Lab 3   Bill Pierce
10-12 Tuesday

NUMERICAL MATHEMATICAL ANALYSIS

NUMERICAL

MATHEMATICAL

ANALYSIS

BY

JAMES B. SCARBOROUGH, Ph. D.

PROFESSOR EMERITUS OF MATHEMATICS

AT THE U. S. NAVAL ACADEMY

BALTIMORE: THE JOHNS HOPKINS PRESS

LONDON: GEOFFREY CUMBERLEGE

OXFORD UNIVERSITY PRESS

1955

To the memory
of my son

JAMES BLAINE SCARBOROUGH, JR.
(1919-1927)

PREFACE

Applied mathematics comes down ultimately to numerical results, and the student of any branch of applied mathematics will do well to supplement his usual mathematical equipment with a definite knowledge of the numerical side of mathematical analysis. He should, in particular, be able to estimate the reliability of any numerical result he may arrive at. The object of this book is to set forth in a systematic manner and as clearly as possible the most important principles, methods, and processes used for obtaining numerical results; and also methods and means for estimating the accuracy of such results. The book is concerned only with fundamental principles and processes, and is not a treatise on computation. For this reason little attention is paid to computation forms, the assumption being that the reader who has much computation of a particular kind to do will be able to devise his own form.

The plan of treatment followed throughout the book may be briefly stated as follows: Each major subject or topic is introduced by a short statement of " what it is all about." Then follows a brief statement of the underlying theory of the subject under consideration. With this theory as a basis, the processes and formulas are then developed in the simplest and most direct manner. Formulas and methods for checking or estimating the accuracy of results are also worked out wherever possible. The reader is then shown just *how to use* the formulas and processes developed, by applying them to a variety of examples. Finally, the limitations of the formulas and the pitfalls connected with the processes are carefully pointed out by means of appropriate examples. Notes and remarks are also added wherever they will throw further light on the subjects under consideration.

The treatment of all topics has been made as elementary as was consistent with soundness, and in some instances the explanations may seem unnecessarily detailed. For such detailed explanations no apology is offered, as the book is meant to be understood with a minimum of effort on the part of the reader. Moreover, experience in teaching certain topics has shown that even a good student must receive considerable assistance from teacher, textbook, or some other source. I have tried everywhere to clear up the difficulties before the student meets them, so that no teacher or other source of information will be needed. In order to make the book everywhere as readable as possible I have purposely refrained from using notations peculiar to certain subjects, and from employing symbolic methods and divided differences in deriving the standard formulas of interpolation.

vii

A knowledge of calculus to the extent of the usual first course is all that is needed for the understanding of anything in the book.

The more important formulas throughout the book are numbered in heavy black type to distinguish them from those of less importance.

The worker who is to obtain numerical results with a minimum of effort must provide himself with every possible aid for lessening the labor of his task. In addition to such aids as slide rules, computing machines, and logarithmic tables, the computer will find that Barlow's tables of squares, cubes, etc., and the Smithsonian Mathematical Tables are practically indispensable. Crelle's "Calculating Tables," Jahnke and Emde's "Funktionentafeln," and Jordan's "Opus Palatinum" (tables of natural sines and cosines to seven decimal places) will also prove their worth in many instances.

In the preparation of the book I have consulted the writings of the majority of previous writers on the subjects treated, and am indebted to many of them for ideas and methods; but my greatest debt is to the writings of the late and great Carl Runge, who undoubtedly contributed more to numerical mathematical analysis than any other man since Gauss. References to the works of other writers will be found here and there in the text and in footnotes.

It is a pleasure to record my thanks to the U. S. Naval Institute for permission to use certain copyrighted material which I originally prepared for *Engineering Mathematics* (1925, 1926); to Dr. L. M. Kells, of the U. S. Naval Academy, for helpful criticism on parts of the manuscript; and to the Johns Hopkins Press and the George Banta Publishing Company for their hearty cooperation in meeting my wishes concerning the make-up and publication of the book.

J. B. SCARBOROUGH

Annapolis, Md.
November, 1930

PREFACE TO THE SECOND EDITION

In this revision all known errors and misprints in the first edition have been corrected. A considerable amount of new material has been added, and a small amount of material in the previous edition has been left out.

The chapter on numerical integration in the original edition has been rewritten and augmented to a considerable extent. All the material dealing with the numerical solution of ordinary differential equations has been completely recast and augmented in various directions. Much more attention has been given to methods of starting the solutions, and all the best methods for that purpose have been treated in detail.

The major part of the new material consists of a section on the accuracy of the solutions of systems of linear equations, the new material dealing with numerical integration, the new material dealing with the numerical solution of ordinary differential equations, including the derivation of the equations of exterior ballistics, a rather lengthy chapter on the numerical solution of partial differential equations, and a shorter chapter on the numerical solution of integral equations. Other new material in smaller amounts has been added in various places.

In all new material, as well as in the old, an effort has been made to make the treatment unmistakably clear and understandable everywhere and in all respects. Although the utmost clarity was aimed at in the first edition, clarity has received even more attention in this revision.

The exercises at the ends of the chapters have been changed and augmented to some extent, and the answers to the majority of them are given.

During the past fifteen years the computer has been provided with great and revolutionary aids. The many volumes of W. P. A. Tables, sponsored by the National Bureau of Standards, have met a real need of long standing; the great automatic calculating machines have performed with ease and rapidity many calculations that were prohibitive in labor and time by the older hand methods and hand machines, and they have turned out volumes of tables in a matter of weeks; and, finally, the important journal *Mathematical Tables and Other Aids to Computation* serves as a clearing house in matters of computation and enables the computer to keep up with progress in computation throughout the world. The computer will be wise to make use of these aids whenever possible. It seems no exaggeration to say that during no other fifteen-year period in the world's history have such great strides been made in the art of getting numerical results. May the strides continue!

I wish here to thank those readers in various parts of the world who have kindly pointed out errors and misprints in the first edition of this work. I shall be grateful to future readers who may notify me of errors or misprints in the present edition.

It is a pleasure to record my thanks to Professors A. E. Currier and S. S. Saslaw for putting at my disposal their unusual knowledge of mathematical analysis, and to Professor J. M. Holme for his excellent work in drawing the figures in their final form.

Finally, I wish to extend my thanks to the Johns Hopkins Press and the ·J. H. Furst Company for their hearty cooperation in meeting my wishes relative to the make-up of the book.

J. B. SCARBOROUGH

August, 1950

PREFACE TO THE THIRD EDITION

This edition is mostly an enlargement of the previous edition. The new material consists mainly of an article on the errors in determinants and a chapter on the numerical solution of simultaneous linear equations. All known misprints and errors in the second edition have been corrected and a few other minor improvements have been made.

In recent years the numerical solution of systems of linear equations has become a subject of major importance, due mainily to the widespread use of automatic computing machines. In the new chapter of this book several of the best methods of solving such equations have been treated in detail and illustrated by numerical examples. An attempt has been made to make the treatment as clear and direct as possible.

Here I wish to record my thanks and indebtedness to Dr. Morris Newman, of the National Bureau of Standards, for bringing to my attention the method of inverting matrices used at the Bureau of Standards and for explaining certain points connected with the method. I also wish to thank all readers who have kindly brought to my attention some of the errors and misprints in the second edition.

Finally, I wish to record my thanks to the Director of the Johns Hopkins Press for his interest, encouragement, and cooperation in bringing out this edition.

J. B. S.

September, 1955

CONTENTS

CHAPTER I

THE ACCURACY OF APPROXIMATE CALCULATIONS

CHAPTER II

INTERPOLATION

DIFFERENCES. NEWTON'S FORMULAS OF INTERPOLATION

CHAPTER III

INTERPOLATION

CENTRAL-DIFFERENCE FORMULAS

CHAPTER IV

INTERPOLATION

LAGRANGE'S FORMULA. INVERSE INTERPOLATION

I. LAGRANGE'S FORMULA OF INTERPOLATION

II. INVERSE INTERPOLATION

CHAPTER V

THE ACCURACY OF INTERPOLATION FORMULAS

CHAPTER VI

INTERPOLATION WITH TWO INDEPENDENT VARIABLES
TRIGONOMETRIC INTERPOLATION

CHAPTER VII

NUMERICAL DIFFERENTIATION AND INTEGRATION
I. NUMERICAL DIFFERENTIATION

II. NUMERICAL INTEGRATION

CHAPTER VIII

THE ACCURACY OF QUADRATURE FORMULAS

CHAPTER IX

THE SOLUTION OF NUMERICAL ALGEBRAIC AND TRANSCENDENTAL EQUATIONS

I. EQUATIONS IN ONE UNKNOWN

II. SIMULTANEOUS EQUATIONS

CHAPTER X

GRAEFFE'S ROOT-SQUARING METHOD FOR SOLVING ALGEBRAIC EQUATIONS

CHAPTER XI

THE NUMERICAL SOLUTION OF ORDINARY DIFFERENTIAL EQUATIONS

I. EQUATIONS OF THE FIRST ORDER

II. EQUATIONS OF THE SECOND ORDER AND SYSTEMS OF SIMULTANEOUS EQUATIONS

III. THE DIFFERENTIAL EQUATIONS OF EXTERIOR BALLISTICS

IV. OTHER METHODS OF SOLVING DIFFERENTIAL EQUATIONS NUMERICALLY

CHAPTER XII

THE NUMERICAL SOLUTION OF PARTIAL DIFFERENTIAL EQUATIONS

CHAPTER XIII

THE NUMERICAL SOLUTION OF INTEGRAL EQUATIONS

CHAPTER XIV

THE NORMAL LAW OF ERROR AND THE PRINCIPLE OF LEAST SQUARES

CHAPTER XV

THE PRECISION OF MEASUREMENTS

I. DIRECT MEASUREMENTS

II. INDIRECT MEASUREMENTS

CHAPTER XVI

EMPIRICAL FORMULAS

CHAPTER XVII

HARMONIC ANALYSIS OF EMPIRICAL FUNCTIONS

CHAPTER XVIII

NUMERICAL SOLUTION OF SIMULTANEOUS LINEAR EQUATIONS

I. SOLUTION BY DETERMINANTS

II. SOLUTION BY SUCCESSIVE ELIMINATION OF THE UNKNOWNS

III. SOLUTION BY INVERSION OF MATRICES

IV. SOLUTION BY ITERATION

NUMERICAL MATHEMATICAL
ANALYSIS

NUMERICAL MATHEMATICAL ANALYSIS

CHAPTER I

THE ACCURACY OF APPROXIMATE CALCULATIONS

1. Introduction. Since applied mathematics comes down ultimately to numerical results, the worker in applied mathematics will encounter all kinds of numbers and all kinds of formulas. He must be able to use the numbers and evaluate the formulas so .as to get the best possible result in any situation. What he learned about numerical calculation in his earlier study of arithmetic is inadequate for handling the numerical side of applied mathematics. For example, the numerical data used in solving the problems of everyday life are usually not exact, and the numbers expressing such data are therefore not exact. They are merely approximations, true to two, three, or more figures.

Not only are the data of practical problems usually approximate, but sometimes the methods and processes by which the desired result is to be found are also approximate. An approximate calculation is one which involves approximate data, approximate methods, or both.

It is therefore evident that the error in a computed result may be due to one or both of two sources: errors in the data and errors of calculation. Errors of the first type cannot be remedied, but those of the second type can usually be made as small as we please. Thus, when such a number as π is replaced by its approximate value in a computation, we can decrease the error due to the approximation by taking π to as many figures as desired, and similarly in most other cases. We shall therefore assume in this chapter that the calculations are always carried out in such a manner as to make the errors of calculation negligible.

Nearly all numerical calculations are in some way approximate, and the aim of the computer should be to obtain results consistent with the data with a minimum of labor. The object of the present chapter is to set forth some basic ideas and methods relating to approximate calculations and to give methods for estimating the accuracy of the results obtained.

2. Approximate Numbers and Significant Figures.

(a) *Approximate Numbers.* In the discussion of approximate computation, it is convenient to make a distinction between numbers which are absolutely exact and those which express approximate values. Such numbers as 2, 1/3, 100, etc. are exact numbers because there is no approximation or uncertainty associated with them. Although such numbers as π, $\sqrt{2}$, e, etc. are exact numbers, they cannot be expressed exactly by a finite number of digits. When expressed in digital form, they must be written as 3.1416, 1.4142, 2.7183, etc. Such numbers are therefore only approximations to the true values and in such cases are called approximate numbers. An approximate number is therefore defined as a number which is used as an approximation to an exact number and differs only slightly from the exact number for which it stands.*

(b) *Significant Figures.* A *significant figure* is any one of the digits 1, 2, 3, $\cdots$ 9; and 0 is a significant figure except when it is used to fix the decimal point or to fill the places of unknown or discarded digits. Thus, in the number 0.00263 the significant figures are 2, 6, 3; the zeros are used merely to fix the decimal point and are therefore not significant. In the number 3809, however, all the digits, including the zero, are significant figures. In a number like 46300 there is nothing in the number as written to show whether or not the zeros are significant figures. The ambiguity can be removed by writing the number in the powers-of-ten notation as 4.63×10^4, 4.630×10^4, or 4.6300×10^4, the number of significant figures being indicated by the factor at the left.

3. Rounding of Numbers.
If we attempt to divide 27 by 13.1, we get

$$27/13.1 = 2.061068702 \cdots ,$$

a quotient which never terminates. In order to use such a number in a practical computation, we must cut it down to a manageable form, such as 2.06, or 2.061, or 2.06107, etc. This process of cutting off superfluous digits and retaining as many as desired is called rounding off.

To *round off* or simply *round* a number is to retain a certain number of digits, *counted from the left*, and drop the others. Thus, to round off π to three, four, five, and six figures, respectively, we have 3.14, 3.142, 3.1416, 3.14159. Numbers are rounded off so as to cause the *least possible error*. This is attained by rounding according to the following rule:

---

* Some readers may object to the term " approximate number " and insist that one should always say " approximate value " of a number. The shorter term, however, is less cumbrous, is perfectly definite as defined above, and reminds us by its very name that it stands for the approximate value of a number. It has been used in this sense by no less an authority than Jules Tannery in his *Leçons d'Arithmétique.*

To round off a number to n significant figures, discard all digits to the right of the nth place. If the discarded number is less than half a unit in the nth place, leave the nth digit unchanged; if the discarded number is greater than half a unit in the nth place, add 1 to the nth digit. If the discarded number is *exactly* half a unit in the nth place, leave the nth digit unaltered if it is an even number, but increase it by 1 if it is an odd number; in other words, round off so as to leave the nth digit an *even* number in such cases.

When a number has been rounded off according to the rule just stated, it is said to be *correct to* n *significant figures.*

The following numbers are rounded off correctly to four significant figures:

29.63243	becomes	29.63
81.9773	"	81.98
4.4995001	"	4.500
11.64489	"	11.64
48.365	"	48.36
67.495	"	67.50

When the above rule is followed consistently, the errors due to rounding are largely cancelled by one another.

Such is not the case, however, if the computer follows an old rule which is sometimes advocated. The old rule says that when a 5 is dropped the preceding digit should always be increased by 1. This is bad advice and is conducive to an accumulation of rounding errors and therefore to inaccuracy in computation. It should be obvious to any thinking person that when a 5 is cut off, the preceding digit should be increased by 1 in only *half* the cases and should be left unchanged in the other half. Since even and odd digits occur with equal frequency, on the average, the rule that the odd digits be increased by 1 when a 5 is dropped is logically sound.

The case where the number to be discarded is exactly half a unit in the nth place deserves further comment. From purely logical considerations the digit preceding the discarded 5000 · · · might just as well be left odd, but there is a practical aspect to the matter. Rounded numbers must often be divided by other numbers, and it is highly desirable from the stand-point of accuracy that the division be exact as often as possible. An even number is always divisible by 2, it may be divisible by other even numbers, and it may also be divisible by several odd numbers; whereas an odd number is not divisible by any even number and it may not be divisible by any odd number. Hence, in general, even numbers are exactly divisible by many more numbers than are odd numbers, and therefore there will be fewer left-over errors in a computation when the rounded numbers are left even. The rule that the last digit be left even rather than odd is thus conducive to accuracy in computation.

In certain rare instances the rule for cutting off $50000 \cdots$ should be modified. For example, if a 5 is to be cut off from two or more numbers in a column that is to be added, the preceding digit should be increased by 1 in *half* the cases and left unchanged in the other half, regardless of whether the preceding digit is even or odd. Other cases might arise where common sense should be the guide in making the errors neutralize one another.

4. Absolute, Relative, and Percentage Errors. The *absolute error* of a number, measurement, or calculation is the numerical difference between the true value of the quantity and its approximate value as given, or obtained by measurement or calculation. The *relative error* is the absolute error divided by the true value of the quantity. The *percentage error* is 100 times the relative error. For example, let Q represent the true value of some quantity. If ΔQ is the absolute error of an approximate value of Q, then

$\Delta Q/Q$ = relative error of the approximate quantity.

$100\Delta Q/Q$ = percentage error of the approximate quantity.

If a number is correct to n significant figures, it is evident that its absolute error can not be greater than half a unit in the nth place. For example, if the number 4.629 is correct to four figures, its absolute error is not greater than $0.001 \times \frac{1}{2} = 0.0005$.

Remark. It is to be noted that relative and percentage errors are independent of the unit of measurement, whereas absolute errors are expressed in terms of the unit used.

5. Relation between Relative Error and the Number of Significant Figures. The belief is widespread, even in scientific circles, that the accuracy of a measurement or of a computed result is indicated by the number of decimals required to express it. This belief is erroneous, for the accuracy of a result is indicated by the number of *significant figures* required to express it. The true index of the accuracy of a measurement or of a calculation is the relative error. For example, if the diameter of a 2-inch steel shaft is measured to the nearest thousandth of an inch, the result is less accurate than the measurement of a mile of railroad track to the nearest foot. For although the absolute errors in the two measurements are 0.0005 inch and 6 inches, respectively, the relative errors are 0.0005/2 = 1/4000 and 1/10,560. Hence in the measurement of the shaft we make an error of one part in 4000, whereas in the case of the railroad we make an error of one part in 10,560. The latter measurement is clearly the more accurate, even though its absolute error is 12,000 times as great.

The relation between the relative error and the number of correct figures is given by the following fundamental theorem:

Theorem I. If the first significant figure of a number is k, *and the number is correct to* n *significant figures, then the relative error is less than* $1/(k \times 10^{n-1})$.

Before giving a literal proof of this theorem we shall first show that it holds for several numbers picked at random. Henceforth we shall denote absolute and relative errors of numbers by the symbols E_a and E_r, respectively.

Example 1. Let us suppose that the number 864.32 is correct to five significant figures. Then $k = 8$, $n = 5$, and $E_a \leqq 0.01 \times \frac{1}{2} = 0.005$. For the relative error we have

$$E_r \leqq \frac{0.005}{864.32 - 0.005} = \frac{5}{864320 - 5} = \frac{1}{2 \times 86432 - 1}$$
$$= \frac{1}{2(86432 - \frac{1}{2})} < \frac{1}{2 \times 8 \times 10^4} < \frac{1}{8 \times 10^4}.$$

Hence the theorem holds here.

Example 2. Next, let us consider the number 369,230. Assuming that the last digit (the zero) is written merely to fill the place of a discarded digit and is therefore not a significant figure, we have $k = 3$, $n = 5$, and $E_a \leqq 10 \times \frac{1}{2} = 5$. Then

$$E_r \leqq \frac{5}{369230 - 5} = \frac{1}{2 \times 36923 - 1} = \frac{1}{2(36923 - \frac{1}{2})}$$
$$< \frac{1}{2 \times 3 \times 10^4} < \frac{1}{3 \times 10^4}.$$

Example 3. Finally, suppose the number 0.0800 is correct to three significant figures. Then $k = 8$, $n = 3$, $E_a \leqq 0.0001 \times \frac{1}{2} = 0.00005$, and

$$E_r \leqq \frac{0.00005}{0.0800 - 0.00005} = \frac{5}{8000 - 5} = \frac{1}{1600 - 1}$$
$$= \frac{1}{2(800 - \frac{1}{2})} < \frac{1}{8 \times 10^2}.$$

It is to be noted that in this example the relative error is not certainly less than $1/(2k \times 10^{n-1})$, as was the case in Examples 1 and 2 above.

To prove the theorem generally, let

$$N = \text{any number (exact value)},$$
$$n = \text{number of correct significant figures},$$
$$m = \text{number of correct decimal places}.$$

Three cases must be distinguished, namely $m < n$, $m = n$, and $m > n$.

Case 1. $m < n$. Here the number of digits in the integral part of N is $n - m$. Denoting the first significant figure of N by k, as before, we have

$$E_a \leqq 1/10^m \times \tfrac{1}{2}, \qquad N \geqq k \times 10^{n-m-1} - 1/10^m \times \tfrac{1}{2}.$$

Hence

$$E_r \leqq \frac{1/10^m \times \tfrac{1}{2}}{k \times 10^{n-m-1} - 1/10^m \times \tfrac{1}{2}} = \frac{10^{-m}}{2k \times 10^{n-1} \times 10^{-m} - 10^{-m}}$$

$$= \frac{1}{2k \times 10^{n-1} - 1} = \frac{1}{2(k \times 10^{n-1} - \tfrac{1}{2})}.$$

Remembering now that n is a *positive integer* and that k stands for any one of the digits from 1 to 9 inclusive, we readily see that $2k \times 10^{n-1} - 1 > k \times 10^{n-1}$ in all cases except $k = 1$ and $n = 1$. But this is the trivial case where $N = 1$, 0.01, etc.; that is, where N contains only one digit different from zero and this digit is 1—a case which would never occur in practice. Hence for all other cases we have $2k \times 10^{n-1} - 1 > k \times 10^{n-1}$; and therefore

$$E_r < \frac{1}{k \times 10^{n-1}}$$

Case 2. $m = n$. Here N is a decimal and k is the first decimal figure. We then have

$$E_a \leqq 1/10^m \times \tfrac{1}{2}, \qquad N \geqq k \times 10^{-1} - 1/10^m \times \tfrac{1}{2}.$$

$$\therefore E_r \leqq \frac{10^{-m} \times \tfrac{1}{2}}{k \times 10^{-1} - 10^{-m} \times \tfrac{1}{2}} = \frac{10^{-m}}{2k \times 10^{-1} - 10^{-m}} = \frac{1}{2k \times 10^{m-1} - 1}$$

$$= \frac{1}{2k \times 10^{n-1} - 1} < \frac{1}{k \times 10^{n-1}}.$$

Case 3. $m > n$. In this case k occupies the $(m - n + 1)$th decimal place and therefore

$$N \geqq k \times 10^{-(m-n+1)} - 1/10^m \times \tfrac{1}{2}, \qquad E_a \leqq 1/10^m \times \tfrac{1}{2}.$$

$$\therefore E_r \leqq \frac{10^{-m} \times \tfrac{1}{2}}{k \times 10^{-m} \times 10^{n-1} - 10^{-m} \times \tfrac{1}{2}} = \frac{10^{-m}}{2k \times 10^{-m} \times 10^{n-1} - 10^{-m}}$$

$$= \frac{1}{2k \times 10^{n-1} - 1} < \frac{1}{k \times 10^{n-1}}.$$

The theorem is therefore true in all cases.

Corollary 1. Except in the case of approximate numbers of the form $k(1.000\cdots)\times 10^p$, in which k is the only digit different from zero, the relative error is less than $1/(2k \times 10^{n-1})$.

Corollary 2. If $k \geqq 5$ and the given approximate number is not of the form $k(1.000\cdots)\times 10^p$, then $E_r < 1/10^n$; for in this case $2k \geqq 10$ and therefore $2k \times 10^{n-1} \geqq 10^n$.

To find the number of correct figures corresponding to a given relative error we can not take the converse of the theorem stated at the beginning of this article, for the converse theorem is not true. In proving the formula for the relative error we took the lower limit for N in order to obtain the upper limit for E_r. Thus, for the lower limit of N we took its first significant figure multiplied by a power of 10. In the converse problem of finding the number of correct figures corresponding to a given relative error we must find the upper limit of the absolute error E_a; and since $E_a = NE_r$, we should use the upper limit for N. This upper limit will be $k+1$ times a power of 10, where k is the first significant figure in N. For example, if the approximate value of N is 6895, the lower limit to be used in finding the relative error is 6×10^3, whereas the upper limit to be used in finding the absolute error is 7×10^3.

To solve the converse problem we utilize Theorem II:

Theorem II. If the relative error in an approximate number is less than $1/[(k+1) \times 10^{n-1}]$, the number is correct to n significant figures, or at least is in error by less than a unit in the nth significant figure.

To prove this theorem let

$$N = \text{the given number (exact value),}$$
$$n = \text{number of correct significant figures in } N,$$
$$k = \text{first significant figure in } N,$$
$$p = \text{number of digits in the integral part of } N.$$

Then

$$n - p = \text{number of decimals in } N,$$

and $N \leqq (k+1)\times 10^{p-1}.$

Let

$$E_r < \frac{1}{(k+1) \times 10^{n-1}}.$$

Then

$$E_a < (k+1) \times 10^{p-1} \times \frac{1}{(k+1) \times 10^{n-1}} = \frac{1}{10^{n-p}}.$$

Now $1/10^{n-p}$ is one unit in the $(n-p)$th decimal place, or in the nth significant figure. Hence the absolute error E_a is less than a unit in the nth significant figure.

If the given number is a pure decimal, let

$p =$ number of zeros between the decimal point and first significant figure. Then $n + p =$ number of decimals in N, and

$$N \leqq \frac{(k+1)}{10^{p+1}}.$$

Hence if

$$E_r < \frac{1}{(k+1) \times 10^{n-1}},$$

we have

$$E_a < \frac{(k+1)}{10^{p+1}} \times \frac{1}{(k+1) \times 10^{n-1}} = \frac{1}{10^{n+p}}.$$

But $1/10^{n+p}$ is one unit in the $(n+p)$th decimal place, or in the nth significant figure. Hence the absolute error E_a is less than a unit in the nth significant figure.

Corollary 3. If $E_r < 1/[2(k+1) \times 10^{n-1}]$, then E_a is less than half a unit in the nth significant figure and the given number is correct to n significant figures in all cases.

Corollary 4. Since k may have any value from 1 to 9 inclusive, it is evident that $k + 1$ may have any value from 2 to 10. Hence the upper and lower limits of the fraction $1/[2(k+1) \times 10^{n-1}]$ are $1/(4 \times 10^{n-1})$ and $1/(2 \times 10^n)$, respectively. We can therefore assert that

If the relative error of any number is not greater than $1/(2 \times 10^n)$ the number is certainly correct to n significant figures.

Remark. The reader can readily see from the preceding discussion that *the absolute error* is connected with the number of *decimal places*, whereas the *relative error* is connected with the number of *significant figures*.

6. The General Formula for Errors. Let

(1) $$N = f(u_1, u_2, u_3, \cdots u_n)$$

denote any function of several independent quantities $u_1, u_2, \cdots u_n$, which are subject to the errors $\Delta u_1, \Delta u_2, \cdots \Delta u_n$, respectively. These errors in the u's will cause an error ΔN in the function N, according to the relation

(2) $N + \Delta N = f(u_1 + \Delta u_1, u_2 + \Delta u_2, \cdots u_n + \Delta u_n)$.

To find an expression for ΔN we must expand the right-hand member of (2) by Taylor's theorem for a function of several variables. Hence we have

$$f(u_1 + \Delta u_1, u_2 + \Delta u_2, \cdots u_n + \Delta u_n) = f(u_1, u_2, \cdots u_n) + \Delta u_1 \frac{\partial f}{\partial u_1}$$

$$+ \Delta u_2 \frac{\partial f}{\partial u_2} + \cdots + \Delta u_n \frac{\partial f}{\partial u_n} + \frac{1}{2}[(\Delta u_1)^2 \frac{\partial^2 f}{\partial u_1^2} + \cdots + (\Delta u_n)^2 \frac{\partial^2 f}{\partial u_n^2}$$

$$+ 2\Delta u_1 \Delta u_2 \frac{\partial^2 f}{\partial u_1 \partial u_2} + \cdots] + \cdots .$$

Now since the errors $\Delta u_1, \Delta u_2, \cdots \Delta u_n$ are always relatively small,* we may neglect their squares, products, and higher powers and write

(3) $N + \Delta N = f(u_1, u_2, u_3, \cdots u_n)$

$$+ \Delta u_1 \frac{\partial f}{\partial u_1} + \Delta u_2 \frac{\partial f}{\partial u_2} + \cdots + \Delta u_n \frac{\partial f}{\partial u_n}$$

Subtracting (1) from (3), we get

$$\Delta N = \frac{\partial f}{\partial u_1} \Delta u_1 + \frac{\partial f}{\partial u_2} \Delta u_2 + \cdots + \frac{\partial f}{\partial u_n} \Delta u_n,$$

or

(6.1) $\Delta N = \frac{\partial N}{\partial u_1} \Delta u_1 + \frac{\partial N}{\partial u_2} \Delta u_2 + \frac{\partial N}{\partial u_3} \Delta u_3 + \cdots + \frac{\partial N}{\partial u_n} \Delta u_n.$

This is the general formula for computing the error of a function, and it includes all possible cases. It will be observed that the right-hand member of (6.1) is merely the total differential of the function N.

For the relative error of the function N we have

(6.2) $E_r = \frac{\Delta N}{N} = \frac{\partial N}{\partial u_1} \frac{\Delta u_1}{N} + \frac{\partial N}{\partial u_2} \frac{\Delta u_2}{N} + \cdots + \frac{\partial N}{\partial u_n} \cdot \frac{\Delta u_n}{N} .$

When N is a function of the form

(6.3) $N = \frac{K a^m b^n c^p}{d^q e^r} ,$

* A quantity P is said to be relatively small in comparison with a second quantity Q when the ratio P/Q is small in comparison with unity. The squares and products of such small ratios ars negligible in most calculations.

then by (6. 2) the relative error is

$$E_r = \Delta N/N = m(\Delta a/a) + n(\Delta b/b) + p(\Delta c/c) - q(\Delta d/d) - r(\Delta e/e).$$

But since the errors $\Delta a, \cdots \Delta e$, etc. are just as likely to be negative as positive, we must take all the terms with the positive sign in order to be sure of the maximum error in the function N. Hence we write

(6. 4) $E_r \leqq m \mid \Delta a/a \mid + n \mid \Delta b/b \mid + p \mid \Delta c/c \mid + q \mid \Delta d/d \mid + r \mid \Delta e/e \mid.$

7. Application of the Error Formulas to the Fundamental Operations of Arithmetic and to Logarithms. We shall now apply the preceding results to the fundamental operations of arithmetic.

7a). Addition. Let

$$N = u_1 + u_2 + \cdots + u_n.$$

Then

(7. 1) $\Delta N = E_a = \Delta u_1 + \Delta u_2 + \cdots + \Delta u_n.$

The absolute error of a sum of approximate numbers is therefore equal to the algebraic sum of their absolute errors.

The proper way to add approximate numbers of different accuracies is shown in the two examples below.

Example 1. Find the sum of the approximate numbers 561.32, 491.6, 86.954, and 3.9462, each being correct to its last figure but no farther.

Solution. Since the second number is known only to the first decimal place, it would be useless and absurd to retain more than two decimals in any of the other numbers. Hence we round them off to two decimals, add the four numbers, and give the result to one decimal place, as shown below:

$$
\begin{array}{r}
491.6 \\
561.32 \\
86.95 \\
3.95 \\
\hline
1143.8
\end{array}
$$

By retaining two decimals in the more accurate numbers we eliminate the errors inherent in these numbers and thus reduce the error of the sum to that of the least accurate number. The final result, however, is uncertain by one unit in its last figure.

Example 2. Find the sum of 36490, 994, 557.32, 29500, and 86939, assuming that the number 29500 is known to only three significant figures.

Solution. Since one of the numbers is known only to the nearest hundred, we round off the others to the nearest ten, add, and give the sum to hundreds, as shown below:

$$
\begin{array}{r}
29500 \\
86940 \\
36490 \\
990 \\
560 \\
\hline
\end{array}
$$

154500 or 1.545×10^5.

The result is uncertain by one unit in the last significant figure.

In general, if we find the sum of m numbers each of which has been rounded off correctly to the same place, the error in the sum may be as great as $m/2$ units in the last significant figure.

7b). Averages. An important case in the addition of numbers must here be considered. Suppose we are to find the mean of several approximate numbers. Is this mean reliable to any more figures than are the numbers from which it was obtained? The answer is yes, but in order to see why let us consider the following concrete case.

The first column below contains the mantissas of ten consecutive logarithms taken from a six-place table. The second column contains these same mantissas rounded off to five decimals. The third column gives the errors due to rounding, expressed in units of the sixth decimal place.

N	N'	E
0.961421	0.96142	1
0.961469	0.96147	— 1
0.961516	0.96152	— 4
0.961563	0.96156	3
0.961611	0.96161	1
0.961658	0.96166	— 2
0.961706	0.96171	— 4
0.961753	0.96175	3
0.961801	0.96180	1
0.961848	0.96185	— 2

Average, 0.9616346   Av., 0.961635   Sum, — 4
      = 0.961635   Av., — 0.4

Here we have the relation

$$N = N' + E$$

for each of the numbers and therefore the further relations

$$\Sigma N = \Sigma N' + \Sigma E$$

and

$$\Sigma N/n = \Sigma N'/n + \Sigma E/n.$$

It will be noticed that the average of the rounded numbers is in error by only 0.4 of a unit in the sixth decimal place. We may therefore call it correct to six decimals, or to one more place than the rounded numbers.

The entries in all numerical tables and the results of all measurements are rounded numbers in which the error is not greater than half a unit in the last significant figure. These errors (due to rounding) are in general as likely to be positive as negative and hence their algebraic sum is never large. Usually it is less than a unit in the last figure.

The foregoing considerations justify the computer in retaining one more figure in the mean of a set of numbers than are given in the numbers themselves. But rarely should he retain the mean to more than one additional figure.

7c). Subtraction. Here

$$N = u_1 - u_2$$

and

(7. 2) $$\Delta N = E_a = \Delta u_1 - \Delta u_2.$$

Since the errors Δu_1 and Δu_2 may be either positive or negative, however, we must take the sum of the absolute values of the errors in order to get the maximum error. We then have the result that the absolute error of the difference of two approximate numbers may equal the *sum* of their absolute errors.

When one approximate number is to be subtracted from another, they must both be rounded off to the same place before subtracting. Thus, to subtract 46.365 from 779.8, assuming that each number is approximate and correct only to its last figure, we have

$$779.8 - 46.4 = 733.4.$$

It would be absurd to write $779.800 - 46.365 = 733.435$, because the last two figures in the larger number as here written are not zeros.

7d). Loss of Significant Figures by Subtraction.

The most serious error connected with the subtraction of approximate numbers arises from the subtraction of numbers which are nearly equal. Suppose, for example, that the numbers 64.395 and 63.994 are each correct to five figures, but no more. Their difference, $64.395 - 63.994 = 0.401$, is correct to only *three* figures. Again, if the numbers 16950 and 16870 are each correct to only four significant figures, their difference $16950 - 16870 = 80$ is correct to only *one* significant figure, and even this figure may be in error by one unit.

Errors arising from the disappearance of the most important figures on the left, as in the two examples of the preceding paragraph, are of frequent occurrence and sometimes render the result of a computation worthless. They must be carefully guarded against and eliminated wherever possible.

The inaccuracy resulting from the loss of the most important significant figures in the subtraction of two nearly equal numbers can be lessened, and sometimes entirely avoided, in one of two ways:

1. By approximating each of the numbers with sufficient accuracy *before* subtraction, when this is possible. Thus, to find the difference $\sqrt{2.03} - \sqrt{2}$ correct to five significant figures, we take $\sqrt{2.03} = 1.424781$ and $\sqrt{2} = 1.414214$. Then $1.424781 - 1.414214 = 0.010567$. Note that a slide-rule computation is worthless in such a case as this.

This method is limited when the two given numbers are approximate and true to only a few digits.

2. By transforming the expression whose value is desired. Thus, to find the value of $1 - \cos x$ when x is small and no extended table is at hand, write $1 - \cos x = 2 \sin^2 (x/2)$ in some cases, and in other cases replace $\cos x$ by its Taylor expansion. Then

$$1 - \cos x = 1 - (1 - \frac{x^2}{2} + \frac{x^4}{4!} - \cdots) = \frac{x^2}{2} - \frac{x^4}{24} + \cdots .$$

In finding the area of a circular segment having a small central angle, replace $\sin \theta$ by its Taylor expansion. Thus

$$\text{Area} = \frac{R^2}{2} (\theta - \sin \theta) = \frac{R^2}{2} [\theta - (\theta - \frac{\theta^3}{3!} + \frac{\theta^5}{5!} - \cdots)]$$

$$= \frac{R^2}{2} \left(\frac{\theta^3}{6} - \frac{\theta^5}{120} + \cdots \right),$$

otherwise the area of a plainly visible segment might turn out to be zero when 4- or 5-place tables are used.

Sometimes in the evaluation of such an expression as $\sqrt{a} - \sqrt{b}$, where b is only slightly less than a, one or more significant figures can be saved by rationalizing the expression as the first step in the calculation. Thus,

$$\sqrt{a} - \sqrt{b} = \frac{a - b}{\sqrt{a} + \sqrt{b}} .$$

This method is of value only when fewer digits are lost by taking $a - b$ than by taking $\sqrt{a} - \sqrt{b}$.

The general solution of a certain type of ladder problem in elementary mechanics is

$$P = \frac{\dfrac{W}{2} \cot \theta - W\mu}{\mu - \left(\dfrac{l-c}{l}\right) \cot \theta}.$$

Here the terms in the numerator may be nearly equal for particular values of W, θ, and μ; and the terms of the denominator may also be nearly equal for certain values of μ, l, c, and θ. In such cases a slide-rule computation may be worthless.

In making a transformation to prevent loss of significant figures by subtraction, each problem must be treated individually. There is no known method or procedure that will fit all cases.

The loss of the leading significant figures in the subtraction of two nearly equal numbers is the greatest source of inaccuracy in most computations, and it forms the weakest links in a chain computation where it occurs. The computer must be on his guard against it at all times.

In general, if we desire the difference of two approximate numbers to n significant figures, and if it is known beforehand that the first m figures at the left will disappear by subtraction, we must start with $m + n$ significant figures in *each* of the given numbers.

7e). Multiplication. In this case

$$N = u_1 u_2 u_3 \cdots u_n.$$

Since this is of the form (6.3), in which $m = n = \cdots = r = 1$, we have by (6.4)

(7.3) $E_r = \Delta N/N = \Delta u_1/u_1 + \Delta u_2/u_2 + \cdots + \Delta u_n/u_n.$

The relative error of a product of n approximate numbers is therefore equal to the algebraic sum of the relative errors of the separate numbers.

The accuracy of a product should always be investigated by means of the relative error. The absolute error, if desired, can be found from the relation $E_a = E_r N$.

When it is desired to find the product of two or more approximate numbers of different accuracies, the more accurate numbers should be rounded off so as to contain *one more* significant figure than the least accurate factor, for by so doing we eliminate the error due to the more accurate factors and thus make the error of the product due solely to the errors of the less accurate numbers. The final result should be given to as many significant figures as are contained in the least accurate factor, and no more. The proper method of procedure in such cases will be illustrated by examples later on.

7f). *Division.* Here we have

$$N = u_1/u_2 .$$

This is also of the form (6.3), where the exponents are all unity. Hence by (6.4)

(7.4) $$E_r = \Delta u_1/u_1 + \Delta u_2/u_2 .$$

The relative error of a quotient is therefore equal to the algebraic sum of the relative errors of divisor and dividend, but in order to get the maximum error one should take the arithmetical sum of the errors.

A simple formula for the absolute error of a quotient can be found directly, as follows:

Let $\Delta Q =$ absolute error of the quotient u_1/u_2. Then

$$\Delta Q = \frac{u_1 + \Delta u_1}{u_2 + \Delta u_2} - \frac{u_1}{u_2} = \frac{u_2 \Delta u_1 - u_1 \Delta u_2}{u_2 (u_2 + \Delta u_2)} = \frac{u_1 \left(\dfrac{\Delta u_1}{u_1} - \dfrac{\Delta u_2}{u_2} \right)}{u_2 + \Delta u_2} .$$

Now let ω denote the greatest absolute value of either $\Delta u_1/u_1$ or $\Delta u_2/u_2$, and take the signs of Δu_1 and Δu_2 so as to get the greatest value of ΔQ. Then since $\Delta u_2/u_2 \leqq \omega$, we have $\Delta u_2 \leqq \omega u_2$; and therefore if u_1 and u_2 are *both* subject to errors of the *same order of magnitude* we have

$$\Delta Q \leqq \frac{u_1 (\omega + \omega)}{u_2 - \omega u_2} = \frac{2 u_1 \omega}{u_2 (1 - \omega)} .$$

If only u_1 or u_2 is subject to error and the other is free from error in comparison with it, then

$$\Delta Q \leqq \frac{u_1 (\omega)}{u_2 - \omega u_2} = \frac{u_1 \omega}{u_2 (1 - \omega)} .$$

Finally, if ω is negligible in comparison with 1, we get

(7.5) $$\Delta Q \leqq 2 (u_1/u_2) \omega$$

if u_1 and u_2 are both subject to errors of the same order of magnitude; and

(7.6) $$\Delta Q \leqq (u_1/u_2) \omega$$

if only u_1 or u_2 is subject to error.

As in the case of products, the accuracy of a quotient should always be investigated by means of the relative error, and all the statements made above in regard to products hold for quotients. In particular, if one of the numbers (divisor or dividend) is more accurate than the other, the more accurate number should be rounded off so as to contain *one more* significant figure than the less accurate one. The result should be given to as many significant figures as the less accurate number, and no more. The following examples will illustrate the proper methods of investigating the accuracy of products and quotients.

Example 1. Find the product of 349.1×863.4 and state how many figures of the result are trustworthy.

Solution. Assuming that each number is correct to four figures but no more, we have $\Delta u_1 \leqq 0.05$, $\Delta u_2 \leqq 0.05$. Hence

$$E_r \leqq \frac{0.05}{349.1} + \frac{0.05}{863.4} = 0.000143 + 0.000057 = 0.00020.$$

The product of the given numbers is 301413 to six figures. The absolute error of this product is

$$E_a = 301413 \times 0.00020 = 60, \text{ possibly.}$$

The true result therefore lies between 301473 and 301353, and the best we can do is to take the mean of these numbers to four significant figures, or

$$349.1 \times 863.4 = 301400 = 3.014 \times 10^5.$$

Even then there is some uncertainty about the last figure.

Theorem II of Art. 5 also tells us that the above result is uncertain in the fourth figure, but that the error in that figure is less than a unit.

Example 2. Find the number of correct figures in the quotient $56.3/\sqrt{5}$, assuming that the numerator is correct to its last figure but no farther.

Solution. Here we take $\sqrt{5} = 2.236$ so as to make the divisor free from error in comparison with the dividend. Then

$$E_r \leqq \frac{0.05}{56.3} < 0.0009;$$

and since $56.3/2.236 = 25.2$ we have

$$E_a < 25.2 \times 0.0009 < 0.023.$$

Since this error does not affect the third figure of the quotient, we take 25.2 as the correct result.

Note that formula (7. 6) also gives this result.

We could have seen at a glance, without any investigation, that the error of the quotient in this example would be less than 0.025; for the denominator is free from error and the possible error of 0.05 in the numerator is to be divided by 2.236, thereby making the error of the quotient less than half that amount.

Example 3. Find how many figures of the quotient $4.89\pi/6.7$ are trustworthy, assuming that the denominator is true to only two figures.

Solution. The only appreciable error to be considered here is the possible 0.05 in the denominator. The corresponding relative error is

$$E_r \leqq \frac{0.05}{6.7} < 0.0075.$$

The quotient to three figures is

$$\frac{4.89 \times 3.14}{6.7} = 2.29.$$

Hence the possible absolute error is $E_a \leqq 2.29 \times 0.0075 < 0.02$. Since the third figure of the quotient may be in error by nearly two units, we are not justified in calling the result anything but 2. 3, or

$$\frac{4.89\pi}{6.7} = 2.3.$$

Formula (7. 6) also gives this same result.

Example 4. Find the number of trustworthy figures in the quotient of $876.3/494.2$, assuming that both numbers are approximate and true only to the number of digits given.

Solution. Here the largest relative error is

$$\omega = \frac{0.05}{494.2} = 0.000101,$$

and the quotient is

$$\frac{876.3}{494.2} = 1.7732.$$

Hence by (7. 5)

$$\Delta Q = 2(1.7732)(0.000101) = 0.000358.$$

Since this error affects the fourth decimal place but not the third, we take the quotient to be 1.773.

Note. The greatest and least values of the above quotient are

$$\frac{876.35}{494.15} = 1.7734 \quad \text{and} \quad \frac{876.25}{494.25} = 1.7729.$$

These values agree to four significant figures and both give 1.773.

7g). *Powers and Roots.* Here N has the form

$$N = u^m.$$

Hence by (6.4)

$$E_r \leqq m(\Delta u/u).$$

For the pth power of a number we put $m = p$ and have

$$E_r \leqq p(\Delta u/u).$$

The relative error of the pth power of a number is thus p times the relative error of the given number.

For the rth root of a number we put $m = 1/r$ and get

$$E_r \leqq \frac{1}{r}\ \frac{\Delta u}{u}.$$

Hence the relative error of the rth root of an approximate number is only $1/r$th of the relative error of the given number.

Example. Find the number of trustworthy figures in $(0.3862)^4$, assuming that the number in parentheses is correct to its last figure but no farther.

Solution. Here the relative error of the given number is

$$E_r = \frac{0.00005}{0.3862} < 0.00013.$$

The relative error of the result is therefore less than 4×0.00013, or 0.00052.

The required number to five figures is $(0.3862)^4 = 0.022246$. Hence the absolute error of the result is $0.022246 \times 0.00052 = 0.000012$. Since this error affects the fourth significant figure of the result, the best we can do is to write

$$(0.3862)^4 = 0.02225$$

and say that the last figure is uncertain by one unit.

The relative error of the fourth root of 0.3862 is less than $\frac{1}{4}(0.00013)$ $= 0.000032$, and since this fourth root is 0.78832 the absolute error of the result is about $0.78832 \times 0.000032 = 0.000026$. Hence the fourth root is 0.7883 correct to four figures.

7h). Logarithms. Here we have

$$N = \log_{10} u = 0.43429 \log_e u.$$

Hence

$$\Delta N = 0.43429 (\Delta u / u),$$

or

$$\Delta N < \frac{1}{2} \frac{\Delta u}{u}.$$

The absolute error in the common logarithm of a number is thus less than half the relative error of the given number.

An error in a logarithm may cause a disastrous error in the anti-logarithm or corresponding number, for from the first formula for ΔN above we have

$$\Delta u = \frac{u \Delta N}{0.43429} = 2.3026 u \Delta N.$$

The error in the antilog may thus be many times the error in the logarithm. For this reason it is of the utmost importance that the logarithm of a result be as free from error as possible.

Example 1. Suppose $N = \log_{10} u = 3.49853$ and $\Delta N < 0.000005$, so that the given logarithm is correct to its last figure. Then $u = 3151.6$ and therefore

$$\Delta u = 2.3 \times 3151.6 \times 0.000005 = 0.036.$$

Since this error does not affect the fifth figure in u, the antilog is correct to five figures.

Example 2. Suppose $N = \log_{10} u = 2.96384$ and $\Delta N = 0.00001$. Then $u = 920.11$ and

$$\Delta u = 2.3 \times 920.11 \times 0.00001 = 0.021.$$

This error affects the fifth figure in u and makes it uncertain by two units.

Inasmuch as the logarithm of most results is obtained by the addition of other logarithms, it is evident that such a logarithm is likely to be in error by a unit in the last figure, due to the addition of rounded numbers. Hence the corresponding number may frequently be in error by one or two units in its last significant figure when the number of significant figures in the antilog is the same as the number of decimals in the logarithm.

Remarks. The reader should bear in mind the fact that the number of correct figures in the antilog corresponds to the number of correct *decimals* in the logarithm. The integral part, or characteristic, of the logarithm plays no part in determining the accuracy of the antilog. This fact is at once evident from a consideration of the equation

$$\Delta u/u = 2.3 \Delta N.$$

For inasmuch as the number of correct figures in the antilog u is measured by its relative error, and since this latter quantity depends only on the absolute error ΔN and not at all on the characteristic, it is plain that the accuracy of the antilog depends only on the number of correct decimals in the mantissa.

It is an easy matter to determine the number of correct figures in any antilog when the number of correct decimals in the mantissa is given. Suppose, for example, that we are using m-place log tables and that the possible error in the logarithm of a result is one unit in the last decimal place, as is usually the case. Then $\Delta N = 1/10^m$ and we have

$$\Delta u/u = \frac{2.3}{10^m} = \frac{2.3}{10 \times 10^{m-1}} = \frac{1}{4.34 \times 10^{m-1}} < \frac{1}{2 \times 10^{m-1}} \cdot$$

Hence by Corollary 4, Art. 5, the antilog u is certainly correct to $m-1$ significant figures.

The equation $\Delta u/u = 1/(4.34 \times 10^{m-1})$ shows that if the mantissa is in error by two units in its last figure the antilog is still correct to $m-1$ significant figures, for in this case the relative error of the antilog is

$$\Delta u/u = \frac{1}{2.17 \times 10^{m-1}},$$

which is less than $1/(2 \times 10^{m-1})$. We are therefore justified in asserting that if the mantissa of a logarithm is not in error by more than two units in the last decimal place the antilog is certainly correct to $m-1$ significant figures.

8. The Impossibility, in General, of Obtaining a Result More Accurate than the Data Used. The reader will have observed that in all the examples worked in the preceding pages no result has been more accurate than the numbers used in obtaining it. This, of course, is what we should have expected, but sometimes computers seem to try to get more figures in the result than are used in the data. When we apply Corollaries 1 and 4 of Art. 5 to the errors of products, quotients, powers, roots, logarithms, and antilogarithms, we find that in no case is the result true to more figures than are the numbers used in computing it. The results for these operations are as follows:

(a) *Products and Quotients.* If k_1 and k_2 are the first significant figures of two numbers which are each correct to n significant figures, and if neither number is of the form $k(1.000\cdots) \times 10^p$, then their product or quotient is correct to

$n-1$ significant figures if $k_1 \geqq 2$ and $k_2 \geqq 2$,

$n-2$ significant figures if either $k_1 = 1$ or $k_2 = 1$.

(b) *Powers and Roots.* If k is the first significant figure of a number which is correct to n significant figures, and if this number contains more than one digit different from zero, then its pth power is correct to

$n-1$ significant figures if $p \leqq k$,

$n-2$ significant figures if $p \leqq 10k$;

and its rth root is correct to

n significant figures if $rk \geqq 10$,

$n-1$ significant figures if $rk < 10$.

(c) *Logs and Antilogs.* If k is the first significant figure of a number which is correct to n significant figures, and if this number contains more than one digit different from zero, then for the absolute error in its common logarithm we have

$$E_a < \frac{1}{4k \times 10^{n-1}}.$$

If a logarithm (to the base 10) is not in error by more than two units in the mth decimal place, the antilog is certainly correct to $m-1$ significant figures.

To prove the foregoing results for the accuracy of products and quotients, let k_1 and k_2 represent the first significant figures of the given numbers. Then by Corollary 1 of Art. 5 the relative errors of the numbers are less than $1/(2k_1 \times 10^{n-1})$ and $1/(2k_2 \times 10^{n-1})$, respectively; and since the relative error of the product or quotient of two numbers may equal the sum of their relative errors, we have

Relative error of result

$$< \frac{1}{2k_1 \times 10^{n-1}} + \frac{1}{2k_2 \times 10^{n-1}} = \left(\frac{1}{k_1} + \frac{1}{k_2}\right) \frac{1}{2 \times 10^{n-1}}.$$

Now if $(1/k_1 + 1/k_2) \leqq 1$ we have $E_r < 1/(2 \times 10^{n-1})$, and the product or quotient is certainly correct to $n-1$ significant figures. But this quantity is not greater than 1 if $k_1 \geqq 2$ and $k_2 \geqq 2$. Hence in this case the result is correct to $n-1$ significant figures. If, however, either $k_1 = 1$

or $k_2 = 1$, the quantity $(1/k_1 + 1/k_2) > 1$ and therefore the relative error of the result may be greater than $1/(2 \times 10^{n-1})$. Hence the result may not be correct to $n - 1$ significant figures, but it is certainly correct to $n - 2$ figures.

To prove the above results for the accuracy of powers and roots let k represent the first significant figure of the given number. Then the relative error of this number is less than $1/(2k \times 10^{n-1})$. Hence the relative error of its pth power is less than

$$\frac{p}{2k \times 10^{n-1}} = \frac{p}{k} \frac{1}{2 \times 10^{n-1}} .$$

The result will therefore be correct to $n - 1$ significant figures if $(p/k) \leqq 1$, or $p \leqq k$, and to $n - 2$ significant figures if $p \leqq 10k$.

The error of the rth root is less than

$$\frac{1}{r} \frac{1}{2k \times 10^{n-1}} = \frac{1}{rk} \frac{1}{2 \times 10^{n-1}} = \frac{10}{rk} \frac{1}{2 \times 10^{n}} .$$

Hence the result will be correct to n significant figures if $rk \geqq 10$ and to $n - 1$ significant figures if $rk < 10$.

To prove the result for the error of the common logarithm we recall that $\Delta N < \frac{1}{2}(\Delta u/u)$, and since $\Delta u/u < 1/(2k \times 10^{n-1})$ we have

$$\Delta N < \frac{1}{4k \times 10^{n-1}} .$$

The proof for the accuracy of the antilog has already been given at the end of Art. 7.

Since the separate processes of multiplication, division, raising to powers, and extraction of roots can not give a result more accurate than the data used in obtaining it, no combination of these processes could be expected to give a more accurate result except by accident. Hence when only these processes are involved in a computation, the result should never be given to more significant figures than are contained in the least accurate of the factors used. Even then the last significant figure will usually be uncertain. In a computation involving several distinct steps, retain at the end of each step one more significant figure than is required in the final result.

While it is true in general that a computed result is not more accurate than the numbers used in obtaining it, an exception must be made in the cases of addition and subtraction. When only these processes are involved, the result may be much more accurate than one of the quantities added or subtracted. For example, the sum $3463 + \sqrt{3} = 3463 + 1.7 = 3464.7$ is correct to five significant figures (assuming 3463 to be an exact number) even though one of the numbers used in obtaining it is correct to only two figures. A similar result would evidently follow in the case of subtraction.

9. Further Considerations on the Accuracy of a Computed Result. In commenting on formulas (7.1) and (7.3), it was stated that the absolute error of a sum is equal to the *algebraic* sum of the errors of the numbers added, and that the relative error of a product is equal to the *algebraic* sum of the relative errors of the factors. The word "algebraic" deserves emphasis in these cases because errors of measuremnt and errors due to rounding are compensating to a very great extent, so that in most cases the error in a computed result is not equal to the arithmetical sum of the errors of the numbers from which the result was obtained.

We saw in (7b) that the error in a sum was only a small fraction of the arithmetic sum of the separate errors. That the errors of the factors in a product are also compensating may be seen by considering the product of two *exact* numbers:

$$649.3 \times 675.8 = 438,796.94.$$

Now suppose we round off these numbers to 649 and 676. Their product is then $649 \times 676 = 438,724$. The actual error of this product is 72.94, and the relative error is

$$\frac{72.94}{438,796.94} = 0.000166.$$

The relative errors of the factors are $0.3/649.3 = 0.000462$ and $-0.2/675.8 = -0.000296$. The relative error of the product is thus *less* than the relative error of either factor and is actually equal to their *algebraic* sum. The product in this case is more accurate than either factor.

When a long computation is carried out in several steps and the intermediate results are properly rounded at the end of each step, there is no accumulation of rounding errors. If there were, long astronomical computations, such as those of eclipses and the orbits of comets, would be worthless. Time and experience have proved the correctness of such astronomical computations. In a chain computation the loss of significant figures by subtraction is the chief source of error.

Bad advice is sometimes given in regard to computation. In the addition of numbers of unequal accuracy, some writers advise that all the numbers first be rounded off to the number of decimal places given in the least accurate number. When this is done, the computer throws away definite information and replaces it with uncertainty. In adding a column of several numbers, the uncertainties might largely cancel one another, but this would not be the case with only a few numbers. The proper method is to add the more accurate numbers separately and then round off their sum to the same decimal place as the least accurate number or numbers. In this way, the sum is as accurate as the least accurate of the numbers added.

Similar bad advice is given in the case of multiplication and division. When multiplying or dividing numbers of unequal accuracy, some writers advise that all numbers first be rounded off to the same number of significant figures as contained in the least accurate factor. To make all factors as rough as the roughest one is folly. There is no sense in throwing away perfectly definite information and replacing it with a question mark. The more accurate factors should be kept with *one more* significant figure than the least accurate factor. Then the result will usually be as accurate as the least accurate factor. The correct procedure in all ordinary computations can be stated in

A Sound and Safe Rule: When computing with rounded or approximate numbers of unequal accuracy, retain from the beginning *one more* significant figure in the more accurate numbers than are contained in the least accurate number. Then round off the result to the same number of significant figures as the least accurate number.

In the case of addition, retain in the more accurate numbers one more *decimal* digit than is contained in the least accurate number.

This rule follows from equations (7. 1), (7. 3), and (7. 4). By retaining one more digit in the more accurate numbers, we reduce to zero the errors of those terms and thus reduce the error of the final result.

In the case of subtraction or of addition of only *two* numbers, round off the more accurate number to the same number of decimal places as the less accurate one *before* subtracting or adding.

10. Accuracy in the Evaluation of a Formula or Complex Expression. The two fundamental problems under this head are the following:

(a) Given the errors of several independent quantities or approximate numbers, to find the error of any function of these quantities.

(b) To find the allowable errors in several independent quantities in order to obtain a prescribed degree of accuracy in any function of these quantities.

10a). The Direct Problem. The first of these problems is solved by replacing the given *approximate* numbers by the letters $a, b, c, \cdots$ or u_1, u_2, u_3, taking the partial derivatives of the function with respect to each of these letters, and then substituting in formula (6. 1) or (6. 2). An *exact* number, such as 2, 3, 10, etc., is *not* replaced by a letter before taking the derivatives.* We shall now work some examples to show the method of procedure.

Example 1. Find the error in the evaluation of the fraction $\cos 7° 10'/\log_{10} 242.7$, assuming that the angle may be in error by $1'$ and that the number 242.7 may be in error by a unit in its last figure.

Solution. Since this is a quotient of two functions, it is better to compute the relative error from the formula $E_r \leqq \Delta u_1/u_1 + \Delta u_2/u_2$ and then find the absolute error from the relation $E_a = NE_r$. Hence if we write

$$N = \frac{\cos 7° 10'}{\log_{10} 242.7} = \frac{\cos x}{\log_{10} y} = u_1/u_2$$

we have

$$\Delta u_1 = \Delta \cos x = - \sin x \Delta x,$$

$$\Delta u_2 = \Delta \log_{10} y = 0.43429\,(\Delta y/y).$$

$$\therefore E_r \leqq \frac{\sin x}{\cos x}\,\Delta x + \frac{0.43429}{y \log y}\,\Delta y,$$

or

$$E_r \leqq \tan x \Delta x + \frac{0.435}{y \log y}\,\Delta y.$$

Now taking $x = 7° 10'$, $\Delta x = 1' = 0.000291$ radian, $y = 242$, $\Delta y = 0.1$, and using a slide rule for the computation, we have

$$E_r < 0.126 \times 0.000291 + \frac{0.435 \times 0.1}{242 \times 2.38} = 0.00011.$$

Since $N = \cos 7° 10'/\log 242.7 = 0.41599$, we have

$$E_a = 0.00011 \times 0.416 = 0.000046,$$

or $E_a < 0.00005$.

The value of the fraction is therefore between 0.41604 and 0.41594, and we take the mean of these numbers to four figures as the best value of the fraction, or

$$N = 0.4160.$$

Example 2. The hypotenuse and a side of a right triangle are found by measurement to be 75 and 32, respectively. If the possible error in

---

* Adopted or accepted values of physical, chemical, and astronomical constants are to be treated as exact numbers, but results obtained by using these numbers as multipliers or divisors are not to be relied upon to more significant figures than are used in the constants themselves.

the hypotenuse is 0.2 and that in the side is 0.1, find the possible error in the computed angle A.

Solution. Lettering the triangle in the usual manner, we have

$$\sin A = 32/75 = a/c.$$

$$\therefore A = \sin^{-1}(a/c),$$

and

$$\Delta A = (\partial A/\partial a)\Delta a + (\partial A/\partial c)\Delta c.$$

Now

$$\partial A/\partial a = 1/\sqrt{c^2 - a^2},$$

$$\partial A/\partial c = - a/(c\sqrt{c^2 - a^2}).$$

Taking the numerical values of c and a in such a manner as to give the upper limits for $\partial A/\partial a$ and $\partial A/\partial c$, and remembering that $\Delta a = 0.1$, $\Delta c = 0.2$, we have

$$\Delta A < \frac{1}{\sqrt{(74.8)^2 - (32.1)^2}} \times 0.1 + \frac{32.1}{74.8\sqrt{(74.8)^2 - (32.1)^2}} \times 0.2 = 0.00275,$$

or

$$\Delta A < 0.0028 \text{ radian} = \underline{9' 38''}.$$

The possible error in A is therefore less than 9' 38''.

10b). The Inverse Problem. We now turn our attention to the second fundamental problem mentioned at the beginning of this article: that of finding the allowable errors in $u_1, u_2, \cdots u_n$ when the function N is desired to a given degree of accuracy. This problem is mathematically indeterminate, since it would be possible to choose the errors Δu_1, Δu_2, etc. in a variety of ways so as to make ΔN less than any prescribed quantity. The problem is solved with the least labor by using what is known as the *principle of equal effects.** This principle assumes that all the partial differentials $(\partial N/\partial u_1)\Delta u_1$, $(\partial N/\partial u_2)\Delta u_2$, etc., contribute an equal amount in making up the total error ΔN. Under these conditions all the terms in the right-hand member of equation (6.1) are equal to one another, so that

$$\Delta N = n \frac{\partial N}{\partial u} \Delta u_1 = n \frac{\partial N}{\partial u_2} \Delta u_2 = \cdots = n \frac{\partial N}{\partial u_n} \Delta u_n.$$

Hence

$$\Delta u_1 = \frac{\Delta N}{n \dfrac{\partial N}{\partial u_1}}, \quad \Delta u_2 = \frac{\Delta N}{n \dfrac{\partial N}{\partial u_2}}, \cdots \Delta u_n = \frac{\Delta N}{n \dfrac{\partial N}{\partial u_n}}.$$

* See Palmer's *Theory of Measurements*, pp. 147-148.

Example 3. Two sides and the included angle of a trianglar city lot are approximately 96 ft., 87 ft., and 36°, respectively. Find the allowable errors in these quantities in order that the area of the lot may be determined to the nearest square foot.

Solution. Writing $b = 96$, $c = 87$, $A = 36°$, and denoting the area by u, we have

$$u = \tfrac{1}{2}bc \sin A = \tfrac{1}{2}(96 \times 87 \sin 36°) = 2455 \text{ sq. ft.}$$

Hence

$$\partial u/\partial b = \tfrac{1}{2}c \sin A, \quad \partial u/\partial c = \tfrac{1}{2}b \sin A, \quad \partial u/\partial A = \tfrac{1}{2}bc \cos A.$$

Substituting these quantities in (6. 2), we find

$$\Delta u/u = \Delta b/b + \Delta c/c + \Delta A/\tan A.$$

Now since the area is to be determined to the nearest square foot we must have $\Delta u < 0.5$; and by the principle of equal effects we must have

$$\frac{\Delta b}{b} = \frac{1}{3}\frac{\Delta u}{u} < \frac{0.5}{3 \times 2455} = \frac{1}{14730} < 0.000068.$$

Hence $\Delta b < 96 \times 0.000068 = 0.0065$ ft.

In like manner ,

$$\frac{\Delta c}{c} = \frac{1}{3}\frac{\Delta u}{u}, \text{ or } \Delta c < 87 \times 0.000068 = 0.0059 \text{ ft.};$$

and

$$\frac{3}{1}\frac{u}{\Delta u} = \frac{\Delta A}{\tan A}, \text{ or } \Delta A < \tan 36° \times 0.000068 = 0.000049 \text{ radian.}$$

Hence from a table for converting radians to degrees we find $\Delta A = 10''$.

It thus appears that in order to attain the desired accuracy in the area the sides must be measured to the nearest hundredth of a foot and the included angle to the nearest 20″ of arc.

This problem could also be solved by assuming that the possible errors in the measured sides might be 0.005 ft. and then computing the permissible error in the measured angle.

Example 4. The value of the function $6x^2(\log_{10} x - \sin 2y)$ is required correct to two decimal places. If the approximate values of x and y are 15.2 and 57°, respectively, find the permissible errors in these quantities.

Solution. Putting

$$u = 6x^2(\log_{10} x - \sin 2y) = 6(15.2)^2(\log_{10} 15.2 - \sin 114°)$$
$$= 371.9,$$

we have

$$\partial u/\partial x = 12x\,(\log_{10} x - \sin 2y) + 6x \times 0.43429 = 88.54,$$

$$\partial u/\partial y = -12x^2 \cos 2y = 1127.7.$$

Hence

$$\Delta u = (\partial u/\partial x)\,\Delta x + (\partial u/\partial y)\,\Delta y = 88.54\Delta x + 1127.7\Delta y.$$

In order that the required result be correct to two decimal places we must have $\Delta u < 0.005$. Then by the principle of equal effects we have

$$\Delta x = \frac{\Delta u}{2\,\dfrac{\partial u}{\partial x}} < \frac{0.005}{2 \times 88.54} = 0.000028,$$

$$\Delta y = \frac{\Delta u}{2\,\dfrac{\partial u}{\partial y}} < \frac{0.005}{2 \times 1127.7} = 0.0000022 \text{ rad.}$$

$$= 0''.45.$$

Since the permissible error in x is only 0.00003, it will be necessary to take x to seven significant figures in order to attain the required degree of accuracy in the result. The value of y can then be taken to the nearest second.

The reason why the permissible errors in x and y are so small in this example is that the factor $\log_{10}x - \sin 2y$ causes the loss of one significant figure by subtraction.

Remark. It is neither necessary nor desirable to investigate the accuracy of all proposed computations. But when we are in doubt about the possibility of attaining a certain degree of accuracy in the final result, we should make the necessary investigation. It usually suffices to carry all computations to one more figure than is desired in the final result and then round off the result to the desired number of figures, if the accuracy of the given independent quantities is such as to permit this.

11. Accuracy in the Determination of Arguments from a Tabulated Function. In many problems it is necessary to compute some function of an unknown quantity and then determine the quantity from tabulated values of the function. Examples of this kind are the determination of numbers from a table of logarithms, and angles from trigonometric tables. If the computed function happens to be affected with an error, the argument determined from this function is necessarily incorrect in some degree. The purpose of this article is to investigate the accuracy of the argument whose value is required.

In tables of single entry are tabulated functions of a single argument. Calling x the argument and y the tabulated function, we have

$$y = f(x).$$

From this we get the relation

$$\Delta y = f'(x)\Delta x, \text{ approximately,}$$

from which we have

(11. 1) $\Delta x = \Delta y / f'(x).$

This is the *fundamental equation* for computing the error in arguments taken from a table. Here Δy represents the error in the computed function whose values are tabulated, and Δx is the corresponding error in the argument. It will be noted that the magnitude of Δx depends upon three things: the error in the function, the nature of the function, and the magnitude of the argument itself. We shall now apply (11. 1) to several functions whose values are tabulated.

1. Logarithms.

$\qquad$ (a) $\qquad\qquad\qquad\qquad f(x) = \log_e x.$

$\qquad\qquad\qquad\qquad\qquad f'(x) = 1/x.$

(1) $\qquad\qquad\qquad \therefore \Delta x = x\Delta y, \text{ from } (11.1).$

$\qquad$ (b) $\qquad\qquad\qquad f(x) = \log_{10} x.$

$\qquad\qquad\qquad\qquad\qquad f'(x) = M/x, \text{ where } M = 0.43429.$

$\qquad\qquad\qquad\qquad\qquad \therefore \Delta x = x\Delta y/M = 2.3026x\Delta y.$

Hence

(2) $\qquad\qquad\qquad\qquad \Delta x < 2.31x\Delta y.$

2. Trigonometric Functions.

$\qquad$ (a) $\qquad\qquad\qquad\qquad f(x) = \sin x.$

$\qquad\qquad\qquad\qquad\qquad f'(x) = \cos x.$

(3) $\qquad\qquad \therefore \Delta x = \Delta y/\cos x = \sec x\Delta y \text{ radians,}$

or

(4) $\qquad\qquad (\Delta x)'' = 206264.8 \sec x\Delta y \text{ seconds.}$

$\qquad$ (b) $\qquad\qquad\qquad\qquad f(x) = \tan x.$

$\qquad\qquad\qquad\qquad\qquad f'(x) = \sec^2 x.$

(5) $\therefore \Delta x = \cos^2 x \Delta y$ radians,

or

(6) $(\Delta x)'' = 206264.8 \cos^2 x \Delta y$ seconds.

(c) $f(x) = \log_{10} \sin x.$

$$f'(x) = M \frac{\cos x}{\sin x} = M \cot x.$$

(7) $\therefore \Delta x = \dfrac{\Delta y}{M \cot x} = 2.3026 \tan x \Delta y$ radians,

or

(8) $(\Delta x)'' < 475000 \tan x \Delta y$ seconds.

(d) $f(x) = \log_{10} \tan x.$

$$f'(x) = M \frac{\sec^2 x}{\tan x} = \frac{M}{\sin x \cos x} = \frac{2M}{\sin 2x}.$$

$$\therefore \Delta x = \frac{\sin 2x \Delta y}{2M} = 1.1513 \sin 2x \Delta y,$$

or

(9) $\Delta x < 1.16 \sin 2x \Delta y$ radians;

and

(10) $(\Delta x)'' < 238000 \sin 2x \Delta y$ seconds.

3. Exponential Functions.

$$f(x) = e^x.$$
$$f'(x) = e^x.$$

(11) $\therefore \Delta x = \Delta y / e^x.$

4. Other Tabulated Functions. By means of the fundamental equation
(11. 1) we can compute the error in any argument when the derivative of
the given function is given or can be easily found. In Jahnke and
Emde's *Funktionentafeln,* for instance, are tabulated the derivatives of
$\log \Gamma(x + 1)$, the error function $\int_0^x e^{-x^2} dx$, the Weierstrass p-function,
$p(u)$, and Legendre's polynomials $P_n(x)$. Hence by means of these tables
we can determine the arugment and also its error.

Elliptic integrals are functions of two arguments. The error in each
of these arguments can not be determined uniquely, but by using formula
(6. 1) and assuming the principle of equal effects we can find definite
formulas for the errors in the arguments. Thus, denoting an elliptic
integral by I and the function of the arguments by $F(\theta, \phi)$, we have

$$I = F(\theta, \phi).$$

Hence

$$\Delta I = (\partial F/\partial\theta)\Delta\theta + (\partial F/\partial\phi)\Delta\phi.$$

By assuming that the two terms on the right-hand side are equal, we get

$$\Delta\theta = \frac{\Delta I}{2\dfrac{\partial F}{\partial\theta}}, \qquad \Delta\phi = \frac{\Delta I}{2\dfrac{\partial F}{\partial\phi}}.$$

Knowing the error ΔI of the integral, we can find from these formulas the corresponding errors in θ and ϕ.

Remarks. Comparison of formulas (3) and (5) shows that the error made in finding an angle from its tangent is always less than when finding it from its sine, because $\cos^2 x$ is less than sec x. The latter may have any value from 1 to ∞, whereas the value of the former never exceeds 1.

Formulas (7) and (9) show still more clearly the advantage of determining an angle from its tangent. It is evident from (9) that the error in x can rarely exceed the error in y, since sin $2x$ can not exceed 1, but (7) shows that when the angle is determined from its log sine the error in x may be many times that in y.

Let us consider a numerical case. Suppose we are to find x from a 5-place table of log sines. Since all the tabular values are rounded numbers, the value of Δy may be as large as 0.000005, due to the inherent errors of the table itself. Taking $x = 60°$ and substituting in (7), we get

$$\Delta x = 2.3026\sqrt{3} \times 0.000005$$
$$= 0.00002 \text{ radian, about,}$$
$$= 4''.1.$$

The unavoidable error may therefore be as great as 4 seconds if we find x from its log sine.

If, on the other hand, we find x from a table of log tangents we have from (9)

$$\Delta x < 1.16 \times \tfrac{1}{2}\sqrt{3} \times 0.000005 = 0.000005 \text{ rad.}$$
$$= 1''.$$

The error is thus only one-fourth as great as in the preceding case.

The foregoing formulas simply substantiate what has long been known by computers: that an angle can be determined more accurately from its tangent or cotangent than from its sine or cosine.

Note. The problem of determining the maximum possible error in a result found by means of tables is rather involved. The reader will find a masterly treatment of this matter in J. Lüroth's *Vorlesungen über numerisches Rechen,* Leipzig, 1900.

However, the problem is of little practical importance, because the errors in such a computation rarely if ever combine so as to produce their maximum aggregate effect. They neutralize one another as the calculation proceeds.

12. The Accuracy of Series Approximations. It is frequently easier to find the numerical value of a function by expanding it into a power series and evaluating the first few terms than by any other method. In fact, this is sometimes the only possible method of computing it. The general method for expanding functions into power series is by means of Taylor's formula. The two standard forms of this formula are the following:

$$(1) \quad f(x) = f(a) + (x-a)f'(a) + \frac{(x-a)^2}{2!}f''(a) + \cdots + \frac{(x-a)^{n-1}}{(n-1)!}f^{(n-1)}$$

$$+ \frac{(x-a)^n}{n!}f^{(n)}[a + \theta(x-a)], \quad 0 < \theta < 1.$$

$$(2) \quad f(x+h) = f(x) + hf'(x) + \frac{h^2}{2!}f''(x) + \cdots + \frac{h^{n-1}}{(n-1)!}f^{(n-1)}(x)$$

$$+ \frac{h^n}{n!}f^{(n)}(x + \theta h), \quad 0 < \theta < 1.$$

On putting $a = 0$ in (1) we get Maclaurin's formula:

$$(3) \quad f(x) = f(0) + xf'(0) + \frac{x^2}{2!}f''(0) + \cdots + \frac{x^{n-1}}{(n-1)!}f^{(n-1)}(0)$$

$$+ \frac{x^n}{n!}f^{(n)}(\theta x), \quad 0 < \theta < 1.$$

The last term in each of these three formulas is the *remainder after n terms.* This remainder term is the quantity in which we shall be interested in this article. The forms of the remainder given above are not the only ones, however. Another useful form will be given below.

12a). The Remainder Terms in Taylor's and Maclaurin's Series. Denoting by $R_n(x)$ the remainder after n terms in the Taylor and Maclaurin expansions, we have the following useful forms:

1. For Taylor's formula (1):

$$(a) \qquad R_n(x) = \frac{(x-a)^n}{n!}f^{(n)}[a + \theta(x-a)], \quad 0 < \theta < 1.$$

(b) $$R_n(x) = \frac{1}{(n-1)!} \int_0^{x-a} f^{(n)}(x-t) t^{n-1} dt.$$

2. For Taylor's formula (2):

(a) $$R_n(x) = \frac{h^n}{n!} f^{(n)}(x+\theta h), \quad 0 < \theta < 1.$$

(b) $$R_n(x) = \frac{1}{(n-1)!} \int_0^h f^{(n)}(x+h-t) t^{n-1} dt.$$

3. For Maclaurin's formula:

(a) $$R_n(x) = \frac{x^n}{n!} f^{(n)}(\theta x), \quad 0 < \theta < 1.$$

(b) $$R_n(x) = \frac{1}{(n-1)!} \int_0^x f^{(n)}(x-t) t^{n-1} dt.$$

It will be observed that the second form (the integral form) is perfectly definite and contains no uncertain factor θ. In using either form, however, it is necessary first to find the nth derivative of $f(x)$.

Since the integral form of $R_n(x)$ is not usually given in the textbooks on calculus, we shall show how to apply it to an example.

Example. Find the remainder after n terms in the expansion of $\log_e (x+h)$.

Solution. Here

$$f(x) = \log_e x,$$
$$\therefore f'(x) = 1/x,$$
$$f''(x) = -(1/x^2),$$
$$f'''(x) = 2/x^3,$$
$$f^{iv}(x) = -(6/x^4),$$

. . . .

$$f^{(n)}(x) = \frac{(-1)^{n-1}(n-1)!}{x^n}.$$

$$\therefore R_n(x) = (-1)^{n-1} \frac{(n-1)!}{(n-1)!} \int_0^h \frac{1}{(x+h-t)^n} t^{n-1} dt.$$

Now since t varies from 0 to h, the greatest value of $R_n(x)$ is obtained by putting $t = h$ in the integrand. We then have, omitting the factor $(-1)^{n-1}$, which is never greater than 1,

$$R_n(x) < \int_0^h \frac{t^{n-1}dt}{x^n} = \frac{1}{x^n} \int_0^h t^{n-1}dt = \frac{1}{x^n} \frac{h^n}{n} = \frac{1}{n}\left(\frac{h}{x}\right)^n.$$

Suppose $x = 1$, $h = 0.01$. Then $h/x = 0.01$. If, therefore, we wish to know how many terms in the expansion of $\log_e 1.01$ are necessary in order to get a result correct to seven decimal places we take $R_n \leqq 0.00000005$.

$$\therefore (1/n)(0.01)^n = 0.00000005.$$

It is evident by inspection that $n = 4$ will give a remainder much smaller than the allowable error. Hence we take four terms of the expansion of $\log_e (x + h)$.

The reader can easily verify that the first form of remainder gives the same result as that just found.

12b). Alternating Series. An alternating series is an infinite series in which the terms are alternately positive and negative. Such a series is convergent if (a) each term is numerically less than the preceding and (b) the limit of the nth term is zero when n becomes infinite.

Alternating series are of frequent occurrence in applied mathematics and are the most satisfactory for purposes of computation, because it is always an easy matter to determine the error of a computed result. The rule for determining the error is simply this:

In a convergent alternating series the error committed in stopping with any term is always less than the first term neglected.

Thus, since

$$\log_e (1 + x) = x - x^2/2 + x^3/3 - x^4/4 + x^5/5 - \cdots,$$

we have

$$\log_e (1.01) = 0.01 - \frac{(0.01)^2}{2} + \frac{(0.01)^3}{3} + R,$$

where $R < |(0.01)^4/4| = 0.0000000025$.

We therefore get a result true to eight decimal places by taking only three terms of the expansion.

12c). Some Important Series and Their Remainder Terms. Below are given some of the most useful series and their remainder terms, alternating series not being included because their remainder terms can be computed by the rule given above.

1. The Binomial Series.

$$(1 + x)^m = 1 + mx + \frac{m(m-1)}{2!} x^2 + \frac{m(m-1)(m-2)}{3!} x^3 + \cdots$$
$$+ \frac{m(m-1)(m-2)\cdots(m-n+2)}{(n-1)!} x^{n-1} + R_n,$$

where

(a) $R_n = \dfrac{m(m-1)(m-2)\cdots(m-n+1)}{n!}\, x^n (1+\theta x)^{m-n}, \quad 0 < \theta < 1,$

in all cases.

(b) $R_n < \left| \dfrac{m(m-1)(m-2)\cdots(m-n+1)}{n!}\, x^n \right| \text{ if } x > 0.$

(c) $R_n < \left| \dfrac{m(m-1)(m-2)\cdots(m-n+1)}{n!} \dfrac{x^n}{(1+x)^{n-m}} \right|$

if $x < 0$ and $n > m$.

(d) $R_n < |x^n| (1+x)^m \text{ if } -1 < m < 0.$

If m is a fraction, positive or negative, or a negative integer, the binomial expansion is valid only when $|x| < 1$. Also, except when m is a *positive integer*, a binomial such as $(a+b)^m$ must be written in the form

$$a^m \left(1 + \frac{b}{a}\right)^m \text{ if } a > b, \text{ or } b^m \left(1 + \frac{a}{b}\right)^m \text{ if } b > a,$$

before expanding it.

2. *Exponential Series.*

(a) $e^x = 1 + x + \dfrac{x^2}{2!} + \dfrac{x^3}{3!} + \cdots + \dfrac{x^{n-1}}{(n-1)!} + \dfrac{x^n}{n!}\, e^{\theta x}.$

(b) $a^x = 1 + x \log a + \dfrac{(x \log a)^2}{2!} + \cdots + \dfrac{(x \log a)^{n-1}}{(n-1)!} + \dfrac{(x \log a)^n}{n!}\, a^{\theta x}.$

If in (a) we put $x = 1$ we get the following series for computing e:

(c) $e = 1 + 1 + \dfrac{1}{2} + \dfrac{1}{3!} + \dfrac{1}{4!} + \cdots + \dfrac{1}{(n-1)!} + \dfrac{e^\theta}{n!}.$

Here

$$R_n = \frac{e^\theta}{n!}.$$

But since $e < 3$ and $\theta \leq 1$, it is plain that

(d) $R_n < \dfrac{3}{n!}.$

A more definite formula for R_n can be found as follows:
Writing more than n terms of the series (c), we have

$$e = \left[1 + 1 + \frac{1}{2!} + \frac{1}{3!} + \cdots + \frac{1}{(n-1)!} \right]$$
$$+ \frac{1}{n!} + \frac{1}{(n+1)!} + \frac{1}{(n+2)!} + \cdots,$$

where the remainder after n terms is

$$R_n = \frac{1}{n!} + \frac{1}{(n+1)!} + \frac{1}{(n+2)!} + \cdots$$
$$= \frac{1}{n!}\left(1 + \frac{1}{n+1} + \frac{1}{(n+1)(n+2)} + \cdots\right).$$

The quantity in parenthesis on the right is clearly less than the sum of the geometric series

$$1 + 1/n + 1/n^2 + 1/n^3 + \cdots,$$

the sum of which is

$$\frac{1}{1 - 1/n} = \frac{n}{n-1}.$$

Hence

(e) $$R_n < \frac{1}{n!}\,\frac{n}{n-1}, \text{ or } R_n < \frac{1}{(n-1)(n-1)!}.$$

By means of this formula (e) we can find the requisite number of terms in the expansion (c) to give the value of e correct to any desired number of decimal places. Thus, if we wished to find e correct to ten decimal places by means of the series (c) we would find n from the equation $1/(n-1)(n-1)! = 0.00000000005$. With the aid of a table of the reciprocals of the factorials we find that $n-1 = 13$, or $n = 14$. We should therefore take 14 terms of the series (c). We find in like manner that in order to compute e correct to 100 decimal places we should take 71 terms of the series (c).

3. Logarithmic Series.

(a) $$\log_e(m+1) = \log_e m + 2\left[\frac{1}{2m+1} + \frac{1}{3(2m+1)^3} + \frac{1}{5(2m+1)^5}\right.$$
$$\left. + \cdots \quad \frac{1}{(2n-1)(2m+1)^{2n-1}}\right] + R_n,$$

To find an upper limit for R_n we have

$$R_n = 2\left[\frac{1}{(2n+1)(2m+1)^{2n+1}} + \frac{1}{(2n+3)(2m+1)^{2n+3}}\right.$$
$$\left. + \frac{1}{(2n+5)(2m+1)^{2n+5}} + \cdots\right]$$

Each term of the series in brackets, after the first, is less than the corresponding term of the series

$$\frac{1}{(2n+1)(2m+1)^{2n+1}} + \frac{1}{(2n+1)(2m+1)^{2n+3}}$$
$$+ \frac{1}{(2n+1)(2m+1)^{2n+5}} + \cdots ,$$

or

$$\frac{1}{(2n+1)(2m+1)^{2n+1}}\left[1 + \frac{1}{(2m+1)^2} + \frac{1}{(2m+1)^4} + \cdots \right],$$

which is a geometric series with ratio $\dfrac{1}{(2m+1)^2}$ and sum

$$\frac{1}{1 - \dfrac{1}{(2m+1)^2}}, \quad \text{or} \quad \frac{(2m+1)^2}{4m(m+1)}. \quad \text{Hence}$$

$$R_n < 2\left(\frac{1}{(2n+1)(2m+1)^{2n+1}}\right)\frac{(2m+1)^2}{4m(m+1)}$$
$$= \frac{1}{2}\,\frac{1}{m(m+1)(2n+1)(2m+1)^{2n-1}}.$$

Therefore

(b) $$R_n < \frac{1}{2}\,\frac{1}{m(m+1)(2n+1)(2m+1)^{2n-1}}.$$

Example 1. To compute ln 2 * by taking three terms of (a) we have, since $m=1$, $n=3$,

$$\ln 2 = 2\left[\frac{1}{3} + \frac{1}{3(3)^3} + \frac{1}{5(3)^5}\right] = 0.693004;$$

and by (b),

$$R_n < \frac{1}{2}\,\frac{1}{2(7)(3)^5} = 0.000147,$$

which affects the fourth decimal place. Since the true value of ln 2 to eight decimal places is 0.69314718, the error in the value found above is 0.000143, which is less than 0.000147.

Example 2. To find ln 5 correct to ten decimal places we have $m=4$, $R_n = (1/2) \cdot (1/10^{10})$. Hence, by (b),

$$\frac{1}{2}\,\frac{1}{4 \times 5(2n+1)(9)^{2n-1}} = \frac{1}{2}\,\frac{1}{10^{10}},$$

or

$$(2n+1)(9)^{2n-1} = 5 \times 10^8 = 500{,}000{,}000.$$

We find by trial that n is about 4. 1, and that for $n=5$ the logarithm will be correct to 11 decimal places.

* Frequently in this book we shall write ln for $\log_e$.

12d). Some nth Derivatives. In computing the remainder term in a series it is necessary to have the nth derivative of the given function. To facilitate the calculation of R_n we therefore give below a list of nth derivatives of some simple functions. The symbol D denotes differentiation with respect to x, or $D = d/dx$.

(a) $$D^n a^x = a^x (\log_e a)^n.$$

(b) $$D^n \sin x = \sin[x + n(\pi/2)].$$

(c) $$D^n \cos x = \cos[x + n(\pi/2)].$$

(d) $$D_n \left(\frac{1}{a + bx} \right) = \frac{(-1)^n n! b^n}{(a + bx)^{n+1}}.$$

(e) $$D^n \left(\frac{1}{\sqrt{a + bx}} \right) = \frac{(-1)^n 1 \cdot 3 \cdot 5 \cdots (2n - 1)}{2^n (a + bx)^{(2n+1)/2}} b^n.$$

(f) $$D^n \log_e (a + bx) = \frac{(-1)^n (n - 1)! b^n}{(a + bx)^n}.$$

(g) $$D^n \left(\frac{\log_e x}{x} \right) = \frac{(-1)^n n!}{x^{n+1}} [\log_e x - (1 + \tfrac{1}{2} + \tfrac{1}{3} + \cdots + 1/n)].$$

(h) $$D^n \log_e (1 + x^2) = \frac{(-1)^{n-1} 2(n - 1)! \cos \left[n \sin^{-1} \left(\dfrac{1}{\sqrt{1 + x^2}} \right) \right]}{(1 + x^2)^{n/2}}.$$

(i) $$D^n \tan^{-1} x = \frac{(-1)^{n-1} (n - 1)!}{(1 + x^2)^{n/2}} \cdot \sin \left[n \sin^{-1} \left(\frac{1}{\sqrt{1 + x^2}} \right) \right].$$

(j) $$D^n \frac{1}{1 + x^2} = \frac{(-1)^n n!}{(1 + x^2)^{(n+1)/2}} \sin \left[(n + 1) \sin^{-1} \left(\frac{1}{\sqrt{1 + x^2}} \right) \right].$$

(k) $$D^n \left(\frac{\alpha + \beta x}{(x - a)^2 + b^2} \right) = \frac{(-1)^n n!}{b \rho^{n+1}} [\beta b \cos(n + 1)\theta$$
$$+ (\alpha + \beta a) \sin(n + 1)\theta],$$

where

$$\rho = \sqrt{(x - a)^2 + b^2}$$

$$\theta = \tan^{-1} \frac{b}{x - a}$$

For an extensive investigation of nth derivatives the reader is referred to Steffensen's *Interpolation*, pp. 231-241.

13. Accuracy of the Solution of Simultaneous Linear Equations.
In some fields of applied mathematics one encounters systems of linear

equations in which the coefficients and constant terms are subject to small errors. Such errors may be due to uncertainties in experimental data or to rounding off. The solutions of such systems of equations will therefore be inaccurate in some degree, and it is very desirable to have a method of estimating the inherent errors of such solutions.

Consider the simple system

(1)
$$\begin{cases} a_1x + b_1y = c_1 \\ a_2x + b_2y = c_2 . \end{cases}$$

If the exact values of the constants are $a_1 + \Delta a_1$, $b_1 + \Delta b_1$, etc., and the corresponding true values of x and y are $x + \Delta x$ and $y + \Delta y$, then the system (1) becomes

(2)
$$\begin{cases} (a_1 + \Delta a_1)(x + \Delta x) + (b_1 + \Delta b_1)(y + \Delta y) = c_1 + \Delta c_1 \\ (a_2 + \Delta a_2)(x + \Delta x) + (b_2 + \Delta b_2)(y + \Delta y) = c_2 + \Delta c_2 . \end{cases}$$

Multiplying out, dropping the terms involving the products of two errors (such as $\Delta a_1 \Delta x$ etc., since they are negligible), and making use of (1), we get

(3)
$$\begin{cases} a_1\Delta x + x\Delta a_1 + b_1\Delta y + y\Delta b_1 = \Delta c_1 \\ a_2\Delta x + x\Delta a_2 + b_2\Delta y + y\Delta b_2 = \Delta c_2 . \end{cases}$$

Now since Δa_1, Δb_1, etc. are supposed to be known, and x and y can be found from (1), we have

(4)
$$\begin{cases} a_1\Delta x + b_1\Delta y = \Delta c_1 - (x\Delta a_1 + y\Delta b_1), \\ a_2\Delta x + b_2\Delta y = \Delta c_2 - (x\Delta a_2 + y\Delta b_2). \end{cases}$$

Since the right-hand members of these equations are known, one can readily find Δx and Δy from (4).

It is to be noted that the coefficients of Δx and Δy in (4) are the same as those of x and y in (1). Hence if the equations are solved by determinants (Cramer's Rule), the determinant

$$\begin{vmatrix} a_1 & b_1 \\ a_2 & b_2 \end{vmatrix}$$

serves for both sets of equations.

Since the values of x and y in (1) are

$$x = \frac{c_1b_2 - c_2b_1}{a_1b_2 - a_2b_1}, \qquad y = \frac{c_2a_1 - c_1a_2}{a_1b_2 - a_2b_1},$$

it is evident that the magnitudes of x and y vary directly with the magnitudes of the c's, a fact which is obvious if we put $c_1 = c_2 = k$. Then

$$x = \frac{k(b_2 - b_1)}{a_1 b_2 - a_2 b_1}, \qquad y = \frac{k(a_1 - a_2)}{a_1 b_2 - a_2 b_1}.$$

Hence in order to get the upper limits of the errors Δx and Δy, we should make the right-hand members of (4) as large as possible. This is done by taking the sum of the absolute values of the quantities in the right-hand members of (4).

It is to be further noted that *equations* (3) *are merely the differentials of* (1) and can therefore be written down at once by differentiating the given equations.

The upper limits of the inherent errors in the solution of a system of simultaneous linear equations can now be found by the following procedure:

1. Solve the given system for the unknowns in the usual manner.

2. Take the differentials of the equations of the given system and write the results in the form (4).

3. Substitute in the differential system found in step 2 the assumed values of the errors Δa_1, etc. and the values of x and y found in step 1.

4. Taking the arithmetic sum (sum of the absolute values) of the quantities in the right-hand members of the equations found in step 3, solve the system for Δx, Δy, etc.

Example 1. Solve the system

$$3.21x - 4.36y = 5.73$$

$$2.13x + 8.63y = 12.65,$$

assuming that all the numerical values are rounded numbers and correct to two decimal places.

Solution. Solving these equations by determinants, we have

$$x = \frac{\begin{vmatrix} 5.73 & -4.36 \\ 12.65 & 8.63 \end{vmatrix}}{\begin{vmatrix} 3.21 & -4.36 \\ 2.13 & 8.63 \end{vmatrix}} = \frac{49.4499 + 55.1540}{27.7023 + 9.2868} = 2.828,$$

$$y = \frac{\begin{vmatrix} 3.21 & 5.73 \\ 2.13 & 12.65 \end{vmatrix}}{36.9891} = \frac{40.6065 - 12.2049}{36.9891} = 0.768.$$

Before proceeding further we substitute these values of x and y in the given equations to see whether they satisfy those equations.   It will be found that they do.

Since the given equations are correct to two decimal places, the errors Δa_1, Δb_1, etc. are not greater than 0.005.   Hence the equations for finding the possible errors in x and y are

$$3.21\Delta x - 4.36\Delta y = 0.005 + (2.828 + 0.768)(0.005)$$
$$= 0.005(1 + 2.828 + 0.768) = 0.0230,$$
$$2.13\Delta x + 8.63\Delta y = 0.005 + (2.828 + 0.768)(0.005) = 0.0230.$$

Then

$$\Delta x = \frac{\begin{vmatrix} 0.0230 & -4.36 \\ 0.0230 & 8.63 \end{vmatrix}}{37.0} = \frac{0.0230}{37.0} \begin{vmatrix} 1 & -4.36 \\ 1 & 8.63 \end{vmatrix} = 0.0081,$$

$$\Delta y = \frac{\begin{vmatrix} 3.21 & 0.0230 \\ 2.13 & 0.0230 \end{vmatrix}}{37.0} = \frac{0.0230}{37.0} \begin{vmatrix} 3.21 & 1 \\ 2.13 & 1 \end{vmatrix} = 0.00067.$$

These errors affect the second decimal in x and the third decimal in y. Hence we may take $x = 2.83$ and $y = 0.768$ with the understanding that the last digit in each is slightly uncertain.

If we change the sign of the coefficient of y in the first of the given equations and then solve the set, we find $\Delta x = 0.0033$ and $\Delta y = 0.00084$.

Example 2.   Solve the system

$$\begin{cases} 1.22x - 1.32y + 3.96z = 2.12 \\ 2.12x - 3.52y + 1.62z = -1.26 \\ 4.23x - 1.21y + 1.09z = 3.22, \end{cases}$$

all numbers being rounded and correct to the number of digits given.

Solution.   Here

$$D = \begin{vmatrix} 1.22 & -1.32 & 3.96 \\ 2.12 & -3.52 & 1.62 \\ 4.23 & -1.21 & 1.09 \end{vmatrix} = 64.404516 - 23.884520$$
$$= 40.520,$$

$$x = \frac{55.077264 - 16.832552}{40.520} = 0.9438,$$

$$y = \frac{62.666064 - 12.938452}{40.520} = 1.227,$$

$$z = \frac{47.612136 - 21.126204}{40.520} = 0.65365.$$

The solutions are written as above to indicate that there was no loss of significant figures by subtraction.

It will be found that the above values satisfy the given equations, except for 0.001 in the second equation.

Since the possible errors in the coefficients and constant terms do not exceed 0.005, the error equations are

$$\begin{cases} 1.22\Delta x - 1.32\Delta y + 3.96\Delta z = 0.005 \\ \qquad\qquad + (0.944 + 1.227 + 0.654)(0.005) = 0.01412 \\ 2.12\Delta x - 3.52\Delta y + 1.62\Delta z = 0.01412 \\ 4.23\Delta x - 1.21\Delta y + 1.09\Delta z = 0.01412. \end{cases}$$

Then

$$\Delta x = \frac{\begin{vmatrix} 0.01412 & -1.32 & 3.96 \\ 0.01412 & -3.52 & 1.62 \\ 0.01412 & -1.21 & 1.09 \end{vmatrix}}{40.52} = \frac{0.01412}{40.52} \begin{vmatrix} 1 & -1.32 & 3.96 \\ 1 & -3.52 & 1.62 \\ 1 & -1.21 & 1.09 \end{vmatrix} = 0.0023.$$

Similarly, $\Delta y = 0.0015$, $\Delta z = 0.0023$. Hence x, y, and z are true to 2 decimal places and we take them to be

$$x = 0.94, \qquad y = 1.23, \qquad z = 0.65.$$

Note. The values found for Δx, Δy, and Δz are the maximum possible errors for x, y, and z. The true errors in these quantities may be, and probably are, much smaller than these maximum errors.

Example 3. Solve the system

$$\begin{cases} 47.11x + 13.72y = 40.44 \\ 13.72x + \quad 4y = 11.78, \end{cases}$$

the coefficient of y in the second equation being an exact number and all the other numbers being rounded but correct to the number of digits given.

Solution. Solving by determinants we have

$$x = \frac{\begin{vmatrix} 40.44 & 13.72 \\ 11.78 & 4 \end{vmatrix}}{\begin{vmatrix} 47.11 & 13.72 \\ 13.72 & 4 \end{vmatrix}} = \frac{161.76 - 161.6216}{188.44 - 188.2384} = \frac{0.1384}{0.2016} = 0.6865.$$

$$y = \frac{\begin{vmatrix} 47.11 & 40.44 \\ 13.72 & 11.78 \end{vmatrix}}{0.2016} = \frac{554.9588 - 554.8368}{0.2016} = \frac{0.1190}{0.2016} = 0.5903.$$

Note that the first three significant figures were lost by subtraction in this example. Nevertheless, the values found satisfy the given equations.

Note also that no numbers were rounded in the above computation. *In the solution of systems of simultaneous equations no numbers should be rounded or shortened in any way until the final results are reached,* otherwise errors of computation will be introduced and the results found will not satisfy the given equations.

For the computation of the errors in x and y, we have

$$\Delta a_1 = \Delta b_1 = \Delta c_1 = \Delta a_2 = \Delta c_2 \leqq 0.005, \text{ and } \Delta b_2 = 0.$$

Hence the error equations are

$$\begin{cases} 47.11\Delta x + 13.72\Delta y = 0.005 + (0.6865 + 0.5903)(0.005) = 0.01138 \\ 13.72\Delta x + 4\Delta y = 0.005 + 0.6865 \times 0.005 = 0.00843. \end{cases}$$

Therefore

$$\Delta x = \frac{\begin{vmatrix} 0.01138 & 13.72 \\ 0.00843 & 4 \end{vmatrix}}{0.2016} = \frac{0.04552 - 0.11566}{0.2016} = -0.35,$$

$$\Delta y = \frac{\begin{vmatrix} 47.11 & 0.01138 \\ 13.72 & 0.00843 \end{vmatrix}}{0.2016} = \frac{0.3971 - 0.1561}{0.2016} = 1.20.$$

The possible errors in x and y are thus larger than the quantities themselves. This might mean that the values found for x and y are worthless, but it is known from additional information that the value of x is roughly correct. The value of y is practically worthless.*

Geometrical considerations help to explain some of the trouble in this example. A glance at the given equations shows that the graphs of those equations are almost parallel straight lines. Hence slight changes in their positions, due to altering their coefficients, will cause their point of intersection to change greatly. The only way to get more dependable results is to have coefficients of greater accuracy.

The real source of the inherent errors in the solution of systems of linear equations is the loss of leading significant figures by subtraction. Any method † of solving the equations will necessitate the subtraction of numbers of the same order of magnitude, and when two such numbers are nearly equal there will be a loss of leading digits. This loss produces an inherent error in the solution.

---

* This example is a slight variation of Example 3, p. 456.
† Except iteration. See Art. 164.

Such a loss of leading digits can be seen at a glance if the equations are solved by determinants and the determinants are expanded by the method of minors. In systems involving several equations, however, such a method of solution is impracticable and therefore the loss of leading digits can not be detected. Hence it is necessary to have a method of computing the maximum inherent errors in the solution.

Example 3 serves to bring out the fact that the solution of a system of linear equations may be much less reliable than the coefficients and constant terms. Hence in solving a system of linear equations the solution should be carried through without dropping any seemingly surplus digits until the end is reached. Then the results found should be substituted in the given equations to see if they satisfy those equations. And, finally, the upper limits of the errors of the solutions should be computed. The final results should not be given to more digits than the errors justify.

13a. Errors in Determinants. In Example 3 of the preceding article we have seen that when the elements in a determinant are inexact numbers, due to rounding or otherwise, the value of the determinant may be seriously affected by the loss of the most important significant figures in the expansion or evaluation process. The amount of such losses cannot be determined in advance. We can, however, determine the upper limit of the error in a determinant whose elements are subject to given possible errors. For purposes of illustration we consider a determinant of the third order.

Let

$$(1) \qquad D = \begin{vmatrix} x_1 & x_2 & x_3 \\ y_1 & y_2 & y_3 \\ z_1 & z_2 & z_3 \end{vmatrix} .$$

Now if the elements are subject to possible errors of unknown signs but of magnitudes Δx_1, Δy_1, etc., which are small in comparison with x_1, y_1, etc., then the value of D will be subject to the possible error ΔD such that

$$(2) \qquad D + \Delta D = \begin{vmatrix} x_1 + \Delta x_1 & x_2 + \Delta x_2 & x_3 + \Delta x_3 \\ y_1 + \Delta y_1 & y_2 + \Delta y_2 & y_3 + \Delta y_3 \\ z_1 + \Delta z_1 & z_2 + \Delta z_2 & z_3 + \Delta z_3 \end{vmatrix} .$$

By the addition theorem of determinants the right member of (2) can be expressed as the sum of eight determinants, the first of which is the original determinant D. Each of three of the remaining determinants contains one column of error elements, each of three of the others contains two columns of error elements, and the remaining determinant has three columns of error elements. All determinants containing more than one column of error elements will be neglected, because, when expanded, the resulting terms will all contain second and third powers of the errors and will therefore be negligible in comparison with terms containing only the first powers of the errors. The value of ΔD is thus the sum of three determinants each containing a single column of error elements.

But those determinants are only the *differential* of D, and we therefore have

$$
(3) \qquad dD = \begin{vmatrix} dx_1 & x_2 & x_3 \\ dy_1 & y_2 & y_3 \\ dz_1 & z_2 & z_3 \end{vmatrix} + \begin{vmatrix} x_1 & dx_2 & x_3 \\ y_1 & dy_2 & y_3 \\ z_1 & dz_2 & z_3 \end{vmatrix} + \begin{vmatrix} x_1 & x_2 & dx_3 \\ y_1 & y_2 & dy_3 \\ z_1 & z_2 & dz_3 \end{vmatrix},
$$

or

$$
\begin{aligned}
(4) \qquad dD =\; & (y_2 z_3 - y_3 z_2)\,dx_1 - (x_2 z_3 - x_3 z_2)\,dy_1 + (x_2 y_3 - x_3 y_2)\,dz_1 \\
& - (y_1 z_3 - y_3 z_1)\,dx_2 + (x_1 z_3 - x_3 z_1)\,dy_2 - (x_1 y_3 - x_3 y_1)\,dz_2 \\
& + (y_1 z_2 - y_2 z_1)\,dx_3 - (x_1 z_2 - x_2 z_1)\,dy_3 + (x_1 y_2 - x_2 y_1)\,dz_3.
\end{aligned}
$$

The maximum possible error would occur when the signs of the elements and the signs of the errors were such that all the eighteen terms in the right member of (4) were of the same sign—a very remote possibility.

Equation (4) shows that the error in a determinant composed of inexact elements may be anything from zero up to a number of considerable magnitude. It must be borne in mind, however, that the terms in (4) will largely cancel one another so that, in general, dD will not be large.

14. A Final Remark. The present chapter may appropriately close with the following lines from Alexander Pope:

> A little learning is a dangerous thing;
> Drink deep, or taste not the Pierian spring:
> There shallow draughts intoxicate the brain,
> And drinking largely sobers us again.

Pope was probably not thinking of approximate calculation when he wrote those lines, but no better advice could be given with respect to that subject. A smatter of knowledge of approximate calculation is worse than no knowledge at all. Fragmentary knowledge may lead to rough results that cannot be trusted. The author has seen students and teachers obtain far worse results from applying hazy ideas of the subject than if they had never heard of it. Their faulty work was due mostly to drastic rounding of numbers (at the beginning of a computation or at intermediate steps) or to dropping non-negligible terms in a series.

The essence of this chapter cannot be given in one or two recitations, nor in two or three. If the teacher has only two or three recitations to devote to it, he had better leave it out entirely.

EXERCISES I

1. Round off the following numbers correctly to four significant figures:

63.8543, 93487, 0.0063945, 83615, 363042, 0.090038, 53908.

2. A carpenter measures a 10-foot beam to the nearest eighth of an inch, and a machinist measures a $\frac{1}{2}$-inch bolt to the nearest thousandth of an inch.* Which measurement is the more accurate?

3. The following numbers are all approximate and are correct as far as their last digits only. Find their sum.

136.421, 28.3, 321, 68.243, 17.482.

4. Find the sum of the following approximate numbers, each being correct only to the number of significant figures given:

0.15625, 86.43, 191.6, 432.0 $\times$ 10, 930.42.

5. The numbers 48.392 and 6852.4 are both approximate and true only to their last digits. Find their difference and state how many figures in the result are trustworthy.

6. Find the value of $\sqrt{10} - \pi$ correct to five significant figures.

7. The theoretical horsepower available in a stream is given by the formula

$$H.P. = \frac{whQ}{550},$$

where h = head in feet, Q = discharge in cubic feet per second, and w =

---

* When a measurement is recorded to the nearest unit, the absolute error of the measurement is not more than *half* a unit.

weight of a cubic foot of water. The weight of fresh water varies from 62.3 to 62.5 lbs. per cubic foot, depending upon its temperature and purity.

If the measured values of Q and h are $Q = 463$ cu. ft./sec. and $h = 16.42$ ft., find the H. P. of the stream and indicate how many figures of the result are reliable.

8. The velocity of water flowing in long pipes is given by the formula

$$v = \sqrt{\frac{2ghd}{fl}} \text{ ft./sec.,}$$

where $g =$ acceleration of gravity $= 32.2$ ft./sec.^{2}
               $h =$ head in feet,
               $d =$ diameter of pipe in feet,
               $l =$ length of pipe in feet,
               $f =$ coefficient of pipe friction.

In this problem the factor f is the most uncertain. It varies from 0.01 to 0.05 and is usually somewhere between 0.02 and 0.03. Assuming that f is within the limits 0.02 and 0.03 and taking

$$g = 32.2,$$
$$h = 112 \text{ feet,}$$
$$d = \tfrac{1}{2} \text{ foot,}$$
$$l = 1865 \text{ feet,}$$

find v and indicate its reliability.

9. The velocity of water in a short pipe is given by the formula

$$v = \sqrt{\frac{2gh}{1.5 + fl/d}}$$

where g, h, f, l, and d have the same meanings as in the preceding example. Taking $l = 75$ feet and the other data the same as in Ex. 8, find v and indicate its reliability.

10. The acceleration of gravity at any point on the earth's surface is given by the formula

$$g = 32.1721 - 0.08211 \cos 2L - 0.000003H,$$

where $H =$ altitude in feet above sea level, and $L =$ latitude of the place. It thus appears that the value of g is not 32, nor 32.2, nor even 32.17.

Compute the kinetic energy of a 100-pound projectile moving with a velocity of 2000 feet per second by taking g equal to 32, 32.2, and 32.17 in succession and note the extent to which the results disagree after the first two or three figures.

11. How accurately should the length and time of vibration of a seconds pendulum be measured in order that the computed value of g be correct to 0.05 per cent?

12. If in the formula

$$R = \frac{r^2}{2h} + \frac{h}{2}$$

the percentage error in R is not to exceed 0.3 per cent, find the allowable percentage errors in r and h when $r = 48$ mm. and $h = 56$ mm.

13. When the index of refraction of a liquid is determined by means of a refractometer, the index n is given by the formula

$$n = \sqrt{N^2 - \sin^2 \theta}.$$

If $N = 1.62200$ with an uncertainty of 0.00004 and $\theta = 38°$ approximately, find $\Delta\theta$ in order that n may be reliable to 0.02 per cent.

14. The area of the cross section of a rod is desired to 0.2 per cent. How accurately should the diameter be measured?

15. The approximate latitude of a place can be easily found by measuring the altitude h of Polaris at a known time t and using the formula

$$L = h - p \cos t,$$

where $p =$ polar distance $= 90° -$ declination.

Treating p as a constant and equal to $1°07'30''$, and taking $h = 41°25'$, $t = 0°38'42''$, find the error in L due to errors of $1'$ in h and 5^s in t.

16. In the preceding example find the allowable errors in h and t in order that the error in L shall not exceed $1'$, using the same values of p, t, and h as before.

17. The distance between any two points P_1 and P_2 on the earth's surface is given by the formula

$$\cos D = \sin L_1 \sin L_2 + \cos L_1 \cos L_2 \cos(\lambda_1 - \lambda_2),$$

where L_1, L_2 and λ_1, λ_2 denote the respective latitudes and longitudes of the two places. Find the allowable errors in L_1, L_2, λ_1, λ_2 in order that the error in D shall not exceed $1'$ (a geographical mile), taking

$$L_1 = 36°10' N, \quad L_2 = 58°43' N, \quad \lambda_1 = 82°15' W, \quad \lambda_2 = 125°42' W.$$

18. The fundamental equations of practical astronomy are:

(1) $\sin h = \sin \delta \sin L + \cos \delta \cos L \cos t,$

(2) $\cos h \cos A = -\sin \delta \cos L + \cos \delta \sin L \cos t,$

(3) $\cos h \sin A = \cos \delta \sin t,$

where δ denotes declination, t hour angle, h altitude, and A azimuth of a celestial body and L denotes the latitude of a place on the earth. The declination δ is always accurately known and may therefore be considered free from error.

Differentiating (1) by considering δ constant and h, L, t as variables, we have

$$\cos h\, dh = \sin \delta \cos L\, dL - \cos \delta \sin L \cos t\, dL - \cos \delta \cos L \sin t\, dt.$$

Replacing $\cos \delta \sin L \cos t$ and $\cos \delta \sin t$ on the right by their values from (2) and (3), respectively, we get

$$dh = -(\cos A\, dL + \sin A \cos L\, dt).$$

Solving for dL,

(4) $dL = -(\sec A\, dh + \tan A \cos L\, dt).$

This equation shows that the numerical value of dL is least when A is near $0°$ or $180°$, that is, when the body is near the *meridian*. If A should be near $90°$, that is, if the body should be near the prime vertical, the error in L might be enormous. Hence when determining latitude the observed body should be as near the meridian as possible.

Using equation (4), compute dL when $dh = 1'$, $dt = 10^s$, $L = 40°$, $A = 10°$, and $A = 80°$.

19. Using the formula $dL = -(\sec A dh + \tan A \cos L dt)$, find the allowable errors in t and h in order that the error in L may not exceed $1'$ when $L = 40°$ and (a) $A = 10°$ and (b) $A = 75°$.

20. From the relation

$$\cos h dh = (\sin \delta \cos L - \cos \delta \sin L \cos t)\, dL - \cos \delta \cos L \sin t dt$$

we find by means of (2) and (3) of Ex. 18

$$dt = -\frac{dh + \cos A dL}{\sin A \cos L}.$$

This equation shows that dt is least numerically when A is near $90°$, that is, when the observed body is near the prime vertical; it also shows that when the body is on or near the prime vertical an error in the assumed latitude has practically no effect on the error in t.

Compute dt when $dh = 1'$, $dL = 5'$, $L = 40°$, $A = 10°$, and $A = 80°$.

21. Using the formula for dt in the preceding example, find the allowable errors in L and h in order that dt may not exceed 3^s, taking $L = 40°$, $A = 10°$, and $A = 80°$.

22. Using the formula of Ex. 20, take $dt = 3^s$, $dh = 1'$, and find dL for $A = 10°$ and $A = 80°$.

23. In the equation

$$x = a \sin (kt + \alpha)$$

suppose a, k and α are subject to the errors Δa, Δk, $\Delta \alpha$, respectively. Compute Δx and see which of the errors Δa, Δk, $\Delta \alpha$ is the most potent in causing an error in x.

24. Find the value of

$$I = \int_0^{0.8} (\sin x/x)\, dx$$

correct to five decimal places.

25. Compute the value of the integral

$$I = \int_0^{\pi/2} \sqrt{1 - 0.162 \sin^2 \phi}\, d\phi$$

correct to five significant figures by first expanding the integrand by the binomial theorem and then integrating the result term by term.

26. Solve the following system of equations and determine the possible errors in your solutions:

$$3.15x - 1.96y + 3.85z = 12.95$$
$$2.13x + 5.12y - 2.89z = -8.61$$
$$5.92x + 3.05y + 2.15z = 6.88.$$

27. Solve the following system and determine the possible errors in your solutions:

$$2.22x - 3.96y + 3.11z + 3.86u = -3.08$$
$$3.09x - 1.97y + 6.23z + 5.17u = -1.13$$
$$4.91x + 7.83y + 9.15z + 2.74u = 8.69$$
$$1.34x - 9.86y - 2.89z - 7.23u = 2.15.$$

CHAPTER II

INTERPOLATION

DIFFERENCES. NEWTON'S FORMULAS OF INTERPOLATION

15. Introduction. Interpolation has been defined as the art of reading between the lines of a table, and in elementary mathematics the term usually denotes the process of computing intermediate values of a function from a set of given or tabular values of that function. The general problem of interpolation, however, is much larger than this. In higher mathematics we frequently have to deal with functions whose analytical form is either totally unknown or else is of such a nature (complicated or otherwise) that the function can not easily be subjected to such operations as may be required. In either case it is desirable to replace the given function by another which can be more readily handled. This operation of replacing or representing a given function by a simpler one constitutes interpolation in the broad sense of the term.*

The general problem of interpolation consists, then, in representing a function, known or unknown, in a form chosen in advance, with the aid of given values which this function takes for definite values of the independent variable.

Thus, let $y = f(x)$ be a function given by the values $y_0, y_1, y_2, \cdots y_n$ which it takes for the values $x_0, x_1, x_2, \cdots x_n$ of the independent variable x, and let $\phi(x)$ denote an arbitrary simpler function so constructed that it takes the same values as $f(x)$ for the values $x_0, x_1, x_2, \cdots x_n$. Then if $f(x)$ is replaced by $\phi(x)$ over a given interval, the process constitutes interpolation, and the function $\phi(x)$ is a formula of interpolation.

The function $\phi(x)$ can take a variety of forms. When $\phi(x)$ is a polynomial, the process of representing $f(x)$ by $\phi(x)$ is called *parabolic* or *polynomial* interpolation; and when $\phi(x)$ is a finite trigonometric series, the process is trigonometric interpolation. In like manner, $\phi(x)$ may be a series of exponential functions, Legendre polynomials, Bessel functions, etc. In practical problems we always choose for $\phi(x)$ the simplest function which will represent the given function over the interval in question. Since polynomials are the simplest functions, we usually take a polynomial for $\phi(x)$, and nearly all the standard formulas of interpolation are poly-

---

* The author thinks that this process of replacing a complicated function by a simpler one should be called the principle of *analytical replacement* or the principle of *functional substitution*.

51

nomial formulas. In case the given function is known to be periodic, however, it is better to represent it by a trigonometric series.

The justification for replacing a given function by a polynomial or by a trigonometric series rests on two theorems proved by Weierstrass * in 1885. These theorems may be stated as follows:

I. Every function which is continuous in an interval (a, b) can be represented in that interval, to any desired degree of accuracy, by a polynomial; that is, it is possible to find a polynomial $P(x)$ such that $|f(x) - P(x)| < \epsilon$ for every value of x in the interval (a, b), where ϵ is any preassigned positive quantity.

II. Every continuous function of period 2π can be represented by a finite trigonometric series of the form

$$g(x) = a_0 + a_1 \sin x + a_2 \sin 2x + \cdots + a_n \sin nx$$
$$+ b_1 \cos x + b_2 \cos 2x + \cdots + b_n \cos nx;$$

or $|f(x) - g(x)| < \delta$ for all values of x in the interval considered, where δ represents any preassigned positive quantity.

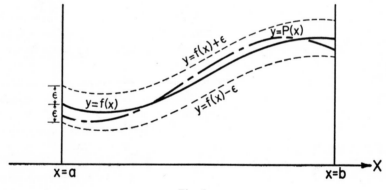

Fig. 1.

Geometrically these theorems mean that, having drawn the graphs of $y = f(x)$, $y = f(x) + \epsilon$, and $y = f(x) - \epsilon$, it is possible to find a polynomial or a finite trigonometric series whose graph remains within the region bounded by $y = f(x) + \epsilon$ and $y = f(x) - \epsilon$ for all values of x between a and b, however small ϵ may be. (See Fig. 1.) These theorems mean, therefore, that the given function may be replaced by a polynomial or by a finite trigonometric series to any desired degree of accuracy.

* Über die analytische Darstellbarkeit sogenannter willkürlicher Funktionen einer reelen Veränderlichen (Sitzungsberichte der Kgl. Ak. der Wiss., 1885).

16. Differences. If $y_0, y_1, y_2, \cdots y_n$ denote a set of values of any function $y = f(x)$, then $y_1 - y_0, y_2 - y_1, y_3 - y_2, \cdots y_n - y_{n-1}$ are called the *first differences* of the function y. Denoting these differences by Δy_0, Δy_1, Δy_2, etc., we have $\Delta y_0 = y_1 - y_0$, $\Delta y_1 = y_2 - y_1$, $\cdots \Delta y_{n-1} = y_n - y_{n-1}$, $\Delta y_n = y_{n+1} - y_n$.

The differences of these first differences are called *second differences*. Denoting them by $\Delta^2 y_0$, $\Delta^2 y_1$, etc., we have

$$\Delta^2 y_0 = \Delta y_1 - \Delta y_0 = y_2 - 2y_1 + y_0,$$
$$\Delta^2 y_1 = \Delta y_2 - \Delta y_1 = y_3 - 2y_2 + y_1,$$

etc.

In like manner, the *third differences* are

$$\Delta^3 y_0 = \Delta^2 y_1 - \Delta^2 y_0 = y_3 - 3y_2 + 3y_1 - y_0,$$
$$\Delta^3 y_1 = \Delta^2 y_2 - \Delta^2 y_1 = y_4 - 3y_3 + 3y_2 - y_1,$$

etc.

The following *difference table* shows how the differences of all orders are formed:

x	y	Δy	$\Delta^2 y$	$\Delta^3 y$	$\Delta^4 y$	$\Delta^5 y$	$\Delta^6 y$	$\Delta^7 y$	$\Delta^8 y$
x_0	y_0								
		Δy_0							
x_1	y_1		$\Delta^2 y_0$						
		Δy_1		$\Delta^3 y_0$					
x_2	y_2		$\Delta^2 y_1$		$\Delta^4 y_0$				
		Δy_2		$\Delta^3 y_1$		$\Delta^5 y_0$			
x_3	y_3		$\Delta^2 y_2$		$\Delta^4 y_1$		$\Delta^6 y_0$		
		Δy_3		$\Delta^3 y_2$		$\Delta^5 y_1$		$\Delta^7 y_0$	
x_4	y_4		$\Delta^2 y_3$		$\Delta^4 y_2$		$\Delta^6 y_1$		$\Delta^8 y_0$
		Δy_4		$\Delta^3 y_3$		$\Delta^5 y_2$		$\Delta^7 y_1$	
x_5	y_5		$\Delta^2 y_4$		$\Delta^4 y_3$		$\Delta^6 y_2$		
		Δy_5		$\Delta^3 y_4$		$\Delta^5 y_3$			
x_6	y_6		$\Delta^2 y_5$		$\Delta^4 y_4$				
		Δy_6		$\Delta^3 y_5$					
x_7	y_7		$\Delta^2 y_6$						
		Δy_7							
x_8	y_8								

TABLE 1. Diagonal Difference Table.

This table is called a *diagonal* difference table. The majority of difference tables are of this kind, but for many purposes a more compact table, called a *horizontal* difference table, is preferable. In the horizontal difference tables the differences of different order are denoted by subscripts instead of exponents. Using the notation for horizontal differences, we can rewrite the preceding difference table in the horizontal form as follows·

x	y	$\Delta_1 y$	$\Delta_2 y$	$\Delta_3 y$	$\Delta_4 y$	$\Delta_5 y$	$\Delta_6 y$	$\Delta_7 y$	$\Delta_8 y$
x_0	y_0								
x_1	y_1	$\Delta_1 y_1$							
x_2	y_2	$\Delta_1 y_2$	$\Delta_2 y_2$						
x_3	y_3	$\Delta_1 y_3$	$\Delta_2 y_3$	$\Delta_3 y_3$					
x_4	y_4	$\Delta_1 y_4$	$\Delta_2 y_4$	$\Delta_3 y_4$	$\Delta_4 y_4$				
x_5	y_5	$\Delta_1 y_5$	$\Delta_2 y_5$	$\Delta_3 y_5$	$\Delta_4 y_5$	$\Delta_5 y_5$			
x_6	y_6	$\Delta_1 y_6$	$\Delta_2 y_6$	$\Delta_3 y_6$	$\Delta_4 y_6$	$\Delta_5 y_6$	$\Delta_6 y_6$		
x_7	y_7	$\Delta_1 y_7$	$\Delta_2 y_7$	$\Delta_3 y_7$	$\Delta_4 y_7$	$\Delta_5 y_7$	$\Delta_6 y_7$	$\Delta_7 y_7$	
x_8	y_8	$\Delta_1 y_8$	$\Delta_2 y_8$	$\Delta_3 y_8$	$\Delta_4 y_8$	$\Delta_5 y_8$	$\Delta_6 y_8$	$\Delta_7 y_8$	$\Delta_8 y_8$

TABLE 2. Horizontal Difference Table.

In order to see the relation between horizontal and diagonal differences of the same order, we give in Tables 3 and 4 the differences of both kinds in terms of the y's.

Inspection of these tables shows that the top diagonal line is the same in both, but that the bottom upwardly inclined diagonal in Table 3 is the same as the bottom horizontal line in Table 4. Also, from Table 3 we have, for example,

$$\Delta^3 y_1 = y_4 - 3y_3 + 3y_2 - y_1.$$

Likewise, from Table 4 we have

$$\Delta_3 y_4 = y_4 - 3y_3 + 3y_2 - y_1.$$

Hence

$$\Delta^3 y_1 = \Delta_3 y_4.$$

A glance at Tables 3 and 4 will show that the general relation between the Δ's affected with exponents and those affected with subscripts is

$$\Delta^m y_k = \Delta_m y_{k+m} \qquad \text{(going forward from } y_k\text{)},$$

or

$$\Delta_m y_n = \Delta^m y_{n-m} \qquad \text{(going backward from } y_n\text{)},$$

where m denotes the order of differences and k and n the number of the tabulated value.

The relation between diagonal differences and horizontal differences can be illustrated still further by a numerical example. The tables on page 56 show both kinds of differences for a set of equidistant values of the function $y = \sinh x$.

TABLE 3. Diagonal Differences.

y	Δy	$\Delta^2 y$	$\Delta^3 y$	$\Delta^4 y$	$\Delta^5 y$
y_0	$y_1 - y_0$	$y_2 - 2y_1 + y_0$	$y_3 - 3y_2 + 3y_1 - y_0$	$y_4 - 4y_3 + 6y_2 - 4y_1 + y_0$	$y_5 - 5y_4 + 10y_3 - 10y_2 + 5y_1 - y_0$
y_1	$y_2 - y_1$	$y_3 - 2y_2 + y_1$	$y_4 - 3y_3 + 3y_2 - y_1$	$y_5 - 4y_4 + 6y_3 - 4y_2 + y_1$	$y_6 - 5y_5 + 10y_4 - 10y_3 + 5y_2 - y_1$
y_2	$y_3 - y_2$	$y_4 - 2y_3 + y_2$	$y_5 - 3y_4 + 3y_3 - y_2$	$y_6 - 4y_5 + 6y_4 - 4y_3 + y_2$	$y_7 - 5y_6 + 10y_5 - 10y_4 + 5y_3 - y_2$
y_3	$y_4 - y_3$	$y_5 - 2y_4 + y_3$	$y_6 - 3y_5 + 3y_4 - y_3$	$y_7 - 4y_6 + 6y_5 - 4y_4 + y_3$	$y_8 - 5y_7 + 10y_6 - 10y_5 + 5y_4 - y_3$
y_4	$y_5 - y_4$	$y_6 - 2y_5 + y_4$	$y_7 - 3y_6 + 3y_5 - y_4$	$y_8 - 4y_7 + 6y_6 - 4y_5 + y_4$	
y_5	$y_6 - y_5$	$y_7 - 2y_6 + y_5$	$y_8 - 3y_7 + 3y_6 - y_5$		
y_6	$y_7 - y_6$	$y_8 - 2y_7 + y_6$			
y_7	$y_8 - y_7$				
y_8					

TABLE 4. Horizontal Differences.

y	$\Delta_1 y$	$\Delta_2 y$	$\Delta_3 y$	$\Delta_4 y$	$\Delta_6 y$
y_0	$y_1 - y_0$	$y_2 - 2y_1 + y_0$	$y_3 - 3y_2 + 3y_1 - y_0$	$y_4 - 4y_3 + 6y_2 - 4y_1 + y_0$	$y_5 - 5y_4 + 10y_3 - 10y_2 + 5y_1 - y_0$
y_1	$y_2 - y_1$	$y_3 - 2y_2 + y_1$	$y_4 - 3y_3 + 3y_2 - y_1$	$y_5 - 4y_4 + 6y_3 - y_2 + y_1$	$y_6 - 5y_5 + 10y_4 - 10y_3 + 5y_2 - y_1$
y_2	$y_3 - y_2$	$y_4 - 2y_3 + y_2$	$y_5 - 3y_4 + 3y_3 - y_2$	$y_6 - 4y_5 + 6y_4 - 4y_3 + y_2$	$y_7 - 5y_6 + 10y_5 - 10y_4 + 5y_3 - y_2$
y_3	$y_4 - y_3$	$y_5 - 2y_4 + y_3$	$y_6 - 3y_5 + 3y_4 - y_3$	$y_7 - 4y_6 + 6y_5 - 4y_4 + y_3$	$y_8 - 5y_7 + 10y_6 - 10y_5 + 5y_4 - y_3$
y_4	$y_5 - y_4$	$y_6 - 2y_5 + y_4$	$y_7 - 3y_6 + 3y_5 - y_4$	$y_8 - 4y_7 + 6y_6 - 4y_5 + y_4$	
y_5	$y_6 - y_5$	$y_7 - 2y_6 + y_5$	$y_8 - 3y_7 + 3y_6 - y_5$		
y_6	$y_7 - y_6$	$y_8 - 2y_7 + y_6$			
y_7	$y_8 - y_7$				
y_8					

x	y	Δy	$\Delta^2 y$	$\Delta^3 y$	$\Delta^4 y$	$\Delta^5 y$	$\Delta^6 y$
1.5	2.12928						
		24629					
1.6	2.37557		2377				
		27006		271			
1.7	2.64563		2648		26		
		29654		297		3	
1.8	2.94217		2945		29		1
		32599		326		4	
1.9	3.26816		3271		33		
		35870		359			
2.0	3.62686		3630				
		39500					
2.1	4.02186						

x	y	$\Delta_1 y$	$\Delta_2 y$	$\Delta_3 y$	$\Delta_4 y$	$\Delta_5 y$	$\Delta_6 y$
1.5	2.12928						
1.6	2.37557	24629					
1.7	2.64536	27006	2377				
1.8	2.94217	29654	2648	271			
1.9	3.26816	32599	2945	297	26		
2.0	3.62686	35870	3271	326	29	3	
2.1	4.02186	39500	3630	359	33	4	1

It will be observed that the differences for the seven functional values are the same whether written as diagonal differences or as horizontal differences.

In certain work, however, horizontal difference tables have distinct advantages. In the numerical solution of differential equations, for example, the functional values behind us are always known, but those ahead of us are always unknown. Here the horizontal difference table shows all orders of differences on the same line as the last known value of the function, and these differences are used for finding the next computed value of the function. The horizontal type of difference table is more compact and convenient in this case than the diagonal type would be.

On the other hand, when we take up the study of central-difference interpolation in the next chapter, we shall find that a diagonal difference table is much better for that purpose.

17. Effect of an Error in a Tabular Value. Let $y_0, y_1, y_2, \cdots y_n$ be the true values of a function, and suppose the value y_5 to be affected with an error ϵ, so that its erroneous value is $y_5 + \epsilon$. Then the successive differences of the y's are as shown below:

y	Δy	$\Delta^2 y'$	$\Delta^3 y$	$\Delta^4 y$
y_0				
	Δy_0			
y_1		$\Delta^2 y_0$		
	Δy_1		$\Delta^3 y_0$	
y_2		$\Delta^2 y_1$		$\Delta^4 y_0$
	Δy_2		$\Delta^3 y_1$	
y_3		$\Delta^2 y_2$		$\Delta^4 y_1 + \epsilon$
	Δy_3		$\Delta^3 y_2 + \epsilon$	
y_4		$\Delta^2 y_3 + \epsilon$		$\Delta^4 y_2 - 4\epsilon$
	$\Delta y_4 + \epsilon$		$\Delta^3 y_3 - 3\epsilon$	
$y_5 + \epsilon$		$\Delta^2 y_4 - 2\epsilon$		$\Delta^4 y_3 + 6\epsilon$
	$\Delta y_5 - \epsilon$		$\Delta^3 y_4 + 3\epsilon$	
y_6		$\Delta^2 y_5 + \epsilon$		$\Delta^4 y_4 - 4\epsilon$
	Δy_6		$\Delta^3 y_5 - \epsilon$	
y_7		$\Delta^2 y_6$		$\Delta^4 y_5 + \epsilon$
	Δy_7		$\Delta^3 y_6$	
y_8		$\Delta^2 y_7$		$\Delta^4 y_6$
	Δy_8		$\Delta^3 y_7$	
y_9		$\Delta^2 y_8$		
	Δy_9			
y_{10}				

TABLE 5. Showing the effect of an error in the tabular values.

This table shows that the effect of an error increases with the successive differences, that the coefficients of the ϵ's are the binomial coefficients with alternating signs, and that *the algebraic sum of the errors in any difference column is zero.* It shows also that *the maximum error in the differences is in the same horizontal line as the erroneous tabular value.*

The following table shows the effect of an error in a horizontal difference table:

y	$\Delta_1 y$	$\Delta_2 y$	$\Delta_3 y$	$\Delta_4 y$
y_0				
y_1	$\Delta_1 y_1$			
y_2	$\Delta_1 y_2$	$\Delta_2 y_2$		
y_3	$\Delta_1 y_3$	$\Delta_2 y_3$	$\Delta_3 y_3$	
y_4	$\Delta_1 y_4$	$\Delta_2 y_4$	$\Delta_3 y_4$	$\Delta_4 y_4$
$y_5 + \epsilon$	$\Delta_1 y_5 + \epsilon$	$\Delta_2 y_5 + \epsilon$	$\Delta_3 y_5 + \epsilon$	$\Delta_4 y_5 + \epsilon$
y_6	$\Delta_1 y_6 - \epsilon$	$\Delta_2 y_6 - 2\epsilon$	$\Delta_3 y_6 - 3\epsilon$	$\Delta_4 y_6 - 4\epsilon$
y_7	$\Delta_1 y_7$	$\Delta_2 y_7 + \epsilon$	$\Delta_3 y_7 + 3\epsilon$	$\Delta_4 y_7 + 6\epsilon$
y_8	$\Delta_1 y_8$	$\Delta_2 y_8$	$\Delta_3 y_8 - \epsilon$	$\Delta_4 y_8 - 4\epsilon$
y_9	$\Delta_1 y_9$	$\Delta_2 y_9$	$\Delta_3 y_9$	$\Delta_4 y_9 + \epsilon$
y_{10}	$\Delta_1 y_{10}$	$\Delta_2 y_{10}$	$\Delta_3 y_{10}$	$\Delta_4 y_{10}$

TABLE 6.

Here, again, the effect of the error is the same as in the preceding table, but in this table *the first erroneous difference of any order is in the same horizontal line as the erroneous tabular value.*

The law according to which an error is propagated in a difference table enables us to trace such an error to its source and correct it. As an illustration of the process of detecting and correcting an error in a tabulated function, let us consider the following table: *

x	y	$\Delta_1 y$	$\Delta_2 y$	$\Delta_3 y$	$\Delta_4 y$	ϵ
0.10	0.09983					
0.15	0.14944	4961				
0.20	0.19867	4923	− 38			
0.25	0.24740	4873	− 50	−12		
0.30	0.29552	4812	− 61	−11	1	
0.35	0.34290	4738	− 74	−13	− 2	
0.40	0.38945	4655	− 83	− 9	4	ϵ
0.45	0.43497	4552	−103	−20	−11	-4ϵ
0.50	0.47943	4446	−106	− 3	17	6ϵ
0.55	0.52269	4326	−120	−14	−11	-4ϵ
0.60	0.56464	4195	−131	−11	3	ϵ
0.65	0.60519	4055	−140	− 9	2	
0.70	0.64422	3903	−152	−12	− 3	

Here the third differences are quite irregular near the middle of the column, and the fourth differences are still more irregular. The irregularity begins in each column on the horizontal line corresponding to $x = 0.40$.

Since the algebraic sum of the fourth differences is 1, the average value of the fourth differences is only about 0.1 of a unit in the fifth decimal place. Hence the fourth differences found in this example are mostly accumulated errors. Referring now to Table 6, we have

$$- 4\epsilon = - 11, \qquad 6\epsilon = 17, \text{ etc.}$$

Hence, $\epsilon = 3$ to the nearest unit. The true value of y corresponding to $x = 0.40$ is therefore $0.38945 - 0.00003 = 0.38942$, since $(y_k + \epsilon) - \epsilon = y_k$. The columns of differences can now be corrected, and it will be found that the third differences are practically constant.

* *Note.* When writing numerical difference tables, or when substituting numerical differences in formulas, it is customary to omit the zeros between the decimal point and the first significant figure to the right of it; in other words, the differences are expressed in units of the last figure retained. Thus, instead of writing —0.00038 as the first number in the column $\Delta_2 y$ we write simply —38. This practice will be followed throughout this book, except in a few instances where the zeros are written for the sake of clearness.

If several tabular values of the function are affected with errors the successive differences of the function will become irregular, but it is not an easy matter to determine the sources and magnitudes of the separate errors.

In the case where *each* of the tabulated y's is affected with an error of magnitude ϵ, each of the third differences is affected with an error $\epsilon_k - 3\epsilon_{k-1} + 3\epsilon_{k-2} - \epsilon_{k-3}$, each of the fourth differences with an error $\epsilon_k - 4\epsilon_{k-1} + 6\epsilon_{k-2} - 4\epsilon_{k-3} + \epsilon_{k-4}$, etc., as is evident from Tables 3 and 4. In practical problems the tabulated values of the function y are obtained by measurement or by computation. They are thus liable to be affected with errors of measurement or with errors due to rounding off the computed results to the given number of figures. In either case these errors would be magnified in the process of taking differences and they alone would be sufficient to cause the higher differences to become irregular.* For this reason it is usually not advisable to use differences higher than the fourth.

18. Relation Between Differences and Derivatives. It is sometimes desirable to know the relations which exist between differences and derivatives. The fundamental relations between them are:

(18. 1) $$\Delta^n f(x) = (\Delta x)^n f^{(n)}(x + \theta n \Delta x), \qquad 0 < \theta < 1$$
and

$$\lim_{\Delta x \to 0} \frac{\Delta^n f(x)}{(\Delta x)^n} = f^{(n)}(x).$$

These relations are derived in Vallée-Poussin's *Cours d'Analyse Infinitésimale*, I (fourth edition, 1921), pp. 72-73.

19. Differences of a Polynomial. Let us now compute the successive differences of a polynomial of the nth degree. We have

(1) $$y = f(x) = ax^n + bx^{n-1} + cx^{n-2} + \cdots + kx + l.$$

(2) $$\therefore \ y + \Delta y = a(x + h)^n + b(x + h)^{n-1} + c(x + h)^{n-2} + \cdots + k(x + h) + l,$$
where $h = \Delta x$.

Subtracting (1) from (2), we get

$$\Delta y = a[(x + h)^n - x^n] + b[(x + h)^{n-1} - x^{n-1}] + c[(x + h)^{n-2} - x^{n-2}] + \cdots + kh.$$

---

* For an exhaustive discussion of errors in the tabular values of a function, see Rice's *Theory and Practice of Interpolation*, pp. 7-15 and 46-62. Also O. Biermann's *Vorlesungen über Mathematische Näherungsmethoden*, p. 136.

Expanding the quantities $(x + h)^n$, $(x + h)^{n-1}$, etc. by the binomial theorem, we have

$$\Delta y = a \left[x^n + nhx^{n-1} + \frac{n(n-1)}{2} h^2 x^{n-2} + \frac{n(n-1)(n-2)}{3!} h^3 x^{n-3} \right.$$

$$\left. + \cdots - x^n \right] + b \left[x^{n-1} + (n-1)hx^{n-2} + \frac{(n-1)(n-2)}{2} h^2 x^{n-3} \right.$$

$$\left. + \cdots - x^{n-1} \right] + c \left[x^{n-2} + (n-2)hx^{n-3} + \frac{(n-2)(n-3)}{2} h^2 x^{n-4} \right.$$

$$\left. + \cdots - x^{n-2} \right] + \cdots + kh,$$

or

$$\Delta y = anhx^{n-1} + \left[ah^2 \frac{n(n-1)}{2} + b(n-1)h \right] x^{n-2}$$

$$+ \left[ah^3 \frac{n(n-1)(n-2)}{3!} + bh^2 \frac{(n-1)(n-2)}{2} + ch(n-2) \right] x^{n-3} + \cdots .$$

Now if $\Delta x (= h)$ is constant, the bracketed coefficients of x^{n-2}, x^{n-3}, etc. are constants, so that we may replace them by the single constant coefficients b', c', etc. Hence we have

$$(3) \qquad \Delta y = anhx^{n-1} + b'x^{n-2} + c'x^{n-3} + \cdots + k'x + l'.$$

The first difference of a polynomial of the nth degree is thus another polynomial of degree $n-1$.

To find the second difference we give x an increment $\Delta x = h$ in (3) and therefore have

$$(4) \quad \Delta y + \Delta(\Delta y) = anh(x+h)^{n-1} + b'(x+h)^{n-2}$$

$$+ c'(x+h)^{n-3} + \cdots + k'(x+h) + l'.$$

Subtracting (3) from (4), we get

$$\Delta(\Delta y) = \Delta^2 y = anh[(x+h)^{n-1} - x^{n-1}]$$

$$+ b'[(x+h)^{n-2} - x^{n-2}] + c'[(x+h)^{n-3} - x^{n-3}] + \cdots + k'h.$$

Expanding $(x + h)^{n-1}$, $(x + h)^{n-2}$, etc. by the binomial theorem and replacing the constant coefficients of x^{n-3}, x^{n-4}, etc. by a single letter as before, we have

$$\Delta^2 y = an(n-1)h^2 x^{n-2} + b''x^{n-3} + c''x^{n-4} \cdots + k''x + l''.$$

The second difference is thus a polynomial of degree $n-2$.

By continuing the calculation in this manner we arrive at a polynomial of zero degree for the nth difference; that is,

$$\Delta^n y = a[n(n-1)(n-2)\cdots 1]h^n x^{n-n} = an!h^n x^0 = ah^n n!.$$

The nth difference is therefore constant, and all higher differences are zero.

The reader should bear in mind that this result is true only when h is a constant, that is, when the values of x are in arithmetic progression.

The proposition which we have just proved may be stated as follows:

The nth differences of a polynomial of the nth degree are constant when the values of the independent variable are taken in arithmetic progression, that is, at equal intervals apart.

The converse of this proposition is also true, namely:

If the nth differences of a tabulated function are constant when the values of the independent variable are taken in arithmetic progression, the function is a polynomial of degree n. *

This second proposition enables us to replace any function by a polynomial if its differences of some order become constant or nearly so. Thus, the function tabulated in Art. 17 can be represented by a polynomial of the third degree, since the corrected third differences are approximately constant.

20. Newton's Formula for Forward Interpolation. Our next problem is to find suitable polynomials for replacing any given function over a given interval. Let $y = f(x)$ denote a function which takes the values $y_0, y_1, y_2, \cdots y_n$ for the equidistant values $x_0, x_1, x_2, \cdots x_n$ of the independent variable x, and let $\phi(x)$ denote a polynomial of the nth degree. This polynomial may be written in the form

$$(1) \quad \phi(x) = a_0 + a_1(x-x_0) + a_2(x-x_0)(x-x_1)$$
$$+ a_3(x-x_0)(x-x_1)(x-x_2)$$
$$+ a_4(x-x_0)(x-x_1)(x-x_2)(x-x_3)$$
$$+ \cdots + a_n(x-x_0)(x-x_1)(x-x_2)\cdots(x-x_{n-1}).$$

We shall now determine the coefficients $a_0, a_1, a_2, \cdots a_n$ so as to make $\phi(x_0) = y_0$, $\phi(x_1) = y_1$, $\phi(x_2) = y_2, \cdots \phi(x_n) = y_n$.

Substituting in (1) the successive values $x_0, x_1, x_2, \cdots x_n$ for x, at the same time putting $\phi(x_0) = y_0$, $\phi(x_1) = y_1$, etc., and remembering that $x_1 - x_0 = h$, $x_2 - x_0 = 2h$, etc., we have

* For the proof of this proposition see Rice's *Theory and Practice of Interpolation*, p. 24.

$y_0 = a_0,$ or $a_0 = y_0.$

$y_1 = a_0 + a_1(x_1 - x_0) = y_0 + a_1 h.$

$$\therefore a_1 = \frac{y_1 - y_0}{h} = \frac{\Delta y_0}{h}.$$

$$y_2 = a_0 + a_1(x_2 - x_0) + a_2(x_2 - x_0)(x_2 - x_1) = y_0 + \frac{y_1 - y_0}{h}(2h)$$
$$+ a_2(2h)(h).$$

$$\therefore a_2 = \frac{y_2 - 2y_1 + y_0}{2h^2} = \frac{\Delta^2 y_0}{2h^2}.$$

$$y_3 = a_0 + a_1(x_3 - x_0) + a_2(x_3 - x_0)(x_3 - x_1)$$
$$+ a_3(x_3 - x_0)(x_3 - x_1)(x_3 - x_2)$$
$$= y_0 + \frac{y_1 - y_0}{h}(3h) + \frac{y_2 - 2y_1 + y_0}{2h^2}(3h)(2h) + a_3(3h)(2h)(h).$$

$$\therefore a_3 = \frac{y_3 - 3y_2 + 3y_1 - y_0}{6h^3} = \frac{\Delta^3 y_0}{3!h^3}.$$

$$y_4 = a_0 + a_1(x_4 - x_0) + a_2(x_4 - x_0)(x_4 - x_1)$$
$$+ a_3(x_4 - x_0)(x_4 - x_1)(x_4 - x_2)$$
$$+ a_4(x_4 - x_0)(x_4 - x_1)(x_4 - x_2)(x_4 - x_3)$$
$$= y_0 + \frac{y_1 - y_0}{h}(4h) + \frac{y_2 - 2y_1 + y_0}{2h^2}(4h)(3h)$$
$$+ \frac{y_3 - 3y_2 + 3y_1 - y_0}{6h^3}(4h)(3h)(2h) + a_4(4h)(3h)(2h)(h).$$

$$\therefore a_4 = \frac{y_4 - 4y_3 + 6y_2 - 4y_1 + y_0}{4!h^4} = \frac{\Delta^4 y_0}{4!h^4}.$$

By continuing this method of calculating the coefficients we shall find that

$$a_5 = \frac{\Delta^5 y_0}{5!h^5}, \qquad a_6 = \frac{\Delta^6 y_0}{6!h^6}, \cdots \qquad a_n = \frac{\Delta^n y_0}{n!h^n}.$$

Substituting these values of $a_0, a_1, \cdots a_n$ in (1), we get

$$(2) \quad \phi(x) = y_0 + \frac{\Delta y_0}{h}(x - x_0) + \frac{\Delta^2 y_0}{2h^2}(x - x_0)(x - x_1)$$

$$+ \frac{\Delta^3 y_0}{3!h^3}(x - x_0)(x - x_1)(x - x_2)$$

$$+ \frac{\Delta^4 y_0}{4!h^4}(x - x_0)(x - x_1)(x - x_2)(x - x_3) + \cdots$$

$$+ \frac{\Delta^n y_0}{n!h^n}(x - x_0)(x - x_1)(x - x_2) \cdots (x - x_{n-1}).$$

This is Newton's formula for *forward* interpolation, written in terms of x.

The formula can be simplified by a change of variable. Let us first write (2) in the following equivalent form:

$$(3) \quad \phi(x) = y_0 + \Delta y_0 \left(\frac{x - x_0}{h}\right) + \frac{\Delta^2 y_0}{2}\left(\frac{x - x_0}{h}\right)\left(\frac{x - x_1}{h}\right)$$

$$+ \frac{\Delta^3 y_0}{3!}\left(\frac{x - x_0}{h}\right)\left(\frac{x - x_1}{h}\right)\left(\frac{x - x_2}{h}\right)$$

$$+ \frac{\Delta^4 y_0}{4!}\left(\frac{x - x_0}{h}\right)\left(\frac{x - x_1}{h}\right)\left(\frac{x - x_2}{h}\right)\left(\frac{x - x_3}{h}\right) + \cdots$$

Now put

$$\frac{x - x_0}{h} = u, \quad \text{or} \quad x = x_0 + hu.$$

Then since $x_1 = x_0 + h$, $x_2 = x_0 + 2h$, etc., we have

$$\frac{x - x_1}{h} = \frac{x - (x_0 + h)}{h} = \frac{x - x_0 - h}{h} = \frac{x - x_0}{h} - \frac{h}{h} = u - 1,$$

$$\frac{x - x_2}{h} = \frac{x - (x_0 + 2h)}{h} = \frac{x - x_0}{h} - \frac{2h}{h} = u - 2,$$

$$\cdots \cdots \cdots \cdots \cdots \cdots \cdots \cdots \cdots$$

$$\frac{x - x_{n-1}}{h} = \frac{x - [x_0 + (n-1)h]}{h} = \frac{x - x_0}{h} - \frac{(n-1)h}{h}$$

$$= u - (n-1) = u - n + 1.$$

Substituting in (3) these values of $(x - x_0)/h$, $(x - x_1)/h$, etc., we get

$$(\text{I}) \quad \phi(x) = \phi(x_0 + hu) = g(u) = y_0 + u\Delta y_0 + \frac{u(u-1)}{2!}\Delta^2 y_0$$

$$+ \frac{u(u-1)(u-2)}{3!}\Delta^3 y_0 + \frac{u(u-1)(u-2)(u-3)}{4!}\Delta^4 y_0$$

$$+ \cdots + \frac{u(u-1)(u-2)\cdots(u-n+1)}{n!}\Delta^n y_0.$$

This is the form in which Newton's formula for forward interpolation is usually written. We shall refer to it hereafter as Newton's formula (I).* It will be observed that the coefficients of the Δ's are the binomial coefficients.

---

* Recent historical investigation has shown that this formula was really first discovered by James Gregory as early as 1670.

The reason for the name "forward" interpolation formula lies in the fact that the formula contains values of the tabulated function from y_0 onward to the right (forward from y_0) and none to the left of this value. Because of this fact this formula is used mainly for interpolating the values of y near the *beginning* of a set of tabular values and for extrapolating values of y a short distance backward (to the left) from y_0.

The starting point y_0 may be any tabular value, but then the formula will contain only those values of y which come *after* the value chosen as starting point.

21. Newton's Formula for Backward Interpolation. The formulas of the preceding section can not be used for interpolating a value of y near the end of the tabular values. To derive a formula for this case we write the polynomial $\phi(x)$ in the following form:

$$(1) \quad \phi(x) = a_0 + a_1(x - x_n) + a_2(x - x_n)(x - x_{n-1})$$
$$+ a_3(x - x_n)(x - x_{n-1})(x - x_{n-2})$$
$$+ a_4(x - x_n)(x - x_{n-1})(x - x_{n-2})(x - x_{n-3}) + \cdots$$
$$+ a_n(x - x_n)(x - x_{n-1}) \cdots (x - x_1).$$

Then we determine the coefficients $a_0, a_1, a_2, \cdots a_n$ so as to make $\phi(x_n) = y_n$, $\phi(x_{n-1}) = y_{n-1}$, etc. Substituting in (1) the values x_n, x_{n-1}, etc. for x and at the same time putting $\phi(x_n) = y_n$, $\phi(x_{n-1}) = y_{n-1}$, etc., we have

$$y_n = a_0, \quad \text{or} \quad a_0 = y_n.$$

$$y_{n-1} = a_0 + a_1(x_{n-1} - x_n) = y_n + a_1(-h).$$

$$\therefore a_1 = \frac{y_n - y_{n-1}}{h} = \frac{\Delta_1 y_n}{h}.$$

$$y_{n-2} = a_0 + a_1(x_{n-2} - x_n) + a_2(x_{n-2} - x_n)(x_{n-2} - x_{n-1})$$

$$= y_n + \frac{y_n - y_{n-1}}{h}(-2h) + a_2(-2h)(-h).$$

$$\therefore a_2 = \frac{y_n - 2y_{n-1} + y_{n-2}}{2h^2} = \frac{\Delta_2 y_n}{2h^2}.$$

By continuing the calculation of the coefficients in this manner we shall find

$$a_3 = \frac{\Delta_3 y_n}{3!h^3}, \qquad a_4 = \frac{\Delta_4 y_n}{4!h^4}, \cdots \qquad a_n = \frac{\Delta_n y_n}{n!h^n}.$$

Substituting these values of a_0, a_1, a_2, etc. in (1), we have

(2) $\phi(x) = y_n + \dfrac{\Delta_1 y_n}{h}(x - x_n) + \dfrac{\Delta_2 y_n}{2h^2}(x - x_n)(x - x_{n-1})$

$\qquad + \dfrac{\Delta_3 y_n}{3!h^3}(x - x_n)(x - x_{n-1})(x - x_{n-2})$

$\qquad + \dfrac{\Delta_4 y_n}{4!h^4}(x - x_n)(x - x_{n-1})(x - x_{n-2})(x - x_{n-3}) + \cdots$

$\qquad \cdots \cdots \cdots \cdots \cdots \cdots \cdots \cdots$

$\qquad + \dfrac{\Delta_n y_n}{n!h^n}(x - x_n)(x - x_{n-1})\cdots(x - x_1).$

This is Newton's formula for *backward* interpolation, written in terms of x. It can be simplified by making a change of variable, as was done in Art. 20.

Let us first write (2) in the equivalent form

(3) $\phi(x) = y_n + \Delta_1 y_n\left(\dfrac{x - x_n}{h}\right) + \dfrac{\Delta_2 y_n}{2}\left(\dfrac{x - x_n}{h}\right)\left(\dfrac{x - x_{n-1}}{h}\right)$

$\qquad + \dfrac{\Delta_3 y_n}{3!}\left(\dfrac{x - x_n}{h}\right)\left(\dfrac{x - x_{n-1}}{h}\right)\left(\dfrac{x - x_{n-2}}{h}\right)$

$\qquad + \dfrac{\Delta_4 y_n}{4!}\left(\dfrac{x - x_n}{h}\right)\left(\dfrac{x - x_{n-1}}{h}\right)\left(\dfrac{x - x_{n-2}}{h}\right)\left(\dfrac{x - x_{n-3}}{h}\right) + \cdots$

$\qquad + \dfrac{\Delta_n y_n}{n!}\left(\dfrac{x - x_n}{h}\right)\left(\dfrac{x - x_{n-1}}{h}\right)\cdots\left(\dfrac{x - x_1}{h}\right).$

Now put

$$u = \frac{x - x_n}{h}, \quad \text{or} \quad x = x_n + hu.$$

Then since $x_{n-1} = x_n - h$, $x_{n-2} = x_n - 2h$, etc., we have

$$\frac{x - x_{n-1}}{h} = \frac{x - (x_n - h)}{h} = \frac{x - x_n + h}{h} = \frac{x - x_n}{h} + \frac{h}{h} = u + 1,$$

$$\frac{x - x_{n-2}}{h} = \frac{x - (x_n - 2h)}{h} = \frac{x - x_n}{h} + \frac{2h}{h} = u + 2,$$

$$\cdots \cdots \cdots \cdots \cdots \cdots \cdots$$

$$\frac{x - x_1}{h} = \frac{x - [x_n - (n-1)h]}{h} = \frac{x - x_n}{h} + \frac{(n-1)h}{h} = u + n - 1.$$

Substituting in (3) these values of $(x - x_n)/h$, $(x - x_{n-1})/h$, etc., we get

(II) $\phi(x) = \phi(x_n + hu) = \psi(u) = y_n + u\Delta_1 y_n + \dfrac{u(u+1)}{2}\Delta_2 y_n$

$\qquad + \dfrac{u(u+1)(u+2)}{3!}\Delta_3 y_n + \dfrac{u(u+1)(u+2)(u+3)}{4!}\Delta_4 y_n + \cdots$

$\qquad + \dfrac{u(u+1)(u+2)\cdots(u+n-1)}{n!}\Delta_n y_n.$

This is the form in which Newton's formula for background interpolation is usually written. We shall refer to this formula hereafter as Newton's formula (II). It is to be observed that this formula employs *horizontal* differences, whereas the formula for forward interpolation employs diagonal differences.

(II) is called the formula for " backward " interpolation because it contains values of the tabulated function from y_n *backward* to the left and none to the right of y_n. This formula is used mainly for interpolating values of y near the *end* of a set of tabular values, and also for extrapolating values of y a short distance ahead (to the right) of y_n.

We shall now illustrate the use of Newton's formulas by working some examples.

Example 1. Find $\log_{10}\pi$, having given

$$\log 3.141 = 0.4970679364,$$
$$\log 3.142 = 0.4972061807,$$
$$\log 3.143 = 0.4973443810,$$
$$\log 3.144 = 0.4974825374,$$
$$\log 3.145 = 0.4976206498.$$

Solution. We first form the table of differences, as shown below:

x	$y = \log x$	Δy	$\Delta^2 y$	$\Delta^3 y$
3.141	0.4970679364			
		1382443		
3.142	0.4972061807		— 440	
		1382003		1
3.143	0.4973443810		— 439	
		1381564		— 1
3.144	0.4974825374		— 440	
		1381124		
3.145	0.4976206498			

Here $x = \pi = 3.1415926536$, $x_0 = 3.141$, $h = 0.001$. Hence

$$u = \frac{x - x_0}{h} = \frac{3.1415926536 - 3.141}{0.001} = 0.5926536,$$
$$u - 1 = -0.4073464, \text{ etc.}$$

Substituting these values in (I), Art. 20, we get

$$\log_{10} \pi = 0.4970679364 + 0.5926536(1382443)$$
$$+ \frac{0.5926536(-0.4073464)(-440)}{2}$$
$$= 0.4970679364 + 0.0000819310 + 0.0000000053$$
$$= 0.4971498727.$$

This result is correct to its last figure.

Example 2. Using the tabular values of the preceding example, find $\log_{10} 3.140$.

Solution. Here $x = x_{-1} = 3.140$, $x_0 = 3.141$, $h = 0.001$. Hence

$$u = \frac{x - x_0}{h} = \frac{x_{-1} - x_0}{h} = \frac{-h}{h} = -1,$$
$$u - 1 = -2, \text{ etc.}$$

$$\therefore \log_{10} 3.140 = 0.4970679364 + (-1)(1382443) + \frac{(-1)(-2)}{2}(-440)$$
$$= 0.4970679364 - 0.0001382443 - 0.0000000440$$
$$= 0.4969296481.$$

This result is also correct to its last figure.

Note. The process of computing the value of a function outside the range of given values, as in the example above, is called *extrapolation.* It should be used with caution, but if the function is known to run smoothly near the ends of the range of given values, and if h is taken as small as it should be, we are usually safe in extrapolating for a distance h outside the range of given values.

Example 3. The hourly declination of the moon for January 1, 1918, is given in the following table. Find the declination at $3^h\ 35^m\ 15^s$.

Hour	Declination	Δ_1	Δ_2	Δ_3
0	8° 29′ 53″.7			
1	8 18 19 .4	−11′ 34″.3		
2	8 6 43 .5	−11 35 .9	−1″.6	
3	7 55 6 .1	−11 37 .4	−1 .5	0″.1
4	7 43 27 .2	−11 38 .9	−1 .5	0 .0

Solution. Since the desired declination is near the *end* of the values given we use Newton's formula (II), and we therefore form a horizontal difference table, as shown above. Denoting the time in hours by t, we have $t_n = 4$, $t = 3^h\ 35^m\ 15^s$, $h = 1$. Hence

$$u = \frac{t - t_n}{h} = \frac{-0^h\ 24^m\ 45^s}{1^h} = \frac{-1485^s}{3600^s} = -0.3569.$$

$$\therefore\ u + 1 = 0.6431.$$

Substituting these values in (II) and denoting the required declination by δ, we get

$$\delta = 7° 43' 27''.2 + (-0.3569)(-11' 38''.9) + \frac{(0.6431)(-0.3569)}{2}(-1''.5)$$

$$= 7° 43' 27''.2 + 4' 9''.4 + 0''.2$$

$$= 7° 47' 36''.8.$$

Example 4. Using the data of the preceding problem, find the declination of the moon at $t = 5^h$.

Solution. Here $t = t_{n+1} = 5$, $t_n = 4$.

$$\therefore\ u = \frac{t_{n+1} - t_n}{h} = \frac{h}{h} = 1,\ u + 1 = 2.$$

Substituting in (II), we have

$$\delta_{n+1} = 7° 43' 27''.2 + (1)(-11' 38''.9) + \frac{(1)(2)}{2}(-1''.5)$$

$$= 7° 31' 46''.8.$$

The true value, as given in the *American Ephemeris and Nautical Almanac*, is $7° 31' 46''.9$, the error in the extrapolated value thus being only $0''.1$.

EXERCISES II

1. Find and correct by means of differences the error in the following table:

20736

28561

38416

50625

65540

83521

104976

130321

160000.

2. Correct the error in this table:

$$
\begin{array}{rrr}
19° & 12' & 22''.4 \\
19 & 25 & 54\ .7 \\
19 & 39 & 7\ .3 \\
19 & 51 & 53\ .8 \\
20 & 4 & 31\ .9 \\
20 & 16 & 43\ .5 \\
20 & 28 & 34\ .3.
\end{array}
$$

3. Find $\log_{10} \sin 37' 23''$, given

$$
\begin{array}{rcl}
\log \sin 37' &=& 8.0319195 - 10 \\
"\quad" \quad 38' &=& 8.0435009 - 10 \\
"\quad" \quad 39' &=& 8.0547814 - 10 \\
"\quad" \quad 40' &=& 8.0657763 - 10 \\
"\quad" \quad 41' &=& 8.0764997 - 10 \\
"\quad" \quad 42' &=& 8.0869646 - 10 \\
"\quad" \quad 43' &=& 8.0971832 - 10.
\end{array}
$$

4. The following table gives the longitude of the moon at twelve-hour intervals for the first four days of April, 1918. Find the moon's longitude at 8:50 P. M. on April 2, the day beginning at noon.

$$
\begin{array}{lrrrrr}
\text{Apr. 1} & 0 & 244° & 44' & 20''.5 \\
"\quad 1 & 12 & 250 & 57 & 35\ .7 \\
"\quad 2 & 0 & 257 & 14 & 22\ .1 \\
"\quad 2 & 12 & 263 & 35 & 8\ .6 \\
"\quad 3 & 0 & 270 & 0 & 24\ .6 \\
"\quad 3 & 12 & 276 & 30 & 39\ .6 \\
"\quad 4 & 0 & 283 & 6 & 22\ .1.
\end{array}
$$

5. Using the data of Exercise 3, find $\log \sin 42' 13''$.

6. Using the data of Exercise 4, find the moon's longitude at 8:43 P. M., Apr. 3.

CHAPTER III

INTERPOLATION

CENTRAL-DIFFERENCE FORMULAS

22. Introduction. Newton's formulas (I) and (II) are fundamental and are applicable to nearly all cases of interpolation, but in general they do not converge as rapidly as another class of formulas called *central-difference* formulas. These latter formulas employ differences taken as nearly as possible from a horizontal line through a diagonal difference table, and a glance at Table 3 shows that these differences contain values of the function both preceding and following the value through which the horizontal line is drawn. The central-difference formulas are therefore particularly suited for interpolating values of the function near the *middle* of a tabulated set.

The most important central-difference formulas are the two known as Stirling's formula and Bessel's formula, respectively. They can be derived in several ways, but are most simply derived by an algebraic transformation of Newton's formula (I).

23. Stirling's Interpolation Formula. To derive Stirling's formula we first write a diagonal difference table and mark for special consideration the tabular value y_0 and the differences lying as near as possible to the horizontal line through y_0. These quantities are printed in heavy type in the table given below.

y	Δy	$\Delta^2 y$	$\Delta^3 y$	$\Delta^4 y$	$\Delta^5 y$	$\Delta^6 y$	$\Delta^7 y$	$\Delta^8 y$
y_{-4}								
	Δy_{-4}							
y_{-3}		$\Delta^2 y_{-4}$						
	Δy_{-3}		$\Delta^3 y_{-4}$					
y_{-2}		$\Delta^2 y_{-3}$		$\Delta^4 y_{-4}$				
	Δy_{-2}		$\Delta^3 y_{-3}$		$\Delta^5 y_{-4}$			
y_{-1}		$\Delta^2 y_{-2}$		$\Delta^4 y_{-3}$		$\Delta^6 y_{-4}$		
	$\mathbf{\Delta y_{-1}}$		$\mathbf{\Delta^3 y_{-2}}$		$\mathbf{\Delta^5 y_{-3}}$		$\mathbf{\Delta^7 y_{-4}}$	
$\mathbf{y_0}$		$\mathbf{\Delta^2 y_{-1}}$		$\mathbf{\Delta^4 y_{-2}}$		$\mathbf{\Delta^6 y_{-3}}$		$\mathbf{\Delta^8 y_{-4}}$
	$\mathbf{\Delta y_0}$		$\mathbf{\Delta^3 y_{-1}}$		$\mathbf{\Delta^5 y_{-2}}$		$\mathbf{\Delta^7 y_{-3}}$	
y_1		$\mathbf{\Delta^2 y_0}$		$\mathbf{\Delta^4 y_{-1}}$		$\mathbf{\Delta^6 y_{-2}}$		$\mathbf{\Delta^8 y_{-3}}$
	Δy_1		$\Delta^3 y_0$		$\Delta^5 y_{-1}$		$\Delta^7 y_{-2}$	
y_2		$\Delta^2 y_1$		$\Delta^4 y_0$		$\Delta^6 y_{-1}$		
	Δy_2		$\Delta^3 y_1$		$\Delta^5 y_0$			
y_3		$\Delta^2 y_2$		$\Delta^4 y_1$				
	Δy_3		$\Delta^3 y_2$					
y_4		$\Delta^2 y_3$						
	Δy_4							
y_5								

TABLE 7.

Newton's formula (I), when setting out from y_0, is

(A) $\qquad y = y_0 + u\Delta y_0 + \dfrac{u(u-1)}{2}\,\Delta^2 y_0 + \dfrac{u(u-1)(u-2)}{3!}\,\Delta^3 y_0$

$\qquad\qquad + \dfrac{u(u-1)(u-2)(u-3)}{4!}\,\Delta^4 y_0$

$\qquad\qquad + \dfrac{u(u-1)(u-2)(u-3)(u-4)}{5!}\,\Delta^5 y_0 + \cdots,$

which may be written in the form

(B) $\quad y = y_0 + C_1\Delta y_0 + C_2\Delta^2 y_0 + C_3\Delta^3 y_0 + C_4\Delta^4 y_0 + C_5\Delta^5 y_0 + \cdots,$

where the C's denote the binomial coefficients.

Let us now put

(a) $\qquad m_1 = \dfrac{\Delta y_{-1} + \Delta y_0}{2},$ $\qquad\qquad$ (b) $\qquad m_3 = \dfrac{\Delta^3 y_{-2} + \Delta^3 y_{-1}}{2},$

(c) $\qquad m_5 = \dfrac{\Delta^5 y_{-3} + \Delta^5 y_{-2}}{2},$ $\qquad\qquad$ (d) $\qquad m_7 = \dfrac{\Delta^7 y_{-4} + \Delta^7 y_{-3}}{2},$

etc.

These m's are thus the arithmetic means of the *odd* differences immediately above and below the horizontal line through y_0.

Our immediate object now is to express Δy_0, $\Delta^2 y_0$, $\Delta^3 y_0$, etc. in terms of the m's and the *even* differences lying on the horizontal line through y_0. This will be done by a process of elimination by working from Δy_0, $\Delta^2 y_0$, etc. diagonally upward to the right until the quantities in the horizontal line are reached. As an aid to this we shall underline the even differences $\Delta^2 y_{-1}$, $\Delta^4 y_{-2}$, $\Delta^6 y_{-3}$, $\Delta^8 y_{-4}$ wherever they occur in the algebraic work which follows, the purpose of the underlining being to call attention to the fact that the underlined quantities are *not* to be eliminated.

From the definition of differences we have

$$\Delta^2 y_{-1} = \Delta y_0 - \Delta y_{-1}.$$

$$\therefore \Delta y_0 = \underline{\Delta^2 y_{-1}} + \Delta y_{-1}.$$

But $\qquad\qquad\qquad \Delta y_{-1} = 2m_1 - \Delta y_0$, from (a).

$$\therefore \Delta y_0 = \underline{\Delta^2 y_{-1}} + 2m_1 - \Delta y_0.$$

(1) $\qquad\qquad\qquad \therefore \Delta y_0 = m_1 + \tfrac{1}{2}\underline{\Delta^2 y_{-1}}.$

To find the value of $\Delta^2 y_0$ in terms of the desired quantities we have

$$\Delta^3 y_{-1} = \Delta^2 y_0 - \underline{\Delta^2 y_{-1}},$$

(e) or $\qquad\qquad \Delta^2 y_0 = \underline{\Delta^2 y_{-1}} + \Delta^3 y_{-1}.$

But

(f) $\qquad \Delta^4 y_{-2} = \Delta^3 y_{-1} - \Delta^3 y_{-2}$, by definition,

(g) and $\qquad \Delta^3 y_{-1} = 2m_3 - \Delta^3 y_{-2}$, from (b).

Subtracting (f) from (g) and solving for $\Delta^3 y_{-1}$,

(h) $\qquad \Delta^3 y_{-1} = m_3 + \frac{1}{2}\Delta^4 y_{-2}$.

Substituting (h) in (e),

(2) $\qquad\qquad\qquad \Delta^2 y_0 = \Delta^2 y_{-1} + m_3 + \frac{1}{2}\Delta^4 y_{-2}$.

To find $\Delta^3 y_0$ we start with

$$\Delta^4 y_{-1} = \Delta^3 y_0 - \Delta^3 y_{-1},$$

(i) or $\qquad \Delta^3 y_0 = \Delta^3 y_{-1} + \Delta^4 y_{-1}$

$$= m_3 + \frac{1}{2}\Delta^4 y_{-2} + \Delta^4 y_{-1}, \text{ from (h)}$$

But

$$\Delta^5 y_{-2} = \Delta^4 y_{-1} - \Delta^4 y_{-2},$$

(j) or $\qquad \Delta^4 y_{-1} = \Delta^4 y_{-2} + \Delta^5 y_{-2}$.

(k) Also, $\qquad \Delta^6 y_{-3} = \Delta^5 y_{-2} - \Delta^5 y_{-3}$

(l) and $\qquad \Delta^5 y_{-2} = 2m_5 - \Delta^5 y_{-3}$, from (c).

Subtracting (k) from (l) and solving for $\Delta^5 y_{-2}$,

(m) $\qquad \Delta^5 y_{-2} = m_5 + \frac{1}{2}\Delta^6 y_{-3}$.

Substituting (m) in (j),

(n) $\qquad \Delta^4 y_{-1} = \Delta^4 y_{-2} + m_5 + \frac{1}{2}\Delta^6 y_{-3}$.

Substituting (n) in (i),

(3) $\qquad\qquad \Delta^3 y_0 = m_3 + \frac{3}{2}\Delta^4 y_{-2} + m_5 + \frac{1}{2}\Delta^6 y_{-3}$.

For $\Delta^4 y_0$ we start with

$$\Delta^5 y_{-1} = \Delta^4 y_0 - \Delta^4 y_{-1},$$

(o) or $\qquad \Delta^4 y_0 = \Delta^4 y_{-1} + \Delta^5 y_{-1}$

$$= \Delta^4 y_{-2} + m_5 + \frac{1}{2}\Delta^6 y_{-3} + \Delta^5 y_{-1}, \text{ from (n).}$$

But

(p) $\qquad \Delta^6 y_{-2} = \Delta^5 y_{-1} - \Delta^5 y_{-2}$

$$= \Delta^5 y_{-1} - m_5 - \frac{1}{2}\Delta^6 y_{-3}, \text{ from (m);}$$

(q) and $\qquad \Delta^7 y_{-3} = \Delta^6 y_{-2} - \Delta^6 y_{-3}$.

(r) Also, $\qquad \Delta^8 y_{-4} = \Delta^7 y_{-3} - \Delta^7 y_{-4}$

(s) and $\qquad \Delta^7 y_{-3} = 2m_7 - \Delta y_{-4}$, from (d).

Subtracting (r) from (s) and solving for $\Delta^7 y_{-3}$,

(t) $\qquad \Delta^7 y_{-3} = m_7 + \tfrac{1}{2}\Delta^8 y_{-4}$.

Substituting (t) in (q) and solving for $\Delta^6 y_{-2}$,

(u) $\qquad \Delta^6 y_{-2} = \underline{\Delta^6 y_{-3}} + m_7 + \tfrac{1}{2}\Delta^8 y_{-4}$.

Substituting (u) in (p) and solving for $\Delta^5 y_{-1}$,

(v) $\qquad \Delta^5 y_{-1} = m_5 + \underline{\tfrac{3}{2}\Delta^6 y_{-3}} + m_7 + \tfrac{1}{2}\Delta^8 y_{-4}$.

Substituting (v) in (o),

(4) $\qquad \Delta^4 y_0 = \underline{\Delta^4 y_{-2}} + 2m_5 + \underline{2\Delta^6 y_{-3}} + m_7 + \tfrac{1}{2}\Delta^8 y_{-4}$.

Now substituting (1), (2), (3), (4) in (B), we get

$$y = y_0 + C_1(m_1 + \tfrac{1}{2}\Delta^2 y_{-1}) + C_2(m_3 + \Delta^2 y_{-1} + \tfrac{1}{2}\Delta^4 y_{-2})$$
$$+ C_3(m_3 + m_5 + \tfrac{3}{2}\Delta^4 y_{-2} + \tfrac{1}{2}\Delta^6 y_{-3})$$
$$+ C_4(2m_5 + m_7 + \Delta^4 y_{-2} + 2\Delta^6 y_{-3} + \tfrac{1}{2}\Delta^8 y_{-4}),$$

or

$$y = y_0 + C_1 m_1 + \left(\frac{C_1}{2} + C_2\right)\Delta^2 y_{-1} + (C_2 + C_3)m_3$$
$$+ \left(\frac{C_2}{2} + \frac{3C_3}{2} + C_4\right)\Delta^4 y_{-2} + \text{terms in } m_5, \ \Delta^6 y_{-3}, \ \text{etc.}$$

Replacing the C's and m's by their values, we get

$$y = y_0 + u\frac{\Delta y_{-1} + \Delta y_0}{2} + \left(\frac{u}{2} + \frac{u(u-1)}{2}\right)\Delta^2 y_{-1}$$
$$+ \left(\frac{u(u-1)}{2} + \frac{u(u-1)(u-2)}{6}\right)\frac{\Delta^3 y_{-2} + \Delta^3 y_{-1}}{2}$$
$$+ \left(\frac{u(u-1)}{4} + \frac{3u(u-1)(u-2)}{12} + \frac{u(u-1)(u-2)(u-3)}{24}\right)\Delta^4 y_{-2} + \cdots,$$

or

$$y = y_0 + w\frac{\Delta y_{-1} + \Delta y_0}{2} + \frac{u^2}{2}\Delta^2 y_{-1} + \frac{u(u^2-1)}{3!}\frac{\Delta^3 y_{-2} + \Delta^3 y_{-1}}{2}$$
$$+ \frac{u^2(w^2-1)}{4!}\Delta^4 y_{-2} + \cdots.$$

By continuing the calculation as above outlined we arrive at *Stirling's* formula, namely:

$$\textbf{(III)} \quad y = y_0 + u\frac{\Delta y_{-1} + \Delta y_0}{2} + \frac{u^2}{2}\Delta^2 y_{-1} + \frac{u(u^2 - 1^2)}{3!}\frac{\Delta^3 y_{-2} + \Delta^3 y_{-1}}{2}$$

$$+ \frac{u^2(u^2 - 1^2)}{4!}\Delta^4 y_{-2} + \frac{u(u^2 - 1^2)(u^2 - 2^2)}{5!}\frac{\Delta^5 y_{-3} + \Delta^5 y_{-2}}{2}$$

$$+ \frac{u^2(u^2 - 1^2)(u^2 - 2^2)}{6!}\Delta^6 y_{-3} + \cdots\cdots$$

$$+ \frac{u(u^2 - 1^2)(u^2 - 2^2)(u^2 - 3^2)\cdots[u^2 - (n-1)^2]}{(2n-1)!}$$

$$\times \frac{\Delta^{2n-1} y_{-n} + \Delta^{2n-1} y_{-(n-1)}}{2}$$

$$+ \frac{u^2(u^2 - 1^2)(u^2 - 2^2)(u^2 - 3^2)\cdots[u^2 - (n-1)^2]}{(2n)!}\Delta^{2n} y_{-n},$$

where $u = (x - x_0)/h$.

In this formula there are $2n + 1$ terms, and the polynomial coincides with the given function at the $2n + 1$ points

$$u = -n, -(n-1), -(n-2), \cdots -2, -1, 0, 1, 2, \cdots n-2, n-1, n;$$

or

$$x = x_0 - nh, x_0 - (n-1)h, \cdots x_0 - h, x_0, x_0 + h, \cdots x_0 + (n-1)h, x_0 + nh$$

24. Bessel's Interpolation Formulas. The derivation of Bessel's formula of interpolation is similar to that of Stirling's. We first write down a diagonal difference table as before, and mark for special consideration the quantities lying as near as possible to the horizontal line drawn halfway between y_0 and y_1. These quantities are printed in heavy type in the table below.

y	Δy	$\Delta^2 y$	$\Delta^3 y$	$\Delta^4 y$	$\Delta^5 y$	$\Delta^6 y$	$\Delta^7 y$	$\Delta^8 y$
y_{-4}								
	Δy_{-4}							
y_{-3}		$\Delta^2 y_{-4}$						
	Δy_{-3}		$\Delta^3 y_{-4}$					
y_{-2}		$\Delta^2 y_{-3}$		$\Delta^4 y_{-4}$				
	Δy_{-2}		$\Delta^3 y_{-3}$		$\Delta^5 y_{-4}$			
y_{-1}		$\Delta^2 y_{-2}$		$\Delta^4 y_{-3}$		$\Delta^6 y_{-4}$		
	Δy_{-1}		$\Delta^3 y_{-2}$		$\Delta^5 y_{-3}$		$\Delta^7 y_{-4}$	
$\mathbf{y_0}$		$\mathbf{\Delta^2 y_{-1}}$		$\mathbf{\Delta^4 y_{-2}}$		$\mathbf{\Delta^6 y_{-3}}$		$\mathbf{\Delta^8 y_{-4}}$
	$\mathbf{\Delta y_0}$		$\mathbf{\Delta^3 y_{-1}}$		$\mathbf{\Delta^5 y_{-2}}$		$\mathbf{\Delta^7 y_{-3}}$	
$\mathbf{y_1}$		$\mathbf{\Delta^2 y_0}$		$\mathbf{\Delta^4 y_{-1}}$		$\mathbf{\Delta^6 y_{-2}}$		$\mathbf{\Delta^8 y_{-3}}$
	Δy_1		$\Delta^3 y_0$		$\Delta^5 y_{-1}$		$\Delta^7 y_{-2}$	
y_2		$\Delta^2 y_1$		$\Delta^4 y_0$		$\Delta^6 y_{-1}$		
	Δy_2		$\Delta^3 y_1$		$\Delta^5 y_0$			
y_3		$\Delta^2 y_2$		$\Delta^4 y_1$				
	Δy_3		$\Delta^3 y_2$					
y_4		$\Delta^2 y_3$						
	Δy_4							
y_5								

TABLE 8.

Let us now put

$(a) \qquad m_0 = \dfrac{y_0 + y_1}{2},$ $\qquad\qquad (b) \qquad m_2 = \dfrac{\Delta^2 y_{-1} + \Delta^2 y_0}{2},$

$(c) \qquad m_4 = \dfrac{\Delta^4 y_{-2} + \Delta^4 y_{-1}}{2},$ $\qquad (d) \qquad m_6 = \dfrac{\Delta^6 y_{-3} + \Delta^6 y_{-2}}{2},$

$(e) \qquad m_8 = \dfrac{\Delta^8 y_{-4} + \Delta^8 y_{-3}}{2}, \text{ etc.}$

The m's in this case are thus the arithmetic means of the ordinates y_0 and y_1, and of the *even* differences just above and below the horizontal line through $y_{1/2}$.

We next write down Newton's formula (I), starting from the entry y_0, as was done in Art. 23. Our problem is to express $y_0, \Delta y_0, \Delta^2 y_0, \cdots \Delta^n y_0$ in terms of the m's and the *odd* differences lying on the horizontal line through $y_{1/2}$. This will be done by an elimination process, by working from $\Delta^2 y_0, \Delta^3 y_0$, etc. diagonally upward to the right until we reach the quantities in the horizontal line. The odd differences in the horizontal line will be underlined in the work which follows, to indicate that they are *not* to be eliminated.

By definition we have

$$\underline{\Delta y_0} = y_1 - y_0.$$

$$\therefore \; y_0 = y_1 - \underline{\Delta y_0}.$$

But $\qquad\qquad y_1 = 2m_0 - y_0, \text{ from } (a).$

$$\therefore \; y_0 = 2m_0 - y_0 - \underline{\Delta y_0}.$$

$(1) \qquad\qquad\qquad \therefore \; \underline{y_0 = m_0 - \tfrac{1}{2}\Delta y_0}.$

To find $\Delta^2 y_0$ we start with

$$\underline{\Delta^3 y_{-1}} = \Delta^2 y_0 - \Delta^2 y_{-1}, \text{ by definition.}$$

$$\therefore \; \Delta^2 y_0 = \underline{\Delta^3 y_{-1}} + \Delta^2 y_{-1}.$$

But $\qquad\qquad \Delta^2 y_{-1} = 2m_2 - \Delta^2 y_0, \text{ from } (b).$

$$\therefore \; \Delta^2 y_0 = \underline{\Delta^3 y_{-1}} + 2m_2 - \Delta^2 y_0,$$

or

$(2) \qquad\qquad\qquad \Delta^2 y_0 = m_2 + \tfrac{1}{2}\Delta^3 y_{-1}.$

For $\Delta^3 y_0$ we have

$$\Delta^4 y_{-1} = \Delta^3 y_0 - \underline{\Delta^3 y_{-1}}, \text{ by definition.}$$

$(f) \qquad\qquad \therefore \; \Delta^3 y_0 = \underline{\Delta^3 y_{-1}} + \Delta^4 y_{-1}.$

(g) But $\qquad \Delta^4 y_{-1} = 2m_4 - \Delta^4 y_{-2}$, from (c),

(h) and $\qquad \underline{\Delta^5 y_{-2}} = \Delta^4 y_{-1} - \Delta^4 y_{-2}$, by definition.

Subtracting (h) from (g) and solving for $\Delta^4 y_{-1}$,

(i) $\qquad \Delta^4 y_{-1} = m_4 + \tfrac{1}{2}\Delta^5 y_{-2}$.

Substituting (i) in (f),

(3) $\qquad \Delta^3 y_0 = \underline{\Delta^3 y_{-1}} + m_4 + \underline{\tfrac{1}{2}\Delta^5 y_{-2}}$.

To find $\Delta^4 y_0$ we start with

$$\Delta^5 y_{-1} = \Delta^4 y_0 - \Delta^4 y_{-1}, \text{ by definition.}$$

(j) $\qquad \therefore\ \Delta^4 y_0 = \Delta^4 y_{-1} + \Delta^5 y_{-1}$

$$= m_4 + \tfrac{1}{2}\underline{\Delta^5 y_{-2}} + \Delta^5 y_{-1}, \text{ from (i).}$$

(k) Now $\qquad \Delta^6 y_{-2} = \Delta^5 y_{-1} - \underline{\Delta^5 y_{-2}}$, by definition.

(l) Also $\qquad \underline{\Delta^7 y_{-3}} = \Delta^6 y_{-2} - \Delta^6 y_{-3}$, by definition,

(m) and $\qquad \Delta^6 y_{-2} = 2m_6 - \Delta^6 y_{-3}$, from (d).

Subtracting (l) from (m) and solving for $\Delta^6 y_{-2}$,

(n) $\qquad \Delta^6 y_{-2} = m_6 + \tfrac{1}{2}\Delta^7 y_{-3}$.

Equating (k) and (n) and solving for $\Delta^5 y_{-1}$,

(o) $\qquad \Delta^5 y_{-1} = \underline{\Delta^5 y_{-2}} + m_6 + \tfrac{1}{2}\Delta^7 y_{-3}$.

Substituting (o) in (j), we get

(4) $\qquad \Delta^4 y_0 = m_4 + \tfrac{3}{2}\Delta^5 y_{-2} + m_6 + \tfrac{1}{2}\Delta^7 y_{-3}$.

Now substituting these values of y_0, $\Delta^2 y_0$, $\Delta^3 y_0$, etc. in (A) of Art. 23, we have

$$y = m_0 - \tfrac{1}{2}\Delta y_0 + u\Delta y_0 + \frac{u(u-1)}{2}(m_2 + \tfrac{1}{2}\Delta^3 y_{-1})$$

$$+ \frac{u(u-1)(u-2)}{6}(m_4 + \Delta^3 y_{-1} + \tfrac{1}{2}\Delta^5 y_{-2})$$

$$+ \frac{u(u-1)(u-2)(u-3)}{24}(m_4 + \tfrac{3}{2}\Delta^5 y_{-2} + m_6 + \tfrac{1}{2}\Delta^7 y_{-3}),$$

or, rearranging,

$$y = m_0 + (u - \tfrac{1}{2})\Delta y_0 + \frac{u(u-1)}{2}m_2 + \left[\frac{u(u-1)}{4} + \frac{u(u-1)(u-2)}{6}\right]\Delta^3$$

$$+ \left[\frac{u(u-1)(u-2)}{6} + \frac{u(u-1)(u-2)(u-3)}{24}\right]m_4$$

$$\left[\frac{u(u-1)(u-2)}{12} + \frac{u(u-1)(u-2)(u-3)}{16}\right]\Delta^5 y_{-2}$$

$\qquad +$ terms in $\Delta^5 y$, m_6, and $\Delta^7 y_{-3}$.

Simplifying and replacing the m's by their values, we get

$$y = \frac{y_0 + y_1}{2} + (u - \tfrac{1}{2})\Delta y_0 + \frac{u(u-1)}{2} \frac{\Delta^2 y_{-1} + \Delta^2 y_0}{2}$$

$$+ \frac{u(u-1)(u-\tfrac{1}{2})}{3!} \Delta^3 y_{-1} + \frac{u(u-1)(u+1)(u-2)}{4!} \frac{\Delta^4 y_{-2} + \Delta^4 y_{-1}}{2}$$

$$+ \cdots .$$

Now since $\Delta y_0 = y_1 - y_0$, the first two terms can be transformed to $y_0 + u\Delta y_0$. Hence

$$y = y_0 + u\Delta y_0 + \frac{u(u-1)}{2} \frac{\Delta^2 y_{-1} + \Delta^2 y_0}{2} + \frac{u(u-1)(u-\tfrac{1}{2})}{3!} \Delta^3 y_{-1}$$

$$+ \frac{u(u-1)(u+1)(u-2)}{4!} \frac{\Delta^4 y_{-2} + \Delta^4 y_{-1}}{2} + \cdots .$$

By continuing the calculation as carried out above we arrive at *Bessel's* formula of interpolation:

(IV) $y = y_0 + u\Delta y_0 + \dfrac{u(u-1)}{2} \dfrac{\Delta^2 y_{-1} + \Delta^2 y_0}{2}$

$$+ \frac{(u-\tfrac{1}{2})u(u-1)}{3!} \Delta^3 y_{-1} + \frac{u(u-1)(u+1)(u-2)}{4!} \frac{\Delta^4 y_{-2} + \Delta^4 y_{-1}}{2}$$

$$+ \frac{(u-\tfrac{1}{2})u(u-1)(u+1)(u-2)}{5!} \Delta^5 y_{-2}$$

$$+ \frac{u(u-1)(u+1)(u-2)(u+2)(u-3)}{6!} \frac{\Delta^6 y_{-3} + \Delta^6 y_{-2}}{2} + \cdots$$

$$+ \frac{u(u-1)(u+1)(u-2)(u+2)\cdots(u-n)(u+n-1)}{(2n)!}$$

$$\times \frac{\Delta^{2n} y_{-n} + \Delta^{2n} y_{-n+1}}{2}$$

$$+ \frac{(u-\tfrac{1}{2})u(u-1)(u+1)(u-2)(u+2)\cdots(u-n)(u+n-1)}{(2n+1)!} \Delta^{2n+1} y_{-n} .$$

If in this formula we put $u = \tfrac{1}{2}$, we get the simple formula

(V) $\quad y = \dfrac{y_0 + y_1}{2} - \dfrac{1}{8} \dfrac{\Delta^2 y_{-1} + \Delta^2 y_0}{2} + \dfrac{3}{128} \dfrac{\Delta^4 y_{-2} + \Delta^4 y_{-1}}{2}$

$$- \frac{5}{1024} \frac{\Delta^6 y_{-3} + \Delta^6 y_{-2}}{2} + \cdots$$

$$+ (-1)^n \frac{[1 \cdot 3 \cdot 5 \cdots (2n-1)]^2}{2^{2n}(2n)!} \frac{\Delta^{2n} y_{-n} + \Delta^{2n} y_{-n+1}}{2} .$$

This important special case of Bessel's formula is called the *formula for interpolating to halves*. It is used for computing values of the function midway between any two given values.

A more symmetrical and convenient form of Bessel's formula is obtained by putting $u - \frac{1}{2} = v$, or $u = v + \frac{1}{2}$. Making this substitution in (IV), we get

$$\textbf{(VI)} \quad y = \frac{y_0 + y_1}{2} + v\Delta y_0 + \frac{(v^2 - \frac{1}{4})}{2} \frac{\Delta^2 y_{-1} + \Delta^2 y_0}{2} + \frac{v(v^2 - \frac{1}{4})}{3!} \Delta^3 y_{-1}$$

$$+ \frac{(v^2 - \frac{1}{4})(v^2 - \frac{9}{4})}{4!} \frac{\Delta^4 y_{-2} + \Delta^4 y_{-1}}{2} + \frac{v(v^2 - \frac{1}{4})(v^2 - \frac{9}{4})}{5!} \Delta^5 y_{-2}$$

$$+ \frac{(v^2 - \frac{1}{4})(v^2 - \frac{9}{4})(v^2 - \frac{25}{4})}{6!} \frac{\Delta^6 y_{-3} + \Delta^6 y_{-2}}{2} + \cdots :$$

$$+ \frac{(v^2 - \frac{1}{4})(v^2 - \frac{9}{4}) \cdots [v^2 - (2n-1)^2/4]}{(2n)!} \frac{\Delta^{2n} y_{-n} + \Delta^{2n} y_{-n+1}}{2}$$

$$+ \frac{v(v^2 - \frac{1}{4})(v^2 - \frac{9}{4}) \cdots [v^2 - (2n-1)^2/4]}{(2n+1)!} \Delta^{2n+1} y_{-n}.$$

In formulas (IV) and (VI) there are $2n + 2$ terms, and the polynomials represented by them coincide with the given function at the $2n + 2$ points

$$u = -n, \ -n+1, \ -n+2, \cdots -1, \ 0, \ 1, \ 2, \cdots n, n+1;$$

$$v = -\frac{2n+1}{2}, \ -\frac{2n-1}{2}, \cdots -\frac{3}{2}, \ -\frac{1}{2}, \frac{1}{2}, \frac{3}{2}, \cdots \frac{2n-1}{2}, \frac{2n+1}{2};$$

$$x = x_0 - nh, x_0 - (n-1)h, \cdots x_0 - h, x_0, x_0 + h, \cdots x_0 + nh, x_0 + (n+1)h.$$

The zero point for the v's is $x_0 + h/2$, whereas for the u's it is x_0.

We shall now apply Stirling's and Bessel's formulas to some numerical examples.

Example 1. The following table gives the values of the probability integral

$$f(x) = \frac{2}{\sqrt{\pi}} \int_0^x e^{-x^2} dx$$

for certain equidistant values of x. Find the value of this integral when $x = 0.5437$.

x	$f(x)$	$\Delta f(x)$	$\Delta^2 f(x)$	$\Delta^3 f(x)$	$\Delta^4 f(x)$
0.51	0.5292437				
		86550			
0.52	0.5378987		−896		
		85654		−7	
0.53	0.5464641		−903		0
		84751		−7	
0.54	0.5549392		−910		0
		83841		−7	
0.55	0.5633233		−917		1
		82924		−6	
0.56	0.5716157		−923		
		82001			
0.57	0.5798158				

Solution. Here we take $x_0 = 0.54$ and $x = 0.5437$. Since $h = 0.01$, we have

$$u = \frac{x - x_0}{h} = \frac{0.5437 - 0.54}{0.01} = \frac{0.0037}{0.01} = 0.37.$$

(a) Using Stirling's formula, (III), we have

$$f(0.5437) = 0.5549392 + 0.37 \frac{(84751 + 83841)}{2}$$

$$+ \frac{(0.37)^2}{2}(-910) + \frac{0.37(0.37^2 - 1)}{2} \frac{(-7 - 7)}{6}$$

$$= 0.5549392 + 0.00311895 - 0.00000623 + 0.00000004.$$

$$= \underline{0.5580520.}$$

(b) To find $f(0.5437)$ by Bessel's formula it is more convenient to use (VI). Here

$$v = u - \tfrac{1}{2} = 0.37 - 0.50 = -0.13.$$

Substituting in (VI), we have

$$f(0.5437) = \frac{0.5549392 + 0.5633233}{2} + (-0.13)(83841)$$

$$+ \frac{0.0169 - 0.25}{2}\left(\frac{-910 - 917}{2}\right) + \frac{-0.13(0.0169 - 0.25)(-7)}{6}$$

$$= 0.55913125 - 0.00108993 + 0.00001065$$

$$= 0.5580520.$$

Example 2. The values of e^{-x} for certain equidistant values of x are given in the following table. Find the value of e^{-x} when $x = 1.7489$.

x	e^{-x}	Δ	Δ^2	Δ^3	Δ^4
1.72	0.1790661479				
		−17817379			
1.73	0.1772844100		177285		
		−17640094		−1762	
1.74	0.1755204006		175523		+13
		−17464571		−1749	
1.75	0.1737739435		173774		+22
		−17290797		−1727	
1.76	0.1720448638		172047		+15
		−17118750		−1712	
1.77	0.1703329888		170335		
		−16948415			
1.78	0.1686381473				

Solution.

(a) By Stirling's formula.

Here we take $x = 1.7489$, $x_0 = 1.75$, $h = 0.01$.

Hence

$$u = \frac{1.7489 - 1.75}{0.01} = -\frac{0.0011}{0.01} = -0.11.$$

Substituting in (III), we have

$$f(1.7489) = 0.1737739435 - 0.11\,\frac{(-17464571 - 17290797)}{2}$$

$$+ \frac{0.0121}{2}\,(173774) - 0.11\left(\frac{0.0121 - 1}{6}\right)\left(\frac{-1749 - 1727}{2}\right)$$

$$+ 0.0121\left(\frac{0.0121 - 1}{24}\right)(22)$$

$$= 0.1737739435 + 0.00019115452$$

$$+ 0.00000010513 - 0.00000000315\,;$$

or $f(1.7489) = e^{-1.7489} = \underline{0.1739652000}.$

This value is correct to ten decimal places.

(b) By Bessel's formula.

Since the value 1.7489 is nearer to the middle of the interval 1.74 — 1.75 than it is to the middle of the interval 1.75 — 1.76, we take $x_0 = 1.74$ so as to make v as small as possible. Hence we have

$$u = \frac{1.7489 - 1.74}{0.01} = 0.89,$$

$$v = u - \tfrac{1}{2} = 0.89 - 0.50 = 0.39.$$

$$\therefore \; f(1.7489) = \frac{0.1755204006 + 0.1737739435}{2} + 0.39(-17464571)$$

$$+ \left(\frac{0.39^2 - 0.25}{2}\right)\left(\frac{175523 + 173774}{2}\right)$$

$$+ 0.39\left(\frac{0.39^2 - 0.25}{6}\right)(-1749)$$

$$+ \frac{(0.39^2 - 0.25)(0.39^2 - 2.25)}{24}\left(\frac{13 + 22}{2}\right)$$

$$= 0.17464717205 - 0.00068111827$$

$$- 0.00000085490 + 0.00000000111$$

$$+ 0.00000000001 \,;$$

or $f(1.7489) = 0.1739652000$, as before.

We could also take $x_0 = 1.75$, in which case we should have $v = -0.61$. This would give

$$f(1.7489) = 0.17290940365 + 0.00105473862$$

$$+ 0.00000105562 + 0.00000000214$$

$$- 0.00000000002 = 0.1739652000.$$

This value is also correct to ten decimal places, but the series converges slightly less rapidly than in the preceding case; and both of these series given by Bessel's formula converge a little less rapidly than the one given by Stirling's formula.

Remark. The question naturally arises at this point as to which is the more accurate, Stirling's formula or Bessel's. The answer is that one is about as accurate as the other. For a given table of differences the rapidity of convergence depends upon the magnitude of u in the case of formula (III) and upon the magnitude of v in the case of formula (VI). The smaller the values of u and v the more rapidly the series converge. We should therefore always choose the starting point x_0 so as to make u and v as small as possible. In most cases it is possible to choose the starting point so as to make $-0.5 \leqq u \leqq 0.5$ and $-0.5 \leqq v \leqq 0.5$. Thus, in Example 1 the starting point was so chosen that $u = 0.37$, $v = -0.13$; and in Example 2 we had $u = -0.11$, $v = 0.39$. It is to be noted that Bessel's formula converged the more rapidly in the first example and Stirling's the more rapidly in the second, the reason being that v was smaller than u in the first case and u smaller than v in the second.

As a general rule it may be stated that Bessel's formula will give a more accurate result when interpolating near the middle of an interval, say from $u = 0.25$ *to* 0.75 *(*$v = -0.25$ *to* 0.25*); whereas Stirling's formula will give the better result when interpolating near the beginning or end of an interval, from* $u = -0.25$ *to* 0.25*, say.*

For another phase of this question see Chapter V.

Example 3.   The following table gives the values of the elliptic integral

$$F(\phi) = \int_0^\phi \frac{d\phi}{\sqrt{1 - \tfrac{1}{2}\sin^2\phi}}$$

for certain equidistant values of ϕ.   Find the value of $F(23°.5)$.

ϕ	$F(\phi)$	ΔF	$\Delta^2 F$	$\Delta^3 F$	$\Delta^4 F$
21°	0.370634373				
		18070778			
22	0.388705151		59002		
		18129780		2707	
23	0.406834931		61709		4
		18191489		2711	
24	0.425026420		64420		−7
		18255909		2704	
25	0.443282329		67124		
		18323033			
26	0.461605362				

Solution.   Since we are to find the value of the function halfway between two given tabular values, we use formula (V) for interpolating to halves. Hence we have

$$F(23°.5) = \frac{0.406834931 + 0.425026420}{2} - \frac{1}{8}\,\frac{61709 + 64420}{2}$$

$$+ \frac{3}{128}\,\frac{4-7}{2}$$

$$= 0.4159306755 - 0.0000078831 = 0.415922792.$$

This result is probably correct to its last figure, since the differences in the table are perfectly regular and decrease rapidly.

EXERCISES III

1. Find $\log_{10} \tan 56' 43''.5$ by Bessel's formula (IV) or (VI), given

$$\log \tan 52' = 8.1797626 - 10$$
$$"\quad" \quad 53 = 8.1880364 - 10$$
$$"\quad" \quad 54 = 8.1961556 - 10$$
$$"\quad" \quad 55 = 8.2041259 - 10$$
$$"\quad" \quad 56 = 8.2119526 - 10$$
$$"\quad" \quad 57 = 8.2196408 - 10$$
$$"\quad" \quad 58 = 8.2271953 - 10$$
$$"\quad" \quad 59 = 8.2346208 - 10.$$

2. Find $\cos 0.806595$ by Stirling's formula, given

$$\cos 0.8050 = 0.693111235$$
$$"\quad 0.8055 = 0.692750733$$
$$"\quad 0.8060 = 0.692390058$$
$$"\quad 0.8065 = 0.692029210$$
$$"\quad 0.8070 = 0.691668188$$
$$"\quad 0.8075 = 0.691306994$$
$$"\quad 0.8080 = 0.690945627.$$

3. Compute the value of $(2/\sqrt{\pi}) \int_0^x e^{-x^2} dx$ when $x = 0.6538$, given the following table:

x	$(2/\cdot\sqrt{\pi}) \int_0^x e^{-x^2} dx$
0.62	0.6194114
0.63	0.6270463
0.64	0.6345857
0.65	0.6420292
0.66	0.6493765
0.67	0.6566275
0.68	0.6637820

4. The mean atmospheric refraction, R, for a star at various altitudes $h°$ above the horizon is given in the table below. Using Bessel's formula for interpolation to halves, find the refraction for a star at an altitude of $27°$ above the horizon.

h	R
22°	2′ 23″ .3
24	2 10 .2
26	1 58 .9
28	1 49 .2
30	1 40 .6
32	1 33 .0

5. The declination of the moon at the beginning (noon) of certain days in August, 1918, was as given below. Compute the declination for 9:35 P. M., August 25.

Aug.	20,	— 16°	0′	51″	.0
"	21	— 11	24	51	.8
"	22	— 6	3	29	.4
"	23	— 0	17	25	.8
"	24	+ 5	30	21	.5
"	25	10	56	40	.3
"	26	15	39	57	.8
"	27	19	22	3	.7
"	28	21	49	48	.3
"	29	22	56	22	.8
"	30	22	41	54	.1

6. The values of an elliptic integral for certain values of the amplitude ϕ are given in the table below. Compute the value of the integral when $\phi = 24° 36′ 42″$.

ϕ	$F(\phi)$
21°	0.370634373
22	0.388705151
23	0.406834931
24	0.425026420
25	0.443282329
26	0.461605362
27	0.479998225

CHAPTER IV

LAGRANGE'S FORMULA. INVERSE INTERPOLATION

I. LAGRANGE'S FORMULA OF INTERPOLATION

25. Introduction. The interpolation formulas derived in the preceding sections are applicable only when the values of the independent variable are given at equidistant intervals. It is sometimes inconvenient or even impossible to obtain values of a function for equidistant values of the independent variable, and in such cases it is desirable to have an interpolation formula which involves only such data as may be at hand. We shall now derive such a formula.

26. Lagrange's Formula. Let (x_0, y_0), (x_1, y_1), (x_2, y_2), $\cdots$ (x_n, y_n) denote $n + 1$ corresponding pairs of values of any two variables x and y, where $y = f(x)$. We replace the given function by a polynomial of the nth degree, which may be written in the following form:

$$(1) \quad \phi(x) = A_0(x - x_1)(x - x_2)(x - x_3) \cdots (x - x_n)$$
$$+ A_1(x - x_0)(x - x_2)(x - x_3) \cdots (x - x_n)$$
$$+ A_2(x - x_0)(x - x_1)(x - x_3) \cdots (x - x_n)$$
$$+ \cdots$$
$$+ A_n(x - x_0)(x - x_1)(x - x_2) \cdots (x - x_{n-1}).$$

Here there are $n + 1$ terms and n factors in each term.

We next determine the $n + 1$ constants A_0, A_1, A_2, $\cdots A_n$ so as to make $\phi(x_0) = y_0$, $\phi(x_1) = y_1$, $\cdots \phi(x_n) = y_n$. Putting $x = x_0$ and $\phi(x_0) = y_0$ in (1), we get

$$y_0 = A_0(x_0 - x_1)(x_0 - x_2) \cdots (x_0 - x_n).$$

$$\therefore A_0 = \frac{y_0}{(x_0 - x_1)(x_0 - x_2) \cdots (x_0 - x_n)}.$$

Again, putting $x = x_1$, $\phi(x_1) = y_1$ in (1), we have

$$y_1 = A_1(x_1 - x_0)(x_1 - x_2) \cdots (x_1 - x_n).$$

$$\therefore A_1 = \frac{y_1}{(x_1 - x_0)(x_1 - x_2) \cdots (x_1 - x_n)}.$$

In a similar manner we find

$$A_2 = \frac{y_2}{(x_2 - x_0)(x_2 - x_1)(x_2 - x_3) \cdots (x_2 - x_n)},$$

$$\cdots \cdots \cdots \cdots \cdots \cdots$$

$$A_n = \frac{y_n}{(x_n - x_0)(x_n - x_1) \cdots (x_n - x_{n-1})}.$$

Substituting in (1) these values of the A's, we get

(VII) $\quad \phi(x) = \dfrac{(x - x_1)(x - x_2) \cdots (x - x_n)}{(x_0 - x_1)(x_0 - x_2) \cdots (x_0 - x_n)} y_0$

$\qquad + \dfrac{(x - x_0)(x - x_2) \cdots (x - x_n)}{(x_1 - x_0)(x_1 - x_2) \cdots (x_1 - x_n)} y_1$

$\qquad + \dfrac{(x - x_0)(x - x_1)(x - x_3) \cdots (x - x_n)}{(x_2 - x_0)(x_2 - x_1)(x_2 - x_3) \cdots (x_2 - x_n)} y_2 + \cdots$

$\qquad + \dfrac{(x - x_0)(x - x_1) \cdots (x - x_{n-1})}{(x_n - x_0)(x_n - x_1) \cdots (x_n - x_{n-1})} y_n.$

This formula can also be written in the form

(VIII) $\qquad \phi(x) = \sum\limits_{i=0}^{n} \dfrac{II_n(x)}{(x - x_i)II'_n(x)} y_i, \qquad\qquad i = 0, 1, \cdots n,$

where $\qquad\qquad II_n(x) = (x - x_0)(x - x_1) \cdots (x - x_n),$

$$II'_n(x) = \frac{d}{dx} II_n(x).$$

Formulas (VII) and (VIII) are known as *Lagrange's formula of interpolation*. The values of the independent variable may or may not be equidistant. It is to be noted that Lagrange's formula does not involve the successive differences of the function concerned, and that there is nothing in it by which we can estimate the reliability of the results obtained.

Since Lagrange's formula is merely a relation between two variables, either of which may be taken as the independent variable, it is evident that by considering y as the independent variable we can write a formula giving x as a function of y. Hence, on interchanging x and y in the right-hand member of (VII) we get

(IX) $\qquad \psi(y) = \dfrac{(y - y_1)(y - y_2) \cdots (y - y_n)}{(y_0 - y_1)(y_0 - y_2) \cdots (y_0 - y_n)} x_0$

$\qquad + \dfrac{(y - y_0)(y - y_2) \cdots (y - y_n)}{(y_1 - y_0)(y_1 - y_2) \cdots (y_1 - y_n)} x_1$

$\qquad + \dfrac{(y - y_0)(y - y_1) \cdots (y - y_n)}{(y_2 - y_0)(y_2 - y_1) \cdots (y_2 - y_n)} x_2 + \cdots$

$\qquad + \dfrac{(y - y_0)(y - y_1) \cdots (y - y_{n-1})}{(y_n - y_0)(y_n - y_1) \cdots (y_n - y_{n-1})} x_n.$

The chief uses of Lagrange's formula are two: (1) to find any value of a function when the given values of the independent variable are not equidistant, and (2) to find the value of the independent variable corresponding to a given value of the function. This second problem is solved by means of formula (IX).

We shall now work two examples to illustrate these uses.

Example 1. The following table gives certain corresponding values of x and $\log_{10} x$. Compute the value of log 323.5.

x	321.0	322.8	324.2	325.0
$\log_{10} x$	2.50651	2.50893	2.51081	2.51188

Solution. Here $x = 323.5$, $x_0 = 321.0$, $x_1 = 322.8$, $x_2 = 324.2$, $x_3 = 325.0$. Substituting these values in (VII), we get

$$\log_{10} 323.5 = \frac{(323.5 - 322.8)(323.5 - 324.2)(323.5 - 325.0)}{(321 - 322.8)(321 - 324.2)(321 - 325)} \times 2.50651$$

$$+ \frac{(323.5 - 321)(323.5 - 324.2)(323.5 - 325)}{(322.8 - 321)(322.8 - 324.2)(322.8 - 325)} \times 2.50893$$

$$+ \frac{(323.5 - 321)(323.5 - 322.8)(323.5 - 325)}{(324.2 - 321)(324.2 - 322.8)(324.2 - 325)} \times 2.51081$$

$$+ \frac{(323.5 - 321)(323.5 - 322.8)(323.5 - 324.2)}{(325 - 321)(325 - 322.8)(325 - 324.2)} \times 2.51188$$

$$= -0.07996 + 1.18794 + 1.83897 - 0.43708$$

$$= 2.50987.$$

This result is correct to the last figure.

Example 2. The following table gives the values of the probability integral $(2/\sqrt{\pi}) \int_0^x e^{-x^2} dx$ corresponding to certain values of x. For what value of x is this integral equal to $\frac{1}{2}$?

$(2/\sqrt{\pi}) \int_0^x e^{-x^2} dx$	x
0.4846555	0.46
0.4937452	0.47
0.5027498	0.48
0.5116683	0.49

Solution. Calling y the value of the probability integral, we have

$$y = \tfrac{1}{2} = 0.5, \quad x_0 = 0.46, \quad x_1 = 0.47, \quad x_2 = 0.48, \quad x_3 = 0.49.$$

Substituting these in (IX), we get

$$x = \frac{(0.5 - 0.4937452)(0.5 - 0.5027498)(0.5 - 0.5116683)}{(0.4846555 - 0.4937452)(0.4846555 - 0.5027498)(0.4846555 - 0.5116683)} \times 0.46$$

$$+ \frac{(0.5 - 0.4846555)(0.5 - 0.5027498)(0.5 - 0.5116683)}{(0.4937452 - 0.4846555)(0.4937452 - 0.5027498)(0.4937452 - 0.5116683)} \times 0.47$$

$$+ \frac{(0.5 - 0.4846555)(0.5 - 0.4937452)(0.5 - 0.5116683)}{(0.5027498 - 0.4846555)(0.5027498 - 0.4937452)(0.5027498 - 0.5116683)} \times 0.48$$

$$+ \frac{(0.5 - 0.4846555)(0.5 - 0.4937452)(0.5 - 0.5027498)}{(0.5116683 - 0.4846555)(0.5116683 - 0.4937452)(0.5116683 - 0.5027498)} \times 0.49$$

$$= -\frac{62548 \times 27498 \times 116683}{90897 \times 180943 \times 270128} \times 0.46$$

$$+ \frac{153445 \times 27498 \times 116683}{90897 \times 90046 \times 179231} \times 0.47$$

$$+ \frac{153445 \times 62548 \times 116683}{180943 \times 90046 \times 89185} \times 0.48$$

$$- \frac{153445 \times 62548 \times 27498}{270128 \times 179231 \times 89185} \times 0.49$$

$$= -0.0207787 + 0.157737 + 0.369928 - 0.0299495$$

$$= 0.476937.$$

The true value to six decimal places is 0.476936.

Note. The computation in this problem should be performed by logarithms unless a calculating machine is available.

Remark. The reader who has followed through the computation in the two preceding examples will have noticed that Lagrange's formula is tedious to apply and involves a great deal of computation. It must also be used with care and caution, for if the values of the independent variable are not taken close together the results are liable to be very inaccurate. For these reasons Lagrange's formula should not be used except in cases where Newton's, Stirling's, and Bessel's formulas are inapplicable.

II. INVERSE INTERPOLATION

27. Definition. *Inverse interpolation* is the process of finding the value of the *argument* corresponding to a given value of the function when the latter is intermediate between two tabulated values. The problem of inverse interpolation can be solved by several methods, but in this book we shall explain only three.

28. By Lagrange's Formula. One method of dealing with the problem is to use Lagrange's interpolation formula in the form (IX), in which x is expressed as a function of y. Example 2 of the preceding article was really a problem in inverse interpolation. We shall therefore not explain this method further.

29. By Successive Approximations. A second method is that of *successive approximations* or *iteration*. To see how this method is applied let us consider Newton's formula (I), namely,

$$y = y_0 + u\Delta y_0 + \frac{u(u-1)}{2}\Delta^2 y_0 + \frac{u(u-1)(u-2)}{3!}\Delta^3 y_0$$
$$+ \frac{u(u-1)(u-2)(u-3)}{4!}\Delta^4 y_0 + \cdots.$$

Transposing and dividing through by Δy_0, we have

$$(1) \qquad u = \frac{y-y_0}{\Delta y_0} - \frac{u(u-1)\Delta^2 y_0}{2\Delta y_0} - \frac{u(u-1)(u-2)\Delta^3 y_0}{3!\ \Delta y_0}$$
$$- \frac{u(u-1)(u-2)(u-3)}{4!}\frac{\Delta^4 y_0}{\Delta y_0}.$$

To get a first approximation for u, we neglect all differences higher than the first and therefore have

$$u^{(1)} = \frac{y-y_0}{\Delta y_0}.$$

The second approximation is obtained by substituting $u^{(1)}$ in the right-hand side of (1). We then have

$$(2) \quad u^{(2)} = \frac{y-y_0}{\Delta y_0} - \frac{u^{(1)}(u^{(1)}-1)}{2}\frac{\Delta^2 y_0}{\Delta y_0} - \frac{u^{(1)}(u^{(1)}-1)(u^{(1)}-2)}{3!}\frac{\Delta^3 y_0}{\Delta y_0}$$
$$- \frac{u^{(1)}(u^{(1)}-1)(u^{(1)}-2)(u^{(1)}-3)}{4!}\frac{\Delta^4 y_0}{\Delta y_0}.$$

The third approximation is

$$(3) \quad u^{(3)} = \frac{y-y_0}{\Delta y_0} - \frac{u^{(2)}(u^{(2)}-1)}{2}\frac{\Delta^2 y_0}{\Delta y_0} - \frac{u^{(2)}(u^{(2)}-1)(u^{(2)}-2)}{3!}\frac{\Delta^3 y_0}{\Delta y_0}$$
$$- \frac{u^{(2)}(u^{(2)}-1)(u^{(2)}-2)(u^{(2)}-3)}{4!}\frac{\Delta^4 y_0}{\Delta y_0}.$$

And so on for higher approximations.

We shall now illustrate the method by working an example.

Example 1. Given a table of values of the probability integral $(2/\sqrt{\pi})\int_0^x e^{-x^2}dx$, for what value of x is this integral equal to $\frac{1}{2}$?

x	y	Δy	$\Delta^2 y$	$\Delta^3 y$	$\Delta^4 y$
0.45	0.4754818				
		91737			
0.46	0.4846555		−840		
		90897		−11	
0.47	0.4937452		−851		1
		90046		−10	
0.48	0.5027498		−861		2
		89185		− 8	
0.49	0.5116683		−869		
		88316			
0.50	0.5204999				

Solution. Here it is better to use a central-difference formula. Inspection shows that the desired value of x lies between 0.47 and 0.48, and a rough linear interpolation shows that it is about 0.47$\frac{2}{3}$. Hence we take $x_0 = 0.47$ and use Bessel's formula. We therefore have

$$x_0 = 0.47, \quad h = 0.01, \quad y = \tfrac{1}{2} = 0.5.$$

Substituting in Bessel's formula (VI) this value of y and the appropriate quantities from the table, we have

$$0.5 = 0.4982475 + 0.0090046v + \frac{(v^2 - 0.25)}{2}(-0.0000856)$$
$$+ \frac{v(v^2 - 0.25)}{6}(-0.0000010).$$

Transposing and dividing through by 0.0090046, we get

(4) $\quad v = 0.194623 - (v^2 - 0.25)(-0.004753) - v(v^2 - 0.25)(-0.0000185).$

A first approximation for v is obtained by neglecting all terms beyond the first in the right-hand member of (4). Hence

$$v^{(1)} = 0.194623.$$

Substituting this for v in the right-hand member of (4), we find the second approximation to be

$$v^{(2)} = 0.194623 - [(0.194623)^2 - 0.25](-0.004753)$$
$$- 0.194623[(0.194623)^2 - 0.25](-0.0000185)$$
$$= 0.194623 - 0.001008 - 0.000001 = 0.193614.$$

Now substituting this value for v in the right-hand member of (4), we find

$$v^{(3)} = 0.194623 - 0.0010101 - 0.000001 = 0.193612.$$

This value differs only slightly from the preceding, and we therefore make no further approximations.

Since $u = v + \frac{1}{2}$ and $x = x_0 + hu$, we have

$$u = 0.693612,$$

$$x = 0.47 + 0.01(0.693612) = 0.47693612.$$

This value is correct to six decimal places.

Note. In this example it is not possible to obtain more than five trustworthy figures in the value of v, because the right-hand member of (4) is the result of a division by the approximate number 0.0090046, the fifth significant figure of which is uncertain. As a matter of fact, only the first four figures in v are correct.

If all differences higher than the second are negligible, the problem of inverse interpolation amounts only to the solution of a quadratic equation. The following example illustrates this.

Example 2. Given $\sinh x = 62$, to find x.

Solution. Forming a difference table as shown below, we find that all differences above the second are zero. We also notice that the required value of x is slightly greater than 4.82. Hence we take $x_0 = 4.82$ and use Stirling's formula.

x	$y = \sinh x$	Δy	$\Delta^2 y$	$\Delta^3 y$
4.80	60.7511			
		6106		
4.81	61.3617		62	
		6168		0
4.82	61.9785		62	
		6230		0
4.83	62.6015		62	
		6292		
4.84	63.2307			

Substituting $y = 62$ in Stirling's formula, (III), we have

$$62 = 61.9785 + 0.6199u + 0.0031u^2,$$

or $$31u^2 + 6199u = 215.$$

$$\therefore \quad u = \frac{-6199 + \sqrt{(6199)^2 + 4 \times 31 \times 215}}{62} = \frac{-6199 + 6201.15}{62}$$

$$= \frac{2.15}{62} = 0.0347.$$

Since $h = 0.01$ and $x = x_0 + hu$, we get
$$x = 4.82 + 0.01(0.0347) = \underline{4.8203}.$$

30. By Reversion of Series. The most obvious method of solving the problem of inverse interpolation is by reversion of series; for all the interpolation formulas thus far developed are in the form of a power series, and any convergent power series can be reverted. Thus, the power series

(1) $$y = a_0 + a_1 x + a_2 x^2 + a_3 x^3 + \cdots a_n x^n + \cdots$$

when reverted becomes

(2) $$x = \left(\frac{y - a_0}{a_1}\right) + c_1 \left(\frac{y - a_0}{a_1}\right)^2 + c_2 \left(\frac{y - a_0}{a_1}\right)^3$$
$$+ c_3 \left(\frac{y - a_0}{a_1}\right)^4 + \cdots + c_{n-1} \left(\frac{y - a_0}{a_1}\right)^n + \cdots,$$

where

(3) $$\begin{cases} c_1 = -\dfrac{a_2}{a_1}, \\[2mm] c_2 = -\dfrac{a_3}{a_1} + 2\left(\dfrac{a_2}{a_1}\right)^2, \\[2mm] c_3 = -\dfrac{a_4}{a_1} + 5\left(\dfrac{a_2 a_3}{a_1^2}\right) - 5\left(\dfrac{a_2}{a_1}\right)^3, \\[2mm] c_4 = -\dfrac{a_5}{a_1} + 6\dfrac{a_2 a_4}{a_1^2} + 3\left(\dfrac{a_3}{a_1}\right)^2 - 21\dfrac{a_2^2 a_3}{a_1^3} + 14\left(\dfrac{a_2}{a_1}\right)^4, \\[2mm] c_5 = -\dfrac{a_6}{a_1} + 7\left(\dfrac{a_2 a_5 + a_3 a_4}{a_1^2}\right) - 28\left(\dfrac{a_2^2 a_4 + a_2 a_3^2}{a_1^3}\right) + 84\dfrac{a_2^3 a_3}{a_1^4} \\[2mm] \qquad - 42\left(\dfrac{a_2}{a_1}\right)^5, \text{ etc.} \end{cases}$$

When reverting a series with numerical coefficients, it is better to compute the c's from equations (3) and then substitute their values in (2).

We shall now write Newton's, Stirling's, and Bessel's formulas in the form of power series and then write down the values of $a_0, a_1, \cdots a_4$ in each case. We stop with fourth differences, but the reader will have no difficulty in extending them to higher differences if necessary.

a) Newton's Formula (I).

$$y = y_0 + u\Delta y_0 + \frac{u(u-1)}{2}\Delta^2 y_0 + \frac{u(u-1)(u-2)}{3!}\Delta^3 y_0$$
$$+ \frac{u(u-1)(u-2)(u-3)}{4!}\Delta^4 y_0$$
$$= y_0 + \left(\Delta y_0 - \frac{\Delta^2 y_0}{2} + \frac{\Delta^3 y_0}{3} - \frac{\Delta^4 y_0}{4}\right)u + \left(\frac{\Delta^2 y_0}{2} - \frac{\Delta^3 y_0}{2} + \frac{11\Delta^4 y_0}{24}\right)u^2$$
$$+ \left(\frac{\Delta^3 y_0}{6} - \frac{\Delta^4 y_0}{4}\right)u^3 + \frac{\Delta^4 y_0}{24}u^4.$$

Here

$$a_0 = y_0 ,$$

$$a_1 = \Delta y_0 - \frac{\Delta^2 y_0}{2} + \frac{\Delta^3 y_0}{3} - \frac{\Delta^4 y_0}{4} ,$$

$$a_2 = \frac{\Delta^2 y_0}{2} - \frac{\Delta^3 y_0}{2} + \frac{11 \Delta^4 y_0}{24} ,$$

$$a_3 = \frac{\Delta^3 y_0}{6} - \frac{\Delta^4 y_0}{4} ,$$

$$a_4 = \frac{\Delta^4 y_0}{24} .$$

b) Stirling's Formula.

$$y = y_0 + u m_1 + \frac{u^2}{2} \Delta^2 y_{-1} + \frac{u(u^2-1)}{3!} m_3 + \frac{u^2(u^2-1)}{4!} \Delta^4 y_{-2}$$

$$= y_0 + \left(m_1 - \frac{m_3}{6} \right) u + \left(\frac{\Delta^2 y_{-1}}{2} - \frac{\Delta^4 y_{-2}}{24} \right) u^2 + \frac{m_3 u^3}{6} + \frac{\Delta^4 y_{-2}}{24} u^4,$$

where m_1 and m_3 have the values given in Art 23. Here

$$a_0 = y_0, \quad a_1 = m_1 - \frac{m_3}{6}, \quad a_2 = \frac{\Delta^2 y_{-1}}{2} - \frac{\Delta^4 y_{-1}}{24} ,$$

$$a_3 = \frac{m_3}{6} , \quad a_4 = \frac{\Delta^4 y_{-2}}{24} .$$

c) Bessel's Formula (VI).

$$y = m_0 + v \Delta y_0 + \frac{(v^2 - \frac{1}{4})}{2} m_2 + v \frac{(v^2 - \frac{1}{4})}{3!} \Delta^3 y_{-1} + \frac{(v^2 - \frac{1}{4})(v^2 - \frac{9}{4})}{4!} m_4$$

$$= \left(m_0 - \frac{m_2}{8} + \frac{3m_4}{128} \right) + \left(\Delta y_0 - \frac{\Delta^3 y_{-1}}{24} \right) v + \left(\frac{m_2}{2} - \frac{5m_4}{48} \right) v^2$$

$$+ \frac{\Delta^3 y_{-1}}{6} v^3 + \frac{m_4}{24} v^4,$$

where m_0, m_2, m_4 have the values given in Art. 24. Here

$$a_0 = m_0 - \frac{m_2}{8} + \frac{3m_4}{128} , \qquad a_1 = \Delta y_0 - \frac{\Delta^3 y_{-1}}{24} ,$$

$$a_2 = \frac{m_2}{2} - \frac{5m_4}{48} , \qquad a_3 = \frac{\Delta^3 y_{-1}}{6} , \qquad a_4 = \frac{m_4}{24} .$$

We shall now work Examples 1 and 2 of the preceding article by reverting the series. For Example 1 we use Bessel's formula as before. From the table on page 90 we get

$$m_0 = 0.4982475, \qquad m_2 = -0.0000856, \qquad m_4 = 0.00000015.$$

Hence

$$a_0 = 0.4982475 + \frac{0.0000856}{8} = 0.4982582,$$

$$a_1 = 0.0090046 + \frac{0.0000010}{24} = 9.00900464,$$

$$a_2 = -\frac{0.0000856}{2} = -0.0000428,$$

$$a_3 = -\frac{0.0000010}{6} = -0.00000017,$$

$$a_4 = 0, \text{ practically.}$$

Since $y = \frac{1}{2} = 0.5$, we have

$$\frac{y - a_0}{a_1} = \frac{0.5 - 0.4982582}{0.00900464} = 0.1934336.$$

Also

$$\frac{a_2}{a_1} = -\frac{0.0000428}{0.00900464} = -0.004753.$$

$$\therefore \left(\frac{a_2}{a_1}\right)^2 = (-0.004753)^2 = 0.0000225910,$$

$$\left(\frac{a_2}{a_1}\right)^3 = -0.0000001074,$$

$$\frac{a_3}{a_1} = -\frac{0.00000017}{0.00900464} = -0.00001888.$$

Hence

$$c_1 = -\frac{a_2}{a_1} = 0.004753,$$
$$c_2 = 0.00001888 + 2(0.000022591) = 0.00006406,$$
$$c_3 = 0 + 5(-0.004753)(-0.00001888) - 5(-0.0000001074)$$
$$= 0.000000986.$$

Substituting these quantities in (2), we get

$$v = 0.1934336 + 0.004753(0.1934336)^2 + 0.00006406(0.1934336)^3$$
$$= 0.1934336 + 0.0001778 + 0.00000046$$
$$= 0.193612.$$

Hence

$$u = v + \tfrac{1}{2} = 0.693612$$

and

$$x = x_0 + hu = 0.47 + 0.01(0.693612) = \underline{0.47693612,}$$

which is the same value as found by the method of successive approximations.

To solve Example 2 we use Stirling's formula, as before. Here

$$a_0 = y_0 = 61.9785,$$
$$a_1 = 0.6199,$$
$$a_2 = \frac{0.0062}{2} = 0.0031,$$
$$a_3 = a_4 = 0.$$

Since $y = 62$, we have

$$y - a_0 = 62 - 61.9785 = 0.0215.$$

$$\therefore \frac{y - a_0}{a_1} = \frac{0.0215}{0.6199} = 0.034683,$$

$$\frac{a_2}{a_1} = \frac{0.0031}{0.6199} = 0.005001.$$

Hence

$$c_1 = -0.005001, \quad c_2 = 2(0.005001)^2 = 0.00005002,$$
$$c_3 = 0, \text{ practically.}$$

Substituting these values in (2), we have

$$u = 0.034683 - 0.005001(0.034683)^2$$
$$= 0.0347.$$

$$\therefore x = 4.82 + 0.01(0.0347) = \underline{4.8203,}$$

as previously found by the method of iteration.

Remark. The problem of inverse interpolation should be dealt with in practice by the iteration process when only a few digits are to be substituted in the right-hand member, and by reversion of series when the number of digits involved is large.

EXERCISES IV

1. From the data in the following table find by Lagrange's formulas the value of y when $x = 102$ and the value of x when $y = 13.5$.

x	y
93.0	11.38
96.2	12.80
100.0	14.70
104.2	17.07
108.7	19.91

2. If cosh $x = 1.285$, find x by inverse interpolation, using the data in the following table:

x	cosh x
0.735	1.2824937
0.736	1.2832974
0.737	1.2841023
0.738	1.2849085
0.739	1.2857159
0.740	1.2865247
0.741	1.2873348
0.742	1.2881461

CHAPTER V

THE ACCURACY OF INTERPOLATION FORMULAS

31. Introduction. In the preceding articles we have dealt with polynomial formulas for representing a given function over an interval. These polynomials coincide with the given function at the points (x_0, y_0), (x_1, y_1), (x_2, y_2), etc. Hence it is reasonable to suppose that we can make these polynomials approximate the given function as closely as desired by merely increasing the number of coinciding points. Such indeed is the case if we don't attempt to spread over too wide an interval, but the necessity for caution in this matter will appear from the following considerations.

When the number of points $x_0, x_1, x_2, \cdots x_n$ increases indefinitely, the polynomial interpolation formulas become infinite series, called *interpolation series*; and just as a power series converges in a certain interval and diverges outside the interval, so likewise an interpolation series converges and represents the given function over a certain interval but fails to represent it outside of that interval. For example, if we should attempt to represent the function $1/(1 + x^2)$ over the interval $-5 \leqq x \leqq 5$ by an interpolation series, we should find that the series would not represent the function at all when $x = 4$. As a matter of fact, the series would converge and represent the function to any desired degree of accuracy between $x = -3.63$ and $x = +3.63$, but would diverge and fail to represent it outside of this interval.* The investigation of the convergence of interpolation series is a somewhat lengthy matter and requires the use of functions of a complex variable.† We shall therefore not enter into it, but shall merely derive expressions for the remainder terms in the polynomial formulas previously considered.

32. Remainder Term in Newton's Formula (I) and in Lagrange's Formula. The derivation of the remainder term in a polynomial interpolation formula is very similar to that of finding the remainder in Taylor's

---

* Runge, " über empirische Funktionen und die Interpolation zwischen äquidistanten Ordinaten." *Zeitschrift für Math. und Physik*, vol. XLVI (1901), p. 229. See also Steffensen's *Interpolation*, pp. 35-38.

† The interested reader should consult the paper by Runge, cited above, and also the following Borel Monographs: Nörlund, *Leçons sur les Series d'Interpolation*, Paris, 1926. Borel, *Leçons sur les Fonctions de Variables Réelles et les Developpements en Séries de Polynomes*, Paris, 1905. Montel, *Leçons sur les Séries de Polynomes à une Variable Complexe*, Paris, 1910. Also Runge's *Theorie und Praxis der Reihe*, Leipzig, 1904.

expansion. Thus, to find the remainder term in Newton's formula (I) and in Lagrange's formula, we write down the arbitrary function.

$$(1) \quad F(z) = f(z) - \phi(z) - [f(x) - \phi(x)] \frac{(z-x_0)(z-x_1) \cdots (z-x_n)}{(x-x_0)(x-x_1) \cdots (x-x_n)},$$

where $f(x)$ denotes the given function, $\phi(x)$ a polynomial interpolation formula, and z a real variable. We shall assume that $f(x)$ is continuous and possesses continuous derivatives of all orders within the interval from x_0 to x_n.

Now $F(z)$ vanishes for the $n+2$ values $z = x, x_0, x_1, \cdots x_n$; and since $f(x)$ is continuous and has continuous derivatives of all orders, the same is true of $f(z)$ and hence of $F(z)$. $F(z)$ therefore satisfies the conditions of Rolle's theorem. Hence the first derivative of $F(z)$ vanishes at least once between every two consecutive zero values of $F(z)$. Therefore in the interval from x_0 to x_n, $F'(z)$ must vanish $n+1$ times; $F''(z)$, n times; $F'''(z)$, $n-1$ times; etc. Hence the $(n+1)$th derivative of $F(z)$ will vanish at least once at some point whose abscissa is ξ.

Since $\phi(z)$ is a polynomial of the nth degree, its $(n+1)$th derivative is zero. Furthermore, since the expression $(z-x_0)(z-x_1)(z-x_2) \cdots (z-x_n)$ is a polynomial of degree $n+1$, it follows that its $(n+1)$th derivative is the same as the $(n+1)$th derivative of z^{n+1}, which is $(n+1)!$ On differentiating (1) $n+1$ times with respect to z we therefore have

$$F^{(n+1)}(z) = f^{(n+1)}(z) - 0 - [f(x) - \phi(x)] \frac{(n+1)!}{(x-x_0)(x-x_1) \cdots (x-x_n)}.$$

But since $F^{(n+1)}(z) = 0$ at some point $z = \xi$, we have

$$0 = f^{(n+1)}(\xi) - [f(x) - \phi(x)] \frac{(n+1)!}{(x-x_0)(x-x_1) \cdots (x-x_n)}.$$

Hence

$$f(x) - \phi(x) = \frac{f^{(n+1)}(\xi)}{(n+1)!} (x-x_0)(x-x_1) \cdots (x-x_n).$$

Now since $f(x) - \phi(x)$ is the difference between the given function and the polynomial at any point whose abscissa is x, it represents the *error* committed by replacing the given function by the polynomial. Hence we have

$$(2) \qquad \text{Error} = R_n = \frac{f^{(n+1)}(\xi)}{(n+1)!} (x-x_0)(x-x_1) \cdots (x-x_n),$$

where ξ is some value of x between x_0 and x_n. This is the remainder term in formula (2) of Art. 20 and in Lagrange's formula (VII).

To get the remainder term in formula (I) of Art. 20 we recall that

$x - x_0 = hu, x - x_1 = h(u-1), x - x_2 = h(u-2), \cdots x - x_n = h(u-n)$.
Substituting these values of $x - x_0$, $x - x_1$, etc. in (2) above, we have

(3) $$R_n = \frac{h^{n+1} f^{(n+1)}(\xi)}{(n+1)!} u(u-1)(u-2) \cdots (u-n).$$

If the analytical form of the given function $f(x)$ is unknown, then the best we can do is to replace $f^{(n+1)}(\xi)$ by its value in terms of differences. From Article 18 we have

(a) $$\Delta^n f(x) = (\Delta x)^n f^{(n)}(x + \theta n \Delta x), \quad 0 < \theta < 1.$$

Putting $x = x_0$ and $\Delta x = h$, we have from (a)

(b) $$f^{(n)}(x_0 + \theta n h) = \frac{\Delta^n f(x_0)}{h^n}.$$

Now since $x_0 + nh$ and ξ are values of x at points within the interval of interpolation (that is, between x_0 and x_n) we may, for practical purposes, put $\xi = x_0 + \theta n h$. Making this substitution in (b), we get

(c) $$f^{(n)}(\xi) = \frac{\Delta^n f(x)}{h^n}.$$

Hence we have

(d) $$f^{(n+1)}(\xi) = \frac{\Delta^{n+1} f(x_0)}{h^{n+1}},$$

practically. Substituting this value of $f^{(n+1)}(\xi)$ in (3), we get

(4) $$R_n = \frac{\Delta^{n+1} y_0}{(n+1)!} u(u-1)(u-2) \cdots (u-n).$$

The smaller the interval h is taken the more nearly does (4) give the actual error.

33. Remainder Term in Newton's Formula (II). To find a formula for the remainder in Newton's formula for *backward* interpolation we write down the function

$$F(z) = f(z) - \phi(z) - [f(x) - \phi(x)] \frac{(z - x_n)(z - x_{n-1}) \cdots (z - x_0)}{(x - x_n)(x - x_{n-1}) \cdots (x - x_0)},$$

differentiate it $n + 1$ times with respect to z, and put $F^{(n+1)}(z) = 0$ for $z = \xi$. We thus find

$$f(x) - \phi(x) = \frac{f^{(n+1)}(\xi)}{(n+1)!} (x - x_n)(x - x_{n-1}) \cdots (x - x_0),$$

or

(1) $$\text{Error} = R_n = \frac{f^{(n+1)}(\xi)}{(n+1)!} (x - x_n)(x - x_{n-1})(x - x_{n-2}) \cdots (x - x_0).$$

This is the remainder term for formula (2) of Art 21.

To find the corresponding formula in terms of u we recall that

$$\frac{x - x_n}{h} = u, \quad \frac{x - x_{n-1}}{h} = u + 1, \quad \frac{x - x_{n-2}}{h} = u + 2, \cdots \frac{x - x_0}{h} = u + n.$$

Substituting these values for $x - x_n$ etc. in (1) above, we get

$$(2) \qquad R_n = \frac{h^{n+1} f^{(n+1)}(\xi)}{(n+1)!} u(u+1)(u+2) \cdots (u+n).$$

To find a formula for R_n when the analytical form of the given function is unknown, we replace $f^{(n+1)}(\xi)$ by $\Delta_{n+1} y_n / h^{n+1}$ in (2). The result is

$$(3) \qquad R_n = \frac{\Delta_{n+1} y_n}{(n+1)!} u(u+1)(u+2) \cdots (u+n).$$

34. Remainder Term in Stirling's Formula. We next turn our attention to the central-difference formulas of Stirling and Bessel. To find the remainder term in Stirling's formula we write down the arbitrary function

$$(1) \quad F(z) = f(z) - \phi(z)$$

$$- [f(x) - \phi(x)] \frac{(z - x_0)(z - x_1)(z - x_{-1}) \cdots (z - x_n)(z - x_{-n})}{(x - x_0)(x - x_1)(x - x_{-1}) \cdots (x - x_n)(x - x_{-n})}.$$

This function vanishes for the $2n + 2$ values $z = x, x_0, x_1, \cdots x_n, x_{-1}, x_{-2}, \cdots x_{-n}$. We assume that $f(x)$ is continuous and has continuous derivatives of all orders up to $2n + 1$. Hence $F(z)$ satisfies the conditions of Rolle's theorem. Also, since $\phi(z)$ is a polynomial of degree $2n$, its $(2n + 1)$th derivative is zero. Hence on differentiating (1) $2n + 1$ times and putting $F^{(2n+1)}(z) = 0$ for some value $z = \xi$, we get

$$0 = f^{(2n+1)}(\xi) - 0 - [f(x) - \phi(x)] \frac{(2n+1)!}{(x - x_0)(x - x_1)(x - x_{-1}) \cdots (x - x_n)(x - x_{-\cdot}}$$

from which

$$f(x) - \phi(x) = \frac{f^{(2n+1)}(\xi)}{(2n+1)!}(x - x_0)(x - x_1)(x - x_{-1}) \cdots (x - x_n)(x - x_{-n}),$$

or

$$(2) \quad \text{Error} = R_n = \frac{f^{(2n+1)}(\xi)}{(2n+1)!}(x - x_0)(x - x_1)(x - x_{-1}) \cdots (x - x_n)(x - x_{-n}).$$

We write this formula in terms of u as follows: Since

$$x - x_0 = hu, \quad x - x_1 = h(u-1), \cdots x - x_n = h(u-n), \text{ and}$$

$$x - x_{-1} = x - (x_0 - h) = x - x_0 + h = hu + h = h(u+1),$$

$$x - x_{-2} = h(u+2), \cdots x - x_{-n} = h(u+n),$$

we have

(3) $\quad R_n = \dfrac{h^{2n+1}f^{(2n+1)}(\xi)}{(2n+1)!}\, u(u^2-1)(u^2-2^2)(u^2-3^2)\cdots(u^2-n^2),$

where ξ is some value of x between x_{-n} and x_n.

If the analytical form of $f(x)$ is unknown, we replace $f^{(2n+1)}(\xi)$ by m_{2n+1}, where

$$m_{2n+1} = \frac{\Delta^{2n+1}y_{-n-1} + \Delta^{2n+1}y_{-n}}{2}.$$

Hence we get from (3)

(4) $\quad R_n = \dfrac{m_{2n+1}}{(2n+1)!}\, u(u^2-1)(u^2-2^2)\cdots(u^2-n^2).$

In formulas (3) and (4) n is the number of intervals *on each side* of x_0.

35. Remainder Terms in Bessel's Formulas.

The remainder term in Bessel's formulas is derived by first writing down the arbitrary function

(1) $\quad F(z) = f(z) - \phi(z)$

$$-[f(x)-\phi(x)]\frac{(z-x_0)(z-x_1)(z-x_{-1})\cdots(z-x_n)(z-x_{-n})(z-x_{n+1})}{(x-x_0)(x-x_1)(x-x_{-1})\cdots(x-x_n)(x-x_{-n})(x-x_{n+1})}.$$

This function vanishes at the $2n+3$ points $z = x, x_0, x_1, x_{-1}, \cdots x_n,$ x_{-n}, x_{n+1}. Since $\phi(z)$ is a polynomial of degree $2n+1$, its $(2n+2)$th derivative is zero. Hence on differentiating (1) $2n+2$ times with respect to z and putting $F^{(2n+2)}(z) = 0$ for some value $z = \xi$, we get

$$0 = f^{(2n+2)}(\xi) - 0$$

$$-[f(x)-\phi(x)]\frac{(2n+2)!}{(x-x_0)(x-x_1)(x-x_{-1})\cdots(x-x_n)(x-x_{-n})(x-x_{n+1})},$$

from which

$$f(x)-\phi(x) = \frac{f^{(2n+2)}(\xi)}{(2n+2)!}(x-x_0)(x-x_1)(x-x_{-1})\cdots(x-x_n)(x-x_{-n})(x-x_{n+1}),$$

or

(2) $\quad$ Error $= R_n$

$$= \frac{f^{(2n+2)}(\xi)}{(2n+2)!}(x-x_0)(x-x_1)(x-x_{-1})\cdots(x-x_n)(x-x_{-n})(x-x_{n+1}).$$

Putting $x-x_0 = hu,\ x-x_1 = h(u-1),\ x-x_{-1} = h(u+1)$, etc., as in the case of Stirling's formula, we get

(3) $\quad R_n = \dfrac{h^{2n+2}f^{(2n+2)}(\xi)}{(2n+2)!}\, u(u-1)(u+1)(u-2)\cdots(u-n)(u+n)(u-n-1).$

This is the remainder term in formula (IV) of Art. 24. In terms of differences it becomes

(4) $R_n = \dfrac{m_{2n+2}}{(2n+2)!} u(u-1)(u+1)(u-2)(u+2)$
$$\cdots (u-n)(u+n)(u-n-1),$$

where

$$m_{2n+2} = \frac{\Delta^{2n+2} y_{-n-1} + \Delta^{2n+2} y_{-n}}{2}.$$

On putting $u = v + \frac{1}{2}$ in (3) and (4), we get

(5) $R_n = \dfrac{h^{2n+2} f^{(2n+2)}(\xi)}{(2n+2)!} \left(v^2 - \dfrac{1}{4}\right)\left(v^2 - \dfrac{9}{4}\right)\cdots\left(v^2 - \dfrac{(2n+1)^2}{4}\right),$

(6) $R_n = \dfrac{m_{2n+2}}{(2n+2)!} \left(v^2 - \dfrac{1}{4}\right)\left(v^2 - \dfrac{9}{4}\right)\cdots\left(v^2 - \dfrac{(2n+1)^2}{4}\right).$

These are the remainder terms in formula (VI) of Art. 24.

Putting $v = 0$ in (5) and (6), we get the remainder terms in the formula for interpolating to halves, namely

(7) $R_n = \dfrac{h^{2n+2} f^{(2n+2)}(\xi)}{(2n+2)!} (-1)^{n+1} \dfrac{[1 \cdot 3 \cdot 5 \cdots (2n+1)]^2}{2^{2n+2}},$

(8) $R_n = \dfrac{m_{2n+2}}{(2n+2)!} (-1)^{n+1} \dfrac{[1 \cdot 3 \cdot 5 \cdots (2n+1)]^2}{2^{2n+2}}.$

36. Recapitulation of Formulas for the Remainder. We now collect for easy reference the most important of the formulas derived in this chapter.

     1. Newton's Formula (I)

(a) $R_n = \dfrac{h^{n+1} f^{(n+1)}(\xi)}{(n+1)!} u(u-1)(u-2) \cdots (u-n).$

(b) $R_n = \dfrac{\Delta^{n+1} y_0}{(n+1)!} u(u-1)(u-2) \cdots (u-n).$

     2. Newton's Formula (II)

(a) $R_n = \dfrac{h^{n+1} f^{(n+1)}(\xi)}{(n+1)!} u(u+1)(u+2) \cdots (u+n).$

(b) $R_n = \dfrac{\Delta_{n+1} y_n}{(n+1)!} u(u+1)(u+2) \cdots (u+n).$

3. *Stirling's Formula*, (III)

(a) $R_n = \dfrac{h^{2n+1}f^{(2n+1)}(\xi)}{(2n+1)!} u(u^2-1)(u^2-2^2)(u^2-3^2)\cdots(u^2-n^2).$

(b) $R_n = \dfrac{m_{2n+1}}{(2n+1)!} u(u^2-1)(u^2-2^2)(u^2-3^2)\cdots(u^2-n^2).$

4. *Bessel's Formula* in terms of u, (IV)

(a) $R_n = \dfrac{h^{2n+2}f^{(2n+2)}(\xi)}{(2n+2)!} u(u-1)(u+1)(u-2)\cdots(u-n)(u+n)(u-n-1).$

(b) $R_n = \dfrac{m_{2n+2}}{(2n+2)!} u(u-1)(u+1)(u-2)\cdots(u-n)(u+n)(u-n-1).$

5. *Bessel's Formula* in terms of v, (VI)

(a) $R_n = \dfrac{h^{2n+2}f^{(2n+2)}(\xi)}{(2n+2)!}\left(v^2-\dfrac{1}{4}\right)\left(v^2-\dfrac{9}{4}\right)\cdots\left(v^2-\dfrac{(2n+1)^2}{4}\right).$

(b) $R_n = \dfrac{m_{2n+2}}{(2n+2)!}\left(v^2-\dfrac{1}{4}\right)\left(v^2-\dfrac{9}{4}\right)\cdots\left(v^2-\dfrac{(2n+1)^2}{4}\right).$

6. *Formula for Interpolating to Halves*, (V)

(a) $R_n = \dfrac{h^{2n+2}f^{(2n+2)}(\xi)}{(2n+2)!}(-1)^{n+1}\dfrac{[1\cdot3\cdot5\cdots(2n+1)]^2}{2^{2n+2}}.$

(b) $R_n = \dfrac{m_{2n+2}}{(2n+2)!}(-1)^{n+1}\dfrac{[1\cdot3\cdot5\cdots(2n+1)]^2}{2^{2n+2}}.$

7. *Lagrange's Formula*, (VII)

$$R_n = \dfrac{f^{(n+1)}(\xi)}{(n+1)!}(x-x_0)(x-x_1)(x-x_2)\cdots(x-x_n).$$

Where the formulas are given in pairs, the second form (b) should be used when the analytic form of the function is not known.

To lessen the labor of computing R_n from these formulas the student should, when possible, use the expressions for the nth derivatives given on page 38.

It is not worth while to compute the remainder term in many applications of Newton's, Stirling's, and Bessel's formulas, because if the starting point is so chosen that u and v are numerically less than 1 and if the differences of some order are practically constant, the interpolated result will usually be correct to as many figures as are given in the tabular values of the function. This statement is based on the assumption that all available differences are used in the interpolation formula, or at least all differences which will contribute anything to the last figure retained. It is in those cases where the differences do not become constant or where it is impracticable to make use of differences above a certain order that we should compute the remainder term.

When using Lagrange's formula, however, the case is very different. Here there are no differences available and there is nothing in the formula itself by which we can estimate the reliability of the results obtained. We should therefore compute the remainder term in every application of this formula where it is possible to do so.

It is to be observed, however, that the inherent error in Lagrange's formula involves the $(n + 1)$th derivative of the given function. When the analytical form of a function is not known, the inherent error due to the use of Lagrange's formula cannot be estimated.

The student should observe that the remainder term in Stirling's formula contains *odd* differences, whereas in Bessel's formula it contains *even* differences. If, therefore, when using a central difference formula we stop with *even* differences and wish to estimate the error, we should use Stirling's formula; whereas if we stop with *odd* differences, we should use Bessel's formula. If this rule is followed, the remainder term will always be the next term after the one at which we stop.

There should never be any difficulty in determining the proper value of n to be substituted in the remainder formulas. Thus, if we are using Bessel's formula and stop with third differences, the remainder term will contain fourth differences. Hence we must have $2n + 2 = 4$, or $n = 1$. On the other hand, if we are using Stirling's formula and stop with fourth differences, the remainder term will contain fifth differences. Hence we shall then have $2n + 1 = 5$, from which $n = 2$.

We shall now compute the remainder term in an application of Bessel's formula.

Example. The following table contains values of the function $y = x^4 + 10x^5$ for certain values of x. Find y when $x = 2.27$.

x	y	Δy	$\Delta^2 y$	$\Delta^3 y$	$\Delta^4 y$
2.0	336.0000				
		91.8582			
2.1	427.8582		19.0724		
		110.9306		2.8266	
2.2	538.7888		21.8990		0.2664
		132.8296		3.0930	
2.3	671.6184		24.9920		0.2784
		157.8216		3.3714	
2.4	829.4400		28.3634		
		186.1850			
2.5	1015.6250				

Solution. Since we wish to use Bessel's formula and compute the remainder term, we stop with third differences. Taking $x_0 = 2.2$, $x = 2.27$, $h = 0.1$, we have

$$u = \frac{2.27 - 2.20}{0.1} = \frac{0.07}{0.1} = 0.7.$$

$$\therefore \quad v = u - \tfrac{1}{2} = 0.2.$$

$$\therefore \quad y = \frac{538.7888 + 671.6184}{2} + 0.2\,(132.8296)$$

$$+ \left(\frac{0.04 - 0.25}{2}\right)\left(\frac{21.8990 + 24.9920}{2}\right)$$

$$+ 0.2\left(\frac{0.04 - 0.25}{6}\right)(3.0930)$$

$$= 605.2036 + 26.56592 - 2.46178 - 0.02165,$$

or

$$y = 629.28609.$$

To find R_n we have $2n + 2 = 4$, or $n = 1$. Also

$$f^{iv}(x) = 24 + 1200x.$$

Hence

$$f^{iv}(\xi) = 24 + 1200\xi.$$

Now since ξ lies somewhere between 2.0 and 2.5, we can express it in the form

$$\xi = 2.25 + 0.1\eta,$$

where η lies between -2.5 and $+2.5$. Substituting this value of ξ in $f^{iv}(\xi)$ above, we get

$$f^{iv}(\xi) = f^{iv}(2.25 + 0.1\eta) = 24 + 2700 + 120\eta$$
$$= 2724 + 120\eta.$$

Hence by (5) of Art. 35 we have

$$R_n = \frac{h^4 f^{iv}(\xi)}{4!}\left(v^2 - \frac{1}{4}\right)\left(v^2 - \frac{9}{4}\right)$$

$$= \frac{(0.1)^4 (2724 + 120\eta)}{24}\,(0.04 - 0.25)\,(0.04 - 2.25)$$

$$= 0.00527 + 0.000232\eta$$

$$= 0.00527 \pm 0.00058.$$

We therefore have

$$y = 629.28609 + 0.00527 \pm 0.00058$$
$$= 629.29136 \pm 0.00058.$$

The value of y is thus between 629.2919 and 629.2908, or between 629.292 and 629.291. The correct value to four decimal places is 629.2914, and this happens to be the mean of the two limits found above.

If we substitute differences instead of the derivative in R_n, we have $m_{2n+2} = m_4 = (0.2664 + 0.2784)/2 = 0.2724$; and therefore by (6) of Art. 35

$$R_n = \frac{m_4}{4!}\left(v^2 - \frac{1}{4}\right)\left(v^2 - \frac{9}{4}\right)$$

$$= \frac{0.2784}{24}(0.04 - 0.25)(0.04 - 2.25)$$

$$= 0.00527,$$

which is the definite part of the remainder term found by using the derivative. We then have $y = 629.28609 + 0.00527 = 629.29136$, which is correct to four decimal places.

Note. The substitution $\xi = x_m + h\eta$, where x_m denotes the midpoint of the range of given values of the function, gives the remainder as the sum of two terms, the larger of which is perfectly definite and unaffected by the uncertain factor η. It also saves the trouble of finding the greatest and least values of $f^{iv}(x)$ in order to find the limits between which the true value of the computed function lies. For Newton's formulas (I) and (II) we make the substitutions $\xi = x_0 + h\eta$ and $\xi = x_n - h\eta$, respectively, where η is now *positive* in each case. For computing R_n in Lagrange's formula we should put $\xi = x_m + h\eta$, as in the example worked above.

A final remark concerning accuracy must now be made. When the analytical form of a function is totally unknown, and the sum total of our knowledge of the function consists merely of a set of tabular values of the argument, the problem of interpolation is really indeterminate; for it is theoretically possible to construct a large number of functions which would take the values $y_0, y_1, y_2, \cdots y_n$ corresponding to the values $x_0, x_1, x_2, \cdots x_n$ of the argument. Nevertheless, if we have some knowledge of the nature of the function with which we are dealing and have no reason to believe that it behaves in an erratic manner within the range of values considered, we may fairly assume that its graph is a *smooth curve*, in which case the function can safely be replaced by a polynomial.

37. The Accuracy of Linear Interpolation from Tables. We shall now derive a simple formula for the maximum error inherent in linear interpolation from tables.

In the remainder after $n + 1$ terms in Newton's formula (I) let us put $n = 1$. Then R_n becomes

(1) $$R_1 = \frac{h^2 f''(\xi)}{2} u(u - 1) = \frac{h^2 M}{2}(u^2 - u),$$

where M denotes the maximum absolute value of $f''(x)$ in any interval of width h. To find the maximum numerical value of R_1 we differentiate it with respect to u, put the derivative equal to zero, solve for u, and then substitute this value of u in (1). Hence we have

$$\frac{dR_1}{du} = \frac{h^2 M}{2}(2u - 1) = 0.$$

$$\therefore \quad u = \tfrac{1}{2} \quad \text{and}$$

$$|R_{max}| = \frac{h^2 M}{2}\left|\frac{1}{4} - \frac{1}{2}\right| = \frac{h^2 M}{8}.$$

The formula for the maximum error is therefore

(2) $$E \leqq \frac{h^2 M}{8}.$$

Example. The function $1/N$ is tabulated in Barlow's Tables at unit intervals from 1 to 12,500. Find the possible error in the linear interpolation of this function when

$$N = 650.$$

Solution.

$$f(N) = \frac{1}{N}.$$

$$\therefore \quad f''(N) = \frac{2}{N^3}.$$

Taking $h = 1$, $N = 650$, and substituting in (2), we find

$$E \leqq \frac{1}{4 \times (650)^3} = \frac{1}{1,098,500,000},$$

or

$$E < \underline{0.000000001}.$$

Note. The student should ever bear in mind that linear interpolation is permissible only when first differences are constant, or practically so.

He should therefore always compute a few first differences and see if they are constant before using linear interpolation.

EXERCISES V

1. Estimate the error in your answers to Exercises 3 and 4 of Chapter II.

2. Compute the error in your answers to Exercises 2, 3, 4, and 6 of Chapter III.

CHAPTER VI

INTERPOLATION WITH TWO INDEPENDENT VARIABLES
TRIGONOMETRIC INTERPOLATION

38. Introduction. Occasionally it becomes necessary to interpolate a function of two arguments. For example, a table of elliptic integrals contains the two arguments θ and ϕ, on both of which the value of the integral depends.

The problem of double interpolation can be solved in two ways. The simplest method in theory is to interpolate first with respect to one variable and then with respect to the other. In making these interpolations any one of the standard interpolation formulas—Newton's, Stirling's, or Bessel's—may be used for either the first interpolations or the second. We always choose the most suitable formula for the problem at hand.

39. Double Interpolation by a Double Application of Single Interpolation. This method can be explained best by means of examples.

Example 1. The following table * gives the hour angle (t) of the sun corresponding to certain altitudes (a) and declinations (d) at a place in a certain latitude. Find the hour angle corresponding to $d = 12°$, $a = 16°$.

	$a = 10°$	$14°$	$18°$	$22°$
$d = 20°$	6ʰ 11ᵐ 26ˢ	5ʰ 50ᵐ 17ˢ	5ʰ 29ᵐ 27ˢ	5ʰ 8ᵐ 48ˢ
15°	5 55 41	**5 35 5**	5 14 39	4 54 17
10°	5 40 16	5 19 56	4 59 37	4 39 17
5°	5 24 50	5 4 30	4 44 4	4 23 29
0°	5 9 5	4 48 29	4 27 39	4 6 28

Solution. Here we take the entry 5ʰ 35ᵐ 5ˢ as the starting point. Then the initial values of d and a are $d_0 = 15°$, $a_0 = 14°$.

Let $t = f(d, a)$ denote the functional relation connecting t, d, and a. We first find by ordinary interpolation the values of $f(12°, 14°), f(12°, 18°)$, $f(12°, 22°)$. To this end we construct the following difference tables corresponding to $a = 14°$, $a = 18°$, and $a = 22°$.

---

* A table of this kind is called the *function table*. The entries in this table are taken from Whittaker and Robinson's *Calculus of Observations*, p. 374.

$$a = 14°$$

	$f(d, 14°)$	Δf	$\Delta^2 f$	$\Delta^3 f$
(a)	5ʰ 35ᵐ 05ˢ			
		−15ᵐ 09ˢ		
	5 19 56		−17ˢ	
		−15 26		−18ˢ
	5 04 30		−35	
		−16 01		
	4 48 29			

$$a = 18°$$

	$f(d, 18°)$	Δf	$\Delta^2 f$	$\Delta^3 f$
(b)	5ʰ 14ᵐ 39ˢ			
		−15ᵐ 02ˢ		
	4 59 37		−31ˢ	
		−15 33		−21ˢ
	4 44 04		−52	
		−16 25		
	4 27 39			

$$a = 22°$$

	$f(d, 22°)$	Δf	$\Delta^2 f$	$\Delta^3 f$
(c)	4ʰ 54ᵐ 17ˢ			
		−15ᵐ 0ˢ		
	4 39 17		−48ˢ	
		−15 48		−25ˢ
	4 23 29		−1ᵐ 13ˢ	
		−17 01		
	4 06 28			

Since the required value $f(12°, 16°)$ of the function is near the *beginning* of the assigned values of d, we use Newton's formula (I) to find $f(12°, a)$. Furthermore, since the given equidistant values of d decrease by steps of $5°$, we have $h = -5°$ and therefore

$$u = \frac{d - d_0}{h} = \frac{12 - 15}{-5} = 0.6.$$

Now substituting in (I) of Art. 20 this value of u and the other quantities from table (a) above, we have

$$f(12°\ 14°) = 5^h35^m5^s + 0.6(-15^m9^s) + \frac{0.6(-0.4)}{2}(-17^s)$$

$$+ \frac{0.6(-0.4)(-1.4)}{6}(-18^s)$$

$$= 5^h26^m1^s.$$

Using the values in table (b), we get

$$f(12°\ 18°) = 5^h14^m39^s + 0.6(-15^m2^s) + \frac{0.6(-0.4)}{2}(-31^s)$$

$$+ \frac{0.6(-0.4)(-1.4)}{6}(-21^s)$$

$$= 5^h5^m40^s.$$

In like manner, from table (c) we get

$$f(12°, 22°) = 4^h54^m17^s + 0.6(-15^m0^s) + \frac{0.6(-0.4)}{2}(-48^s)$$

$$+ \frac{0.6(-0.4)(-1.4)}{6}(-25^s)$$

$$= 4^h45^m21^s.$$

The next step in the solution is to form a difference table of these functions just computed. Hence we have

$f(12, a)$	Δf	$\Delta^2 f$
$5^h\ 26^m\ 1^s$		
	$-20^m\ 21^s$	
$5\ \ 5\ \ 40$		$+2^s$
	$-20\ \ 19$	
$4\ \ 45\ \ 21$		

Now since the required value of the function is also near the beginning of the assigned values of a, we again use Newton's formula (I). Also, since the equidistant values of a increase by 4°, we have $h = 4°$. Hence

$$u = \frac{a - a_0}{h} = \frac{16° - 14°}{4°} = 0.5.$$

Substituting in (I) of Art. 20 this value of u and the other quantities from the tables above, we finally get

$$f(12°, 16°) = 5^h26^m1^s + 0.5(-20^m21^s) + \frac{0.5(-0.5)}{2}(2^s)$$
$$= 5^h15^m50^s.$$

Note. If it should be required to compute $f(14°, 20°)$, for example, we would set out from the entry $5^h55^m41^s$ and compute $f(14°, 10°)$, $f(14°, 14°)$, $f(14°, 18°)$, and $f(14°, 22°)$ by Newton's formula (I). Then to find $f(14°, 20°)$ we would use Newton's formula (II), because the required value is near the *end* of the given values of a.

Example 2. Find from a table of elliptic integrals the value of

$$\int_0^{\sin^{-1}(12/13)} \frac{d\phi}{\sqrt{1 - 0.78\sin^2\phi}}.$$

Solution. Comparing this integral with the standard elliptic integral of the first kind, namely

$$F(\theta, \phi) = \int_0^\phi \frac{d\phi}{\sqrt{1 - \sin^2\theta \sin^2\phi}},$$

we have

$$\phi = \sin^{-1}\frac{12}{13} = \sin^{-1}(0.9230769) = 67° 22' 48''.5$$
$$= 67°.38014,$$

$$\sin^2\theta = 0.78,$$

$$\sin\theta = 0.8831761,$$

$$\theta = 62° 01' 40''.4 = 62°.02789.$$

In problems of this kind, where extensive tables are at hand, it is better to use central-difference formulas. Hence we write down the appropriate portion of the given function table, compute the necessary difference tables, and from them calculate the values of $F(60°, 67°.38014)$, $F(61°, 67°.38014)$, $F(62°, 67°.38014)$, $F(63°, 67°.38014)$, and $F(64°, 67°.38014)$ by means of Bessel's formula (VI), because $67°.38014$ is near the middle of an interval. Then we form a difference table from these computed functions and find $F(62°.02789, 67°.38014)$ by means of Stirling's formula, (III), because here the value $62°.02789$ is near the beginning of an interval.

The function table is given below, and from it the difference tables following are computed.

ϕ	$\theta=60°$	61°	62°	63°	64°
65°	1.3489264	1.3559464	1.3630180	1.3701309	1.3772732
66	1.3772777	1.3847727	1.3923331	1.3999481	1.4076057
67	1.4059999	1.4139971	1.4220753	1.4302236	1.4384298
68	1.4350955	1.4436231	1.4522494	1.4609635	1.4697532
69	1.4645657	1.4736530	1.4828589	1.4921728	1.5015826
70	1.4944109	1.5040879	1.5139061	1.5238552	1.5339233

$$\theta=60°$$

ϕ	$F(60°, \phi)$	ΔF	$\Delta^2 F$	$\Delta^3 F$	$\Delta^4 F$	$\Delta^5 F$	
65°	1.3489264						
		283513					
66	1.3772777		3709				
		287222		25			
67	**1.4059999**		**3734**		**−11**		(a)
		290956		14		−5	
68	**1.4350955**		**3748**		**−16**		
		294704		− 2			
69	1.4645659		3746				
		298450					
70	1.4944109						

$$\theta=61°$$

ϕ	$F(61°, \phi)$	ΔF	$\Delta^2 F$	$\Delta^3 F$	$\Delta^4 F$	$\Delta^5 F$	
65°	1.3559464						
		288263					
66	1.3847727		3981				
		292244		35			
67	**1.4139971**		**4016**		**−12**		
		296260		23		**+1**	
68	**1.4436231**		**4039**		**−11**		(b)
		300299		11			
69	1.4736530		4050				
		304349					
70	1.5040879						

$\theta = 62°$

ϕ	$F(62°, \phi)$	ΔF	$\Delta^2 F$	$\Delta^3 F$	$\Delta^4 F$	$\Delta^5 F$	
65°	1.3630180						
		293151					
66	1.3923331		4271				
		297422		48			
67	**1.4220753**		**4319**		**−13**		(c)
		301741		**35**		**+1**	
68	**1.4522494**		**4354**		**−12**		
		306095		23			
69	1.4828589		4377				
		310472					
70	1.5139061						

$\theta = 63°$

ϕ	$F(63°, \phi)$	ΔF	$\Delta^2 F$	$\Delta^3 F$	$\Delta^4 F$	$\Delta^5 F$	
65°	1.3701309						
		298172					
66	1.3999481		4593				
		302755		61			
67	**1.4302236**		**4644**		**−11**		(d)
		307399		**50**		**−2**	
68	**1.4609635**		**4694**		**−13**		
		312093		37			
69	1.4921728		4731				
		316824					
70	1.5238552						

$\theta = 64°$

ϕ	$F(64°, \phi)$	ΔF	$\Delta^2 F$	$\Delta^3 F$	$\Delta^4 F$	$\Delta^5 F$	
65°	1.3772732						
		303325					
66	1.4076057		4916				
		308241		77			
67	**1.4384298**		**4993**		**−10**		(e)
		313234		**67**		**−4**	
68	**1.4697532**		**5060**		**−14**		
		318294		53			
69	1.5015826		5113				
		323407					
70	1.5339233						

Here

$$\phi_0 = 67°, \quad \phi = 67°.38014, \quad h = 1°,$$

$$u = 0.38014.$$

$$\therefore \quad v = u - \tfrac{1}{2} = -0.11986.$$

Substituting in Bessel's formula (VI) the quantities given in table (a), we have

$$F(60°, 67°.38014) = 1.4205477 - 0.00348740 - 0.00004408$$

$$+ 0.00000001 - 0.00000003$$

$$= 1.4170162.$$

In a similar manner we get from tables (b), (c), (d), (e),

$$F(61°, 67°.38014) = 1.4252117,$$
$$F(62°, 67°.38014) = 1.4334946,$$
$$F(63°, 67°.38014) = 1.4418540,$$
$$F(64°, 67°.38014) = 1.4502779.$$

Forming now a table of differences from these computed functions, we have

θ	$F(\theta, 67°.38014)$	ΔF	$\Delta^2 F$	$\Delta^3 F$	$\Delta^4 F$
60°	1.4170162				
		81955			
61	1.4252117		874		
		82829		−109	
62	**1.4334946**		765		−11
		83594		−120	
63	1.4418540		645		
		84239			
64	1.4502779				

For this interpolation we have

$$\theta_0 = 62°, \quad \theta = 62°.02789, \quad h = 1°.$$

$$\therefore \quad u = \frac{\theta - \theta_0}{h} = \frac{62°.02789 - 62°}{1°} = 0.02789.$$

Substituting in Stirling's formula, (III), this value of u and the appropriate quantities from the table above, we get

$$F(62°.02789, 67°.38014) = 1.4334946 + 0.00023208$$
$$+ 0.00000003 + 0.00000005$$
$$= 1.4337268.$$

40. Double or Two-Way Differences. Before explaining the second method of dealing with the problem of double interpolation it is necessary to define double or two-way differences, to which we now turn our attention.

Let $z = f(x, y)$ denote any function of two independent variables x and y, and let $z_{rs} = f(x_r, y_s)$. Let us next construct the following function table:

	x_0	x_1	x_2	x_3	x_4				x_m
y_0	z_{00}	z_{10}	z_{20}	z_{30}	z_{40}	...	...	...	z_{m0}
y_1	z_{01}	z_{11}	z_{21}	z_{31}	z_{41}	...	...	...	z_{m1}
y_2	z_{02}	z_{12}	z_{22}	z_{32}	z_{42}	...	...	...	z_{m2}
y_3	z_{03}	z_{13}	z_{23}	z_{33}	z_{43}	...	...	...	z_{m3}
y_4	z_{04}	z_{14}	z_{24}	z_{34}	z_{44}	...	...	...	z_{m4}
...	...	...	...	...	...	...	...	...	...
...	...	...	...	...	...	...	...	...	...
...	...	...	...	...	...	...	...	...	...
...	...	...	...	...	...	...	...	...	...
...	...	...	...	...	...	...	...	...	...
y_n	z_{0n}	z_{1n}	z_{2n}	z_{3n}	z_{4n}	...	...	...	z_{mn}

We now define double or two-way differences as follows:

$$\Delta^{1+0} z_{00} = \Delta_x z_{00} = z_{10} - z_{00},$$
$$\Delta^{1+0} z_{01} = \Delta_x z_{01} = z_{11} - z_{01},$$
$$\Delta^{1+0} z_{02} = \Delta_x z_{02} = z_{12} - z_{02},$$
$$\cdot \quad \cdot \quad \cdot \quad \cdot \quad \cdot \quad \cdot \quad \cdot \quad \cdot \quad \cdot$$
$$\Delta^{0+1} z_{00} = \Delta_y z_{00} = z_{01} - z_{00},$$
$$\Delta^{0+1} z_{10} = \Delta_y z_{10} = z_{11} - z_{10},$$
$$\Delta^{0+1} z_{20} = \Delta_y z_{20} = z_{21} - z_{20}.$$
$$\cdot \quad \cdot \quad \cdot \quad \cdot \quad \cdot \quad \cdot \quad \cdot \quad \cdot \quad \cdot$$

Or, more generally,

$$\Delta^{1+0} z_{rs} = \Delta_x z_{rs} = z_{r+1,s} - z_{rs},$$
$$\Delta^{0+1} z_{rs} = \Delta_y z_{rs} = z_{r,s+1} - z_{rs}.$$

Also,

$$\Delta^{1+1}z_{00} = \Delta^2_{xy}z_{00} = \Delta^{1+0}z_{01} - \Delta^{1+0}z_{00}$$
$$= \Delta^{0+1}z_{10} - \Delta^{0+1}z_{00},$$

$$\Delta^{2+0}z_{00} = \Delta_x{}^2z_{00} = z_{20} - 2z_{10} + z_{00},$$

$$\Delta^{2+0}z_{01} = \Delta_x{}^2z_{01} = z_{21} - 2z_{11} + z_{01},$$

$$\Delta^{2+0}z_{02} = \Delta_x{}^2z_{02} = z_{22} - 2z_{12} + z_{02},$$

$$\Delta^{0+2}z_{00} = \Delta_y{}^2z_{00} = z_{02} - 2z_{01} + z_{00},$$

$$\Delta^{0+2}z_{10} = \Delta_y{}^2z_{10} = z_{12} - 2z_{11} + z_{10},$$

$$\Delta^{0+2}z_{20} = \Delta_y{}^2z_{20} = z_{22} - 2z_{21} + z_{20},$$

$$\Delta^{2+1}z_{00} = \Delta^{2+0}z_{01} - \Delta^{2+0}z_{00},$$

$$\Delta^{1+2}z_{00} = \Delta^{0+2}z_{10} - \Delta^{0+2}z_{00},$$

$$\Delta^{3+0}z_{00} = \Delta_x{}^3z_{00} = z_{30} - 3z_{20} + 3z_{10} - z_{00},$$

$$\Delta^{3+0}z_{01} = \Delta_x{}^3z_{01} = z_{31} - 3z_{21} + 3z_{11} - z_{01},$$

$$\Delta^{0+3}z_{00} = \Delta_y{}^3z_{00} = z_{03} - 3z_{02} + 3z_{01} - z_{00},$$

$$\Delta^{0+3}z_{10} = \Delta_y{}^3z_{10} = z_{13} - 3z_{12} + 3z_{11} - z_{10},$$

$$\Delta^{3+1}z_{00} = \Delta^{3+0}z_{01} - \Delta^{3+0}z_{00},$$

$$\Delta^{1+3}z_{00} = \Delta^{0+3}z_{10} - \Delta^{0+3}z_{00},$$

$$\Delta^{4+0}z_{00} = \Delta_x{}^4z_{00} = z_{40} - 4z_{30} + 6z_{20} - 4z_{10} + z_{00},$$

$$\Delta^{0+4}z_{00} = \Delta_y{}^4z_{00} = z_{04} - 4z_{03} + 6z_{02} - 4z_{01} + z_{00},$$

$$\Delta^{2+2}z_{00} = \Delta^{2+0}z_{02} - 2\Delta^{2+0}z_{01} + \Delta^{2+0}z_{00},$$
$$= \Delta^{0+2}z_{20} - 2\Delta^{0+2}z_{10} + \Delta^{0+2}z_{00}.$$

The general formula for writing down these differences is easily seen to be

$$(1) \quad \Delta^{m+n}z_{00} = \Delta^{m+0}z_{0n} - n\Delta^{m+0}z_{0,n-1} + \frac{n(n-1)}{2}\Delta^{m+0}z_{0,n-2} + \cdots$$
$$+ \Delta^{m+0}z_{00}$$
$$= \Delta^{0+n}z_{m0} - m\Delta^{0+n}z_{m-1,0} + \frac{m(m-1)}{2}\Delta^{0+n}z_{m-2,0} + \cdots$$
$$+ \Delta^{0+n}z_{00}.$$

The symbol $\Delta_x{}^m z_{00}$, for example, means that we find the mth difference of z_{00} *with respect to* x, y being held constant.

41. A General Formula for Double Interpolation. We are now in a position to consider a general formula for double interpolation. The following formula is derived in O. Biermann's *Mathematische Näherungs-methoden*, pages 138-144:

(1) $z = f(x, y) = z_{00} + \dfrac{x - x_0}{h} \Delta^{1+0} z_{00} + \dfrac{y - y_0}{k} \Delta^{0+1} z_{00}$

$\dfrac{1}{2!} \left[\dfrac{(x - x_0)(x - x_1)}{h^2} \Delta^{2+0} z_{00} + \dfrac{2(x - x_0)(y - y_0)}{hk} \Delta^{1+1} z_{00} \right.$

$\left. + \dfrac{(y - y_0)(y - y_1)}{k^2} \Delta^{0+2} z_{00} \right] + \cdots$

$+ \dfrac{1}{m!} \left[\dfrac{(x - x_0)(x - x_1) \cdots (x - x_{m-1})}{h^m} \Delta^{m+0} z_{00} \right.$

$+ \dfrac{m(x - x_0)(x - x_1) \cdots (x - x_{m-2})(y - y_0)}{h^{m-1} k} \Delta^{(m-1)+1} z_{00}$

$+ \dfrac{m(m - 1)(x - x_0)(x - x_1) \cdots (x - x_{m-3})(y - y_0)(y - y_1)}{2 \qquad\qquad\qquad h^{m-2} k^2}$

$\times \Delta^{(m-2)+2} z_{00} + \cdots$

$\left. + \dfrac{(y - y_0)(y - y_1) \cdots (y - y_{m-1})}{k^m} \Delta^{0+m} z_{00} \right] + R(x_0, y_0).$

Here h and k are the intervals between the equidistant values of x and y, respectively, and $R(x_0, y_0)$ is the remainder term.

This formula can be simplified by changing the variables from x and y to u and v, as follows:
Put

$$u = \frac{x - x_0}{h}, \text{ or } x = x_0 + hu.$$

Then

$$\frac{x - x_1}{h} = \frac{x - (x_0 + h)}{h} = \frac{x - x_0}{h} - \frac{h}{h} = u - 1,$$

and

$$\frac{x - x_2}{h} = \frac{x - (x_0 + 2h)}{h} = \frac{x - x_0}{h} - \frac{2h}{h} = u - 2,$$

$$\cdot \quad \cdot \quad \cdot \quad \cdot \quad \cdot \quad \cdot \quad \cdot \quad \cdot \quad \cdot \quad \cdot$$

$$\frac{x - x_{m-1}}{h} = u - (m - 1).$$

Also, put

$$v = \frac{y - y_0}{k}, \text{ or } y = y_0 + kv.$$

Then

$$\frac{y - y_1}{k} = \frac{y - (y_0 + k)}{k} = \frac{y - y_0}{k} - \frac{k}{k} = v - 1,$$

$$\frac{y - y_2}{k} = v - 2, \text{ etc.}$$

Substituting these values of $(x-x_0)/h$, $(y-y_0)/k$, etc. in (1), we get

(X) $z = f(x,y) = f(x_0 + hu, y_0 + kv) = z_{00} + u\Delta^{1+0}z_{00} + v\Delta^{0+1}z_{00}$

$$+\frac{1}{2!}[u(u-1)\Delta^{2+0}z_{00} + 2uv\Delta^{1+1}z_{00} + v(v-1)\Delta^{0+2}z_{00}]$$

$$+\frac{1}{3!}[u(u-1)(u-2)\Delta^{3+0}z_{00} + 3u(u-1)v\Delta^{2+1}z_{00}$$

$$+ 3uv(v-1)\Delta^{1+2}z_{00} + v(v-1)(v-2)\Delta^{0+3}z_{00}]$$

$$+\frac{1}{4!}[u(u-1)(u-2)(u-3)\Delta^{4+0}z_{00} + 4u(u-1)(u-2)v\Delta^{3+1}z_{10}$$

$$+ 6u(u-1)v(v-1)\Delta^{2+2}z_{00} + 4uv(v-1)(v-2)\Delta^{1+3}z_{00}$$

$$+ v(v-1)(v-2)(v-3)\Delta^{0+4}z_{00}] + R_n(x_0, y_0),$$

where

$$R_n(x_0, y_0) = \frac{1}{(n+1)!}[u(u-1)(u-2)\cdots(u-n)\Delta^{(n+1)+0}z_{00}$$

$$+ (n+1)u(u-1)(u-2)\cdots[u-(n-1)]v\Delta^{n+1}z_{00}$$

$$+ \frac{(n+1)n}{2!}u(u-1)\cdots[u-(n-2)]v(v-1)\Delta^{(n-1)+2}z_{00}$$

$$+\cdots+ v(v-1)(v-2)\cdots(v-n)\Delta^{0+(n+1)}z_{00}]$$

This formula (X) corresponds to Newton's formula (I) and reduces to that formula if we put either $u = 0$ or $v = 0$.

In some applications of mathematics, particularly in Navigation, *linear* interpolation with several arguments is of considerable importance. For example, in various navigation tables are tabulated the complete solutions of thousands of astronomical triangles. Here the one or two desired parts are functions of three arguments.

Formulas for linear interpolation with several arguments are readily found from the general formula (1) of Art. 41 and from extensions of that formula. Thus for two arguments, after neglecting all differences higher than the first, we have

$$(2)\qquad z = z_{00} + \frac{x-x_0}{h}(\Delta_x z_{00}) + \frac{y-y_0}{k}(\Delta_y z_{00}).$$

For a function of three arguments, as $u = f(x, y, z)$, we have

$$(3)\quad u = u_{000} + \frac{x-x_0}{h}(\Delta_x u_{000}) + \frac{y-y_0}{k}(\Delta_y u_{000}) + \frac{z-z_0}{l}(\Delta_z u_{000});$$

and so on for any number of arguments.

We shall now apply formula (X) to the two examples which have already been worked by the first method.

Example 3. Solve Example 1 of Art 39 by means of formula (X).

Solution. For the sake of clearness we repeat the function table given in Example 1, and work the problem anew from the start.

d	$a = 14°$	$18°$	$22°$
15°	5ʰ 35ᵐ 5ˢ	5ʰ 14ᵐ 39ˢ	4ʰ 54ᵐ 17ˢ
10°	5 19 56	4 59 37	4 39 17
5°	5 4 30˙	4 44 4	4 23 29
0°	4 48 29	4 27 39	4 6 28

Forming next the necessary difference tables, we have

$$a_0 = 14°$$

	f_{d0}	$\Delta^{1+0}f_{d0}$	$\Delta^{2+0}f_{d0}$	$\Delta^{3+0}f_{d0}$
d_0	5ʰ 35ᵐ 5ˢ			
		−15ᵐ 9ˢ		
d_1	5 19 56		−17ˢ	
		−15 26		−18ˢ
d_2	5 4 30		−35	
		−16 1		
d_3	4 48 29			

$$a_1 = 18°$$

	f_{d1}	$\Delta^{1+0}f_{d1}$	$\Delta^{2+0}f_{d1}$	$\Delta^{3+0}f_{d1}$
d_0	5ʰ 14ᵐ 39ˢ			
		−15ᵐ 2ˢ		
d_1	4 59 37		−31ˢ	
		−15 33		−21ˢ
d_2	4 44 4		−52	
		−16 25		
d_3	4 27 39			

$$a_2 = 22°$$

	f_{d2}	$\Delta^{1+0}f_{d2}$	$\Delta^{2+0}f_{d2}$	$\Delta^{3+0}f_{d2}$
d_0	$4^h\ 54^m\ 17^s$			
		$-15^m\ \ 0^s$		
d_1	4 39 17		-48^s	
		$-15\ \ 48$		-25^s
d_2	4 23 29		$-\ 1^m\ 13$	
		$-17\ \ \ 1$		
d_3	4 6 28			

These three tables, it will be observed, are the same as tables (a), (b), (c) in Example 1.

We next form difference tables by taking constant values of d.

$$d_0 = 15°$$

	f_{0a}	$\Delta^{0+1}f_{0a}$	$\Delta^{0+2}f_{0a}$
a_0	$5^h\ 35^m\ \ 5^s$		
		$-20^m\ 26^s$	
a_1	5 14 39		$+4^s$
		$-20\ \ 22$	
a_2	4 54 17		

$$d_1 = 10°$$

	f_{1a}	$\Delta^{0+1}f_{1a}$	$\Delta^{0+2}f_{1a}$
a_0	$5^h\ 19^m\ 56^s$		
		$-20^m\ 19^s$	
a_1	4 59 37		-1^s
		$-20\ \ 20$	
a_2	4 39 17		

$$d_2 = 5°$$

	f_{2a}	$\Delta^{0+1}f_{2a}$	$\Delta^{0+2}f_{2a}$
a_0	$5^h\ \ 4^m\ 30^s$		
		$-20^m\ 26^s$	
a_1	4 44 4		-9^s
		$-20\ \ 35$	
a_2	4 23 29		

Hence

$$\Delta^{1+1}f_{00} = \Delta^{1+0}f_{01} - \Delta^{1+0}f_{00} = -15^m2^s - (-15^m9^s) = 7^s,$$

$$\Delta^{1+2}f_{00} = \Delta^{0+2}f_{10} - \Delta^{0+2}f_{00} = -1^s - (4^s) = -5^s,$$

$$\Delta^{2+1}f_{00} = \Delta^{2+0}f_{01} - \Delta^{2+0}f_{00} = -31^s - (-17^s) = -14^s,$$

$$\Delta^{1+3}f_{00} = \Delta^{0+3}f_{10} - \Delta^{0+3}f_{00} = 0 - 0 = 0,$$

$$\Delta^{3+1}f_{00} = \Delta^{3+0}f_{01} - \Delta^{3+0}f_{00} = -21^s - (-18^s) = -3^s,$$

$$\Delta^{2+2}f_{00} = \Delta^{2+0}f_{02} - 2\Delta^{2+0}f_{01} + \Delta^{2+0}f_{00}$$
$$= -48^s - 2(-31^s) + (-17^s) = -3^s,$$

$$\Delta^{4+0}f_{00} = 0,$$

$$\Delta^{0+4}f_{00} = 0.$$

We have already found in Example 1 that

$$u = 0.6, \quad v = 0.5.$$

Substituting in (X) these values of u, v, and the computed differences, we get

$$f(12°\ 16°) = 5^h35^m5^s + 0.6(-15^m9^s) + 0.5(-20^m26^s)$$
$$+ \tfrac{1}{2}[0.6(-0.4)(-17^s) + 0.6(7^s) + 0.5(-0.5)(4^s)]$$
$$+ \tfrac{1}{6}[0.6(-0.4)(-1.4)(-18^s) + 0.9(-0.4)(-14^s)$$
$$+ 0.9(-0.5)(-5^s) + 0]$$
$$+ \tfrac{1}{24}[0 + 1.2(-0.4)(-1.4)(-3^s) + 1.8(-0.4)(-0.5)(-3^s)$$
$$+ 0 + 0],$$

or $f(12°, 16°) = 5^h15^m50^s$, as previously found.

Example 4. Solve Example 2 by means of formula (X).

Solution. Since (X) is not a central-difference formula, we do not use the same function table as in Example 2. From the definition of the two-way differences $\Delta^{m+n}z_{00}$ it will be seen that the following triangular function table, starting from $F(62°, 67°)$, is all that is required for finding all differences up to the fourth order inclusive.

ϕ	$\theta = 62°$	63°	64°	65°	66°
67°	1.4220753	1.4302236	1.4384298	1.4466803	1.4549598
68	1.4522494	1.4609635	1.4697532	1.4786046	
69	1.4828589	1.4921728	1.5015826		
70	1.5139061	1.5238552			
71	1.5453920				

The following difference tables are next computed:

$$\theta_0 = 62°$$

	$F_0\phi$	$\Delta^{0+1}F_0\phi$	$\Delta^{0+2}F_0\phi$	$\Delta^{0+3}F_0\phi$	$\Delta^{0+4}F_0\phi$
ϕ_0	1.4220753				
		301741			
ϕ_1	1.4522494		4354		
		306095		23	
ϕ_2	1.4828589		4377		-13
		310472		10	
ϕ_3	1.5139061		4387		
		314859			
ϕ_4	1.5453920				

$$\theta_1 = 63°$$

	$F_1\phi$	$\Delta^{0+1}F_1\phi$	$\Delta^{0+2}F_1\phi$	$\Delta^{0+3}F_1\phi$
ϕ_0	1.4302236			
		307399		
ϕ_1	1.4609635		4694	
		312093		37
ϕ_2	1.4921728		4731	
		316824		
ϕ_3	1.5238552			

$$\theta_2 = 64°$$

	$F_2\phi$	$\Delta^{0+1}F_2\phi$	$\Delta^{0+2}F_2\phi$
ϕ_0	1.4384298		
		313234	
ϕ_1	1.4697532		5060
		318294	
ϕ_2	1.5015826		

$$\phi_0 = 67°$$

	$F_{\theta 0}$	$\Delta^{1+0}F_{\theta 0}$	$\Delta^{2+0}F_{\theta 0}$	$\Delta^{3+0}F_{\theta 0}$	$\Delta^{4+0}F_{\theta 0}$
θ_0	1.4220753				
		81483			
θ_1	1.4302236	.	579		
		82062		-146	
θ_2	1.4384298		433		3
		82505		-143	
θ_3	1.4466803		290		
		82795			
θ_4	1.4549598				

$$\phi_1 = 68°$$

	$F_{\theta 1}$	$\Delta^{1+0}F_{\theta 1}$	$\Delta^{2+0}F_{\theta 1}$	$\Delta^{3+0}F_{\theta 1}$
θ_0	1.4522494			
		87141		
θ_1	1.4609635		756	
		87897		-139
θ_2	1.4697532		617	
		88514		
θ_3	1.4786046			

$$\phi_2 = 69°$$

	$F_{\theta 2}$	$\Delta^{1+0}F_{\theta 2}$	$\Delta^{2+0}F_{\theta 2}$
θ_0	1.4828589		
		93139	
θ_1	1.4921728		959
		94098	
θ_2	1.5015826		

Hence

$$\Delta^{1+1}F_{00} = \Delta^{1+0}F_{01} - \Delta^{1+0}F_{00} = 87141 - 81483 = 5658,$$
$$\Delta^{1+2}F_{00} = \Delta^{0+2}F_{10} - \Delta^{0+2}F_{00} = 4694 - 4354 = 340,$$
$$\Delta^{2+1}F_{00} = \Delta^{2+0}F_{01} - \Delta^{2+0}F_{00} = 756 - 579 = 177,$$
$$\Delta^{1+3}F_{00} = \Delta^{0+3}F_{10} - \Delta^{0+3}F_{00} = 37 - 23 = 14,$$
$$\Delta^{3+1}F_{00} = \Delta^{3+0}F_{01} - \Delta^{3+0}F_{00} = -139 - (-146) = 7,$$
$$\Delta^{2+2}F_{00} = \Delta^{2+0}F_{02} - 2\Delta^{2+0}F_{01} + \Delta^{2+0}F_{00} = 959 - 1512 + 579$$
$$= 26.$$

In Example 2 we found $u = 0.02789$, $v = 0.38014$. Substituting in (X) these values of u, v, and the computed differences, we get

$F(62.°02789, 67.°38014) = 1.4220753 + 0.02789(81483) + 0.38014(301741)$

$\quad + \frac{1}{2}[0.02789(-0.97211)(579) + 2(0.02789)(0.38014)(5658)$

$\quad + 0.38014(-0.61986)(4354)]$

$\quad + \frac{1}{6}[(0.02789)(-0.97211)(-1.97211)(-146)$

$\quad + 3(0.02789)(-0.97211)(0.38014)(177)$

$\quad + 3(0.02789)(0.38014)(-0.61986)(340)$

$\quad + 0.38014(-0.61986)(-1.61986)(23]$

$\quad + \frac{1}{24}[0.02789(-0.97211)(-1.97211)(-2.97211)(3)$

$\quad + 4(0.02789)(-0.97211)(-1.97211)(0.38014)(7)$

$\quad + 6(0.02789)(-0.97211)(0.38014)(-0.61986)(26)$

$\quad + 4(0.02789)(0.38014)(-0.61986)(-1.61986)(14)$

$\quad + 0.38014(-0.61986)(-1.61986)(-2.61986)(-13)]$

$\quad = 1.4337264.$

This value differs from that found in Example 2 by four units in the last decimal place; but in view of the fact that different parts of the function table, different formulas, and different methods were used in the two computations the agreement is as close as could be expected.

Note. The two methods explained in this chapter are sufficient for the solution of all ordinary problems of double interpolation. As to which of these methods is preferable, it may be said that the use of formula (X) is probably shorter if all differences above the second are negligible.

For a more extensive treatment of double interpolation the reader should consult Steffensen's *Interpolation,* pp. 203-223, and *Tracts for Computers* No. III, Part II, by Karl Pearson.

42. Trigonometric Interpolation. When the function we desire to represent by an interpolation formula is known to be periodic, it is better to use trigonometric interpolation. Hermite's formula for interpolating periodic functions is

(XI) $$y = \frac{\sin(x - x_1)\sin(x - x_2)\cdots\sin(x - x_n)}{\sin(x_0 - x_1)\sin(x_0 - x_2)\cdots\sin(x_0 - x_n)}y_0$$

$$+ \frac{\sin(x - x_0)\sin(x - x_2)\cdots\sin(x - x_n)}{\sin(x_1 - x_0)\sin(x_1 - x_2)\cdots\sin(x_1 - x_n)}y_1$$

$$+ \cdots$$

$$+ \frac{\sin(x - x_0)\sin(x - x_1)\cdots\sin(x - x_{n-1})}{\sin(x_n - x_0)\sin(x_n - x_1)\cdots\sin(x_n - x_{n-1})}y_n.$$

This function has the period 2π, as may be seen by replacing x by $x + 2\pi$. It is evident also that $y = y_0$ when $x = x_0$, $y = y_1$ when $x = x_1$, etc.

This formula of Hermite's for periodic functions corresponds to Lagrange's formula for non-periodic functions (Art. 26), and applies whether the given values of x are equidistant or not. By interchanging x and y in Hermite's formula we get a formula for the inverse interpolation of periodic functions, corresponding to (IX) of Art. 26.

Example. Given the following corresponding values of x and y, find the value of y corresponding to $x = 0.6$, the values of x being in radians:

x	0.4	0.5	0.7	0.8
y	0.0977	0.0088	-0.1577	-0.2192

Solution. Here $x_0 = 0.4$, $x_1 = 0.5$, $x_2 = 0.7$, $x_3 = 0.8$, $x = 0.6$. Substituting these values in the formula

$$y = \frac{\sin (x - x_1) \sin (x - x_2) \sin (x - x_3)}{\sin (x_0 - x_1) \sin (x_0 - x_2) \sin (x_0 - x_3)} y_0$$

$$+ \frac{\sin (x - x_0) \sin (x - x_2) \sin (x - x_3)}{\sin (x_1 - x_0) \sin (x_1 - x_2) \sin (x_1 - x_3)} y_1$$

$$+ \frac{\sin (x - x_0) \sin (x - x_1) \sin (x - x_3)}{\sin (x_2 - x_0) \sin (x_2 - x_1) \sin (x_2 - x_3)} y_2$$

$$+ \frac{\sin (x - x_0) \sin (x - x_1) \sin (x - x_2)}{\sin (x_3 - x_0) \sin (x_3 - x_1) \sin (x_3 - x_2)} y_3,$$

we get

$$y = \frac{\sin (0.1) \sin (- 0.1) \sin (- 0.2)}{\sin (- 0.1) \sin (- 0.3) \sin (- 0.4)} (0.0977)$$

$$+ \frac{\sin (0.2) \sin (- 0.1) \sin (- 0.2)}{\sin (0.1) \sin (- 0.2) \sin (- 0.3)} (0.0088)$$

$$+ \frac{\sin (0.2) \sin (0.1) \sin (- 0.2)}{\sin (0.3) \sin (0.2) \sin (- 0.1)} (-0.1577)$$

$$+ \frac{\sin (0.2) \sin (0.1) \sin (- 0.1)}{\sin (0.4) \sin (0.3) \sin (0.1)} (-0.2192),$$

or

$$y = - 0.01684 + 0.00592 - 0.10601 + 0.03778$$

$$= - 0.07915.$$

The computation in this problem is conveniently performed by logarithms, the log sines being given directly in the *Smithsonian Mathematical Tables, Hyperbolic Functions*, Table III.

Note. The problem of trigonometric interpolation was first solved by Gauss,* who derived several formulas similar to Hermite's. The formula usually called Gauss's formula differs from Hermite's only in having the factor $\frac{1}{2}$ written in front of all the angles; thus, $\sin \frac{1}{2}(x - x_0)$ etc. It is believed, however, that Hermite's formula is simpler than any of the Gauss formulas.

EXERCISES VI

1. Using the data of Example 1, Art. 39, find by two methods the hour angle of the sun when $a = 12°$ and $d = 16°$.

---

* *Werke*, Band III, pp. 265-327.

CHAPTER VII

NUMERICAL DIFFERENTIATION AND INTEGRATION

I. NUMERICAL DIFFERENTIATION

43. Numerical Differentiation is the process of calculating the derivatives of a function by means of a set of given values of that function. The problem is solved by representing the function by an interpolation formula and then differentiating this formula as many times as desired.

If the function is given by a table of values for equidistant values of the independent variable, it should be represented by an interpolation formula employing differences, such as Newton's, Stirling's, or Bessel's. But if the given values of the function are not for equidistant values of the independent variable, we must represent the function by Lagrange's or Hermite's formulas.

The considerations governing the choice of a formula employing differences are the same as in the case of interpolation. That is, if we desire the derivative at a point near the *beginning* of a set of tabular values, we use Newton's formula (I). Whereas, if we desire the derivative at a point near the *end* of the table, we use Newton's formula (II). For points near the middle of the table we should use a central-difference formula— Stirling's or Bessel's.

The values of derivatives in terms of differences may also be found by means of those interpolation formulas which employ differences. Thus, from Stirling's formula we have, since

$$u = \frac{x - x_0}{h} \text{ and } \frac{dy}{dx} = \frac{dy}{du} \cdot \frac{du}{dx} = \frac{1}{h} \frac{dy}{du},$$

$$y = y_0 + u \frac{\Delta y_{-1} + \Delta y_0}{2} + \frac{u^2}{2} \Delta^2 y_{-1} + \frac{u(u^2 - 1)}{3!} \frac{\Delta^3 y_{-2} + \Delta^3 y_{-1}}{2}$$

$$+ \frac{u^2(u^2 - 1)}{4!} \Delta^4 y_{-2} + \frac{u(u^2 - 1)(u^2 - 2^2)}{5!} \frac{\Delta^5 y_{-3} + \Delta^5 y_{-2}}{2}$$

$$+ \frac{u^2(u^2 - 1)(u^2 - 2^2)}{6!} \Delta^6 y_{-3} + \cdots,$$

$$\frac{dy}{dx} = \frac{1}{h} \left[\frac{\Delta y_{-1} + \Delta y_0}{2} + u\Delta^2 y_{-1} + \frac{3u^2 - 1}{3!} \frac{\Delta^3 y_{-2} + \Delta^3 y_{-1}}{2} \right.$$

$$+ \frac{4u^3 - 2u}{4!} \Delta^4 y_{-2} + \frac{5u^4 - 15u^2 + 4}{5!} \frac{\Delta^5 y_{-3} + \Delta^5 y_{-2}}{2}$$

$$\left. + \frac{6u^5 - 20u^3 + 8u}{6!} \Delta^6 y_{-3} + \cdots \right],$$

$$\frac{d^2y}{dx^2} = \frac{1}{h^2}\left[\Delta^2 y_{-1} + u\frac{\Delta^3 y_{-2} + \Delta^3 y_{-1}}{2} + \frac{12u^2 - 2}{4!}\Delta^4 y_{-2}\right.$$

$$\left. + \frac{20u^3 - 30u}{5!}\frac{\Delta^5 y_{-3} + \Delta^5 y_{-2}}{2} + \frac{30u^4 - 60u^2 + 8}{6!}\Delta^6 y_{-3} + \cdots\right],$$

$$\frac{d^3y}{dx^3} = \frac{1}{h^3}\left[\frac{\Delta^3 y_{-2} + \Delta^3 y_{-1}}{2} + u\Delta^4 y_{-2} + \frac{60u^2 - 30}{5!}\frac{\Delta^5 y_{-3} + \Delta^5 y_{-2}}{2}\right.$$

$$\left. + \frac{120u^3 - 120u}{6!}\Delta^6 y_{-3} + \cdots\right],$$

$$\frac{d^4y}{dx^4} = \frac{1}{h^4}\left[\Delta^4 y_{-2} + u\frac{\Delta^5 y_{-3} + \Delta^5 y_{-2}}{2} + \frac{360u^2 - 120}{6!}\Delta^6 y_{-3} + \cdots\right],$$

$$\frac{d^5y}{dx^5} = \frac{1}{h^5}\left[\frac{\Delta^5 y_{-3} + \Delta^5 y_{-2}}{2} + u\Delta^6 y_{-3} + \cdots\right],$$

$$\frac{d^6y}{dx^6} = \frac{1}{h^6}\left[\Delta^6 y_{-3} + \cdots\right].$$

For the point $x = x_0$ we have $u = 0$. Hence on substituting this value of u in the formulas above, we get

$$\left(\frac{dy}{dx}\right)_{x_0} = \frac{1}{h}\left[\frac{\Delta y_{-1} + \Delta y_0}{2} - \frac{1}{3!}\frac{\Delta^3 y_{-2} + \Delta^3 y_{-1}}{2} + \frac{4}{5!}\frac{\Delta^5 y_{-3} + \Delta^5 y_{-2}}{2} + \cdots\right],$$

$$\left(\frac{d^2y}{dx^2}\right)_{x_0} = \frac{1}{h_2}\left[\Delta^2 y_{-1} - \frac{1}{12}\Delta^4 y_{-2} + \frac{8}{6!}\Delta^6 y_{-3} + \cdots\right],$$

$$\left(\frac{d^3y}{dx^3}\right)_{x_0} = \frac{1}{h^3}\left[\frac{\Delta^3 y_{-2} + \Delta^3 y_{-1}}{2} - \frac{30}{5!}\frac{\Delta^5 y_{-3} + \Delta^5 y_{-2}}{2}\right],$$

$$\left(\frac{d^4y}{dx^4}\right)_{x_0} = \frac{1}{h^4}\left[\Delta^4 y_{-2} - \frac{120}{6!}\Delta^6 y_{-3} + \cdots\right],$$

$$\left(\frac{d^5y}{dx^5}\right)_{x_0} = \frac{1}{h^5}\left[\frac{\Delta^5 y_{-3} + \Delta^5 y_{-2}}{2} + \cdots\right],$$

$$\left(\frac{d^6y}{dx^6}\right)_{x_0} = \frac{1}{h^6}\left[\Delta^6 y_{-3} + \cdots\right].$$

Evidently we can find the derivatives in exactly the same way by differentiating Newton's, Bessel's, and Lagrange's formulas.

To find the maximum or minimum value of a tabulated function we compute the necessary differences from the given table, substitute them in the appropriate interpolation formula, put the first derivative of this formula equal to zero, and solve for u. Then x is found from the relation $x = x_0 + hu$.

We can also find the maximum or minimum value of a function by equating to zero the first derivative of Lagrange's formula.

Example. Find the first and second derivatives of the function tabulated below, at the point $x = 0.6$.

x	y	Δy	$\Delta^2 y$	$\Delta^3 y$	$\Delta^4 y$
0.4	1.5836494				
		2137932			
0.5	1.7974426		330018		
		2467950		34710	
0.6	2.0442376		364728		3648
		2832678		38358	
0.7	2.3275054		403086		
		3235764			
0.8	2.6510818				

Solution. Here $x_0 = 0.6$, $u = 0$, $h = 0.1$. Substituting in the formulas for the first and second derivatives at $x = x_0$ the appropriate differences from the table above, we get

$$\frac{dy}{dx} = 10[0.2650314 - 0.0006089] = 2.644225,$$

$$\frac{d^2y}{dx^2} = 100[0.0364728 - 0.0000304] = 3.64424.$$

The function tabulated above is

$$y = 2e^x - x - 1.$$

Hence

$$\frac{dy}{dx} = 2e^x - 1, \quad \frac{d^2y}{dx^2} = 2e^x.$$

Putting $x = 0.6$ in these, we get

$$\frac{dy}{dx} = 2.644238, \quad \frac{d^2y}{dx^2} = 3.644238$$

as the correct values for the first and second derivatives. The values found by numerical differentiation are therefore correct to five significant figures in the case of the first derivative and to six significant figures in the case of the second derivative.

Partial derivatives of a tabulated function of two independent variables can be found by differentiating partially formula (X) of Art. 41.

II. NUMERICAL INTEGRATION

44. Introduction. Numerical integration is the process of computing the value of a definite integral from a set of numerical values of the integrand. When applied to the integration of a function of a single variable, the process is sometimes called *mechanical quadrature*; when applied to the computation of a double integral of a function of two independent variables it is called *mechanical cubature*.

The problem of numerical integration, like that of numerical differentiation, is solved by representing the integrand by an interpolation formula and then integrating this formula between the desired limits. Thus, to find the value of the definite integral $\int_a^b y\,dx$, we replace the function y by an interpolation formula, usually one involving differences, and then integrate this formula between the limits a and b. In this way we can derive *quadrature formulas* for the approximate integration of any function for which numerical values are known. We shall now derive some of the simplest and most useful of the quadrature formulas.

45. A General Quadrature Formula for Equidistant Ordinates. In Newton's, Stirling's, and Bessel's interpolation formulas the relation connecting x and u is

$$(1) \qquad\qquad x = x_0 + hu,$$

from which we get

$$(2) \qquad\qquad dx = h\,du.$$

Let us now integrate Newton's formula (I) over n equidistant intervals of width $h\,(= \Delta x)$. The limits of integration for x are x_0 and $x_0 + nh$. Hence from (1) the corresponding limits for u are 0 and n. We therefore have

$$\int_{x_0}^{x_0+nh} y\,dx = h \int_0^n \left(y_0 + u\Delta y_0 + \frac{u(u-1)}{2!}\Delta^2 y_0 + \frac{u(u-1)(u-2)}{3!}\Delta^3 y_0 \right.$$
$$+ \frac{u(u-1)(u-2)(u-3)}{4!}\Delta^4 y_0 + \frac{u(u-1)(u-2)(u-3)(u-4)}{5!}\Delta^5 y_0$$
$$\left. + \frac{u(u-1)(u-2)(u-3)(u-4)(u-5)}{6!}\Delta^6 y_0 + \cdots \right) du,$$

or

$$(45.1) \quad \int_{x_0}^{x_0+nh} y\,dx = h\left[ny_0 + \frac{n^2}{2}\Delta y_0 + \left(\frac{n^3}{3} - \frac{n^2}{2}\right)\frac{\Delta^2 y_0}{2} \right.$$
$$+ \left(\frac{n^4}{4} - n^3 + n^2\right)\frac{\Delta^3 y_0}{3!} + \left(\frac{n^5}{5} - \frac{3n^4}{2} + \frac{11n^3}{3} - 3n^2\right)\frac{\Delta^4 y_0}{4!}$$
$$+ \left(\frac{n^6}{6} - 2n^5 + \frac{35n^4}{4} - \frac{50n^3}{3} + 12n^2\right)\frac{\Delta^5 y_0}{5!}$$
$$\left. + \left(\frac{n^7}{7} - \frac{15n^6}{6} + 17n^5 - \frac{225n^4}{4} + \frac{274n^3}{3} - 60n^2\right)\frac{\Delta^6 y_0}{6!}\right].$$

From this general formula (45.1), we can obtain a variety of quadrature formulas by putting $n = 1, 2, \cdots$, etc. The best two are found by putting $n = 2$ and $n = 6$.

46. Simpson's Rule. Putting $n = 2$ in (45.1) and neglecting all differences above the second,* we get

$$\int_{x_0}^{x_0+2h} y\,dx = h\left[\,2y_0 + 2\Delta y_0 + \left(\frac{8}{3} - 2\right)\frac{\Delta^2 y_0}{2}\,\right]$$

$$= h[2y_0 + 2y_1 - 2y_0 + \tfrac{1}{3}(y_2 - 2y_1 + y_0)]$$

$$= \frac{h}{3}(y_0 + 4y_1 + y_2).$$

For the next two intervals from x_2 to $x_2 + 2h$ we get in like manner

$$\int_{x_2}^{x_2+2h} y\,dx = \frac{h}{3}(y_2 + 4y_3 + y_4).$$

Similarly for the third pair of intervals we have

$$\int_{x_4}^{x_4+2h} y\,dx = \frac{h}{3}(y_4 + 4y_5 + y_6)\,;$$

and so on. Adding all such expressions as these from x_0 to x_n, where n is *even*, we get

$$\int_{x_0}^{x_0+nh} y\,dx = \frac{h}{3}(y_0 + 4y_1 + y_2 + y_2 + 4y_3 + y_4 + y_4 + 4y_5 + y_6 + \cdots),$$

or

$$\textbf{(46.1)} \quad \int_{x_0}^{x_0+nh} y\,dx = \frac{h}{3}(y_0 + 4y_1 + 2y_2 + 4y_3 + 2y_4 + \cdots + 2y_{n-2} + 4y_{n-1} + y_n)$$

$$= \frac{h}{3}\left[y_0 + 4(y_1 + y_3 + \cdots + y_{n-1}) + 2(y_2 + y_4 + \cdots\right.$$

$$\left. \cdots + y_{n-2}) + y_n\right].$$

$$= \frac{h}{3}\sum_0^n cy,$$

where $c = 1, 4, 2, \cdots 2, 4, 1$.

This important formula is known as *Simpson's Rule*. It is probably the most useful of all the formulas for mechanical quadrature.

---

* Since the interval of integration extends only from x_0 to $x_0 + 2h$, there are only the functional values y_0, y_1, y_2 in this interval. Hence with only three values, there can be no differences higher than the second.

When using this formula the student must bear in mind that the interval of integration must be divided into an *even* number of sub-intervals of width h.

The geometric significance of Simpson's Rule is that we replace the graph of the given function by $n/2$ arcs of second-degree polynomials, or parabolas with vertical axes.

47. Weddle's Rule. Putting $n = 6$ in (45. 1) and neglecting all differences above the sixth, we have

$$\int_{x_0}^{x_0+6h} y\, dx = h\left[6y_0 + 18\Delta y_0 + 27\Delta^2 y_0 + 24\Delta^3 y_0 + \frac{123}{10}\Delta^4 y_0 \right.$$

$$\left. + \frac{33}{10}\Delta^5 y_0 + \frac{41}{140}\Delta^6 y_0 \right].$$

Here the coefficient of $\Delta^6 y_0$ differs from 3/10 by the small fraction 1/140. Hence if we replace this coefficient by 3/10, we commit an error of only $\frac{h}{140}\Delta^6 y_0$. If the value of h is such that the sixth differences are small, the error committed will be negligible. We therefore change the last term to $(3/10)\Delta^6 y_0$ and replace all differences by their values in terms of the given y's. The result reduces down to

$$\int_{x_0}^{x_0+6h} y\, dx = \frac{3h}{10}[y_0 + 5y_1 + y_2 + 6y_3 + y_4 + 5y_5 + y_6].$$

For the next set of six intervals from x_6 to x_{12} we get in the same way

$$\int_{x_6}^{x_{12}} y\, dx = \frac{3h}{10}[y_6 + 5y_7 + y_8 + 6y_9 + y_{10} + 5y_{11} + y_{12}].$$

Adding all such expressions as these from x_0 to x_n, where n is now a *multiple of six*, we get

(47. 1) $\displaystyle\int_{x_0}^{x_0+nh} y\, dx = \frac{3h}{10}[y_0 + 5y_1 + y_2 + 6y_3 + y_4 + 5y_5 + 2y_6 + 5y_7 + y_8$

$$+ 6y_9 + y_{10} + 5y_{11} + 2y_{12} + \cdots$$

$$+ 2y_{n-6} + 5y_{n-5} + y_{n-4} + 6y_{n-3} + y_{n-2} + 5y_{n-1} + y_n].$$

$$= \frac{3h}{10}\sum_0^n ky,$$

where $k = 1, 5, 1, 6, 1, 5, 2, 5, 1, 6, 1, 5, 2$, etc.

This formula is known as *Weddle's Rule*. It is more accurate, in general, than Simpson's Rule, but it requires at least seven consecutive values of the function.

The geometric meaning of Weddle's Rule is that we replace the graph of the given function by $n/6$ arcs of sixth-degree polynomials.

We shall now apply these formulas to two examples, chosen at random.

Example 1. Compute the value of the definite integral

$$\int_4^{5.2} \ln x \, dx.$$

Solution. We divide the interval of integration into six equal parts each of width 0.2. Hence $h = 0.2$. The values of the function $y = \ln x$ are next computed for each point of subdivision. These values are given in the table below.

x	$\ln x$	x	$\ln x$
4.0	1.38629436	4.8	1.56861592
4.2	1.43508453	5.0	1.60943791
4.4	1.48160454	5.2	1.64865863
4.6	1.52605630		

(a) By Simpson's rule we have

$$I_S = \frac{0.2}{3}[3.03495299 + 4(4.57057874) + 2(3.05022046)] = \underline{1.82784726}.$$

(b) By Weddle's rule we get

$$I_W = (0.3)(0.2)[3.03495299 + 5(3.04452244)$$
$$+ 3.05022046 + 6(1.52605630)] = \underline{1.82784741}.$$

The true value of the integral is

$$I = \int_4^{5.2} \ln x \, dx = x(\ln x - 1) \Big]_{4.0}^{5.2} = 1.82784741.$$

Hence the errors are

$$E_S = 0.00000015 = 15 \times 10^{-8},$$

$$E_W = 0.$$

Example 2. Compute the value of the definite integral

$$\int_{0.2}^{1.4} (\sin x - \ln x + e^x) \, dx.$$

Solution. We shall divide the interval of integration into twelve equal parts by taking $h = 0.1$. The values of the function $y = \sin x - \ln x + e^x$ are then computed for each point of subdivision. These values are given in the table below.

x	y	x	y
0.2	3.02951	0.9	3.34830
0.3	2.84936	1.0	3.55975
0.4	2.79754	1.1	3.80007
0.5	2.82130	1.2	4.06984
0.6	2.89759	1.3	4.37050
0.7	3.01465	1.4	4.70418
0.8	3.16605		

(a) By Simpson's rule:

$$I_S = \frac{0.1}{3}\,[3.02951 + 4.70418 + 4(20.20418) + 2(16.49077)] = \underline{4.05106}.$$

(b) By Weddle's rule:

$$I_W = 0.03[21.05841 + 5(13.58281) + 6(6.62137) + 2(3.16605)] = \underline{4.05098}.$$

The true value of the integral is

$$I = \int_{0.2}^{1.4} (\sin x - \ln x + e^x)\,dx = -\cos x - x(\ln x - 1) + e^x \Big]_{0.2}^{1.4}$$

$$= 4.05095.$$

Hence the errors are:

$$E_S = -0.00011,$$
$$E_W = -0.00003.$$

It will be noted that Weddle's rule is more accurate than Simpson's in both examples.

Although Weddle's rule is simple in form and very accurate, it has the disadvantage of requiring that the number of subdivisions be a multiple of six. This means that when computing the values of y in many problems the assigned values of x can not be taken as simple tenths, as was done in the two examples worked above. The subdivision by tenths is nearly always possible when using Simpson's rule. However, when Simpson's rule can not give the desired degree of accuracy, Weddle's rule should be used.

When several values of the function are given, as in the above examples, it is better to make the computation in tabular form, as shown below for Simpson's rule in Ex. 1.

x	$\ln x$	c	$c \ln x$
4.0	1.38629436	1	1.38629436
4.2	1.43508453	4	5.74033812
4.4	1.48160454	2	2.96320908
4.6	1.52605630	4	6.10422520
4.8	1.56861592	2	3.13723184
5.0	1.60943791	4	6.43775164
5.2	1.64865863	1	1.64865863

$$27.41770887 \times \frac{0.2}{3} = 1.82784726.$$

The reader is cautioned against thinking of quadrature formulas as simply methods of computing areas under curves. These formulas are *methods for computing the values of definite integrals.* They give areas only when the integrands are the ordinates of a curve. The integrand may be any function of x, provided it is known for equidistant values of x. This fact is illustrated by the following example.

Example 3. Find by Simpson's Rule the coordinates of the centroid and the moment of inertia about the x-axis for the plane area shown below.

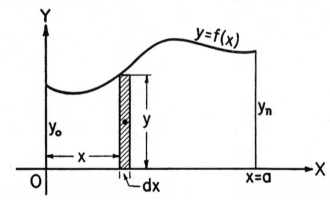

Fig. 2

Solution. The formulas for the centroid give

$$\bar{x} = \frac{\int_0^a x \, dA}{\int_0^a dA} = \frac{\int_0^a (xy) \, dx}{\int_0^a y \, dx} = \frac{(h/3)(x_0 y_0 + 4x_1 y_1 + 2x_2 y_2 + \cdots)}{(h/3)(y_0 + 4y_1 + 2y_2 + \cdots)} = \frac{\Sigma c x y}{\Sigma c y}$$

$$\bar{y} = \frac{\int_0^a (y/2) \, dA}{\int_0^a dA} = \tfrac{1}{2} \frac{\int_0^a y^2 \, dx}{\int_0^a y \, dx} = \tfrac{1}{2} \frac{(h/3)(y_0^2 + 4y_1^2 + 2y_2^2 + \cdots)}{(h/3)(y_0 + 4y_1 + 2y_2 + \cdots)} = \tfrac{1}{2} \frac{\Sigma c y^2}{\Sigma c y}$$

Since the moment of inertia of a rectangle about its base is $bh^3/3$, the moment of inertia of the elementary area $y\,dx$ about the x-axis is $y^3dx/3$. Hence for the whole area we have

$$I_x = 1/3 \int_0^a y^3\,dx = 1/3 \times (h/3)(y_0{}^3 + 4y_1{}^3 + 2y_1{}^3 + \cdots) = (h/9)\,\Sigma cy^3.$$

The computation form for this example is therefore as shown below:

x	y	xy	y^2	y^3	c	cy	cxy	cy^2	cy^3
x_0	y_0	x_0y_0	$y_0{}^2$	$y_0{}^3$	1	y_0	x_0y_0	$y_0{}^2$	$y_0{}^3$
x_1	y_1	x_1y_1	$y_1{}^2$	$y_1{}^3$	4	$4y_1$	$4x_1y_1$	$4y_1{}^2$	$4y_1{}^3$
x_2	y_2	x_2y_2	$y_2{}^2$	$y_2{}^3$	2	$2y_2$	$2x_2y_2$	$2y_2{}^2$	$2y_2{}^3$
x_3	y_3	x_3y_3	$y_3{}^2$	$y_3{}^3$	4	$4y_3$	$4x_3y_3$	$4y_3{}^2$	$4y_2{}^3$
$\cdot$	$\cdot$	$\cdot$	$\cdot$	$\cdot$	$\cdot$	$\cdot$	$\cdot$	$\cdot$	$\cdot$
						S_1	S_2	S_3	S_4

Hence

$$\bar{x} = S_2/S_1, \quad \bar{y} = \tfrac{1}{2} S_3/S_1, \quad I_x = (h/9)S_4,$$

where the S's denote the sums of the numbers in the columns above them.

Any other example can be handled in a similar manner after it has been set up as a definite integral.

Note 1. By putting $n = 1$ in (45. 1) and neglecting all differences above the first, we can derive a simple but crude formula known as the Trapezoidal Rule. This formula replaces a curve by a series of chords. For small values of h it will give fair results, but it is inherently too inaccurate for general use. For this reason it is not considered in this book.

Note 2. A quadrature formula derived from an algebraic polynomial will not give a reliable result in regions where the graph of the given function is vertical, because an algebraic polynomial is never vertical and therefore cannot be made to coincide with a vertical segment of a curve. A simple and satisfactory way of handling such a case is to replace the curve in the vertical region by a parabola having a horizontal axis. Thus, for the curve shown in Fig. 3 we replace the arc MP by an arc of the parabola $y^2 = 2px$. Then the area of the segment MPN is $(2/3)x_1y_1$.

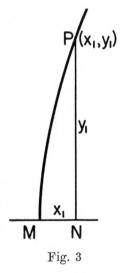

Fig. 3

48. Central-Difference Quadrature Formulas. By integrating Stirling's and Bessel's interpolation formulas we can derive rapidly converging quadrature formulas in terms of differences. Thus, integrating Stirling's formula from $x = x_0 - h$ to $x = x_0 + h$, or $u = -1$ to $u = 1$, we have

$$I = \int_{-h}^{h} \phi(x)\,dx = h \int_{-1}^{1} \left(y_0 + u \frac{\Delta y_{-1} + \Delta y_0}{2} + \frac{u^2}{2} \Delta^2 y_{-1} \right.$$

$$+ \frac{u(u^2 - 1)}{3!} \frac{\Delta^3 y_{-2} + \Delta^3 y_{-1}}{2} + \frac{u^2(u^2 - 1)}{4!} \Delta^4 y_{-2}$$

$$+ \frac{u(u^2 - 1)(u^2 - 4)}{5!} \frac{\Delta^5 y_{-3} + \Delta^5 y_{-2}}{2}$$

$$\left. + \frac{u^2(u^2 - 1)(u^2 - 4)}{6!} \Delta^6 y_{-3} + \cdots \right) du$$

$$= h \left[2y_0 + \frac{1}{3} \Delta^2 y_{-1} + \frac{2}{24} \left(\frac{1}{5} - \frac{1}{3} \right) \Delta^4 y_{-2} + \frac{2}{720} \left(\frac{1}{7} - 1 + \frac{4}{3} \right) \Delta^6 y_{-3} \right]$$

$$= 2h \left[y_0 + \frac{1}{6} \Delta^2 y_{-1} - \frac{1}{180} \Delta^4 y_{-2} + \frac{1}{1512} \Delta^6 y_{-3} + \cdots \right].$$

This formula gives the approximate value of the integral from $x = x_0 - h$ to $x = x_0 + h$. By advancing the subscripts of the y's by one unit we get the value of the integral from $x = x_0$ to $x = x_0 + 2h$. Denoting this integral by I_0^2, we have

$$I_0^2 = 2h \left[y_1 + \frac{1}{6} \Delta^2 y_0 - \frac{1}{180} \Delta^4 y_{-1} + \frac{1}{1512} \Delta^6 y_{-2} \right].$$

The integrals $I_2^4, I_4^6, \cdots I^n{}_{n-2}$ are likewise seen to be

$$I_2^4 = 2h \left[y_3 + \frac{1}{6} \Delta^2 y_2 - \frac{1}{180} \Delta^4 y_1 + \frac{1}{1512} \Delta^6 y_0 \right],$$

$$I_4^6 = 2h \left[y_5 + \frac{1}{6} \Delta^2 y_4 - \frac{1}{180} \Delta^4 y_3 + \frac{1}{1512} \Delta^6 y_2 \right],$$

$$\cdots \cdots \cdots \cdots \cdots \cdots \cdots \cdots \cdots$$

$$I^n{}_{n-2} = 2h \left[y_{n-1} + \frac{1}{6} \Delta^2 y_{n-2} - \frac{1}{180} \Delta^4 y_{n-3} + \frac{1}{1512} \Delta^6 y_{n-4} \right].$$

Adding all these separate integrals, we get

$$(48.1) \quad I_0^n = 2h \left[y_1 + y_3 + y_5 + \cdots + y_{n-1} \right.$$

$$+ \frac{1}{6} (\Delta^2 y_0 + \Delta^2 y_2 + \cdots + \Delta^2 y_{n-2})$$

$$- \frac{1}{180} (\Delta^4 y_{-1} + \Delta^4 y_1 + \Delta^4 y_3 + \cdots + \Delta^4 y_{n-3})$$

$$\left. + \frac{1}{1512} (\Delta^6 y_{-2} + \Delta^6 y_0 + \Delta^6 y_2 + \cdots + \Delta^6 y_{n-4}) \right],$$

where

$$I_0{}^n = \int_{x_0}^{x_0+nh} y\,dx$$

and n is *even*.

Integrating Bessel's formula (VI) over the interval $x = x_0$ to $x = x_0 + h$, or $v = -\frac{1}{2}$ to $v = \frac{1}{2}$, we have

$$I_0{}^1 = \int_{x_0}^{x_0+h} \phi(x)dx = h\int_{-\frac{1}{2}}^{\frac{1}{2}} \left(\frac{y_0 + y_1}{2} + v\Delta y_0 + \frac{(v^2 - \frac{1}{4})}{2} \frac{\Delta^2 y_{-1} + \Delta^2 y_0}{2} \right.$$

$$+ \frac{v(v^2 - \frac{1}{4})}{3!} \Delta^3 y_{-1} + \frac{(v^2 - \frac{1}{4})(v^2 - \frac{9}{4})}{4!} \frac{\Delta^4 y_{-2} + \Delta^4 y_{-1}}{2}$$

$$+ \frac{v(v^2 - \frac{1}{4})(v^2 - \frac{9}{4})}{5!}\Delta^5 y_{-2}$$

$$\left. + \frac{(v^2 - \frac{1}{4})(v^2 - \frac{9}{4})(v^2 - \frac{25}{4})}{6!} \frac{\Delta^6 y_{-3} + \Delta^6 y_{-2}}{2} + \cdots \right) dv$$

$$= h\left[\frac{y_0 + y_1}{2} - \frac{1}{12} \frac{\Delta^2 y_{-1} + \Delta^2 y_0}{2} + \frac{11}{720} \frac{\Delta^4 y_{-2} + \Delta^4 y_{-1}}{2} \right.$$

$$\left. - \frac{191}{60480} \frac{\Delta^6 y_{-3} + \Delta^6 y_{-2}}{2} \right].$$

By advancing the subscripts a unit at a time we find the integrals over the succeeding intervals to be

$$I_1{}^2 = h\left[\frac{y_1 + y_2}{2} - \frac{1}{12} \frac{\Delta^2 y_0 + \Delta^2 y_1}{2} + \frac{11}{720} \frac{\Delta^4 y_{-1} + \Delta^4 y_0}{2} \right.$$

$$\left. - \frac{191}{60480} \frac{\Delta^6 y_{-2} + \Delta^6 y_{-1}}{2} \right],$$

$$I_2{}^3 = h\left[\frac{y_2 + y_3}{2} - \frac{1}{12} \frac{\Delta^2 y_1 + \Delta^2 y_2}{2} + \frac{11}{720} \frac{\Delta^4 y_0 + \Delta^4 y_1}{2} \right.$$

$$\left. - \frac{191}{60480} \frac{\Delta^6 y_{-1} + \Delta^6 y_0}{2} \right],$$

$$\cdot \quad \cdot \quad \cdot \quad \cdot \quad \cdot \quad \cdot \quad \cdot \quad \cdot \quad \cdot \quad \cdot \quad \cdot \quad \cdot \quad \cdot \quad \cdot \quad \cdot$$

$$I^n{}_{n-1} = h\left[\frac{y_{n-1} + y_n}{2} - \frac{1}{12} \frac{\Delta^2 y_{n-2} + \Delta^2 y_{n-1}}{2} + \frac{11}{720} \frac{\Delta^4 y_{n-3} + \Delta^4 y_{n-2}}{2} \right.$$

$$\left. - \frac{191}{60480} \frac{\Delta^6 y_{n-4} + \Delta^6 y_{n-3}}{2} \right].$$

Adding all these separate integrals, we get

$$(48.2) \quad I_0{}^n = h \left[\left(\frac{y_0}{2} + y_1 + y_2 + \cdots + y_{n-1} + \frac{y_n}{2} \right) \right.$$

$$- \frac{1}{12} \left(\frac{\Delta^2 y_{-1}}{2} + \Delta^2 y_0 + \Delta^2 y_1 + \cdots \right.$$

$$\left. + \Delta^2 y_{n-2} + \frac{\Delta^2 y_{n-1}}{2} \right)$$

$$+ \frac{11}{720} \left(\frac{\Delta^4 y_{-2}}{2} + \Delta^4 y_{-1} + \Delta^4 y_0 + \cdots \right.$$

$$\left. + \Delta^4 y_{n-3} + \frac{\Delta^4 y_{n-2}}{2} \right)$$

$$- \frac{191}{60480} \left(\frac{\Delta^6 y_{-3}}{2} + \Delta^6 y_{-2} + \Delta^6 y_{-1} + \cdots \right.$$

$$\left. \left. + \Delta^6 y_{n-4} + \frac{\Delta^6 y_{n-3}}{2} \right) \right],$$

where n is now either even or odd.

It will be observed that formulas (48.1) and (48.2) involve only differences of *even* orders, that (48.2) involves *all* the even differences, whereas (48.1) involves only half of them. Formula (48.2) is too cumbersome for practical use as it stands, but it can be transformed into a much simpler and more useful form, as we shall now show.

From the definition of differences we have

$$\Delta^2 y_{-1} = \Delta y_0 - \Delta y_{-1},$$

$$\Delta^2 y_0 = \Delta y_1 - \Delta y_0,$$

$$\cdots \cdots \cdots \cdots$$

$$\Delta^2 y_{n-1} = \Delta y_n - \Delta y_{n-1},$$

$$\Delta^4 y_{-2} = \Delta^3 y_{-1} - \Delta^3 y_{-2},$$

$$\Delta^4 y_{-1} = \Delta^3 y_0 - \Delta^3 y_{-1},$$

$$\cdots \cdots \cdots \cdots$$

$$\Delta^4 y_{n-2} = \Delta^3 y_{n-1} - \Delta^3 y_{n-2},$$

$$\Delta^6 y_{-3} = \Delta^5 y_{-2} - \Delta^5 y_{-3},$$

$$\Delta^6 y_{-2} = \Delta^5 y_{-1} - \Delta^5 y_{-2},$$

$$\cdots \cdots \cdots \cdots$$

$$\Delta^6 y_{n-3} = \Delta^5 y_{n-2} - \Delta^5 y_{n-3}, \text{ etc.}$$

Substituting in (48.2) these values of the even differences, we find that all differences except those at the beginning and end of the table cancel one another and that formula (48.2) reduces down to

$$I_0{}^n = h \left[\left(\frac{y_0}{2} + y_1 + y_2 + \cdots + y_{n-1} + \frac{y_n}{2} \right) + \frac{1}{12} \left(\frac{\Delta y_{-1} + \Delta y_0}{2} \right) \right.$$

$$- \frac{11}{720} \left(\frac{\Delta^3 y_{-2} + \Delta^3 y_{-1}}{2} \right) + \frac{191}{60480} \left(\frac{\Delta^5 y_{-3} + \Delta^5 y_{-2}}{2} \right)$$

$$- \frac{1}{12} \left(\frac{\Delta y_{n-1} + \Delta y_n}{2} \right) + \frac{11}{720} \left(\frac{\Delta^3 y_{n-2} + \Delta^3 y_{n-1}}{2} \right)$$

$$\left. - \frac{191}{60480} \left(\frac{\Delta^5 y_{n-3} + \Delta^5 y_{n-2}}{2} \right) \right] ,$$

which can be written in the simpler form

$$(48.3) \quad I_0{}^n = h \left[\left(\frac{y_0}{2} + y_1 + y_2 + \cdots + y_{n-1} + \frac{y_n}{2} \right) \right.$$

$$- \frac{1}{12} \left(\frac{\Delta y_{n-1} + \Delta y_n}{2} - \frac{\Delta y_{-1} + \Delta y_0}{2} \right)$$

$$+ \frac{11}{720} \left(\frac{\Delta^3 y_{n-2} + \Delta^3 y_{n-1}}{2} - \frac{\Delta^3 y_{-2} + \Delta^3 y_{-1}}{2} \right)$$

$$\left. - \frac{191}{60480} \left(\frac{\Delta^5 y_{n-3} + \Delta^5 y_{n-2}}{2} - \frac{\Delta^5 y_{-3} + \Delta^5 y_{-2}}{2} \right) . \right.$$

The results given by this formula are identical with those given by (48.2), but the labor involved in obtaining them is only a small fraction of that required when using (48.2).

The geometric significance of formulas (48.1), (48.2), and (48.3) should be noted. Formula (48.1) replaces the graph of the given function by $n/2$ arcs of polynomials of the sixth degree, whereas (48.2) and (48.3) replace the graph by n arcs of sixth-degree polynomials.

By neglecting fourth and sixth differences in (48.1) and replacing the second differences by their values in terms of the y's, we shall find that (48.1) then reduces to Simpson's Rule. This formula therefore represents Simpson's Rule with correction terms.

We shall now apply (48.1) and (48.3) to two examples.

Example 1. Compute the value of π from the formula

$$\frac{\pi}{4} = \int_0^1 \frac{dx}{1 + x^2} .$$

Solution. We first compute the values of the function $y = 1/(1 + x^2)$ from $x = -0.3$ to $x = 1.3$, taking $h = 0.1$, and then form a table of difference as shown on the following page.

Substituting in (48. 1) the appropriate differences, we have

$$\frac{\pi}{4} = 0.2\left[3.9311573 + \frac{1}{6}(-249992) - \frac{1}{180}(-7) + \frac{1}{1512}(778)\right]$$

$$= 0.78539816.$$

$$\therefore \quad \pi = 4 \times 0.78539816 = \underline{3.14159264}.$$

The true value of π to nine figures is

$$\pi = 3.14159265.$$

Difference Table for $y = 1/(1+x^2)$.

x	y	Δy	$\Delta^2 y$	$\Delta^3 y$	$\Delta^4 y$	$\Delta^5 y$	$\Delta^6 y$
-0.3	0.9174312						
		441073					
-0.2	0.9615385		-155468				
		285605		-31127			
-0.1	0.9900990		-186595		$+19702$		
		99010		-11425		$+3148$	
0	1.0000000		-198020		$+22850$		-6296
		-99010		$+11425$		-3148	
0.1	0.9900990		-186595		19702		-4762
		-285605		$+31127$		-7910	
0.2	0.9615385		-155468		11792		-1320
		-441073		42919		-9230	
0.3	0.9174312		-112549		2562		$+1886$
		-553622		45481		-7344	
0.4	0.8620690		-67068		-4782		$+3323$
		-620690		40699		-4021	
0.5	0.8000000		-26369		-8803		3085
		-647059		31896		-936	
0.6	0.7352941		$+5527$		-9739		1983
		-641532		22157		$+1047$	
0.7	0.6711409		$+27684$		-8692		868
		-613848		13465		$+1915$	
0.8	0.6097561		41149		-6777		86
		-572699		6688		2001	
0.9	0.5524862		47837		-4776		-299
		-524862		1912		1702	
1.0	0.5000000		49749		-3074		-416
		-475113		-1162		1286	
1.1	0.4524887		48587		-1788		
		-426526		-2950			
1.2	0.4098361		45637				
		-380889					
1.3	0.3717472						

Substituting in (48. 3) the appropriate differences from the table, we get

$$\frac{\pi}{4} = 0.1[7.8498150 - \frac{1}{12}(-499988) + \frac{11}{720}(375)$$

$$- \frac{191}{60480}(1494)] = 0.78539817.$$

$$\therefore \quad \pi = 4 \times 0.78539817 = \underline{3.14159268}.$$

This value is slightly less accurate than that obtained by (48.1), but either result is correct to as many figures as were used in the computed ordinates.

Simpson's Rule gives for this problem the value

$$\pi = 3.14159260,$$

which is likewise correct to as many figures as are given in the computed ordinates.

Example 2. Compute the approximate value of the integral

$$I = \int_1^2 \frac{dx}{x}$$

Solution. Taking $h = 0.1$, we compute the values of $y = 1/x$ at one-tenth unit intervals from $x = 0.7$ to $x = 2.3$ and form a table of differences.

Substituting in (48.1) the appropriate differences, we get

$$I = 0.2[3.45953943 + \frac{1}{6}(3727034) - \frac{1}{180}(281353)$$

$$+ \frac{1}{1512}(61266)] = \underline{0.693147185.}$$

The correct value is $\ln 2 = 0.693147181$.

Substituting in (48. 3) the appropriate differences from the table, we get

$$I = 0.1[6.93771403 - \frac{1}{12}(7594744) + \frac{11}{720}(593339)$$

$$- \frac{191}{60480}(136810)] = \underline{0.69314714.}$$

It will be seen that formula (48. 1) gave the more accurate value in this example as was the case in the preceding.

Concerning the relative merits of formulas (48. 1) and 48. 3), it may be said that (48. 1) converges more rapidly and is therefore slightly more accurate. It utilitizes fewer ordinates outside the range of integration than does (48. 3). Formula (48. 1) requires that the number of sub-

Difference Table for $y = 1/x$.

x	y	Δy	$\Delta^2 y$	$\Delta^3 y$	$\Delta^4 y$	$\Delta^5 y$	$\Delta^6 y$
0.7	1.42857143						
		−17857143					
0.8	1.25000000		3968254				
		−13888889		−1190476			
0.9	1.11111111		2777778		432900		
		−11111111		− 757576		−180375	
1.0	1.00000000		2020202		252525		83252
		− 9090909		− 505051		− 97123	
1.1	0.90909091		1515151		155402		41618
		− 7575758		− 349649		− 55505	
1.2	0.83333333		1165502		99897		22212
		− 6410256		− 249752		− 33293	
1.3	0.76923077		915750		66604		12472
		− 5494506		− 183148		− 20821	
1.4	0.71428571		732602		45783		7362
		− 4761904		− 137365		− 13459	
1.5	0.66666667		595237		32324		4478
		− 4166667		− 105041		− 8981	
1.6	0.62500000		490196		23343		2834
		− 3676471		− 81698		− 6147	
1.7	0.58823529		408498		17196		1855
		− 3267973		− 64502		− 4292	
1.8	0.55555556		343996		12904		1215
		− 2923977		− 51598		− 3077	
1.9	0.52631579		292398		9827		843
		− 2631579		− 41771		− 2234	
2.0	0.50000000		250627		7593		589
		− 2380952		− 34178		− 1645	
2.1	0.47619048		216449		5948		
		− 2164503		− 28230			
2.2	0.45454545		188219				
		− 1976284					
2.3	0.43478261						

intervals be *even,* and also requires a little more labor in its application than does (48. 3).

Formula (48. 3) has the advantage of being applicable to any number of subintervals and of requiring very little labor in its application. It also gives the same degree of accuracy with third or fifth differences as

(48. 1) gives with fourth or sixth differences. Its chief disadvantage is that it utilizes several ordinates outside the range of integration.

The extra-interval ordinates required in formulas (48. 1) and (48. 3) can usually be found by computation, as in the examples worked above, or by extrapolation by means of Newton's formulas (I) and (II). Usually, however, it is not safe to use extrapolation for finding more than one ordinate at each end of the range.

49. Gauss's Quadrature Formula. The most accurate of the quadrature formulas in ordinary use is known as Gauss's formula. In Simpson's and Weddle's formulas the ordinates are equally spaced, but it occurred to Gauss that some other spacing might give a better result. Hence he set for himself this problem:

If the definite integral $\int_a^b f(x)dx$ is to be computed from a given number of values of $f(x)$, just where should these values be taken in order to get a result of the greatest possible accuracy? In other words, how shall the interval (a, b) be subdivided so as to give the best possible result?

It turns out that the points of subdivision should not be equidistant, but they are symmetrically placed with respect to the midpoint of the interval of integration.

Let $I = \int_a^b y \, dx$ denote the integral to be computed, where $y = f(x)$. On changing the variable by the substitution

$$\textbf{(1)} \qquad x = (b-a)u + \frac{a+b}{2},$$

the limits of integration become $-\frac{1}{2}$ and $\frac{1}{2}$. The new value of y is

$$y = f(x) = f[(b-a)u + \frac{a+b}{2}] = \phi(u), \text{ say.}$$

Then since $dx = (b-a)du$, the integral becomes

$$\textbf{(2)} \qquad I = (b-a)\int_{-\frac{1}{2}}^{\frac{1}{2}} \phi(u)\,du.$$

Gauss's formula is

$$\textbf{(49. 1)} \quad I = \int_{-\frac{1}{2}}^{\frac{1}{2}} \phi(u)du = R_1\phi(u_1) + R_2\phi(u_2) + R_3\phi(u_3) + \cdots + R_n\phi(u_n),$$

where $u_1, u_2, \cdots u_n$ are the points of subdivision of the interval $u = -\frac{1}{2}$ to $u = \frac{1}{2}$. The corresponding values of x are therefore

$$x_1 = (b-a)u_1 + \frac{a+b}{2}, \qquad x_2 = (b-a)u_2 + \frac{a+b}{2}, \text{ etc.}$$

The value of the integral $\int_a^b f(x)$ is therefore

(49. 2) $I = \int_a^b f(x)dx = (b-a)[R_1\phi(u_1) + R_2\phi(u_2) + \cdots + R_n\phi(u_n)].$

We shall not give a detailed derivation of Gauss's formula (49. 1), but merely show how the values of $u_1, u_2, \cdots u_n$ and $R_1, R_2, \cdots R_n$ are found and then show how to apply it to an example.

We assume that $\phi(u)$ can be expanded in a convergent power series in the interval $u = -\frac{1}{2}$ to $u = \frac{1}{2}$. Hence we write

(3) $\qquad \phi(u) = a_0 + a_1 u + a_2 u^2 + a_3 u^3 + \cdots + a_m u^m + \cdots.$

We also assume that the integral can be expressed as a linear function of the ordinates of the form (49. 1). Integrating (3) between the limits $-\frac{1}{2}$ and $\frac{1}{2}$, we have

(4) $\quad I = \int_{-\frac{1}{2}}^{\frac{1}{2}} \phi(u)du = \int_{-\frac{1}{2}}^{\frac{1}{2}} (a_0 + a_1 u + \cdots + a_m u^m + \cdots)du$

$= a_0 + \frac{1}{12} a_2 + \frac{1}{80} a_4 + \frac{1}{448} a_6 + \frac{1}{2304} a_8 + \cdots.$

From (3) we also have

$\phi(u_1) = a_0 + a_1 u_1 + a_2 u_1{}^2 + a_3 u_1{}^3 + a_4 u_1{}^4 + \cdots + a_m u_1{}^m + \cdots,$

$\phi(u_2) = a_0 + a_1 u_2 + a_2 u_2{}^2 + a_3 u_2{}^3 + a_4 u_2{}^4 + \cdots + a_m u_2{}^m + \cdots,$

$\qquad \cdots \cdots \cdots \cdots \cdots \cdots$

$\phi(u_n) = a_0 + a_1 u_n + a_2 u_n{}^2 + a_3 u_n{}^3 + \cdots + a_m u_n{}^m + \cdots.$

Substituting in (49. 1) these values of $\phi(u_1), \phi(u_2), \cdots \phi(u_n)$, we get

$I = R_1(a_0 + a_1 u_1 + a_2 u_1{}^2 + \cdots + a_m u_1{}^m + \cdots)$

$\qquad + R_2(a_0 + a_1 u_2 + a_2 u_2{}^2 + \cdots + a_m u_2{}^m + \cdots)$

$\qquad \cdots \cdots \cdots \cdots \cdots \cdots \cdots$

$\qquad + R_n(a_0 + a_1 u_n + a_2 u_n{}^2 + \cdots + a_m u_n{}^m + \cdots),$

or, rearranging,

(5) $\qquad I = a_0(R_1 + R_2 + R_3 + \cdots + R_n)$

$\qquad + a_1(R_1 u_1 + R_2 u_2 + \cdots + R_n u_n)$

$\qquad + a_2(R_1 u_1{}^2 + R_2 u_2{}^2 + \cdots + R_n u_n{}^2)$

$\qquad \cdots \cdots \cdots \cdots \cdots \cdots \cdots$

$\qquad + a_m(R_1 u_1{}^m + R_2 u_2{}^m + \cdots + R_n u_n{}^m)$

Now if the integral I in (5) is to be identically the same as the I in (4) for *all* values of a_0, a_1, etc.; that is, if (5) is to be identical with (4) regardless of the *form* of the function $\phi(u)$, then corresponding coefficients of a_0, a_1, a_2, etc. in (5) and (4) must be equal. Hence we must have

$$(49.3) \quad \begin{cases} R_1 + R_2 + R_3 + \cdots + R_n = 1, \\ R_1u_1 + R_2u_2 + R_3u_3 + \cdots + R_nu_n = 0, \\ R_1u_1{}^2 + R_2u_2{}^2 + R_3u_3{}^2 + \cdots + R_nu_n{}^2 = \tfrac{1}{12}, \\ R_1u_1{}^3 + R_2u_2{}^3 + R_3u_3{}^3 + \cdots + R_nu_n{}^3 = 0, \\ R_1u_1{}^4 + R_2u_2{}^4 + R_3u_3{}^4 + \cdots + R_nu_n{}^4 = \tfrac{1}{80}, \\ \cdots \cdots \cdots \cdots \cdots \cdots \cdots \cdots \cdots \cdots \cdots \\ \cdots \cdots \cdots \cdots \cdots \cdots \cdots \cdots \cdots \cdots \cdots \end{cases}$$

By taking $2n$ of these equations and solving them simultaneously, it would be theoretically possible to find the $2n$ quantities $u_1, u_2, \cdots u_n$ and $R_1, R_2, \cdots R_n$. However, the labor of solving these equations by the ordinary methods of algebra would be quite prohibitive even for small values of n. Fortunately a formula from higher mathematics makes such labor unnecessary.

It can be shown * without difficulty that if $\phi(u)$ is a polynomial of degree not higher than $2n - 1$, then $u_1, u_2, \cdots u_n$ are the zeros of the Legendre polynomial $P_n(u)$, or the roots of $P_n(u) = 0$. These roots are conveniently found from the equation

$$(6) \qquad \frac{d^n}{du^n} [u^2 - (\tfrac{1}{2})^2]^n = 0.$$

The n roots $u_1, u_2, \cdots u_n$ of this nth-degree equation are all real. On substituting them in (49.3), we can find the R's. We shall do this for the case $n = 3$.

The equation to be solved is

$$\frac{d^3}{du^3} [u^2 - (\tfrac{1}{2})^2]^3 = 0, \quad \text{or} \quad \frac{d^3}{du^3} (u^6 - 3u^4(\tfrac{1}{2})^2 + 3u^2(\tfrac{1}{2})^4 - (\tfrac{1}{2})^6) = 0.$$

Performing the differentiations and simplifying, we get

$$u(20u^2 - 3) = 0, \quad \text{from which}$$
$$u = 0, \ \pm \tfrac{1}{2}\sqrt{3/5}.$$

Hence

$$u_1 = -\tfrac{1}{2}\sqrt{3/5}, \qquad u_2 = 0, \qquad u_3 = \tfrac{1}{2}\sqrt{3/5}.$$

* See, for example, Todhunter's *Functions of Laplace, Lamé, and Bessel*, p. 99.

Then from the first three of equations (49. 3), we have

$$R_1 + R_2 + R_3 = 1$$
$$R_1(-\tfrac{1}{2}\sqrt{3/5}) + R_3(\tfrac{1}{2}\sqrt{3/5}) = 0$$
$$R_1(-\tfrac{1}{2}\sqrt{3/5})^2 + R_3(\tfrac{1}{2}\sqrt{3/5})^2 = 1/12.$$

Solving these equations, we find

$$R_1 = 5/18, \qquad R_2 = 4/9, \qquad R_3 = 5/18.$$

It is to be noted that the u's are symmetrically placed with respect to the midpoint of the interval of integration and that the R's are the same for each symmetric pair of u's. Hence from now on the u's of the points of division will be designated by u_0 for the midpoint, $u_{\pm 1}$ for the pair of symmetric points nearest the midpoint, $u_{\pm 2}$ for the next pair of symmetric points, etc.

The numerical values of the u's and corresponding R's for $n = 2$ to $n = 10$ are given in the table below, where the notation of the form $u_{\pm k} = N$ means $u_k = N$, $u_{-k} = -N$.

	u	R
$n = 2.$		
	$u_{\pm 1} = 0.2886751346$	$R = \tfrac{1}{2}$
$n = 3.$		
	$u_0 = 0$	$R = 4/9$
	$u_{\pm 1} = 0.3872983346$	$R = 5/18$
$n = 4.$		
	$u_{\pm 1} = 0.1699905218$	$R = 0.3260725774$
	$u_{\pm 2} = 0.4305681558$	$R = 0.1739274226$
$n = 5.$		
	$u_0 = 0$	$R = 64/225$
	$u_{\pm 1} = 0.2692346551$	$R = 0.2393143352$
	$u_{\pm 2} = 0.4530899230$	$R = 0.1184634425$
$n = 6.$		
	$u_{\pm 1} = 0.1193095930$	$R = 0.2339569673$
	$u_{\pm 2} = 0.3306046932$	$R = 0.1803807865$
	$u_{\pm 3} = 0.4662347571$	$R = 0.08566224619$
$n = 7.$		
	$u_0 = 0$	$R = 0.2089795918$
	$u_{\pm 1} = 0.2029225757$	$R = 0.1909150253$
	$u_{\pm 2} = 0.3707655928$	$R = 0.1398526957$
	$u_{\pm 3} = 0.4745539562$	$R = 0.06474248308$

	u	R

$n = 8.$

$$u_{\pm 1} = 0.0917173212 \qquad R = 0.1813418917$$
$$u_{\pm 2} = 0.2627662050 \qquad R = 0.1568533229$$
$$u_{\pm 3} = 0.3983332387 \qquad R = 0.1111905172$$
$$u_{\pm 4} = 0.4801449282 \qquad R = 0.05061426815$$

$n = 9.$

$$u_0 = 0 \qquad R = 0.1651196775$$
$$u_{\pm 1} = 0.1621267117 \qquad R = 0.1561735385$$
$$u_{\pm 2} = 0.3066857164 \qquad R = 0.1303053482$$
$$u_{\pm 3} = 0.4180155537 \qquad R = 0.09032408035$$
$$u_{\pm 4} = 0.4840801198 \qquad R = 0.04063719418$$

$n = 10.$

$$u_{\pm 1} = 0.0744371695 \qquad R = 0.1477621124$$
$$u_{\pm 2} = 0.2166976971 \qquad R = 0.1346333597$$
$$u_{\pm 3} = 0.3397047841 \qquad R = 0.1095431813$$
$$u_{\pm 4} = 0.4325316833 \qquad R = 0.07472567458$$
$$u_{\pm 5} = 0.4869532643 \qquad R = 0.03333567215$$

Note. For further tables relating to Gauss's quadrature formula the reader should consult the following literature:

1. " Table of the Zeros of the Legendre Polynomials of Order 1-16 and the Weight Coefficients for Gauss's Mechanical Quadrature Formula," by A. N. Lowan, Norman Davids, and Arthur Levinson, Bulletin of The American Mathematical Society, Vol. 48, No. 10, pp. 739-743, October 1942.

This is the most extensive table of the zeros and Gauss coefficients that has yet been published. All numbers are given to 15 decimal places. This table gives the subdivision points for the interval $u = -1$ to $u = 1$, and the values of u and R must be divided by 2 to agree with those given in the table above.

2. *Valeur Approximative d'une Intégrale Définie,* by B. P. Moors, Paris, 1905. This is the most comprehensive work on approximate quadrature that has ever been written. The roots and coefficients for the Gauss formula are given for $n = 1$ to $n = 10$ to 16 decimal places. The complete formula and its graphic representation are also given for each value of n.

We shall now apply Gauss's formula to a simple example.

Example. Compute the integral

$$I = \int_5^{12} \frac{dx}{x}$$

Solution. Here we put

$$x = (b - a)u + \frac{a + b}{2} = 7u + 8.5$$

$$y = \frac{1}{x} = \frac{1}{7u + 8.5} = \phi(u).$$

Taking $n = 5$, we have

$$y_0 = \phi(u_0) = \frac{1}{8.5} = 0.117647059$$

$$y_1 = \phi(u_1) = \frac{1}{7u_1 + 8.5} = \frac{1}{10.3846426} = 0.0962960439$$

$$y_{-1} = \phi(u_{-1}) = \frac{1}{7u_{-1} + 8.5} = \frac{1}{6.61535741} = 0.151163412$$

$$y_2 = \phi(u_2) = \frac{1}{7u_2 + 8.5} = \frac{1}{11.67162946} = 0.0856778399$$

$$y_{-2} = \phi(u_{-2}) = \frac{1}{7u_{-2} + 8.5} = \frac{1}{5.32837054} = 0.187674636.$$

Substituting these values in (49. 2), together with the corresponding R's for $n = 5$, we get

$$I = 7 \Big[\frac{64}{225} \times 0.117647059 + 0.2393143352(0.151163412 + 0.0962960439)$$

$$+ 0.1184634425(0.187674636 + 0.0856778399) \Big], \quad \text{or}$$

$$I_G = 0.875468458.$$

The true value of the integral is

$$I = \int_5^{12} \frac{dx}{x} = \ln \frac{12}{5} = \ln 2.4 = 0.875468737.$$

The error is therefore

$$E_G = 0.00000028.$$

The value of this integral by Simpson's Rule, using fifteen ordinates, is

$$I_S = 0.87547189.$$

The error in this case is therefore

$$E_S = 0.0000034,$$

or more than ten times as great as with Gauss's formula. The labor required to find the integral by Gauss's formula is, however, many times as great as with Simpson's unless a computing machine is used.

Note. The distance in x-units of any point u_i from the midpoint of the interval of integration is $(b-a)u_i$.

To prove this, let $b-a=L$ and take the midpoint of the interval as origin of coordinates. Then the limits of integration for x are $-L/2$ and $L/2$. On substituting $-L/2$ for a and $L/2$ for b in the transformation formula $x=(b-a)u+\dfrac{a+b}{2}$, we get

$$x=Lu=(b-a)u$$

Gauss's formula is useful for another purpose besides computing definite integrals. Recalling that the mean value of a function is given by the formula

$$y_m=\frac{\displaystyle\int_a^b y\,dx}{b-a},$$

we see that the accuracy of the mean depends on the accuracy with which the integral $\int_a^b y\,dx$ can be computed. The most accurate value of this is obtained by measuring ordinates at the points given by Gauss's formula.

Thus, if we wished to find the best value for the mean daily temperature from only four measurements, we would proceed as follows:

Denoting temperature by T, the hour of the day by t, and taking noon as the middle of the day, we have

$$T=f(t),\qquad T_m=\frac{\displaystyle\int_{-12}^{12}f(t)\,dt}{24}.$$

Taking noon as the midpoint of the 24-hour period and remembering that the time measured from noon is $24u$, we have for $n=4$,

$$t_1=24u_1=24(0.16999)=4.^{h}0798=4^h\,4.^m8$$

$$t_{-1}=24u_{-1}=24(-0.16999)=-4^h\,4.^m8$$

$$t_2=24u_2=24(0.430568)=10.^{h}3336=10^h\,20^m$$

$$t_{-2}=24u_{-2}=24(-0.430568)=-10^h\,20^m.$$

The best times during the day to take measurements are therefore

1:40 A.M., 7:55 A.M., 4:05 P.M., and 10:20 P.M.

In a similar manner we could find the best times of the day for making five, six, or any other number of measurements by taking the proper u's for $n = 5, 6$, etc.

The same method can be applied for finding the best positions or times for taking measurements on any other physical quantity.

Remarks. 1. The reader should bear in mind that Gauss's formula gives an exact result when $f(x)$ is a polynomial of the $(2n-1)$th degree or lower.

2. Although Gauss's method is theoretically beautiful and of great accuracy, it has the disadvantage of being laborious in its application, for three reasons:

(a) If the limits of the given integral are not $-\frac{1}{2}$ and $\frac{1}{2}$, the integral must be transformed to one that has these limits. The transformed integral is usually more complicated than the given one.

(b) If the values of y are to be computed from a formula, the numerical values of u to be substituted in the formula must be given to at least as many significant figures as we wish to obtain in the y's.

(c) After we have found the y's to the desired number of significant figures we must multiply them by R's having at least as many figures.

Gauss's formula thus compels us to deal with large numbers in every step if we desire the accuracy it is capable of giving. In applying this formula it is therefore imperative that we use every available aid for reducing the labor of computation. Whoever doubts this statement has only to work out a simple example to be convinced.

3. Gauss's formula should be used for computing definite integrals only when few ordinates are obtainable or when the importance of the result is such as to justify a great expenditure of labor.

50. Lobatto's Formula. The reader will have noticed that Gauss's formula does not contain the values of the function at the end points of the interval of integration. In certain types of problems it is highly advantageous to utilize the end values of the function. Lobatto * therefore modified Gauss's formula so as to include the end values and also the value of the function at the midpoint of the interval. The modification consisted in finding the points of subdivision (including the midpoint and the end points of the interval) from the equation

(1) $$\frac{d^{n-2}}{du^{n-2}} \left(u^2 - (\tfrac{1}{2})^2\right)^{n-1} = 0,$$

where n denotes the total number of values of the function to be utilized

* *Lessen over de Integraal-Rekening,* §207-210, The Hague, 1852.

(including end values and midpoint values). The values of u found from this equation are then substituted in equations (49.3) to find the corresponding R's. We shall derive Lobatto's formula for the case $n = 5$.

When $n = 5$, (1) becomes

$$\frac{d^3}{du^3} \left(u^2 - \left(\tfrac{1}{2}\right)^2\right)^4 = 0,$$

or

$$\frac{d^3}{du^3} \left[u^8 - 4u^6\left(\tfrac{1}{2}\right)^2 + 6u^4\left(\tfrac{1}{2}\right)^4 - 4u^2\left(\tfrac{1}{2}\right)^6 + \left(\tfrac{1}{2}\right)^8\right] = 0.$$

On performing the indicated differentiations and simplifying, we get

$$u(112u^4 - 40u^2 + 3) = 0,$$

from which

$$u = 0, \quad \pm \tfrac{1}{2}\sqrt{3/7}, \quad \pm \tfrac{1}{2}.$$

Hence

$$u_1 = -\tfrac{1}{2}, \quad u_2 = -\tfrac{1}{2}\sqrt{3/7}, \quad u_3 = 0, \quad u_4 = \tfrac{1}{2}\sqrt{3/7}, \quad u_5 = \tfrac{1}{2}.$$

On substituting these values of u in the first five of equations (49.3) and solving for the R's, we find

$$R_1 = R_5 = 1/20, \quad R_2 = R_4 = 49/180, \quad R_3 = 16/45.$$

Hence Lobatto's formula for $n = 5$ is

$$I = (b - a) \left[\frac{16}{45} y_0 + \frac{49}{180} (y_{-1} + y_1) + \frac{1}{20} (y_{-2} + y_2)\right].$$

The values of u and R for several values of n are as follows:

	u	R
$n = 3.$		
	$u_0 = 0$	$R = 2/3$
	$u_{\pm 1} = \tfrac{1}{2}$	$R = 1/6$
$n = 5.$		
	$u_0 = 0$	$R = 16/45 = 0.355556$
	$u_{\pm 1} = \tfrac{1}{2}\sqrt{3/7} = 0.327327$	$R = 49/180 = 0.272222$
	$u_{\pm 2} = \tfrac{1}{2} = 0.5$	$R = 1/20 = 0.05$
$n = 7.$		
	$u_0 = 0$	$R = 0.2433097$
	$u_{\pm 1} = 0.2344245$	$R = 0.2158727$
	$u_{\pm 2} = 0.415112$	$R = 0.1384129$
	$u_{\pm 3} = 0.5$	$R = 0.02380951$

$$u \qquad\qquad\qquad R$$

$n = 9.$

$u_0 = 0$	$R = 0.1857593$
$u_{\pm 1} = 0.1815585$	$R = 0.1732142$
$u_{\pm 2} = 0.338593$	$R = 0.1372695$
$u_{\pm 3} = 0.449879$	$R = 0.08274774$
$u_{\pm 4} = 0.5$	$R = 0.0138888$

$n = 11.$

$u_0 = 0$	$R = 0.1501037$
$u_{\pm 1} = 0.147876$	$R = 0.1434397$
$u_{\pm 2} = 0.282617$	$R = 0.1240270$
$u_{\pm 3} = 0.392242$	$R = 0.09358390$
$u_{\pm 4} = 0.467000$	$R = 0.05480614$
$u_{\pm 5} = 0.5$	$R = 0.009091366$

These values are to be substituted in formula (49.2).

Lobatto's formula is less accurate than Gauss's for the same n, but it is frequently more convenient for use. If the function happens to be zero at the ends of the interval of integration, as is frequently the case, the end values do not have to be computed. The computation is thereby shortened.

Example. Compute by Lobatto's formula the value of the integral

$$\int_5^{12} \frac{dx}{x},$$

for $n = 5.$

Solution. The integral must first be transformed so that the limits become $-\frac{1}{2}$ and $\frac{1}{2}$, just as was done when using the Gauss formula. From the previous example we have

$$x = 7u + 8.5, \quad y = 1/x, \quad = \frac{1}{7u + 8.5} = \phi(u).$$

Hence

$$y_0 = \phi(u_0) = \frac{1}{8.5} = \frac{2}{17}$$

$$y_1 = \phi(u_1) = \frac{1}{7(0.327327) + 8.5} = \frac{1}{10.79129} = 0.09266725$$

$$y_{-1} = \phi(u_{-1}) = \frac{1}{7(-0.327327) + 8.5} = \frac{1}{6.20871} = 0.161193$$

$$y_2 = \phi(u_2) = \frac{1}{7(0.5) + 8.5} = \frac{1}{12}$$

$$y_{-2} = \phi(u_{-2}) = \frac{1}{7(-0.5) + 8.5} = \frac{1}{5} .$$

Hence

$$I = 7 \left[\frac{16}{45} \times \frac{2}{17} + \frac{49}{180}(0.161193 + 0.092667) + \frac{1}{20}\left(\frac{1}{5} + \frac{1}{12} \right) \right] = 0.87572.$$

The error in this value is 0.00015.

51. Tchebycheff's Formula. Tchebycheff * devised a quadrature formula in which the coefficients of the y's are all equal. His formula is

$$(1) \qquad \int_{-\frac{1}{2}}^{\frac{1}{2}} \phi(u)\, du = (1/n)[\phi(u_1) + \phi(u_2) + \phi(u_3) + \cdots + \phi(u_n)],$$

and therefore

$$(2) \qquad \int_a^b y\, dx = \frac{b-a}{n} [\phi(u_1) + \phi(u_2) + \phi(u_3) + \cdots + \phi(u_n)].$$

The points of subdivision of the interval of integration are symmetrically placed with respect to the midpoint of the interval. The u's are the zeros of certain polynomials, the first few of which, equated to zero, are:

$$(2u)^2 - 1/3 = 0$$
$$(2u)^3 - \tfrac{1}{2}(2u) = 0$$
$$(2u)^4 - (2/3)(2u)^2 + 1/45 = 0$$
$$(2u)^5 - (5/6)(2u)^3 + (7/72)(2u) = 0$$
$$(2u)^6 - (2u)^4 + (1/5)(2u)^2 - 1/105 = 0.$$

The values of the u's for $n = 2$ to $n = 7$ and $n = 9$ are:

$n = 2.$ $u_{\pm 1} = 0.288675$

$n = 3.$ $u_0 = 0,$ $u_{\pm 2} = 0.353553$

$n = 4.$ $u_{\pm 1} = 0.0937962,$ $u_{\pm 2} = 0.397327$

$n = 5.$ $u_0 = 0,$ $u_{\pm 1} = 0.187271,$ $u_{\pm 2} = 0.416249$

$n = 6.$ $u_{\pm 1} = 0.133318,$ $u_{\pm 2} = 0.211259,$ $u_{\pm 3} = 0.433123$

$n = 7.$ $u_0 = 0,$ $u_{\pm 1} = 0.161956,$ $u_{\pm 2} = 0.264828,$ $u_{\pm 3} = 0.441931$

$n = 9.$ $u_0 = 0,$ $u_{\pm 1} = 0.0839531,$ $u_{\pm 2} = 0.264381,$ $u_{\pm 3} = 0.300509,$
   $u_{\pm 4} = 0.455795.$

* P. Tchebichef, " Sur les Quadratures." *Journal de Mathematiques*, 1874, p. 19. Some of the numerical values on p. 25 of that paper are incorrect.

Because of the fact that the functional values all have equal weight (the same coefficient) in Tchebycheff's formula, this formula is particularly appropriate for use when the functional values are found by measurement; for in that case the positive and negative errors of measurement will largely cancel one another. Tchebycheff's formula would be ideal for finding areas from drawings if it were not for the fact that the points of division are not readily located. Even so, these points can probably be located with an accuracy equal to that of the drawing.

Example. Compute by Tchebycheff's formula the value of the integral

$$\int_5^{12} \frac{dx}{x}, \qquad \text{for } n = 5.$$

Solution. Here we must express x in terms of u as in the two preceding examples. We have

$$x = 7u + 8.5, \quad y = 1/x = \frac{1}{7u + 8.5} = \phi(u)$$

Then

$$\phi(u_0) = \frac{1}{8.5} = 0.117647$$

$$\phi(u_1) = \frac{1}{7(0.187271) + 8.5} = \frac{1}{9.810897} = 0.101927$$

$$\phi(u_{-1}) = \frac{1}{7(-0.187271) + 8.5} = \frac{1}{7.189103} = 0.139099$$

$$\phi(u_2) = \frac{1}{7(0.416249) + 8.5} = \frac{1}{11.413743} = 0.087614$$

$$\phi(u_{-2}) = \frac{1}{7(-0.416249) + 8.5} = \frac{1}{5.586257} = 0.179011.$$

Hence

$$I = \frac{7}{5}(0.117647 + 0.101927 + 0.139099 + 0.087614 + 0.179011)$$
$$= 0.875417.$$

The error in this result is 0.000051.

52. Euler's Formula of Summation and Quadrature.

The approximate relation between integrals and sums is expressed by Euler's summation formula. Written as a quadrature formula it is *

---

* For the derivation of Euler's formula see Vallée-Poussin's *Cours d'Analyse Infinitésimale*, II, p. 341; Whittaker and Robinson's *Calculus of Observations*, p. 134; or Charlier's *Mechanik des Himmels*, II, §1.

$$\int_a^b f(x)\,dx = h\left[\frac{f(x_0)}{2} + f(x_1) + f(x_2) + \cdots + f(x_{n-1}) + \frac{f(x_n)}{2}\right.$$

(1)
$$-\frac{h}{12}[f'(b) - f'(a)] + \frac{h^3}{720}[f'''(b) - f'''(a)]$$

$$\left. -\frac{h^5}{30240}[f^v(b) - f^v(a)] + \frac{h^7}{1209600}[f^{vii}(b) - f^{vii}(a)] - \cdots\right]$$

$$\cdots + R.$$

By adding and subtracting $h[f(x_0)/2 + f(x_n)/2]$ on the right-hand side of (1) we have

$$\int_a^b f(x)\,dx = h[f(x_0) + f(x_1) + \cdots + f(x_n)] - \frac{h}{2}[f(x_0) + f(x_n)]$$

$$-\frac{h^2}{12}[f'(b) - f'(a)] + \cdots.$$

Transposing and dividing through by h, we get

$$f(x_0) + f(x_1) + \cdots + f(x_n) = \frac{1}{h}\int_a^b f(x)\,dx + \frac{1}{2}[f(x_0) + f(x_n)]$$

$$+\frac{h}{12}[f'(b) - f'(a)] - \frac{h^3}{720}[f'''(b) - f'''(a)] + \cdots,$$

or, since $x_0 = a$, $x_n = b$,

$$\sum_{i=0}^{i=n} f(x_i) = \frac{1}{h}\int_a^b f(x)\,dx + \frac{1}{2}[f(a) + f(b)] + \frac{h}{12}[f'(b) - f'(a)]$$

(2)
$$-\frac{h^3}{720}[f'''(b) - f'''(a)] + \frac{h^5}{30240}[f^v(b) - f^v(a)]$$

$$-\frac{h^7}{1209600}[f^{vii}(b) - f^{vii}(a)] - R.$$

Formula (2) is *Euler's summation formula*. It is useful for finding the approximate sum of any number of consecutive values of a function when these values are given for equidistant values of x, provided the integral $\int_a^b f(x)\,dx$ can be easily evaluated. In these formulas h is the distance between the equidistant values of x, so that $nh = b - a$.

Note. Formulas (1) and (2) differ in an important respect from the quadrature formulas previously derived. In (1) the terms on the right-hand side, beginning with $(h/12)[f'(b) - f'(a)]$, form an *asymptotic series*. The same is true of (2), beginning with the term $(h/12)[f'(b) - f'(a)]$.

An asymptotic series is an infinite series which converges for a certain number of terms and then begins to diverge. In computing with such a series it is important to know what term to stop with in order to get the most accurate result. We should stop not with the smallest term but with *the term just before the smallest*; for the error committed is usually less than twice the first neglected term * and is therefore least when the first term neglected is the smallest term in the series. For the reason just given it is important that Euler's formula be used with caution, especially when finding sums by (2). We shall now apply each of these formulas to an example.

Example 1. Compute the value of π from the formula

$$\frac{\pi}{4} = \int_0^1 \frac{dx}{1 + x^2}.$$

Solution. We take $h = \frac{1}{6}$ and compute the values of $y = 1/(1 + x^2)$ at each point of subdivision, as shown in the table below.

x	y	x	y
0	1	$\frac{2}{3}$	0.69230769
$\frac{1}{6}$	0.97297297	$\frac{5}{6}$	0.59016393
$\frac{1}{3}$	0.9	1	0.5
$\frac{1}{2}$	0.8		

We next compute the derivatives of $1/(1 + x^2)$, as given below.

$$f(x) = \frac{1}{1 + x^2},$$

$$f'(x) = -\frac{2x}{(1 + x^2)^2},$$

$$f'''(x) = \frac{24x(1 - x^2)}{(1 + x^2)^4},$$

$$f^{v}(x) = \frac{240x}{(1 + x^2)^6}[10x^2 - 3x^4 - 3],$$

$$f^{vii}(x) = -\frac{5760x}{(1 + x^2)^8}[7x^6 - 49x^4 + 49x^2 - 7].$$

Hence

$$f'(0) = 0, \quad f'(1) = -\tfrac{1}{2}.$$
$$f'''(0) = 0, \quad f'''(1) = 0,$$
$$f^{v}(0) = 0, \quad f^{v}(1) = 15,$$
$$f^{vii}(0) = 0, \quad f^{vii}(1) = 0.$$

* See Charlier, loc. cit., p. 14.

Substituting all these values in (1), we get

$$\frac{\pi}{4} = \frac{1}{6}\left[0.75 + 0.97297297 + 0.9 + 0.8 + 0.69230769 + 0.59016393\right]$$

$$- \frac{1}{36 \times 12}\left(-\frac{1}{2}\right) - \frac{1}{6^6 \times 30240}\ (15) = \underline{0.78539816},$$

which is correct to its last figure.

Example 2. Find the sum of

$$\frac{1}{51^2} + \frac{1}{53^2} + \frac{1}{55^2} + \cdots + \frac{1}{99^2}.$$

Solution. Here $f(x) = 1/x^2$ and $h = 2$. Then

$$f'(x) = -\frac{2}{x^3},\ f'''(x) = -\frac{24}{x^5},\ f^{v}(x) = -\frac{72}{x^7},\ f^{vii}(x) = -\frac{40320}{x^9}.$$

Remembering that $a = 51$, $b = 99$, and substituting in (2), we get

$$\sum_{x=51}^{x=99} \frac{1}{x^2} = \frac{1}{2}\int_{51}^{99} \frac{dx}{x^2} + \frac{1}{2}\left[\frac{1}{51^2} + \frac{1}{99^2}\right] + \frac{1}{3}\left[\frac{1}{51^3} - \frac{1}{99^3}\right]$$

$$- \frac{4}{15}\left[\frac{1}{51^5} - \frac{1}{99^5}\right] + \frac{16}{21}\left[\frac{1}{51^7} - \frac{1}{99^7}\right]$$

$$- \frac{64}{15}\left[\frac{1}{51^9} - \frac{1}{99^9}\right]$$

$$= 0.004753416 + 0.0002432490$$

$$+ 0.0000021694 - 0.0000000008$$

$$= \underline{0.004998833}.$$

If we had attempted to find the sum of the squares of the reciprocals of all the odd numbers from 1 to 99 we could not have obtained it accurately, for each bracketed quantity after the second would have been practically unity and therefore the various terms would have been the same as the coefficients 4/15, 16/21, 64/15, etc. To get the greatest accuracy in this case we should have to stop with the third term and even then the error might be nearly 8/15. Hence the necessity for caution in finding sums by means of Euler's formula.

53. Caution in the Use of Quadrature Formulas. The student should ever bear in mind that when computing the value of a definite integral by means of a quadrature formula he is really replacing the given integrand by a polynomial and integrating this polynomial over the given interval of integration. The accuracy of the result will depend upon how well the polynomial represents the integrand over this interval; or, geometrically, on how well the graph of the polynomial coincides with the graph of the integrand. Before beginning the computation of an integral by a quadrature formula the computer should ascertain the nature and behavior of the integrand over the interval of integration. In some instances it may be necessary to construct an accurate graph of the integrand. The computation can then be planned with reference to the nature and behavior of the function to be integrated. The following example will illustrate this point.

Example 1. Find by Simpson's Rule the value of the integral

$$I = \int_{-1}^{1} \frac{x^7 \sqrt{1 - x^2} \, dx}{(2 - x)^{13/2}} \, .$$

Solution. The integrand is evidently negative from $x = -1$ to $x = 0$, and positive from $x = 0$ to $x = 1$. Hence we divide each of these intervals into four equal parts and compute the value of the integrand at each point of subdivision. The results are given in the table below.

x	y	x	y
−1	0	0.25	0.000001555
−0.75	−0.0001231	0.50	0.000485
−0.50	−0.00001753	0.75	0.02070
−0.25	−0.000000304	1	0
0	0		

On applying Simpson's Rule to these tabular values we find

$$I^0_{-1} = -0.0000441,$$

$$I_0^1 = 0.006981,$$

$$\therefore \quad I = -0.0000441 + 0.006981 = 0.006937.$$

This result could be accepted with confidence if the tabular values were of the same order of magnitude, but the table shows that the integrand at $x = 0.50$ is enormously larger than it is for smaller values of x, and that at $x = 0.75$ it is enormously larger than at $x = 0.50$. Hence we had better examine this function more closely in the region from $x = 0.50$ to $x = 1$ and possibly make a new computation of the integral.

x	y	x	y
0.50	0.000485	0.80	0.038468
0.55	0.001136	0.82	0.048654
0.60	0.002514	0.84	0.061016
0.65	0.005297	0.86	0.075765
0.70	0.010688	0.88	0.092918
0.75	0.020701	0.90	0.11221
0.80	0.038468	0.92	0.13259
		0.94	0.15149
		0.96	0.16306
		0.98	0.15190
		1	0

The above table shows the variation of the integrand in the interval $0.50 \leqq x \leqq 1$, and Fig. 4 shows the graph for the whole interval from $x = -1$ to $x = 1$. A glance at the graph shows that in order to obtain

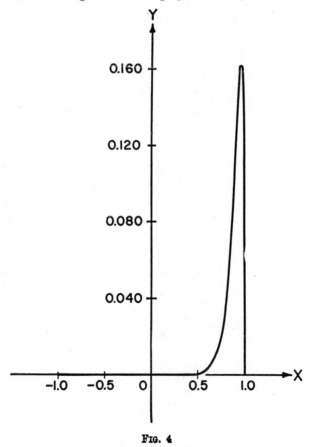

FIG. 4

a trustworthy result we should divide the computation into three distinct parts:

(1) By taking $h = 0.25$ in the interval $-1 < x < 0.5$,

(2) By taking $h = 0.05$ in the interval $0.5 < x < 0.8$,

(3) By taking $h = 0.02$ in the interval $0.8 < x < 1$.

The results of these computations are

$$I_{-1}^{0.5} = -0.0000031,$$

$$I_{0.5}^{0.8} = 0.002898,$$

$$I_{0.8}^{1} = 0.020651,$$

$$\therefore I = -0.0000031 + 0.002898 + 0.020651 = 0.0235.$$

Even when the graph of the integrand is a smooth, regular curve in the interval of integration a quadrature formula may not give a very accurate result unless the subdivisions are very small. This fact is illustrated by the following example.

Example 2. Find by Simpson's Rule the value of

$$I = \int_{-1}^{1} \sqrt{(1 - x^2)(2 - x)}\, dx.$$

Solution. The values of the integrand are given in the table below.

x	y	x	y
-1	0	0.1	1.371496
-0.9	0.742294	0.2	1.314534
-0.8	1.003992	0.3	1.243756
-0.7	1.173456	0.4	1.159310
-0.6	1.289961	0.5	1.060660
-0.5	1.369307	0.6	0.946573
-0.4	1.419859	0.7	0.814248
-0.3	1.446720	0.8	0.657267
-0.2	1.453272	0.9	0.457165
-0.1	1.441874	1	0
0	1.414214		

The correct value of the given integral to five significant figures is found from a table of elliptic integrals to be

$$I = 2.2033.$$

Simpson's Rule gives the following values for different values of h:

(a) $I = 2.0914$ for $h = 0.5$.   Percentage error $= 5.1\%$.

(b) $I = 2.1751$ for $h = 0.2$.   Percentage error $= 1.28\%$.

(c) $I = 2.1934$ for $h = 0.1$.   Percentage error $= 0.42\%$.

It will be observed that when the interval of integration was divided into 20 subintervals the error was nearly a half of one per cent, which is less than slide-rule accuracy. Inasmuch as the tabular values are all correct to six or seven figures, the errors in the results found above are due entirely to the inherent inaccuracy of Simpson's Rule. The trouble with this problem lies in the fact that the integrand cannot be approximated closely by a polynomial near the end points of the range of integration, for at these points the slope of the integrand is infinite. A better approximation can be obtained by using horizontal parabolas for the regions near the ends of the interval (see Note 2 on p. 137). Thus, for the region at the left end of the interval, we have

$$I_1 = (2/3)(0.2 \times 1.003992) = 0.1338656;$$

and for the region at the right end we have

$$I_2 = (2/3)(0.2 \times 0.657267) = 0.0876356.$$

Then the application of Simpson's Rule to the region from $x = -0.8$ to $x = 0.8$ gives

$$I_3 = 1.9780924.$$

The sum of these is

$$I_1 + I_2 + I_3 = I = 2.1996,$$

the percentage error of which is 0.17 per cent.

In Art. 57 several formulas will be derived for the inherent error in Simpson's Rule, but occasionally a problem may arise when the approximte error cannot be easily determined even with the aid of those formulas.

54. Mechanical Cubature.

In this article we shall give two methods for finding the numerical value of a definite double integral of a function of two independent variables. The first method will be by application of a formula which may be regarded as an extension of Simpson's Rule to functions of two variables. The second method is simply by repeated application of the ordinary quadrature formulas for one variable.

To derive the double quadrature formula we start with the formula for double interpolation, namely (X) of Art. 41, and integrate this formula over two intervals in the y-direction and two in the x-direction, first omitting from the formula all terms involving the differences Δ^{3+0}, Δ^{0+3}, Δ^{4+0}, Δ^{3+1}, Δ^{1+3}, Δ^{0+4}, since these differences involve values of the function outside the rectangle over which we are integrating.

Since $dx = h\,du$, $dy = k\,dv$ we have, after omitting the terms just mentioned,

$$
\begin{aligned}
I = \int_{x_0}^{x_0+2h} \int_{y_0}^{y_0+2h} z\,dy\,dx = hk \int_0^2 \int_0^2 \Big\{\ & z_{00} + u\Delta^{1+0}z_{00} + v\Delta^{0+1}z_{00} \\
& + \frac{1}{2}\left[u(u-1)\Delta^{2+0}z_{00} + 2uv\Delta^{1+1}z_{00} + v(v-1)\Delta^{0+2}z_{00}\right] \\
& + \frac{1}{6}\left[3u(u-1)v\Delta^{2+1}z_{00} + 3uv(v-1)\Delta^{1+2}z_{00}\right] \\
& + \frac{1}{24}\left[6u(u-1)v(v-1)\Delta^{2+2}z_{00}\right] \Big\}\, dv\,du.
\end{aligned}
$$

Performing the indicated integrations and replacing the double differences by their values as given in Art. 40, we get

(1) $\quad I = \dfrac{hk}{9}\left[z_{00} + z_{02} + z_{22} + z_{20} + 4(z_{01} + z_{12} + z_{21} + z_{10}) + 16z_{11}\right].$

This is the formula which corresponds to Simpson's Rule for a function of one variable. It can be represented diagramatically as shown in Fig. 5, the coefficients of the several z's being shown on the diagram. By adding any number of unit blocks of this type we could obtain a general formula for double integration, corresponding to Simpson's Rule for n intervals in single integration, but it is not worth while to do this.

Formula (1) can be rewritten in either of the following forms:

(2) $\quad I = \dfrac{h}{3}\left[\dfrac{k}{3}(z_{00}+4z_{01}+z_{02})+4\cdot\dfrac{k}{3}(z_{10}+4z_{11}+z_{12})+ \dfrac{k}{3}(z_{02}+4z_{12}+z_{22})\right],$

(3) $\quad I = \dfrac{h}{3}\left[\dfrac{k}{3}(z_{00}+4z_{10}+z_{20})+4\cdot\dfrac{k}{3}(z_{01}+4z_{11}+z_{21})+ \dfrac{k}{3}(z_{02}+4z_{12}+z_{22})\right].$

Now, such an expression as $(k/3)(z_{00} + 4z_{10} + z_{20})$ is nothing but Simpson's Rule applied to a single row in the diagram, in this case the top horizontal row. Let us put

$$A_0 = \frac{k}{3}(z_{00} + 4z_{10} + z_{20}), \qquad A_1 = \frac{k}{3}(z_{01} + 4z_{11} + z_{21}),\ \text{etc.}$$

Then (3) becomes

(4) $$I = \frac{h}{3}(A_0 + 4A_1 + A_2).$$

This formula shows that formula (1) is equivalent to applying Simpson's Rule to each horizontal row in the diagram and then applying it again to the results thus obtained. These considerations lead to the following general statement:

If we are given a rectangular array of values of a function of two variables, we may apply to each horizontal row or to each vertical column any quadrature formula employing equidistant ordinates, such as Simpson's and Weddle's formulas. Then to the results thus obtained for the rows (or columns) we may again apply a similar formula.

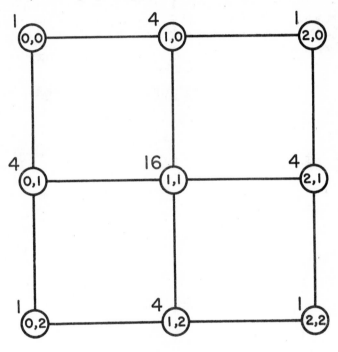

Fig. 5

This important result makes it unnecessary to derive general formulas for approximate double integration.

It is instructive to notice the geometric significance of this general statement. Since the double integral between constant limits of a function of two variables is represented by the volume of a solid having a rectangular base and a height at any point equal to $z[=f(x,y)]$, it is evident that the integrals A_0, A_1, etc. are merely vertical cross-sectional areas of this solid made by equidistant planes. Then when we apply a quadrature formula to these A's we are merely finding the volume of the solid, as if we evaluated the integral $\int_a^b A_s dx$.

An engineering application of mechanical cubature would be the solution of such a problem as the following:

Suppose it were necessary to determine the amount of earth to be moved in making an excavation for a large building on uneven ground, or in grading down or filling in a city block. The area to be excavated would be divided up into small rectangles by running two systems of equidistant parallel lines at right angles to each other. The distances of the corners of these rectangles above or below an asumed datum plane would be the z's of this article. Knowing these z's and the distances between the parallel lines (the h's and k's), we could find the volume of the excavation by the methods given above.

We shall now work two examples by these methods.

Example 1. Find by formula (1) the value of the integral

$$ I = \int_4^{4.4} \int_2^{2.6} \frac{dy\,dx}{xy} . $$

Solution. Taking $h = 0.2$ and $k = 0.3$, we compute the values of $z = 1/xy$ shown in the table below.

x \\ y	4.0	4.2	4.4
2.0	0.125000	0.119048	0.113636
2.3	0.108696	0.103520	0.0988142
2.6	0.096154	0.0915751	0.0874126

Substituting these in (1), we get

$$ I = \frac{0.2 \times 0.3}{9} \, [0.12500 + 0.096154 + 0.0874126 + 0.113636 $$
$$ + 4(0.108696 + 0.0915751 + 0.0988142 $$
$$ + 0.119048) + 16 \times 0.103520] $$
$$ = 0.0250070. $$

The true value of the integral is

$$ \int_4^{4.4} \int_2^{2.6} \frac{dy\,dx}{xy} = \ln 1.1 \times \ln 1.3 $$
$$ = 0.0953108 \times 0.262364 $$
$$ = 0.0250061. $$

The error is therefore

$$E = 0.0250061 - 0.0250070 = -0.0000009.$$

Example 2. Find by numerical integration the value of the integral

$$I = \int_4^{5.2} \int_2^{3.2} \frac{dy\,dx}{xy}.$$

Solution. Here we take $h = 0.2$, $k = 0.3$ as before, and compute the following table of values of $z = 1/xy$.

y \ x	4.0	4.2	4.4	4.6	4.8	5.0	5.2
2.0	0.125000	0.119048	0.113636	0.108696	0.104167	0.100000	0.096154
2.3	0.108696	0.103520	0.0988142	0.0945180	0.0905797	0.0869565	0.0836120
2.6	0.096154	0.0915751	0.0874126	0.0836120	0.0801282	0.0769231	0.0739645
2.9	0.0862069	0.0821018	0.0783699	0.0749625	0.0718391	0.0689655	0.0663130
3.2	0.078125	0.0744048	0.0710227	0.0679348	0.0651042	0.0625000	0.0600962

Applying Weddle's Rule to each horizontal row, we have

$$A_0 = 0.06[0.125000 + 5(0.119048) + 0.113636 + 6(0.108696)$$
$$+ 0.104167 + 5(0.100000) + 0.096154]$$
$$= 0.131182,$$

$$A_1 = 0.114072, \qquad A_2 = 0.100909, \qquad A_3 = 0.090470,$$

$$A_4 = 0.081989.$$

Now applying Simpson's Rule to the A's, we get

$$I = 0.1[0.131182 + 4(0.114072) + 2(0.100909)$$
$$+ 4(0.090470) + 0.081989 = \underline{0.123316}.$$

The true value of this integral is

$$\int_4^{5.2} \int_2^{3.2} \frac{dy\,dx}{xy} = \ln 1.3 \times \ln 1.6 = 0.123321,$$

and the error is therefore

$$E = 0.123321 - 0.123316 = 0.000005.$$

55. Prismoids and the Prismoidal Formula. The formula to be considered in this article is a special form of Simpson's Rule and the oldest form of that rule. It is treated here because of its importance and wide applicability in the mensuration of solids. The formula will be derived with reference to a solid.

A *prismoid* may be defined as a solid whose bases are polygons in parallel planes and whose lateral faces are ruled surfaces, either plane or warped.

If we let one base of the prismoid lie in the yz-plane and let the lateral faces extend in the general direction of the positive x-axis, the volume of the prismoid will be given by the integral

$$V = \int A(x)\,dx,$$

where $A(x)$ denotes the area of a cross section parallel to the bases and at a distance x from the yz-plane. To find $A(x)$, let

(1) $$y = ax + b$$

(2) $$z = cx + d$$

be the equations (in projection form) of any moving straight line. Such a line can move in any manner and will generate a ruled surface as it moves along. In a plane parallel to the yz-plane and distant x to the right of it the area of the cross section of the prismoid is given by the integral

$$A(x) = \int y\,dz,$$

the integration being extended over the entire cross section.

Now, in the fixed plane under consideration x is a constant, and y and z are functions only of the parameters a, b, c, d; that is, in this plane y and z can vary only when and as the parameters vary. Let each of these parameters be a function of a single parameter α. Then y and z become functions of α, and from (2) we have

$$dz = \frac{d}{d\alpha}(cx + d)\,d\alpha = (c'x + d')\,d\alpha.$$

The integral giving the area of the cross section now becomes

$$A(x) = \int y\,dz = \int_{\alpha_0}^{\alpha_1}(ax + b)(c'x + d')\,d\alpha$$

$$= x^2\int_{\alpha_0}^{\alpha_1}ac'd\alpha + x\int_{\alpha_0}^{\alpha_1}(bc' + ad')\,d\alpha + \int_{\alpha_0}^{\alpha_1}bd'd\alpha,$$

where it is assumed that the entire cross section is covered when α varies from α_0 to α_1. Since each side of the cross-sectional polygon is a section of a different ruled surface, the integrands above will change (be replaced by others) as the different sides of the polygon are encountered.* Also,

---

* The integral giving $A(x)$ in this problem is really a line integral. See E. B. Wilson's *Advanced Calculus*, p. 289, or Goursat-Hedrick, *Mathematical Analysis*, Vol. I, pp. 187-189.

since the above integrals in the expression for $A(x)$ are independent of x, they may be denoted by p, q, r, respectively. Hence we have the important result that

(3) $$A(x) = px^2 + qx + r,$$

which shows that the area of the cross section of a prismoid is a quadratic function of its distance from one base and therefore from either of its bases.

To find the volume of a prismoid of length l, we take coordinate axes with the yz-plane coinciding with the midsection of the solid. Then

(4) $$V = \int_{-l/2}^{l/2} A(x)\,dx = \int_{-l/2}^{l/2} (px^2 + qx + r)\,dx = \frac{pl^3}{12} + rl.$$

Let B_1 and B_2 denote the areas of the bases of the prismoid and let M denote the area of the midsection. Then from (3),

$$M = A(0) = r$$

$$B_1 = A\left(-\frac{l}{2}\right) = \frac{pl^2}{4} - \frac{ql}{2} + r.$$

$$B_2 = A\left(\frac{l}{2}\right) = \frac{pl^2}{4} + \frac{ql}{2} + r.$$

Hence

$$B_1 + B_2 = \frac{pl^2}{2} + 2r = \frac{pl^2}{2} + 2M, \qquad \text{from which}$$

$$p = \frac{2}{l^2}(B_1 + B_2 - 2M).$$

Substituting in (4) the values of p and r just found, we get

(5) $$V = \frac{l}{6}(B_1 + B_2 + 4M),$$

which is the *Prismoidal Formula*. The reader should keep in mind the verbal statement of this formula, namely: *The volume of a prismoid is equal to one sixth the product of its length by the sum of its bases and four times its midsection.*

It is to be noted that the prismoidal formula gives the exact volume not only of the prismoid but also of any other solid in which the area of the cross section is a quadratic function of the distance of the cross section from one base. Such solids are cones, pyramids, spheres, spherical segments, frustums of cones and pyramids, wedges, paraboloids of revolution, and other solids of revolution. It also gives with close approximation the volumes of barrels and casks.

Note. Some writers use the terms prismoid and prismatoid interchangeably, as if both terms referred to the same solid. Such is not the case, however. A prismatoid is usually defined as a polyhedron (a solid with *plane* faces)) having for bases two polygons in parallel planes and for lateral faces triangles or trapezoids with one side common with one base and the opposite vertex or side common with the other base. The volume of a prismatoid is found by decomposing the solid into pyramids having their vertices at a point in the midsection. The volume of a prismatoid is given by the prismoidal formula because the area of the cross section of a pyramid made by a plane parallel to its base is proportional to the square of the distance from the section to the vertex (or base) of the pyramid; that is, the area of the section is a quadratic function of its distance from the base.

The prismoidal formula is the fundamental formula for computing the volume of earth in cuts and fills for railroads, highways, canals, etc. The cross-sectional areas of cuts (or fills) are determined at convenient intervals (100 feet apart or less) and then the volume of earth to be excavated (or filled in) is computed by the prismoidal formula.

Example. A proposed railroad cut 100 feet long is represented approximately to scale in Fig. 6. Compute the number of cubic yards of material to be excavated.

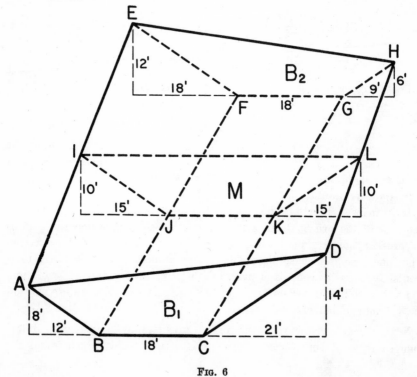

FIG. 6

Solution. The areas of the bases and midsection are found by subtracting the areas of the two triangles from the area of a trapezoid in each case. Hence

$$B_1 = 51 \left(\frac{8 + 14}{2} \right) - \tfrac{1}{2}(8 \times 12) - \tfrac{1}{2}(14 \times 21) = 366 \text{ sq. ft.,}$$

$$B_2 = 45 \left(\frac{6 + 12}{2} \right) - \tfrac{1}{2}(6 \times 9) - \tfrac{1}{2}(12 \times 18) = 270 \text{ sq. ft.,}$$

$$M = 48(10) - 150 = 330 \text{ sq. ft.,}$$

and therefore

$$V = \frac{100}{6} (366 + 270 + 4 \times 330) = 32{,}600 \text{ cu. ft.} = 1207.4 \text{ cu. yd.}$$

When the prismoidal formula is used to find the volume of a solid in which the cross-sectional area does not vary as the square or cube of the distance of the section from one base, the error committed is the same as that in Simpson's Rule (see Art. 57).

EXERCISES VII

1. In the table below are given corresponding values of a variable x and an unknown function y. For what value of x is y a minimum?

x	y
3	-205
4	-240
5	-259
6	-262
7	-250
8	-224

2. For what value of x is the following tabulated function a minimum?

x	y
0.2	0.9182
0.3	0.8975
0.4	0.8873
0.5	0.8862
0.6	0.8935
0.7	0.9086

3. In the year 1918 the declination of the sun at Greenwich mean noon on certain dates was as given below. Find when the declination was a maximum.

Date	Declination
June 19	23° 25′ 23″ .5
" 20	" 26 19 .4
" 21	" 26 50 .5
" 22	" 26 56 .8
" 23	" 26 38 .3
" 24	" 25 55 .1
" 25	" 24 47 .1

4. Compute the value of

$$I = \int_0^{\pi/2} \sqrt{1 - 0.162 \sin^2 \phi}\, d\phi$$

by Simpson's Rule and by Weddle's Rule, taking

$$\phi = 0°, \quad 15°, \quad 30°, \quad 45°, \quad 60°, \quad 75°, \quad 90°.$$

Compare your results with that found by the series method in Exercise 25, Chapter I. Also compare the amount of labor involved in each case.

5. Compute $\int_0^1 \dfrac{dx}{\sqrt{x^4 + 1}}$ by Gauss's method, taking $n = 5$.

6. Compute by Simpson's Rule the value of the integral

$$I = \int_{200}^{1000} \frac{dx}{\log_{10} x},$$

taking eight subintervals.

7. Find by Weddle's Rule the value of the integral

$$I = \int_{0.4}^{1.6} \frac{x\,dx}{\sinh x},$$

taking twelve subintervals.

8. Find by Euler's quadrature formula the value of the integral

$$I = \int_0^1 \cos x^2 \, dx$$

and compare the result with that found by integrating the series for $\cos x^2$.

9. Find by Euler's summation formula the sum of

$$\frac{1}{400} + \frac{1}{402} + \cdots + \frac{1}{498} + \frac{1}{500}.$$

10. Find the value of the integral

$$I = \int_{30°}^{90°} \log_{10} \sin x \, dx$$

by Simpson's Rule, taking ten subintervals.

11. Compute by any method the value of the integral

$$I = \int_0^{\pi/3} \sqrt{\cos \theta} \, d\theta.$$

12. Compute to five decimal places the value of

$$I = \int_0^{\frac{1}{2}} \frac{x \, dx}{\cos x}.$$

13. Using the data of the following table, compute the integrals

(a) $\int_{0.5}^{1.1} xy \, dx,$ (b) $\int_{0.5}^{1.1} y^2 \, dx,$ (c) $\int_{0.5}^{1.1} x^2 y \, dx,$

(d) $\int_{0.5}^{1.1} y^3 \, dx,$

by Simpson's Rule.

x	0.5	0.6	0.7	0.8	0.9	1.0	1.1
y	0.4804	0.5669	0.6490	0.7262	0.7985	0.8658	0.9281

CHAPTER VIII

THE ACCURACY OF QUADRATURE FORMULAS

56. Introduction. A computer should have some means of estimating the reliability of every computed result. It is not always possible to have an explicit formula giving the error committed, but usually there exists some means for ascertaining the magnitude of the majority of unavoidable errors. In the present chapter we consider the accuracy of the more important quadrature formulas and give expressions for the inherent errors in several of them.*

57. Formulas for the Inherent Error in Simpson's Rule. *(a) The General Formula.* Let $f(x)$ denote a function which is finite and continuous in the interval $x = x_0 - h$ to $x = x_0 + h$ and has continuous derivatives of all orders up to and including the fourth in that interval. Furthermore, let $F(x)$ denote the integral of $f(x)$, so that

$$F(x) = \int_k^x f(x)\, dx, \quad F'(x) = f(x), \quad F''(x) = f'(x), \text{ etc.}$$

Then

$$I = \int_{x_0-h}^{x_0+h} f(x)\, dx = F(x_0 + h) - F(x_0 - h).$$

The value of this integral by Simpson's Rule is

$$I_S = \frac{h}{3}\left[f(x_0 - h) + 4f(x_0) + f(x_0 + h) \right].$$

The difference between these results is the inherent error in Simpson's Rule, so that

$$(1) \quad E_S = I - I_S = F(x_0 + h) - F(x_0 - h) - \frac{h}{3}\left[f(x_0 - h) + 4f(x_0) + f(x_0 + h) \right].$$

This formula is of no practical value as it stands, because it is indefinite and cumbersome. It can be reduced to a simple and workable form in either of two ways.

---

* A method for comparing the relative accuracy of quadrature formulas employing equidistant ordinates will be found in the following literature:
1. "On the Relative Accuracy of Simpson's Rules and Weddle's Rule," *American Mathematical Monthly*, Vol. XXXIV, No. 3 (March, 1927), pp. 135-139.
2. The first edition of this book, pp. 153-155.

1. The expression for E_S is clearly a function of h. Hence, following the method of Vallée-Poussin, we denote it by $\phi(h)$ and write

$$\phi(h) = F(x_0 + h) - F(x_0 - h) - \frac{h}{3}\left[f(x_0 - h) + 4f(x_0) + f(x_0 + h)\right].$$

Differentiating both sides successively with respect to h, we have

$$\phi'(h) = f(x_0 + h) + f(x_0 - h) - \frac{h}{3}\left[f'(x_0 + h) - f'(x_0 - h)\right]$$

$$-\frac{1}{3}\left[f(x_0 + h) + 4f(x_0) + f(x_0 - h)\right],$$

$$\phi''(h) = f'(x_0 + h) - f'(x_0 - h) - \frac{h}{3}\left[f''(x_0 + h) + f''(x_0 - h)\right]$$

$$-\frac{2}{3}\left[f'(x_0 + h) - f'(x_0 - h)\right],$$

$$\phi'''(h) = -\frac{h}{3}\left[f'''(x_0 + h) - f'''(x_0 - h)\right].$$

By the theorem of mean value this last expression in brackets is equal to $2hf^{iv}(\xi)$, where $x_0 - h < \xi < x_0 + h$. Hence

$$(2) \qquad\qquad \phi'''(h) = -\frac{2h^2}{3}f^{iv}(\xi).$$

On putting $h = 0$ in the expressions for $\phi(h)$, $\phi'(h)$, $\phi''(h)$, we find that $\phi(h) = \phi'(h) = \phi''(h) = 0$.

We now integrate (2) three times with respect to h, either by integrating from 0 to h or by determining the constant of integration at each step. In either case we make use of the relations $\phi(h) = 0$, $\phi'(h) = 0$, and $\phi''(h) = 0$ for $h = 0$. Although the factor $f^{iv}(\xi)$ depends to some extent on the magnitude of the interval $(0, h)$, we can replace it by its mean value in the interval and remove it from under the integral sign. Assuming that this is done at each step, we have

$$\phi'''(h) = -\frac{2h^2}{3}f^{iv}(\xi),$$

$$\phi''(h) = -\frac{2h^3}{9}f^{iv}(\xi),$$

$$\phi'(h) = -\frac{h^4}{18}f^{iv}(\xi),$$

$$\phi(h) = -\frac{h^5}{90}f^{iv}(\xi).$$

Since this $\phi(h)$ is the inherent error for an interval of width $2h$, the inherent error for a subinterval of width h is half this amount, or

$$-\frac{h^5}{180} f^{iv}(\xi).$$

Then since $b - a = nh$, we have as the inherent error for the whole interval $b - a$:

(57. 1) $E_s = n \left(-\frac{h^5}{180} f^{iv}(\xi) \right) = -\frac{nh^5}{180} f^{iv}(\xi) = -\frac{(b-a)}{180} h^4 f^{iv}(\xi),$

where ξ now lies between a and b, or $a < \xi < b$.

2. Another way of simplifying (1) is by means of Taylor's theorem. Expanding $F(x_0 + h)$ and $F(x_0 - h)$ by Taylor's theorem and remembering that $F'(x_0) = f(x_0)$, $F''(x_0) = f'(x_0)$, etc., we have

$$F(x_0 + h) = F(x_0) + hf(x_0) + \frac{h^2}{2} f'(x_0) + \frac{h^3}{3!} f''(x_0) + \cdots$$

$$F(x_0 - h) = F(x_0) - hf(x_0) + \frac{h^2}{2} f'(x_0) - \frac{h^3}{3!} f''(x_0) + \cdots$$

Also,

$$f(x_0 + h) = f(x_0) + hf'(x_0) + \frac{h^2}{2} f''(x_0) + \frac{h^3}{3!} f'''(x_0) + \cdots$$

$$f(x_0 - h) = f(x_0) - hf'(x_0) + \frac{h^2}{2} f''(x_0) - \frac{h^3}{3!} f'''(x_0) + \cdots.$$

On substituting in (1) these values for $F(x_0 + h)$, $F(x_0 - h)$, $f(x_0 + h)$, and $f(x_0 - h)$, we get

$$E_s = -\frac{h^5}{90} [f^{iv}(x_0) + \cdots].$$

Hence the inherent error for the whole interval $b - a$ is

(3) $E_s = -\frac{h^5}{90} [f^{iv}(x_1) + f^{iv}(x_3) + \cdots + f^{iv}(x_{n-1})] - \cdots.$

Let $f^{iv}(x_m)$ denote the greatest value of any of the $n/2$ quantities within the bracket. Then

(57. 2) $E_s \leqq -\frac{nh^5}{180} f^{iv}(x_m) = -\frac{b-a}{180} h^4 f^{iv}(x_m).$

The values found for E_s show that $E_s = 0$ when $f^{iv}(x) = 0$. Hence when $f(x)$ is a polynomial of the first, second, or third degree, Simpson's Rule gives the *exact* value of $\int_a^b f(x)\,dx$.

(*b*). *A Formula in Terms of Differences.* In many applications of Simpson's Rule the analytical form of the function to be integrated is either totally unknown or else is of such a nature that its fourth derivative is difficult to calculate. In either case formula (3) can not be applied as it stands. We get around the difficulty by transforming it into another form.

Let us replace the derivatives $f^{iv}(x_1)$, $f^{iv}(x_3)$, $\cdots$, etc. by their values in terms of differences. For this purpose we write Stirling's interpolation formula in the form

$$y = f(x) = f(k + hu) = y_k + u\,\frac{\Delta y_k + \Delta y_{k-h}}{2} + \frac{u^2}{2}\,\Delta^2 y_{k-h}$$

$$+ \frac{u(u^2 - 1^2)}{3!}\,\frac{\Delta^3 y_{k-h} + \Delta^3 y_{k-2h}}{2} + \cdots$$

to fourth differences.

Differentiating this formula with respect to x by means of the formula $dy/dx = (dy/du)(du/dx)$ and the relation $x = k + hu$, or $u = (x - k)/h$, and then putting $u = 0$ in each derivative, we get

$$f^{iv}(k) = \frac{\Delta^4 y_{k-2h}}{h^4}.$$

Now putting $k = x_1, x_3, \cdots x_{n-1}$, writing $\Delta^4 y_{x_1-2h} = \Delta^4 y_{-1}$, etc., and substituting in (3) these values of the fourth derivatives, we get

$$(4) \qquad E_S = -\frac{h}{90}\,(\Delta^4 y_{-1} + \Delta^4 y_1 + \Delta^4 y_3 + \cdots + \Delta^4 y_{n-3}).$$

This expression for the error in Simpson's Rule is identical with the third set of terms in our central-difference quadrature formula (48.1). That formula is therefore Simpson's Rule plus its correction terms, as was stated on page 141.

(*c*). *A Formula in Terms of the Given Ordinates.* To get a formula for E_S in terms of the given ordinates, we replace the differences in (4) by their values in terms of the y's as given in Art. 16, Table 3. Since

$$\Delta^4 y_{-1} = y_3 - 4y_2 + 6y_1 - 4y_0 + y_{-1},$$

$$\Delta^4 y_1 = y_5 - 4y_4 + 6y_3 - 4y_2 + y_1,$$

$$\cdot \quad \cdot \quad \cdot \quad \cdot \quad \cdot \quad \cdot \quad \cdot \quad \cdot \quad \cdot \quad \cdot \quad \cdot$$

$$\Delta^4 y_{n-3} = y_{n+1} - 4y_n + 6y_{n-1} - 4y_{n-2} + y_{n-3},$$

we have, on substituting these in (4),

(5) $\quad E_S = -\dfrac{h}{90}\,[y_{-1} + y_{n+1} - 4(y_0 + y_n) + 7(y_1 + y_{n-1})$

$\qquad\qquad -8(y_2 + y_4 + \cdots + y_{n-2}) + 8(y_3 + y_5 + \cdots + y_{n-3})]$

when $n \geqq 6$.

If the number of subintervals be less than six, the formulas for E_S are

(6) $\quad E_S = -\dfrac{h}{90}\,[y_{-1} + y_3 - 4(y_0 + y_2) + 6y_1],$ for $n = 2.$

(7) $\quad E_S = -\dfrac{h}{90}\,[y_{-1} + y_5 - 4(y_0 + y_4) + 7(y_1 + y_3) - 8y_2],$ for $n = 4.$

The ordinates y_{-1} and y_{n+1}, which are outside the interval of integration, can be found in one or more ways. If the values of y are computed from a formula and the formula holds outside the interval of integration, then we merely compute y_{-1} and y_{n+1} from this formula by substituting the proper values of x. But if we are given only a tabular set of y's we find y_{-1} and y_{n+1} by extrapolation, the former by using Newton's formula (I) and the latter by using Newton's formula (II).

(d) *A Formula in Terms of Two Computed Results.* Suppose two computations of a definite integral are made by Simpson's Rule, using a different value of h for each computation. Let R_1, h_1, E_1 denote the result, the value of h, and the error in the first computation, and let R_2, h_2, E_2 denote the corresponding quantities in the second computation. Then by (57.1) or (57.2) we have

$$\frac{E_1}{E_2} = \frac{h_1{}^4}{h_2{}^4}, \text{ or } E_1 = \frac{h_1{}^4}{h_2{}^4}\,E_2\,.$$

Hence if $h_2 = \dfrac{h_1}{2}$, we have

$$E_1 = 16E_2\,.$$

Let I denote the true value of the given integral. Then for the two computations we have

$$I = R_1 + E_1 = R_1 + 16E_2\,,$$
$$I = R_2 + E_2\,.$$

Subtracting the upper equation from the lower and solving for E_2, we get

(8) $$\qquad\qquad\qquad E_2 = \frac{R_2 - R_1}{15}\,.$$

This formula tells us that if we compute the value of a definite integral by using a certain value for h and then compute it again by using twice as many subdivisions, the error of the second result will be about 1/15th of the difference of the two results.

(e) *To Find the Value of* h *for a Stipulated Degree of Accuracy in the Result.* If we wish to know the value of h to obtain a result of stipulated accuracy, we substitute in (57.1) or (57.2) the allowable error E, the maximum value of $f^{iv}(x)$, the value of $b - a$, ignore the negative sign, and solve for h.

In case $f^{iv}(x)$ cannot be found, assume a convenient value h_1 for h, find E_1 by (4) or (5), and use the relation $\dfrac{E_1}{E_p} = \dfrac{h_1^4}{h^4}$, from which

$$\textbf{(9)} \qquad\qquad h = h_1 \left(\frac{E_p}{E_1}\right)^{\frac{1}{4}},$$

where E_p denotes the allowable error.

We shall now apply formulas (5) and (57.1) to the first example worked in Art. 45.

Example. Compute by means of (5) and (57.1) the error in the evaluation of $\int_4^{5.2} \ln x\,dx$ by Simpson's Rule.

Solution. We must first compute y_{-1} and y_{n+1} from the given function $y = \ln x$. For these we have

$$y_{-1} = \ln 3.8 = 1.33500107,$$
$$y_{n+1} = \ln 5.4 = 1.68639895.$$

The values of y from y_0 to y_n inclusive are given in the table on page 134. Substituting these y's in (5), we get

$$\begin{aligned}
E_8 = -\frac{0.2}{90}\,[\,&3.02140002 - 4(3.03495299) \\
&+ 7(3.04452244) - 8(3.05022046) \\
&+ 8(1.52605630)\,] \\
= \;&0.00000015.
\end{aligned}$$

The true error was found in Art. 47 to be 0.00000015.

To compute the error by (57.1) or (57.2) we first find $f^{iv}(x)$ from the equation $f(x) = \ln x$. We thus have

$$f^{iv}(x) = -\frac{6}{x^4}.$$

Hence

$$E_8 \leqq \frac{(5.2 - 4)}{180}\,(0.2)^4 \left(\frac{6}{(4)^4}\right) = 0.00000025.$$

This is of the same order of magnitude as the actual error but greater than it, as it should be.

Suppose we wished to know the value of h necessary to give the integral correct to ten decimal places. Since we have already found the error corresponding to a particular value of h, we can find the desired value by substituting in formula (9). Here

$$h_1 = 0.2, \qquad E_1 = 0.00000015, \qquad E_p < 0.00000000005.$$

Hence we have

$$h < 0.2 \left(\frac{0.00000000005}{0.00000015} \right)^{\frac{1}{4}} = 0.027.$$

Since $b - a = nh$, we find that we should have to divide the interval $(4, 5.2)$ into more than 45 subintervals in order to get a result correct to ten decimal places.

58. The Inherent Error in Weddle's Rule. In deriving Weddle's Rule, we omitted the quantity $-\dfrac{h}{140} \Delta^6 y_0$. This omitted quantity is the principal part of the error inherent in the formula. In terms of derivatives it is

$$-\frac{h^7}{140} f^{vi}(x).$$

Hence

(58. 1) $$E_W = -\frac{h}{140} \Delta^6 y = -\frac{h^7}{140} f^{vi}(x).$$

This means that when $f(x)$ is a polynomial of the 5th degree or lower, Weddle's Rule gives an exact result.

59. The Remainder Terms in Central-Difference Formulas (48. 1) and (48. 3). The remainder terms in these formulas can be found by integrating the remainder terms in Stirling's and Bessel's interpolation fromulas from which (48. 1) and (48. 3) were derived. Since (48. 1) is at least as accurate as (48. 3), and since a more definite formula can be derived for the remainder term in the latter than in the former, we shall derive the remainder term for (48. 3) only and use it for computing the error in both formulas. In Art. 35 we found the remainder term in Bessel's formula (VI) to be

$$R_n = \frac{h^{2n+2} f^{(2n+2)}(\xi)}{(2n + 2)!} \left(v^2 - \frac{1}{4} \right) \left(v^2 - \frac{9}{4} \right) \cdots \left(v^2 - \frac{(2n + 1)^2}{4} \right).$$

Since $f(x)\,dx$ is the quantity that is integrated by a quadrature formula, it is plain that $R_n(x)\,dx$ is the quantity which must be integrated to find the inherent error in the quadrature; and since $dx = h\,dv$, we have for the error in a single subinterval of width h

$$(1) \quad E = \int_{x_0}^{x_0+h} R_n(x)\,dx = h \int^{\frac{1}{2}} \frac{h^{2n+2} f^{(2n+2)}(\xi)}{(2n+2)!} \left(v^2 - \frac{1}{4}\right)\left(v^2 - \frac{9}{4}\right)$$

$$\cdots \left(v^2 - \frac{(2n+1)^2}{4}\right) dv = \frac{2h^{2n+3} f^{(2n+2)}(\xi)}{(2n+2)!}$$

$$\times \int_0^{\frac{1}{2}} \left(v^2 - \frac{1}{4}\right)\left(v^2 - \frac{9}{4}\right)\cdots\left(v^2 - \frac{(2n+1)^2}{4}\right) dv.$$

Let us put

$$(2) \quad V_n = \int_0^{\frac{1}{2}} \left(v^2 - \frac{1}{4}\right)\left(v^2 - \frac{9}{4}\right)\cdots\left(v^2 - \frac{(2n+1)^2}{4}\right) dv.$$

Then

$$E = \frac{2h^{2n+3} f^{(2n+2)}(\xi)}{(2n+2)!} \mid V_n \mid.$$

This is the error for a single subinterval of width h. Let M_n denote the maximum value of $f^{(2n+2)}(x)$ in the interval (a, b). Then since there are $(b-a)/h$ subintervals from $x = a$ to $x = b$, we have for the total error in the interval (a, b)

$$(3) \quad E \leqq \frac{2h^{2n+2} M_n}{(2n+2)!} (b-a) \mid V_n \mid.$$

From this general formula we get particular ones by assigning values to n. Thus, if we include fourth differences in (48.2) and neglect all higher differences, we put $n = 2$. Then (2) becomes

$$V_2 = \int_0^{\frac{1}{2}} \left(v^2 - \frac{1}{4}\right)\left(v^2 - \frac{9}{4}\right)\left(v^2 - \frac{25}{4}\right) dv = -\frac{191}{168},$$

and therefore (3) becomes

$$E \leqq \frac{191 h^6 M_2}{60480} (b-a) ;$$

or, more simply,

$$(4) \quad E_a^b < \frac{h^6 M_2}{316} (b-a).$$

In terms of differences this becomes

$$(5) \quad E_a^b < \frac{\mid \Delta^6 y \mid}{316} (b-a),$$

where $\Delta^6 y$ is the largest of the sixth differences.

If we include sixth differences in (48. 2) and neglect all higher differences, then $n = 3$ and (2) becomes

$$V_3 = \int_0^{\frac{1}{2}} \left(v^2 - \frac{1}{4} \right) \left(v^2 - \frac{9}{4} \right) \left(v^2 - \frac{25}{4} \right) \left(v^2 - \frac{49}{4} \right) dv = \frac{2497}{180} \, .$$

On substituting these in (3) we find

$$E_a{}^b \leqq \frac{2497 h^8 M_3}{3628800} \, (b - a),$$

or

(6)
$$E_a{}^b < \frac{h^8 M_3}{1453} \, (b - a).$$

In terms of differences this becomes

(7)
$$E_a{}^b < \frac{| \Delta^8 y |}{1453} \, (b - a),$$

where $\Delta^8 y$ is the largest of the eighth differences in the interval (a, b).

When we stop with fourth differences in formula (48. 1) or with third differences in (48. 3), the error is to be computed by (5); and when we stop with sixth differences in (48. 1) or with fifth differences in (48. 3), the error is to be computed by (7).

60. The Inherent Errors in the Formulas of Gauss, Lobatto, and Tchebycheff. The inherent errors in the formulas of Gauss, Lobatto, and Tchebycheff are usually given in terms of the coefficients in a power series. To find the error in any given case, it is therefore necessary to expand the function $\phi(u)$ as a power series and pick out the appropriate coefficients, one or more.

For *Gauss's formula* the principal part of the inherent error is *

(1) $$E_G = \frac{b - a}{(2n + 1) 2^{2n}} \left(\frac{n!}{1 \cdot 3 \cdot 5 \cdots (2n - 1)} \right)^2$$
$$\times \left\{ L_{2n} + \frac{L_{2n+2}}{8} \left(\frac{(n + 1)(n + 2)}{2n + 3} + \frac{n(n - 1)}{2n - 1} \right) \right\},$$

where the L's are the coefficients in the power series

(2) $$\phi(u) = L_0 + L_1 u + L_2 u^2 + \cdots + L_{2n} u^{2n} + \cdots.$$

When the series for $\phi(u)$ is rapidly convergent, the term involving L_{2n+2} in formula (1) may be omitted.

If the analytic form of $\phi(u)$ is not known, E_G cannot be determined.

* Derived in Todhunter's *Functions of Laplace, Lamé, and Bessel*, p. 108.

Example. Find E_G for the example in Art. 49, p. 150.

Solution. Here

$$\phi(u) = \frac{1}{7u + 8.5} = \frac{2}{14u + 17} = \frac{2}{17}\left(1 + \frac{14}{17}u\right)^{-1}.$$

Since $n = 5$, $2n + 2 = 12$. We must therefore find the coefficients of u^{10} and u^{12} in the series for $\phi(u)$. We have

$$\phi(u) = \frac{2}{17}\left[1 - \frac{14}{17}u + \left(\frac{14}{17}u\right)^2 - \cdots + \left(\frac{14}{17}u\right)^{10} - \left(\frac{14}{17}u\right)^{11}\right.$$
$$\left. + \left(\frac{14}{17}u\right)^{12} - \cdots\right].$$

From this series we see that

$$L_{2n} = \frac{2}{17}\left(\frac{14}{17}\right)^{10} \text{ and } L_{2n+2} = \frac{2}{17}\left(\frac{14}{17}\right)^{12}$$

Substituting these in (1), we get

$$E_G = \frac{2}{17} \times \frac{7}{11 \times 2^{10}}\left\{\frac{5!}{1\cdot 3\cdot 5\cdot 7\cdot 9}\right\}^2\left\{\left(\frac{14}{17}\right)^{10} + \frac{1}{8}\left(\frac{14}{17}\right)^{12}\left(\frac{42}{13} + \frac{20}{9}\right)\right\}$$
$$= 0.00000017 + 0.00000008 = 0.00000025.$$

This result agrees well with the actual error 0.00000028 found in Art. 49.

There are no simple formulas in terms of n for the inherent errors in the formulas of Lobatto and Tchebycheff. Formulas for particular values of n are given in the tables at the end of the book by B. P. Moors.

61. The Remainder Term in Euler's Formula. Malmsten's expression for the remainder after n terms in Euler's formula of summation and quadrature is

(1) $R_n = A_{2n}h^{2n+1}f^{(2n)}(a + \theta h), \quad 0 < \theta < 1,$

for a single subinterval of width h.

Let M denote the numerically greatest value of $f^{(2n)}(x)$ in the whole interval (a, b). Then for the n subintervals we have

(2) $R_n \leqq nA_{2n}h^{2n+1}M,$

or, since $n = (b - a)/h$,

(3) $R_n \leqq A_{2n}h^{2n}M(b - a).$

Here A_{2n} has the following values:

$$A_2 = -\frac{1}{12}, \quad A_4 = +\frac{1}{720}, \quad A_6 = -\frac{1}{30240}, \quad A_8 = +\frac{1}{1209600},$$

$$A_{10} = -\frac{1}{47900160}.$$

More useful, perhaps, than formula (3) is the following working rule due to Charlier: *

In stopping with any term in Euler's formula the error committed is less than twice the first neglected term.

Hence we get the most accurate result by stopping with the term just before the smallest, so that the first neglected term is the smallest of all.

We shall now show that the first two terms of Euler's formula will give a more accurate result than Simpson's Rule.

Putting $n = 2$ in formula (3), we have

$$R_2 \leqq A_4 h^4 M (b-a) = \frac{h^4 M}{720} (b-a),$$

where M denotes the greatest numerical value of $f^{\text{iv}}(x)$ in the interval (a, b).

The remainder term in Simpson's Rule is (Art. 57)

$$E_S = \frac{h^4 M}{180} (b-a).$$

Hence the inherent error in Euler's formula for only two terms is just one fourth that in Simpson's Rule.

EXERCISES VIII

1. Estimate the inherent errors in your answers to Exercise 4 of Chapter VII and compare these errors with that found in Exercise 25 of Chapter I.

2. Compute the inherent error in your answer to Exercise 6 of Chapter VII.

3. Estimate the accuracy of your answer to Exercise 8, Ch. VII.

---

* *Mechanik des Himmels*, II, pp. 13-16.

CHAPTER IX

THE SOLUTION OF NUMERICAL ALGEBRAIC AND TRANSCENDENTAL EQUATIONS

I. EQUATIONS IN ONE UNKNOWN

62. Introduction. It is shown in algebra how to solve literal equations of all degrees up to and including the fourth; and it is also shown how to compute the roots of numerical equations of any degree. Algebra is silent, however, on the solution of such types of equations as $ax + b \log x = c$, $ae^{-x} + b \tan x = 5$, etc. These are *transcendental equations*, and no general method exists for finding their roots in terms of their coefficients. When the coefficients of such equations are pure numbers, however, it is always possible to compute the roots to any desired degree of accuracy.

The object of the present chapter is to set forth the most useful methods for finding the roots of any equation having numerical coefficients. Since Horner's method is explained in most college algebras, and since it can not be applied to transcendental equations, we shall not consider it here.

63. Finding Approximate Values of the Roots. In finding the real roots of a numerical equation by any method except that of Graeffe, it is necessary first to find an approximate value of the root from a graph or otherwise. Let

$$(1) \qquad\qquad f(x) = 0$$

denote the equation whose roots are to be found. Then if we take a set of rectangular coordinate axes and plot the graph of

$$(2) \qquad\qquad y = f(x),$$

it is evident that the abscissas of the points where the graph crosses the x-axis are the real roots of the given equation, for at these points y is zero and therefore (1) is satisfied. Approximate values for the real roots of any numerical equation can therefore be found from the graph of the given equation. It is not necessary, however, to draw the complete graph. Only the portions in the neighborhood of the points where it crosses the x-axis are needed.

Even more useful and important than a graph is the following fundamental theorem:

If f(x) *is continuous from* x = a *to* x = b *and if* f(a) *and* f(b) *have opposite signs, then there is at least one real root between* a *and* b.

This theorem is evident from an inspection of Fig. 7, for if $f(a)$ and

$f(b)$ have opposite signs the graph must cross the x-axis at least once between $x = a$ and $x = b$.

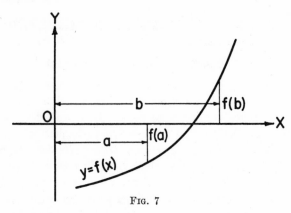

FIG. 7

In most cases the approximate values of the real roots of $f(x) = 0$ are most easily found by writing the equation in the form

(3) $f_1(x) = f_2(x)$

and then plotting on the same axes the two equations

$$y_1 = f_1(x), \qquad y_2 = f_2(x).$$

The abscissas of the points of intersection of these two curves are the real roots of the given equation, for at these points $y_1 = y_2$ and therefore $f_1(x) = f_2(x)$. Hence (3) is satisfied and consequently $f(x) = 0$ is likewise satisfied.

We shall now apply the foregoing methods to two examples.

Example 1. Find approximate values for the real roots of

$$x \log_{10} x = 1.2.$$

Solution. We write the equation in the form $f(x) = x \log_{10} x - 1.2$, assign positive integral values to x, and compute the corresponding values of $f(x)$, as shown in the table below. Since $f(2)$ and $f(3)$ have opposite signs, a root lies between $x = 2$ and $x = 3$, and this is the only real root.

x	1	2	3	4
$f(x)$	-1.2	-0.6	$+0.23$	$+1.21$

The approximate value of the roots can also be found by writing the equation in the form

$$\log_{10} x = \frac{1.2}{x}$$

and then plotting the graphs of $y_1 = \log_{10} x$ and $y_2 = 1.2/x$. The abscissa of the point of intersection of these graphs is the desired root.

Example 2. Find the approximate value of the root of

$$3x - \cos x - 1 = 0.$$

Solution. Since this equation is the difference of two functions, we can write it in the form

$$3x - 1 = \cos x.$$

Then we plot separately on the same set of axes the two equations

$$y_1 = 3x - 1,$$
$$y_2 = \cos x.$$

The abscissa of the point of intersection of the graphs of these equations is seen to be about 0.6 (Fig. 8).

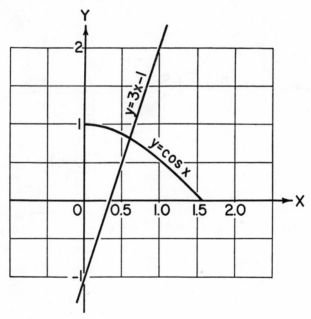

Fig. 8

Of course we could also find this approximate value by computing a table of values of the function $f(x) = 3x - \cos x - 1$ and noting the change in sign of $f(x)$, as in Ex. 1.

64. The Method of Interpolation, or of False Position (Regula Falsi). The oldest method for computing the real roots of a numerical equation is the method of false position, or " regula falsi." In this method we find two numbers x_1 and x_2 between which the root lies. These numbers should be as close together as possible. Since the root lies between x_1 and x_2 the graph of $y = f(x)$ must cross the x-axis between $x = x_1$ and $x = x_2$, and y_1 and y_2 must have opposite signs.

Now since any portion of a smooth curve is practically straight for a short distance, it is legitimate to assume that the change in $f(x)$ is proportional to the change in x over a short interval, as in the case of linear interpolation from logarithmic and trigonometric tables. The method of false position is based on this principle, for it assumes that the graph of $y = f(x)$ is a straight line between the points (x_1, y_1) and (x_2, y_2), these points being on opposite sides of the x-axis.

To derive a formula for computing the root, let Fig. 9 represent a magni-

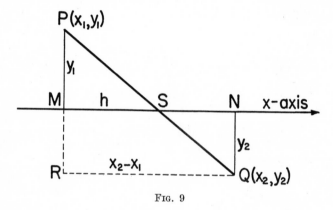

FIG. 9

fied view of that part of the graph between (x_1, y_1) and (x_2, y_2). Then from the similar triangles PMS and PRQ we have

$$\frac{MS}{MP} = \frac{RQ}{RP}, \quad \text{or} \quad \frac{h}{|y_1|} = \frac{x_2 - x_1}{|y_1| + |y_2|}.$$

(1) $$\therefore \quad h = \frac{(x_2 - x_1)\,|y_1|}{|y_1| + |y_2|}.$$

The value of the desired root, under the assumptions made, is

$$x = x_1 + MS = x_1 + h.$$

Hence

(2) $$x = x_1 + \frac{(x_2 - x_1)\,|y_1|}{|y_1| + |y_2|}.$$

This value of x is not, however, the true value of the root, because the graph of $y = f(x)$ is not a perfectly straight line between the points P and Q. It is merely a closer approximation to the true root.

In the practical application of the regula falsi method we compute a short table of corresponding values of x and $f(x)$ for equidistant values of x—units, tenths, hundredths, etc. Then by means of (1) we compute corrections to be applied to the previously obtained approximate values. The following examples should make the method clear.

Example 1. Compute the real root of

$$x \log_{10} x - 1.2 = 0$$

correct to five decimal places.

Solution. The short table in Example 1 of the preceding article shows that the root lies between 2 and 3, and that it is nearer 3. Hence we make out the following table and then compute the corrections by (1).

	x	y
1st	2	-0.6
approx.	3	$+0.23$
Diff.	1	0.83

$$h_1 = \frac{1 \times 0.6}{0.83} = 0.72.$$

$$x^{(1)} = 2 + 0.72 = 2.72.$$

	x	y
2nd	2.7	-0.04
approx.	2.8	$+0.05$
	0.1	0.09

$$h_2 = \frac{0.1 \times 0.04}{0.09} = 0.044.$$

$$x^{(2)} = 2.74.$$

	x	y
3rd	2.74	-0.0006
approx.	2.75	$+0.0081$
	0.01	0.0087

$$h_3 = \frac{0.01 \times 0.0006}{0.0087} = 0.0007.$$

$$x^{(3)} = 2.74 + 0.0007 = 2.7407.$$

	x	y
4th	2.7406	-0.000039
approx.	2.7407	$+0.000045$
	0.0001	0.000084

$$h_4 = \frac{0.0001 \times 0.000039}{0.000084}$$
$$= 0.000046.$$
$$x^{(4)} = 2.7406 + 0.000046$$
$$= 2.74065.$$

Remark. In examples of this kind it is necessary to use logarithms to more decimal places with each succeeding approximation. In this example six-place logarithms were used in the last approximation.

Example 2. Find the real root of the equation

$$3x - \cos x - 1 = 0.$$

Solution. In Ex. 2 of the preceding article we found the approximate value of this root to be 0.6. Hence we begin by computing the following short table of corresponding values of x and $f(x) = 3x - \cos x - 1 = y$. It is evident from the table that the root lies between 0.60 and 0.61. Hence we proceed with the first approximation by the regula falsi method.

x	$f(x)$
0.60	-0.025
0.61	$+0.010$
0.62	$+0.046$

	x	y	
1st	0.60	-0.025	$h_1 = \dfrac{0.01 \times 0.025}{0.035} = 0.0071.$
approx.	0.61	$+0.010$	
Diff.	0.01	0.035	$x^{(1)} = 0.60 + 0.0071 = 0.607.$

2nd	0.607	-0.00036	$h_2 = \dfrac{0.001 \times 0.00036}{0.00357}$
approx.	0.608	$+0.00321$	$= 0.000101.$
	0.001	0.00357	$x^{(2)} = 0.6071.$

3rd	0.6071	0.00000	$h_3 = 0.$
approx.	0.6072	0.00035	$x^{(3)} = 0.60710.$
	0.0001	0.00035	

65. Solution by Repeated Plotting on a Larger Scale. The following method is the graphical equivalent of the regula falsi method and has the advantage of giving a visual representation of the approximating process.

Suppose an approximate value of the root has been found from a graph or otherwise. Plot on a large scale a small part of the graph of $y = f(x)$ for values of x near the desired root, so that one can see more clearly about where the graph crosses the x-axis. An additional figure of the root can be read from this graph. Then plot on a still larger scale a small part of the graph for values of x near the improved value of the root (the value just found), and continue the process in this manner until the root has been found to as many figures as desired. The following example should make the method clear.

Example. Find the positive real root of

$$x - \cos\left(\frac{0.7854 - x\sqrt{1 - x^2}}{1 - 2x^2}\right) = 0.$$

Solution. We first compute the value of the left member for several values of x, as given in table (1). This table shows that a root lies between 0.5 and 0.6. Hence we plot the graph of the given equation from $x = 0.5$ to $x = 0.6$ and assume it to be a straight line within this interval. The result is Fig. 10 (a), and it shows at a glance that the root is about 0.56 or 0.57. We therefore compute table (2) and plot the results as

	x	$f(x)$		x	$f(x)$
(1)	0.4	-0.42	(3)	0.579	-0.001
	0.5	-0.26		0.580	$+0.003$
	0.6	$+0.14$			
(2)	0.56	-0.092	(4)	0.5793	-0.0005
	0.57	-0.030		0.5794	$+0.0003$
	0.58	$+0.003$			

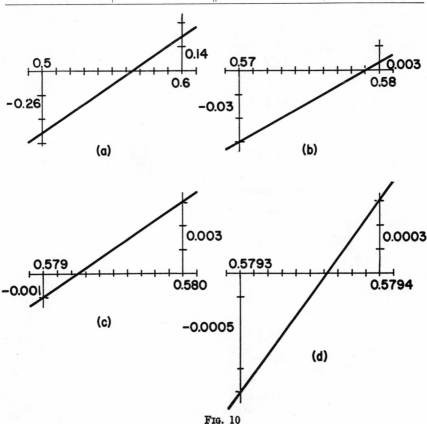

FIG. 10

shown in Fig. 10 (b). This graph shows that the root is about 0.579. Continuing the process in this manner by computing tables (3) and (4) and plotting the results on still larger scales as shown in Figs. 10 (c) and 10 (d), we find the desired root to be $x = 0.57936$ to five figures.

This method and the regula falsi method are particularly valuable for finding the roots of complicated equations such as the one solved above.

66. The Newton-Raphson Method. When the derivative of $f(x)$ is a simple expression and easily found, the real roots of $f(x) = 0$ can be computed rapidly by a process called the Newton-Raphson method. The underlying idea of the method is due to Newton, but the method as now used is due to Raphson.*

To derive a formula for computing real roots by this method let a denote an approximate value of the desired root, and let h denote the correction which must be applied to a to give the exact value of the root, so that

$$x = a + h.$$

The equation $f(x) = 0$ then becomes

$$f(a + h) = 0.$$

Expanding this by Taylor's theorem, we have

$$f(a + h) = f(a) + hf'(a) + \frac{h^2}{2} f''(a + \theta h), \ 0 \leqq \theta \leqq 1.$$

Hence

$$f(a) + hf'(a) + \frac{h^2}{2} f''(a + \theta h) = 0.$$

Now if h is relatively small, we may neglect the term containing h^2 and get the simple relation

$$f(a) + hf'(a) = 0,$$

from which

(1) $$h_1 = - \frac{f(a)}{f'(a)}.$$

The improved value of the root is then

(2) $$a_1 = a + h_1 = a - \frac{f(a)}{f'(a)}.$$

* See Cajori's *History of Mathematics*, p. 203.

The succeeding approximations are

$$a_2 = a_1 + h_2 = a_1 - \frac{f(a_1)}{f'(a_1)}, \qquad a_3 = a_2 - \frac{f(a_2)}{f'(a_2)},$$

$$\ldots a_n = a_{n-1} - \frac{f(a_{n-1})}{f'(a_{n-1})}.$$

Equation (1) is the fundamental formula in the Newton-Raphson process.. It is evident from this formula that the larger the derivative $f'(x)$ the smaller is the correction which must be applied to get the correct value of the root. This means that when the graph is nearly vertical where it crosses the x-axis the correct value of the root can be found with great rapidity and very little labor. If, on the other hand, the numerical value of the derivative $f'(x)$ should be small in the neighborhood of the root, the values of h given by (1) would be large and the computation of the root by this method would be a slow process or might even fail altogether. The Newton-Raphson method should never be used when the graph of $f(x)$ is nearly horizontal where it crosses the x-axis. The process will evidently fail if $f'(x) = 0$ in the neighborhood of the root. In such cases the regula falsi method should be used.

We shall now apply the Newton-Raphson method to two examples.

Example 1. Compute to four decimal places the real root of

$$x^2 + 4 \sin x = 0.$$

Solution. Since the term x^2 is positive for all real values of x, it is evident that the equation will be satisfied only by a negative value of x. We find from a graph that an approximate value of the root is -1.9. Since $f(x) = x^2 + 4 \sin x$ and $f'(x) = 2x + 4 \cos x$, we have from (1)

$$h_1 = -\frac{(-1.9)^2 + 4 \sin(-1.9)}{2(-1.9) + 4 \cos(-1.9)} = -\frac{3.61 - 3.78}{-3.8 - 1.293}$$

$$= -0.03.$$

$$\therefore \quad a_1 = -1.9 - 0.03 = -1.93.$$

$$h_2 = -\frac{(-1.93)^2 + 4 \sin(-1.93)}{2(-1.93) + 4 \cos(-1.93)} = -\frac{-0.0198}{-5.266}$$

$$= -0.0038.$$

$$\therefore \quad \underline{a_2 = -1.9338.}$$

This result is correct to its last figure, as will be shown later.

Example 2.   Find by the Newton-Raphson method the real root of

$$3x - \cos x - 1 = 0.$$

Solution.   Here

$$f(x) = 3x - \cos x - 1,$$
$$f'(x) = 3 + \sin x.$$

We found graphically (Fig. 8) that the approximate value of the root is 0.61.   Hence

$$h_1 = -\frac{3(0.61) - \cos(0.61) - 1}{3 + \sin(0.61)} = -\frac{0.010}{3.57}$$

$$= -0.00290.$$

$$\therefore \quad a_1 = 0.61 - 0.0029 = 0.6071.$$

$$h_2 = -\frac{3(0.6071) - \cos(0.6071) - 1}{3 + \sin(0.6071)}$$

$$= 0.00000381.$$

$$\therefore \quad a_2 = 0.60710381.$$

This result also is true to its last figure.

It will be observed that the root was obtained to a higher degree of accuracy and with less labor by this method than by the regula falsi method.

67. Geometric Significance of the Newton-Raphson Method.   The regula falsi method assumes that the graph of the given function is replaced by the chord joining (x_1, y_1) and (x_2, y_2).   No such geometric assumption was made in deriving the formula for computing the roots by the Newton-Raphson method, but the formula has a simple geometric significance nevertheless.

Let Fig. 11 represent a magnified view of the graph of $y = f(x)$ where it crosses the x-axis.   Suppose we draw a tangent from the point P whose abscissa is a.   This tangent will intersect the x-axis in some point T. Then let us draw another tangent from P_1 whose abscissa is OT.   This tangent will meet the x-axis in some point T_1 between T and S.   Then we may draw a third tangent from P_2 whose abscissa is OT_1, this tangent cutting the x-axis at a point T_2 between T_1 and S, and so on.   It is evident intuitively that if the curvature of the graph does not change sign between P and S the points $T, T_1, T_2, \cdots$ will approach the point S as a limit; that is, the intercepts $OT, OT_1, OT_2, \cdots$ will approach the intercept OS as a limit.   But OS represents the real root of the equation whose graph is drawn. Hence the quantities $OT, OT_1, OT_2, \cdots$ are successive approximations to the desired root. This is the geometric significance of the Newton-Raphson process.

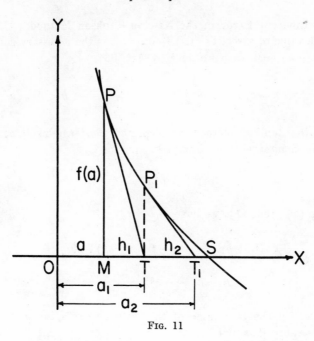

FIG. 11

To derive the fundamental formula from this figure let $MT = h_1$, $TT_1 = h_2$, etc. The slope of the graph at P is $f'(a)$. But from the figure we have

$$PM = f(a), \text{ and slope at } P = \tan \angle XTP = -\frac{f(a)}{h_1}.$$

Hence

$$f'(a) = -\frac{f(a)}{h_1}, \text{ or } h_1 = -\frac{f(a)}{f'(a)},$$

which is the fundamental formula of the Newton-Raphson method. From the triangle P_1TT_1 we find in exactly the same way

$$h_2 = -\frac{f(a_1)}{f'(a_1)}.$$

From the preceding discussion it is evident that in the Newton-Raphson method the graph of the given function is replaced by a tangent at each successive step in the approximation process.

The Newton-Raphson method should not be used when either $f'(x) = 0$ or $f''(x) = 0$ near the desired root. Use the method of enlarged graphs (Art. 65) in such cases.

68. The Inherent Error in the Newton-Raphson Method. If a is an approximate value of a root of $f(x) = 0$ and h is the necessary correction, so that $f(a + h) = 0$, then we have by Art. 66

$$(1) \qquad f(a) + hf'(a) + \frac{h^2}{2} f''(a + \theta h) = 0, \ 0 < \theta < 1.$$

In the Newton-Raphson method we neglected the term involving h^2 and got an approximate value h_1 from the equation

$$(2) \qquad\qquad f(a) + h_1 f'(a) = 0.$$

Subtracting (2) from (1), we have

$$(h - h_1)f'(a) + \frac{h^2}{2} f''(a + \theta h) = 0.$$

$$(3) \qquad\qquad \therefore \quad h - h_1 = - h^2 \frac{f''(a + \theta h)}{2f'(a)}.$$

Now since h is the true value of the required correction and h_1 is its approximate value, it is plain that $h - h_1$ is the error in h_1. The error in h_1 is thus given by (3). Let M denote the maximum value of $f''(x)$ in the neighborhood of $a + h_1$. Then

$$(4) \qquad\qquad h - h_1 = - \frac{h^2 M}{2f'(a)}.$$

Our next problem is to express this error in terms of the known quantity h_1.

Clearing (4) of fractions and transposing, we have

$$M h^2 + 2f'(a)h = 2f'(a)h_1.$$

$$\therefore \quad h = \frac{-f'(a) + \sqrt{[f'(a)]^2 + 2Mf'(a)h_1}}{M}$$

$$= \frac{1}{M}\left[-f'(a) + f'(a)\left(1 + \frac{2Mh_1}{f'(a)} \right)^{\frac{1}{2}} \right].$$

Now expanding the quantity $[1 + 2Mh_1/f'(a)]^{\frac{1}{2}}$ by the binomial theorem, we have

$$h = \frac{1}{M}\left[-f'(a) + f'(a)\left(1 + \frac{Mh_1}{f'(a)} - \frac{1}{2}\frac{M^2h_1{}^2}{[f'(a)]^2} + \frac{1}{2}\frac{M^3h_1{}^3}{[f'(a)]^3}\right)\right]$$

$$= \frac{1}{M}\left(-f'(a) + f'(a) + Mh_1 - \frac{1}{2}\frac{M^2h_1{}^2}{f'(a)} + \frac{1}{2}\frac{M^3h_1{}^3}{[f'(a)]^2}\right)$$

$$= h_1 - \frac{Mh_1{}^2}{2f'(a)} + \frac{M^2h_1{}^3}{2[f'(a)]^2}\cdots$$

Hence

(5) $$\text{Error} = h - h_1 = -\frac{Mh_1{}^2}{2f'(a)} + \frac{M^2h_1{}^3}{2[f'(a)]^2}.$$

Since h_1 is always a small decimal, it is evident that the principal part of the error is contained in the first term on the right-hand side of (5), so that we may neglect the term involving $h_1{}^3$. The formula for the error thus reduces to

(6) $$E_1 \leqq \left|\frac{Mh_1{}^2}{2f'(a)}\right|.$$

This is the error in a_1. The error in a_n is therefore

(7) $$E_n \leqq \left|\frac{Mh_n{}^2}{2f'(a_{n-1})}\right|.$$

Now in most equations which one would solve by the Newton-Raphson method the quantity $M/2f'(a)$ is not greater than 1. Suppose, therefore, that $|M/2f'(a_{n-1})| \leqq 1$. Then (7) reduces to

(8) $$|E_n| \leqq h_n{}^2.$$

This result is most important; for it tells us that if h_n begins with m zeros when expressed as a decimal fraction, then $h_n{}^2$ begins with $2m$ zeros. This means that when the first significant figure in h is less than 7, we may safely carry the division of $f(a_{n-1})/f'(a_{n-1})$ to $2m$ decimal places; for the error in the quotient will be less than half a unit in the $2m$th decimal place. Stated otherwise, *the number of reliable significant figures in* h *is equal to the number of zeros between the decimal point and first significant figure,* provided the number of reliable figures in both $f(a_{n-1})$ and $f'(a_{n-1})$ is as great as the number of zeros preceding the first significant figure in h. Hence in finding the correction h from the relation $h = -\dfrac{f(a)}{f'(a)}$, the divisions of $f(a)$ by $f'(a)$ should be carried out to only one more significant figure than the number of zeros between the decimal point and first significant figure.

We thus have a simple method for determining the accuracy of the roots found by the Newton-Raphson method, and this fact makes this method much superior to the regula falsi method when the root is desired to several decimal places.

It is now clear why we were able to say in Exs. 1 and 2 of Art. 66 that the results obtained were true to the last figure in each case.

69. A Special Procedure for Algebraic Equations. Many algebraic equations can be solved by first removing some of the known real roots by synthetic division and then solving the resulting depressed equation by the easiest method available. For example, if the depressed equation is a quadratic, it can always be solved by the quadratic formula. The following example illustrates the method.

Example. Find all the roots of

$$x^4 - 26x^2 + 49x - 25 = 0$$

Solution. Since the graph of $y = f(x) = x^4 - 26x^2 + 49x - 25$ crosses the y-axis at $(0, -25)$, it is plain that the given equation has at least two real roots. By assigning integral values to x and computing the corresponding values of $f(x)$, we find that these roots are near -6 and 4, respectively. They are found more accurately by the Newton-Raphson method to be -5.916 and 3.876. Now removing these roots from the given equation by synthetic division, we have

1	0	-26	49	-25	
	-5.916	34.999	-53.238	25.072	$(-5.916$
1	-5.916	8.999	-4.238	$(3.876$	
	3.876	-7.907	4.233		
1	-2.040	1.092			

Neglecting the remainder terms in each division, we have

$$x^2 - 2.040x + 1.092 = 0$$

for the depressed equation. Solving this by the quadratic formula, we get

$$x = 1.020 \pm 0.227i$$

as the remaining roots. As a check on the computation, we have

Sum of roots $= 0.000$,

Product of roots $= -25.038$,

which is a satisfactory check.

It is sometimes desirable to know the nature of the roots of a cubic or quartic equation before attempting to find them. For a thorough discussion of the nature of the roots of these equations, see Burnside and Panton's *Theory of Equations*, Vol. I.

70. The Method of Iteration. When a numerical equation $f(x) = 0$ can be expressed in the form

(1) $x = \phi(x)$,

the real roots can be found by the process of *iteration*. This is the method which was used for inverse interpolation in Art. 29. The process is this: We find from a graph or otherwise an approximate value x_0 of the desired root. We then substitute this in the right-hand member of (1) and get a better approximation $x^{(1)}$, given by the equation

$$x^{(1)} = \phi(x_0).$$

Then the succeeding approximations are

$$x^{(2)} = \phi(x^{(1)}),$$
$$x^{(3)} = \phi(x^{(2)}),$$
$$\cdot \quad \cdot \quad \cdot \quad \cdot \quad \cdot \quad \cdot$$
$$x^{(n)} = \phi(x^{(n-1)}).$$

We shall apply the process to two examples.

Example 1. Find by the method of iteration a real root of

$$2x - \log_{10} x = 7.$$

Solution. The given equation can be written in the form

$$x = \tfrac{1}{2}(\log_{10} x + 7).$$

We find from the intersection of the graphs $y_1 = 2x - 7$ and $y_2 = \log_{10} x$ that an approximate value of the root is 3.8. Hence we have

$$x^{(1)} = \tfrac{1}{2}(\log 3.8 + 7) = 3.79,$$
$$x^{(2)} = \tfrac{1}{2}(\log 3.79 + 7) = 3.7893,$$
$$x^{(3)} = \tfrac{1}{2}(\log 3.7893 + 7) = \underline{3.7893}.$$

Since $x^{(3)}$ is the same as $x^{(2)}$, we do not repeat the process but take 3.7893 as the correct result to five figures. The iteration process is the shortest and easiest method for working this example.

Example 2. The method of iteration is especially useful for finding the real roots of an equation given in the form of an infinite series. To find an expression for the probable error (see Art. 133) of a single measurement of a set, one procedure is to find the real root of the following equation (see page 413):

$$\rho - \frac{\rho^3}{3} + \frac{\rho^5}{10} - \frac{\rho^7}{42} + \frac{\rho^9}{216} - \frac{\rho^{11}}{1320} + \cdots = 0.4431135,$$

or

(a) $$\rho = \frac{\rho^3}{3} - \frac{\rho^5}{10} + \frac{\rho^7}{42} - \frac{\rho^9}{216} + \frac{\rho^{11}}{1320} + 0.4431135.$$

We shall now find the value of ρ to six decimal places.

Solution. Neglecting all powers of ρ higher than the first, we find an approximate value of ρ to be 0.44. Hence we start with this value and substitute it in the right-hand member of (a). The result is

$$\rho^{(1)} = \frac{(0.44)^3}{3} - \frac{(0.44)^5}{10} + \frac{(0.44)^7}{42} - \frac{(0.44)^9}{216} + \frac{(0.44)^{11}}{1320} + 0.4431$$

$$= 0.4699 = 0.47, \text{ say.}$$

Then the second approximation is

$$\rho^{(2)} = \frac{(0.47)^3}{3} - \frac{(0.47)^5}{10} + \frac{(0.47)^7}{42} - \frac{(0.47)^9}{216} + \frac{(0.47)^{11}}{1320} + 0.44311$$

$$= 0.47554 = 0.476, \text{ say.}$$

Writing (a) in the form

$$\rho = \phi(\rho),$$

we find the succeeding approximations to be

$$\rho^{(3)} = \phi(0.476) = 0.4767,$$
$$\rho^{(4)} = \phi(0.4767) = 0.47689,$$
$$\rho^{(5)} = \phi(0.47689) = 0.476927,$$
$$\rho^{(6)} = \phi(0.476927) = 0.476934,$$
$$\rho^{(7)} = \phi(0.476934) = 0.476936.$$

This last value is correct to its last figure.*

The reader will observe that the iteration process converges slowly in this example. This is due to the nature of the given equation. In Ex. 1 the convergence was rapid.

Note. Usually there are two or more ways in which an equation $f(x) = 0$ can be written in the form $x = \phi(x)$. It is not a matter of indifference as to which way it is written before starting the iteration process, for in

* The value of ρ correct to ten decimal places is 0.4769362762.

some forms the process will not converge at all. An example of this is given in Art. 74.

71. Convergence of the Iteration Process. We shall now determine the condition under which the iteration process converges. The true value of the root satisfies the equation

$$x = \phi(x),$$

and the first approximation satisfies

$$x^{(1)} = \phi(x_0).$$

Subtracting this equation from the preceding, we have

(1) $$x - x^{(1)} = \phi(x) - \phi(x_0).$$

By the theorem of mean value the right-hand member of (1) can be written

$$\phi(x) - \phi(x_0) = (x - x_0)\phi'(\xi_0), \quad x_0 \leqq \xi_0 \leqq x.$$

Hence (1) becomes

$$x - x^{(1)} = (x - x_0)\phi'(\xi_0).$$

A similar equation holds for all succeeding approximations, so that

$$x - x^{(2)} = (x - x^{(1)})\phi'(\xi_1),$$
$$x - x^{(3)} = (x - x^{(2)})\phi'(\xi_2),$$
$$\cdot \quad \cdot \quad \cdot \quad \cdot \quad \cdot \quad \cdot \quad \cdot \quad \cdot \quad \cdot \quad \cdot$$
$$x - x^{(n)} = (x - x^{(n-1)})\phi'(\xi_{n-1}).$$

Multiplying together all these equations, member for member, and dividing the result through by the common factors $x - x^{(1)}$, $x - x^{(2)}, \cdots x - x^{(n-1)}$, we get

(2) $$x - x^{(n)} = (x - x_0)\phi'(\xi_0)\phi'(\xi_1) \cdots \phi'(\xi_{n-1}).$$

Now if the maximum absolute value of $\phi'(x)$ is less than 1 throughout the interval (x_0, x), so that each of the quantities $\phi'(\xi_0)$, $\phi'(\xi_1)$, etc. is not greater than a proper fraction m, we get from (2)

(3) $$| x - x^{(n)} | \leqq | x - x_0 | \, m^n.$$

Since the right-hand member of (3) approaches zero as n becomes large, we can make the error $x - x^{(n)}$ as small as we please by repeating the iteration process a sufficient number of times.

The condition, then, for convergence is that $| \phi'(x) |$ be less than 1 in the neighborhood of the desired root, the smaller the value of $\phi'(x)$ the more rapid the convergence. This condition was satisfied in Examples 1 and 2 above.

72. Geometry of the Iteration Process. It is instructive to look at the geometric picture of the iteration process. For simplicity we denote the successive approximations to the root by $x_0, x_1, x_2, x_3, \cdots, x_n$. Then the relations

$$x_1 = \phi(x_0)$$
$$x_2 = \phi(x_1)$$
$$x_3 = \phi(x_2), \text{ etc.,}$$

can be pictured as points by the following geometric construction:

Draw the graphs of $y_1 = x$ and $y_2 = \phi(x)$, as shown in Figure 12. Since $|\phi'(x)| < 1$ for convergence, the inclination of the curve $y_2 = \phi(x)$ must be less than $45°$ in the neighborhood of x_0. This fact has been observed in constructing the graph.

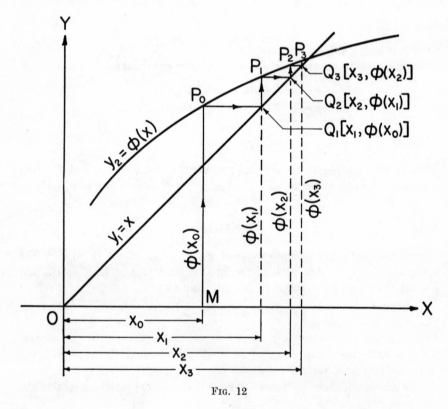

FIG. 12

Now to trace the convergence of the iteration process, draw the ordinate $\phi(x_0)$. Then from the point P_0 draw a line parallel to OX until it intersects the line $y_1 = x$ at the point $Q_1[x_1, \phi(x_0)]$. Note that this point Q_1 is the geometric representation of the first iteration equation $x_1 = \phi(x_0)$. Then draw $Q_1 P_1, P_1 Q_2, Q_2 P_2, P_2 Q_3$, etc., as indicated by the arrows in the figure. The points $Q_1, Q_2, Q_3 \cdots$ thus approach the point of intersection of the curves $y_1 = x$ and $y_2 = \phi(x)$ as the iteration proceeds. Note that the coordinates of these Q's satisfy the corresponding iteration equations.

The reader should draw a curve $y_2 = \phi(x)$ with inclination greater than $45°$ in the neighborhood of x_0 and then proceed with the construction as outlined above. He will find that the points Q_1, Q_2, etc. recede farther and farther away from the intersection point of the graphs and that the successive approximations x_1, x_2, etc. get worse as the iteration proceeds.

II. SIMULTANEOUS EQUATIONS IN SEVERAL UNKNOWNS

The real roots of simultaneous algebraic and transcendental equations in several unknowns can be found either by the Newton-Raphson method or by the method of iteration. We shall give an outline of each method for the cases of two unknowns and three unknowns. The reader will have no difficulty in extending both methods to the case of any number of unknowns should the necessity arise for doing so.

73. The Newton-Raphson Method for Simultaneous Equations.

Let us consider first the case of two equations in two unknowns. Let the given equations be

$$(1) \qquad \phi(x, y) = 0,$$

$$(2) \qquad \psi(x, y) = 0.$$

Now if x_0, y_0 be approximate values of a pair of roots and h, k be corrections, so that

$$x = x_0 + h,$$
$$y = y_0 + k,$$

then (1) and (2) become

$$(3) \qquad \phi(x_0 + h, y_0 + k) = 0,$$
$$(4) \qquad \psi(x_0 + h, y_0 + k) = 0.$$

Expanding (3) and (4) by Taylor's theorem for a function of two variables, we have

$$(5) \qquad \phi(x_0 + h, y_0 + k) = \phi(x_0, y_0) + h\left(\frac{\partial \phi}{\partial x}\right)_0 + k\left(\frac{\partial \phi}{\partial y}\right)_0$$

$+$ terms in higher powers of h and $k = 0$.

(6) $\psi(x_0 + h, y_0 + k) = \psi(x_0, y_0) + h \left(\dfrac{\partial \psi}{\partial x}\right)_0 + k \left(\dfrac{\partial \psi}{\partial y}\right)_0$

$+$ terms in higher powers of h and $k = 0$.

Now since h and k are relatively small, we neglect their squares, products. and higher powers, and then (5) and (6) become simply

(7) $\phi(x_0, y_0) + h \left(\dfrac{\partial \phi}{\partial x}\right)_0 + k \left(\dfrac{\partial \phi}{\partial y}\right)_0 = 0,$

(8) $\psi(x_0, y_0) + h \left(\dfrac{\partial \psi}{\partial x}\right)_0 + k \left(\dfrac{\partial \psi}{\partial y}\right)_0 = 0.$

Solving these by determinants, we find the first corrections to be

(9) $h_1 = \dfrac{\begin{vmatrix} -\phi(x_0, y_0) & \left(\dfrac{\partial \phi}{\partial y}\right)_0 \\[2ex] -\psi(x_0, y_0) & \left(\dfrac{\partial \psi}{\partial y}\right)_0 \end{vmatrix}}{D},$

(10) $k_1 = \dfrac{\begin{vmatrix} \left(\dfrac{\partial \phi}{\partial x}\right)_0 & -\phi(x_0, y_0) \\[2ex] \left(\dfrac{\partial \psi}{\partial x}\right)_0 & -\psi(x_0, y_0) \end{vmatrix}}{D},$

where

(11) $D = \begin{vmatrix} \left(\dfrac{\partial \phi}{\partial x}\right)_0 & \left(\dfrac{\partial \phi}{\partial y}\right)_0 \\[2ex] \left(\dfrac{\partial \psi}{\partial x}\right)_0 & \left(\dfrac{\partial \psi}{\partial y}\right)_0 \end{vmatrix}.$

Additional corrections can be found by repeated applications of these formulas with the improved values of x and y substituted at each step.

The notation $(\partial \phi / \partial x)_0$ means the value of $\partial \phi / \partial x$ when x_0 and y_0 are substituted for x and y. Similarly, $(\partial \phi / \partial x)_1$ means the value of $\partial \phi / \partial x$ when $x = x^{(1)}$, $y = y^{(1)}$; and so on.

In the case of three equations in three unknowns,

$$\phi(x, y, z) = 0,$$
$$\psi(x, y, z) = 0,$$
$$\chi(x, y, z) = 0,$$

let h, k, l, denote corrections to the approximate values x_0, y_0, z_0, respec-

tively. Then proceeding exactly as in the case of two equations, we get
the three simple equations

$$\phi(x_0, y_0, z_0) + h \left(\frac{\partial \phi}{\partial x}\right)_0 + k \left(\frac{\partial \phi}{\partial y}\right)_0 + l \left(\frac{\partial \phi}{\partial z}\right)_0 = 0,$$

$$\psi(x_0, y_0, z_0) + h \left(\frac{\partial \psi}{\partial x}\right)_0 + k \left(\frac{\partial \psi}{\partial y}\right)_0 + l \left(\frac{\partial \psi}{\partial z}\right)_0 = 0,$$

$$\chi(x_0, y_0, z_0) + h \left(\frac{\partial \chi}{\partial x}\right)_0 + k \left(\frac{\partial \chi}{\partial y}\right)_0 + l \left(\frac{\partial \chi}{\partial z}\right)_0 = 0,$$

for determining the first corrections h_1, k_1, l_1. The process may be repeated
as many times as desired.

We shall now apply this method to a pair of simultaneous equations,
one transcendental and the other algebraic.

Example. Compute by the Newton-Raphson method a real solution of
the equations

$$\begin{cases} x + 3 \log_{10} x - y^2 = 0, \\ 2x^2 - xy - 5x + 1 = 0. \end{cases}$$

Solution. On plotting the graphs of these equations on the same set
of axes, we find that they intersect at the points $(1.4, -1.5)$ and $(3.4, 2.2)$.
We shall compute the second set of values correct to four decimal places.
Let

(1) $\phi(x, y) = x + 3 \log_{10} x - y^2$,

(2) $\psi(x, y) = 2x^2 - xy - 5x + 1$.

Then

$$\frac{\partial \phi}{\partial x} = 1 + \frac{3M}{x}, \text{ where } M = 0.43429,$$

$$\frac{\partial \phi}{\partial y} = -2y,$$

$$\frac{\partial \psi}{\partial x} = 4x - y - 5, \frac{\partial \psi}{\partial y} = -x.$$

Now since $x_0 = 3.4$, $y_0 = 2.2$, we have

$$\phi(x_0, y_0) = 0.1545, \qquad \psi(x_0, y_0) = -0.72,$$

$$\left(\frac{\partial \phi}{\partial x}\right)_0 = 1.383, \qquad \left(\frac{\partial \phi}{\partial y}\right)_0 = -4.4, \qquad \left(\frac{\partial \psi}{\partial x}\right)_0 = 6.4,$$

$$\left(\frac{\partial \psi}{\partial y}\right)_0 = -3.4.$$

Substituting these values in (9), (10), (11), we find

$$h_1 = 0.157, \qquad k_1 = 0.085.$$

Hence

$$x^{(1)} = 3.4 + 0.157 = 3.557, \qquad y^{(1)} = 2.285.$$

Now substituting $x^{(1)}$ and $y^{(1)}$ for x and y in $\phi(x, y)$, $\psi(x, y)$, $\partial\phi/\partial x$, etc., we get

$$\phi(x^{(1)}, y^{(1)}) = -0.011, \qquad \psi(x^{(1)}, y^{(1)}) = 0.3945,$$

$$\left(\frac{\partial\phi}{\partial x}\right)_1 = 1.367, \qquad \left(\frac{\partial\phi}{\partial y}\right)_1 = -4.57, \qquad \left(\frac{\partial\psi}{\partial x}\right)_1 = 6.943,$$

$$\left(\frac{\partial\psi}{\partial y}\right)_1 = -3.557.$$

Substituting these in (11), (9), (10), we get

$$h_2 = -0.0685, \qquad k_2 = -0.0229.$$

Hence

$$x^{(2)} = 3.4885, \qquad y^{(2)} = 2.2621.$$

Repeating the computation with these improved values of x and y, we find

$$h_3 = -0.0013, \qquad k_3 = -0.000561.$$

Hence the third approximations are

$$x^{(3)} = \underline{3.4782}, \qquad y^{(3)} = \underline{2.26154},$$

and these are correct to the last figure.

74. The Method of Iteration for Simultaneous Equations. In the case of two equations

$$\phi(x, y) = 0,$$
$$\psi(x, y) = 0,$$

we first write the given equations in the forms

$$x = F_1(x, y),$$
$$y = F_2(x, y).$$

Then if x_0, y_0 be the approximate values of a pair of roots, improved values are found by the steps indicated below:

1st
approx.
$$\begin{cases} x^{(1)} = F_1(x_0, y_0), \\ y^{(1)} = F_2(x^{(1)}, y_0); \end{cases}$$

2nd
approx.
$$\begin{cases} x^{(2)} = F_1(x^{(1)}, y^{(1)}), \\ y^{(2)} = F_2(x^{(2)}, y^{(1)}) ; \end{cases}$$
etc.

If we are given three equations

$$\phi(x, y, z) = 0,$$
$$\psi(x, y, z) = 0,$$
$$\chi(x, y, z) = 0,$$

we would first write them in the forms

$$x = F_1(x, y, z),$$
$$y = F_2(x, y, z),$$
$$z = F_3(x, y, z).$$

The successive steps in the computation would then be:

1st
approximation
$$\begin{cases} x^{(1)} = F_1(x_0, y_0, z_0), \\ y^{(1)} = F_2(x^{(1)}, y_0, z_0), \\ z^{(1)} = F_3(x^{(1)}, y^{(1)}, z_0) ; \end{cases}$$

2nd
approximation
$$\begin{cases} x^{(2)} = F_1(x^{(1)}, y^{(1)}, z^{(1)}), \\ y^{(2)} = F_2(x^{(2)}, y^{(1)}, z^{(1)}), \\ z^{(2)} = F_3(x^{(2)}, y^{(2)}, z^{(1)}) ; \end{cases}$$
etc.

We shall now apply the interation process to the pair of equations which we have already solved (for one pair of roots) by theNewton-Raphson method:

$$\phi(x, y) = x + 3 \log_{10} x - y^2,$$
$$\psi(x, y) = 2x^2 - xy - 5x + 1.$$

Solution. We start with the approximate values $x_0 = 3.4$, $y_0 = 2.2$, as indicated by the intersection of the graphs. In our next step we are confronted with several possibilities, for the two equations can be writen in the forms $x = F_1(x, y)$, $y = F_2(x, y)$ in several ways. In the absence of further information we start out with the simplest forms, namely

$$x = y^2 - 3 \log_{10} x,$$

$$y = \frac{1}{x} + 2x - 5.$$

Then we have

$$x^{(1)} = (2.2)^2 - 3 \log_{10} 3.4 = 3.25,$$

$$y^{(1)} = \frac{1}{3.25} + 2(3.25) - 5 = 1.81;$$

$$x^{(2)} = (1.81)^2 - 3 \log_{10}(3.25) = 1.74, .$$

$$y^{(2)} = \frac{1}{1.74} + 2(1.74) - 5 = 0.95.$$

These values of x and y are evidently getting worse with each application of the iteration process. We must therefore write the given equations in some other form before attempting the iteration process again.

Without trying all possible forms we make a fresh start with the only forms that will make the process converge, namely

$$x = \sqrt{\frac{x(y+5)-1}{2}},$$

$$y = \sqrt{x + 3 \log_{10} x}.$$

Then the successive approximations are

$$\begin{cases} x^{(1)} = \sqrt{\dfrac{3.4(2.2+5)-1}{2}} = 3.426, \\ y^{(1)} = \sqrt{3.426 + 3 \log_{10} 3.426} = 2.243; \end{cases}$$

$$\begin{cases} x^{(2)} = \sqrt{\dfrac{3.426(2.243+5)-1}{2}} = 3.451, \\ y^{(2)} = \sqrt{3.451 + 3 \log_{10} 3.451} = 2.2505; \end{cases}$$

$$x^{(3)} = 3.466, \qquad y^{(3)} = 2.255;$$
$$x^{(4)} = 3.475, \qquad y^{(4)} = 2.258;$$
$$x^{(5)} = 3.480, \qquad y^{(5)} = 2.259;$$
$$x^{(6)} = 3.483, \qquad y^{(6)} = 2.260.$$

Here it is evident that the iteration process converges very slowly in this example, for after having applied the process six times we have added only one reliable figure to the approximate roots with which we started.

This example brings out two important facts in connection with the method of iteration. The first is that we must not start out blindly in working a problem by this method, for instead of improving the roots at each step we might make them decidedly worse. The second important fact brought out is that the iteration process should not be applied at all in some examples, for the convergence might be too slow, as was the case above. All this leads us to a consideration of the conditions under which the process converges. Having these conditions at hand, we can decide in advance as to the advisability of attempting a problem by iteration.

75. Convergence of the Iteration Process in the Case of Several Unknowns. To find the conditions for convergence in the case of two equations, we write them in the forms

$$x = F_1(x, y),$$
$$y = F_2(x, y).$$

These equations are satisfied by the exact values of the pair of roots x, y. The first approximations satisfy the equations

$$x^{(1)} = F_1(x_0, y_0),$$
$$y^{(1)} = F_2(x_0, y_0).$$

Subtracting these equations from the corresponding equations above, we have

(1) $$x - x^{(1)} = F_1(x, y) - F_1(x_0, y_0),$$
(2) $$y - y^{(1)} = F_2(x, y) - F_2(x_0, y_0).$$

Now applying to the right-hand side of the first equation the theorem of mean value for a function of two variables, we have

$$F_1(x, y) - F_1(x_0, y_0) = (x - x_0) \frac{\partial \bar{F}_1}{\partial x} + (y - y_0) \frac{\partial \bar{F}_1}{\partial y},$$

where

$$\frac{\partial \bar{F}_1}{\partial x} = \frac{\partial F_1[x_0 + \theta(x - x_0), y_0 + \theta(y - y_0)]}{\partial x}, \quad 0 \leq \theta \leq 1,$$

and

$$\frac{\partial \bar{F}_1}{\partial y} = \frac{\partial F_1[x_0 + \theta(x - x_0), y_0 + \theta(y - y_0)]}{\partial y}.$$

In a similar manner we get

$$F_2(x, y) - F_2(x_0, y_0) = (x - x_0) \frac{\partial \bar{F}_2}{\partial x} + (y - y_0) \frac{\partial \bar{F}_2}{\partial y}.$$

Substituting these expressions for the right-hand members of (1) and (2), we get

$$x - x^{(1)} = (x - x_0) \frac{\partial \bar{F}_1}{\partial x} + (y - y_0) \frac{\partial \bar{F}_1}{\partial y},$$

$$y - y^{(1)} = (x - x_0) \frac{\partial \bar{F}_2}{\partial x} + (y - y_0) \frac{\partial \bar{F}_2}{\partial y}.$$

Adding these two equations and considering only the absolute values of the several quantities, we have

(3) $| x - x^{(1)} | + | y - y^{(1)} | \leqq | x - x_0 | \left\{ \left| \dfrac{\partial \bar{F}_1}{\partial x} \right| + \left| \dfrac{\partial \bar{F}_2}{\partial x} \right| \right\}$

$\qquad\qquad\qquad + | y - y_0 | \left\{ \left| \dfrac{\partial \bar{F}_1}{\partial y} \right| + \left| \dfrac{\partial \bar{F}_2}{\partial y} \right| \right\}$

Now let the maximum value of either $| \partial F_1/\partial x | + | \partial F_2/\partial x |$ or $| \partial F_1/\partial y | + | \partial F_2/\partial y |$ be a proper fraction m for all points in the region (x_0, x) and (y_0, y). Then (3) becomes

$$| x - x^{(1)} | + | y - y^{(1)} | \leqq m\{ | x - x_0 | + | y - y_0 | \}.$$

This relation holds for the first approximation. For the succeeding approximations we have the similar relations

$$| x - x^{(2)} | + | y - y^{(2)} | \leqq m\{ | x - x^{(1)} | + | y - y^{(1)} | \},$$
$$| x - x^{(3)} | + | y - y^{(3)} | \leqq m\{ | x - x^{(2)} | + | y - y^{(2)} | \},$$
$$\cdots\cdots\cdots\cdots\cdots\cdots\cdots\cdots\cdots\cdots$$
$$| x - x^{(n)} | + | y - y^{(n)} | \leqq m\{ | x - x^{(n-1)} | + | y - y^{(n-1)} | \}.$$

Now multiplying together all these inequalities, member for member, and dividing through by the common factors $\{ | x - x^{(1)} | + | y - y^{(1)} \}$, $\{ | x - x^{(2)} | + | y - y^{(2)} | \}$, etc., we get

$$| x - x^{(n)} | + | y - y^{(n)} | \leqq m^n\{ | x - x_0 | + | y - y_0 | \}.$$

Since m is a proper fraction, it is clear that we can make the right-hand member of this inequality as small as we please by repeating the iteration process a sufficient number of times. This means that the errors $| x - x^{(n)} |$ and $| y - y^{(n)} |$ can be made as small as we like.

The iteration process for two unknowns therefore converges when, and only when, the two conditions $| \partial F_1/\partial x | + | \partial F_2/\partial x | < 1$ and $| \partial F_1/\partial y | + | \partial F_2/\partial y | < 1$ hold for all points in the neighborhood of (x_0, y_0). In order for the convergence to be rapid enough to make the method advisable in any given problem it is necessary that each of the quantities $| \partial F_1/\partial x | + | \partial F_2/\partial x |$ and $| \partial F_1/\partial y | + | \partial F_2/\partial y |$ be much less than 1.

We are now able to see why the convergence was so slow in the example which we attempted to work by the iteration process in Art. 74. For that example the values of the quantities named above are

$$\left| \frac{\partial F_1}{\partial x} \right| + \left| \frac{\partial F_2}{\partial x} \right| = 0.521 + 0.304 = 0.825,$$

$$\left| \frac{\partial F_1}{\partial y} \right| + \left| \frac{\partial F_2}{\partial y} \right| = 0.162 + 0 = 0.162.$$

The first is much too large for rapid convergence.

EXERCISES IX

1. Find graphically or otherwise the approximate value of a real root of the equation

$$2x - \log_{10} x = 7.$$

2. Find the approximate value of a real root of

$$x \sinh \frac{10}{x} - 15 = 0.$$

3. Compute to four decimal places by the interpolation method the root found approximately in Exercise 1 above.

4. Do the same for the root found approximately in Exercise 2.

5. Find to six decimal places by the Newton-Raphson method a real root of

$$2x - 3 \sin x - 5 = 0.$$

6. Solve $x = 0.21 \sin (0.5 + x)$ by the iteration process.

7. Find to three decimal places the smallest positive root of

$$x^x + 2x = 6.$$

8. Find the smallest positive root of

$$x \tan x = 1.28.$$

9. Find to five decimal places a root of

$$x \log_{10} x = -0.125.$$

10. Find all the roots of

$$3x^3 + 5x - 40 = 0.$$

11. Compute to six decimal places a root of

$$6\theta - 5 \sinh \theta = 0.$$

12. Find the smallest root of

$$1 - x + \frac{x^2}{(2\,!)^2} - \frac{x^3}{(3\,!)^2} + \frac{x^4}{(4\,!)^2} - \frac{x^5}{(5\,!)^2} + \cdots = 0.$$

13. Find a real solution of

$$4.2x^2 + 8.8y^2 = 1.42,$$
$$(x - 1.2)^2 + (y - 0.6)^2 = 1.$$

14. Find to five decimal places a solution of

$$\sin x = y - 1.32,$$
$$\cos y = x - 0.85.$$

15. Find all the roots of

$$\frac{d^7}{dx^7}(x^2 - \tfrac{1}{4})^7 = 0.$$

CHAPTER X

GRAEFFE'S ROOT-SQUARING METHOD FOR SOLVING ALGEBRAIC EQUATIONS

76. Introduction. The methods given in the preceding chapter, except that of Art. 69, are applicable only for finding the *real* roots of numerical equations. It is sometimes necessary to find also the complex roots of algebraic equations. In studying the stability of airplanes, for example, it is necessary to solve linear differential equations with constant coefficients. The solution of such a differential equation is effected, as is well known, by first solving an algebraic equation whose degree is equal to the order of the given differential equation. The algebraic equations which arise in stability theory are usually of the fourth, sixth, or eighth degree. A pair of complex roots indicates an oscillation, the real part of the root giving the damping factor and the imaginary part the period of oscillation.

No short and simple method exists for finding the complex roots of algebraic equations of high degree. Probably the root-squaring method of Graeffe * is the best to use in most cases. This method gives all the roots at once, both real and complex.

77. Principle of the Method. The underlying principle of Graeffe's method is this: The given equation is transformed into another whose roots are high powers of those of the original equation. The roots of the transformed equation are widely separated, and because of this fact are easily found. For example, if two of the roots of the original equation are 3 and 2, the corresponding roots of the transformed equation are 3^m and 2^m, where m is the power to which the roots of the given equation have been raised. Thus, if $m = 64$, we have $3^{64} = 10^{30.536}$, $2^{64} = 10^{19.266}$. The two roots of the given equation were of the same order of magnitude, but in the transformed equation the larger root is more than a hundred billion times as large as the smaller one. Stated otherwise, the ratio of the roots in the given equation is $\frac{2}{3}$, but in the transformed equation it is $10^{19.266}/10^{30.536} = 1/10^{11.27}$, or $2^{64}/3^{64} < 0.00000000001$. The smaller root in the transformed equation is therefore negligible in comparison with the larger one. The roots of the transformed equation are said to be separated

* *Auflösung der höheren numerischen Gleichungen*, Zurich (1837).

213

when the ratio of any root to the next larger is negligible in comparison with unity.

78. The Root-Squaring Process. The transformed equation is obtained by repeated application of a root-squaring process. The first application of this process transforms the given equation into another whose roots are the squares of those of the original equation. This second equation is then transformed into a third equation whose roots are the squares of those of the second, and therefore the fourth powers of those of the original equation. The root-squaring process is continued in this manner until the roots of the last transformed equation are completely separated.

We shall now explain the root-squaring process and show the method of applying it.

Let the given equation be

$$(78.1) \quad f(x) = a_0 x^n + a_1 x^{n-1} + a_2 x^{n-2} + \cdots + a_{n-1} x + a_n = 0.$$

Then if $x_1, x_2, \cdots x_n$ be the roots of this equation, we can write it in the equivalent form

$$(1) \qquad f(x) = a_0 (x - x_1)(x - x_2)(x - x_3) \cdots (x - x_n) = 0.$$

Now let us multiply (1) by the function

$$(2) \quad (-1)^n f(-x) = (-1)^n a_0 (-x - x_1)(-x - x_2) \cdots (-x - x_n)$$
$$= a_0 (x + x_1)(x + x_2) \cdots (x + x_n).$$

The result is

$$(78.2) \quad (-1)^n f(-x) f(x) = a_0^2 (x^2 - x_1^2)(x^2 - x_2^2) \cdots (x^2 - x_n^2).$$

Let $x^2 = y$. Then (78.2) becomes

$$(3) \qquad \phi(y) = a_0^2 (y - x_1^2)(y - x_2^2) \cdots (y - x_n^2) = 0.$$

The roots of this equation are $x_1^2, x_2^2, \cdots x_n^2$ and are thus the squares of the roots of the given equation (78.1). Hence to form an equation whose roots are the squares of those of $f(x) = 0$, we merely multiply $f(x) = 0$ by $(-1)^n f(-x)$.

This multiplication can be carried out in a simple routine manner, as we shall now show. Let us first consider the sixth-degree equation

$$f(x) = a_0 x^6 + a_1 x^5 + a_2 x^4 + a_3 x^3 + a_4 x^2 + a_5 x + a_6 = 0.$$
Then

$$(-1)^6 f(-x) = a_0 x^6 - a_1 x^5 + a_2 x^4 - a_3 x^3 + a_4 x^2 - a_5 x + a_6.$$

By actual multiplication we find

(4) $(-1)^6 f(-x) f(x) = a_0^2 x^{12} - a_1^2 \begin{vmatrix} x^{10} \\ + 2a_0 a_2 \end{vmatrix} + a_2^2 \begin{vmatrix} x^8 \\ - 2a_1 a_3 \\ + 2a_0 a_4 \end{vmatrix} - a_3^2 \begin{vmatrix} x^6 \\ 2a_2 a_4 \\ - 2a_1 a_5 \\ + 2a_0 a_6 \end{vmatrix}$

$+ a_4^2 \begin{vmatrix} x^4 \\ - 2a_3 a_5 \\ + 2a_2 a_6 \end{vmatrix} - a_5^2 \begin{vmatrix} x^2 + a_6^2 = 0. \\ + 2a_4 a_6 \end{vmatrix}$

Let us consider next a seventh-degree equation,

$$f(x) = a_0 x^7 + a_1 x^6 + a_2 x^5 + a_3 x^4 + a_4 x^3 + a_5 x^2 + a_6 x + a_7 = 0.$$

Then

$$(-1)^7 f(-x) = a_0 x^7 - a_1 x^6 + a_2 x^5 - a_3 x^4 + a_4 x^3 - a_5 x^2 + a_6 x - a_7.$$

Multiplying these equations together in the ordinary manner, as before, we find

(5) $(-1)^7 f(-x) f(x) = a_0 x^{14} - a_1^2 \begin{vmatrix} x^{12} \\ + 2a_0 a_2 \end{vmatrix} + a_2^2 \begin{vmatrix} x^{10} \\ - 2a_1 a_3 \\ + 2a_0 a_4 \end{vmatrix} - a_3^2 \begin{vmatrix} x^8 \\ + 2a_2 a_4 \\ - 2a_1 a_5 \\ + 2a_0 a_6 \end{vmatrix}$

$+ a_4^2 \begin{vmatrix} x^6 \\ - 2a_3 a_5 \\ + 2a_2 a_6 \\ - 2a_1 a_7 \end{vmatrix} - a_5^2 \begin{vmatrix} x^4 \\ + 2a_4 a_6 \\ - 2a_3 a_7 \end{vmatrix} + a_6^2 \begin{vmatrix} x^2 \\ - 2a_5 a_7 \end{vmatrix} - a_7^2 = 0.$

A glance at equations (4) and (5) shows that the law of formation of the coefficients in the squared equation is the same whether the degree of the given equation be even or odd. In practice the multiplication is carried out with detached coefficients as indicated below:

a_0	a_1	a_2	a_3	a_4	$a_5 \cdots$
a_0	$-a_1$	a_2	$-a_3$	a_4	$-a_5 \cdots$
a_0^2	$-a_1^2$	a_2^2	$-a_3^2$	a_4^2	$-a_5^2 \cdots$
	$+2a_0 a_2$	$-2a_1 a_3$	$+2a_2 a_4$	$-2a_3 a_5$	$+2a_4 a_6 \cdots$
		$+2a_0 a_4$	$-2a_1 a_5$	$+2a_2 a_6$	$-2a_3 a_7 \cdots$
			$+2a_0 a_6$	$-2a_1 a_7$	$+2a_2 a_8 \cdots$
				$+2a_0 a_8$	$-2a_1 a_9 \cdots$
					$+2a_0 a_{10} \cdots$
b_0	$\cdot b_1$	b_2	b_3	b_4	b_5

The coefficients in the new equation are the sums $b_0, b_1, b_2, \cdots b_n$ of the several columns in the scheme above. These coefficients can evidently be written down according to the following rule:

1. *The numbers in the top row are the squares of the coefficients directly above them, with alternating signs—the second, fourth, sixth, etc. squared numbers being negative.*

2. *The quantities directly under these squared numbers are the doubled products of the coefficients equally removed from the one directly overhead, the first being twice the product of the two coefficients adjacent to the one overhead, the second the doubled produce of the next two equally removed coefficients, etc.*

3. *The signs of the doubled products are changed alternately in going along the rows and also in going down the columns, the sign of the first doubled product in each row not being changed.*

We shall now apply Graeffe's method to three cases of algebraic equations.

79. Case I. Roots all Real and Unequal. Since the relations between the roots $x_1, x_2, \cdots x_n$ and coefficients $a_0, a_1, \cdots a_n$ of the general equation of the nth degree.

$$a_0 x^n + a_1 x^{n-1} + \cdots + a_{n-1} x + a_n = 0$$

are

$$\frac{a_1}{a_0} = - (x_1 + x_2 + \cdots + x_n),$$

$$\frac{a_2}{a_0} = + (x_1 x_2 + x_1 x_3 + \cdots),$$

$$\frac{a_3}{a_0} = - (x_1 x_2 x_3 + x_1 x_2 x_4 \cdots),$$

$$\cdot \quad \cdot \quad \cdot \quad \cdot \quad \cdot \quad \cdot \quad \cdot \quad \cdot \quad \cdot \quad \cdot$$

$$\frac{a_n}{a_0} = (-1)^n x_1 x_2 \cdots x_n,$$

it follows that the roots $x_1^m, x_2^m, \cdots x_n^m$ and coefficients $b_0, b_1, \cdots b_n$ of the final transformed equation

$$b_0 (x^m)^n + b_1 (x^m)^{n-1} \cdots + b_{n-1} x^m + b_n = 0$$

are connected by the corresponding relations

$$\frac{b_1}{b_0} = - (x_1^m + x_2^m + \cdots + x_n^m)$$

$$= - x_1^m \left(1 + \frac{x_2^m}{x_1^m} + \frac{x_3^m}{x_1^m} + \cdots + \frac{x_n^m}{x_1^m} \right),$$

$$\frac{b_2}{b_0} = x_1{}^m x_2{}^m + x_1{}^m x_3{}^m + \cdots = x_1{}^m x_2{}^m \left(1 + \frac{x_3{}^m}{x_2{}^m} + \frac{x_4{}^m}{x_2{}^m} + \cdots\right),$$

$$\frac{b_3}{b_0} = -\left(x_1{}^m x_2{}^m x_3{}^m + x_1{}^m x_2{}^m x_4{}^m + \cdots\right) = -x_1{}^m x_2{}^m x_3{}^m \left(1 + \frac{x_4{}^m}{x_3{}^m} + \cdots\right),$$

$$\cdots \cdots \cdots \cdots \cdots \cdots \cdots \cdots$$

$$\frac{b_n}{b_0} = (-1)^n x_1{}^m x_2{}^m \cdots x_n{}^m.$$

Now if the order of magnitude of the roots is

$$|x_1| > |x_2| > |x_3| \cdots > |x_n|,$$

it is evident that when the roots are sufficiently separated the ratios $x_2{}^m/x_1{}^m$, $x_3{}^m/x_2{}^m$, etc. are negligible in comparison with unity. Hence the relations between roots and coefficients in the final transformed equation are

$$\frac{b_1}{b_0} = -x_1{}^m, \quad \frac{b_2}{b_0} = x_1{}^m x_2{}^m, \quad \frac{b_3}{b_0} = -x_1{}^m x_2{}^m x_3{}^m,$$

$$\cdots \cdots \frac{b_n}{b_0} = (-1)^n x_1{}^m x_2{}^m x_3{}^m \cdots x_n{}^m.$$

Dividing each of these equations after the first by the preceding equation, we obtain

$$\frac{b_2}{b_1} = -x_2{}^m, \quad \frac{b_3}{b_2} = -x_3{}^m, \quad \cdots \quad \frac{b_n}{b_{n-1}} = -x_n{}^m.$$

Hence from these and the equation $b_1/b_0 = -x_1{}^m$, we get

(79. 1) $b_0 x_1{}^m + b_1 = 0, \quad b_1 x_2{}^m + b_2 = 0, \quad b_2 x_3{}^m + b_3 = 0, \cdots$

$$b_{n-1} x_n{}^m + b_n = 0.$$

The root-squaring process has thus broken up the original equation into n simple equations from which the desired roots can be found with ease.

The question naturally arises as to how many root-squarings are necessary to break up the original equation into linear fragments. The answer is that the required number of squarings depends upon (1) the ratios of the roots of the given equation and (2) the number of significant figures desired in the computed roots. Since the required roots, and therefore their ratios, are not known in advance, it is not possible to determine beforehand just how many times the root-squaring process must be repeated. This, however, is a matter of no importance, for *in practice we continue the root-*

squaring process until the doubled products in the second row have no effect on the coefficients of the next transformed equation.

Since the coefficients in the given equation are not in general all positive, the signs of the doubled products will not occur in regular order as in the literal equations which we used to illustrate the root-squaring process. The possibilities of making a mistake in the signs of these products are great, and therefore some scheme should be adopted to prevent such mistakes. As a convenient notation for reminding us at each step as to whether or not the sign is to be changed we shall write a " *c* " after each term in which the sign is to be changed and an " *n* " (for no change) after each term where the sign is not to be changed.

Furthermore, as the root-squaring process necessarily increases the coefficients in the transformed equations until they become enormously large numbers, we shall always write these coefficients as simple numbers multiplied by powers of 10.

Finally, in the successive transformations of the equations by the root-squaring process, we shall not write down the multiplier $(-1)^n f(-x)$ as was done in the scheme on page 215, but simply apply the rule stated on page 216. We shall now compute all the roots of an equation by Graeffe's method.

Example 1. Find all the roots of the equation

$$1.23x^5 - 2.52x^4 - 16.1x^3 + 17.3x^2 + 29.4x - 1.34 = 0.$$

Solution. The preliminary work of separating the roots is given on the following page and should be self-explanatory in view of what has been said above. When doubled products are too small to be written down, a star (*) is written instead.

It is evident that further squaring will simply give the squares of the coefficients in the last line of the table, and we therefore stop with the 32d powers of the roots. Then by (79.1) we have the following five simple equations:

$$(7.541 \times 10^2)x_1{}^{32} - 2.346 \times 10^{22} = 0,$$
$$(-2.346 \times 10^{22})x_2{}^{32} + 3.95 \times 10^{37} = 0,$$
$$(3.95 \times 10^{37})x_3{}^{32} - 8.744 \times 10^{46} = 0,$$
$$(-8.744 \times 10^{46})x_4{}^{32} + 2.148 \times 10^{47} = 0,$$
$$(2.148 \times 10^{47})x_5{}^{32} - 1.175 \times 10^4 = 0.$$

	x^5	x^4	x^3	x^2	x^1	x^0
Given equa.	1.23	−2.52	−16.1	17.3	29.4	−1.34
	1.513	−0.635·10 −3.961n	+2.592·10² +0.872c +0.723n	−2.993·10² −9.467n −0.068c	+8.644·10² +0.464c	−1.796
2nd powers	1.513	−4.596·10	+4.187·10²	−1.253·10³	+9.108·10²	−1.796
	2.289	−2.112·10³ +1.267n	+1.753·10⁵ −1.152c +0.028n	−1.570·10⁶ +0.763n *	+8.296·10⁵ −0.045c	−3.226
4th p.	2.289	−0.845·10³	+0.629·10⁵	−0.807·10⁶	+8.251·10⁵	−3.226
	5.240	−0.714·10⁶ +0.288n	+0.396·10¹⁰ −0.136c *	−0.651·10¹² +0.104n *	+6.808·10¹¹ *	−10.41
8th p.	5.240	−0.426·10⁶	+0.260·10¹⁰	−0.547·10¹²	+6.808·10¹¹	−10.41
	2.746·10	−1.815·10¹¹ +0.272n	+6.76·10¹⁸ −0.47c	−2.992·10²³ +0.035n	+4.635·10²³	−1.084·10²
16th p.	2.746·10	−1.543·10¹¹	+6.29·10¹⁸	−2.957·10²³	+4.635·10²³	−1.084·10²
	7.541·10²	−2.381·10²² +0.035n	+3.96·10³⁷ −0.01c	−8.744·10⁴⁶ *	+2.148·10⁴⁷	−1.175·10⁴
32nd p.	7.541·10²	−2.346·10²²	+3.95·10³⁷	−8.744·10⁴⁶	+2.148·10⁴⁷	−1.175·10⁴

Solving these by logarithms, we have

$$\log x_1 = \frac{20 + \log 2.346 - \log 7.541}{32} = 0.60915.$$

$$\therefore \quad x_1 = 4.066.$$

In a similar manner we find

$$x_2 = 2.991, \quad x_3 = 1.959, \quad x_4 = 1.0285, \quad x_5 = 0.04447.$$

The signs of these roots are yet to be determined. To do this we first apply Descartes's rule of signs and find that there can not be more than three positive roots nor more than two negative roots. Then we substitute in the given equation the approximate values ± 4, ± 3, ± 2, ± 1, ± 0.04 and see whether the positive or negative value comes nearer to satisfying the equation. In this manner we find that the roots are

$$x_1 = 4.066,$$
$$x_2 = -2.991,$$
$$x_3 = 1.959,$$
$$x_4 = -1.0285,$$
$$x_5 = 0.0445.$$

The sum of these roots is 2.050, whereas it should be $2.52/1.23 = 2.049$. The agreement is therefore as close as could be expected.

80. A Check on the Coefficients in the Root-Squared Equation. All roots found by Graeffe's method should be carefully checked by some means or other. The coefficients in the root-squared equations can be checked by a process due to H. Rainbow.* The root-squared equation (78. 2) can be written in the form

$$(80. 1) \quad (-1)^n f(x) f(-x) = F(x^2) = A_0(x^2)^n + A_1(x^2)^{n-1}$$
$$+ A_2(x^2)^{n-2} + \cdots + A_{n-1}x^2 + A_n.$$

To derive Rainbow's check formula we put $x = 1$ and $x = -1$ in (78. 1) and (80. 1). Then we have

$$f(1) = a_0 + a_1 + a_2 + \cdots + a_{n-1} + a_n = \sum_{k=0}^{k=n} a_k,$$

$$f(-1) = a_0(-1)^n + a_1(-1)^{n-1} + a_2(-1)^{n-2} + \cdots + a_{n-1}(-1) + a_n$$
$$= \sum_{k=0}^{k=n} (-1)^{n-k} a_k,$$

$$F(1) = A_0 + A_1 + A_2 + \cdots + A_{n-1} + A_n = \sum_{k=0}^{k=n} A_k.$$

* H. Rainbow, mathematician at the Research Laboratory of the Shell Oil Company, Houston, Texas.

On substituting these in (80. 1), we get

(80. 2) $$\sum_0^n A_k = (-1)^n [\sum_0^n a_k] [\sum_0^n (-1)^{n-k} a_k],$$

which is *Rainbow's check formula.*

This formula is applied as follows:

(a) Find the algebraic sum of the coefficients in any equation, either the given equation or an equation whose roots are powers of the roots of the given equation. This gives the factor $\sum_0^n a_k$.

(b) Change the signs of the coefficients of the odd powers of x in the equation mentioned in (a) and then find the algebraic sum of all the coefficients. This gives the factor $\sum_0^n (-1)^{n-k} a_k$.

(c) Find the product of the sums found in (a) and (b) and then multiply this product by $(-1)^n$. The result should agree very closely with the algebraic sum $(\sum_0^n A_k)$ of the coefficients in the root-squared equation next below the given equation.

Example 1. Let us apply Rainbow's check to the first root-squared equation in the table on page 219.

Here

$$n = 5, \qquad \sum_0^n a_k = 27.97, \qquad \sum_0^5 (-1)^{5-k} a_k = -1.09.$$

Hence
$$(-1)^5 (27.97) (-1.09) = 30.4873.$$

The sum of the coefficients in the root-squared equation is

$$\sum_0^k A_k = 30.257.$$

The lack of agreement is due to the fact that the coefficients in the root-squared equation are rounded numbers multiplied by powers of 10. If the root-squaring process is carried through without rounding any numbers, we find $\sum A = 30.4873$, as the formula requires.

Example 2. Applying Rainbow's formula to the coefficients in the 4th-power equation of p. 219, we have

$$\sum_0^5 a_k = 80,000, \qquad \sum(-1)^{5-k}a_k = -1,696,000.$$

Then

$$(-1)^5[\sum a_k][\sum(-1)^{n-k}a_k] = 136,000,000,000.$$

Now finding the sum of the coefficients in the 8th-power equation, we get $A_k = 136,000,000,000$. Here the agreement seems perfect, but such is not quite the case. The zeros occupy places of unknown digits which were cut off in rounding the squares and products. The only reliable significant figures in these sums came from the largest coefficients; that is, the coefficients containing the highest powers of 10.

Although the Rainbow formula cannot give an accurate check in a numerical example, because the coefficients in high-powered equations are so large that they must be expressed by a few digits multiplied by powers of 10, it will nevertheless detect any large error in the process of squaring the roots.

81. Case II. Complex Roots. When some of the roots of an algebraic equation are complex, the equation can not be expressed as a product of linear factors with real coefficients. Such an equation can, however, always be expressed as a product of real linear and real quadratic factors, each quadratic factor corresponding to a pair of complex roots. The root-squaring process can therefore never break up such an equation into linear fragments as in the case when all the roots are real and unequal.

When an equation has complex roots, the root-squaring process always breaks it up into linear and quadratic fragments. The real roots, if any, are found from the linear fragments as in Case I, while the complex roots are found from the quadratic fragments.

In transforming an equation by the root-squaring process the presence of complex roots is revealed in two ways: (1) the doubled products do not all disappear from the first row and (2) the signs of some of the coefficients fluctuate as the transformations continue. The reason for these peculiarities can be seen by considering a typical example.

81a). Detection of Complex Roots. Let us consider an equation having two distinct real roots and two pairs of complex roots. Let these roots be x_1, $r_1e^{i\theta_1}$, $r_1e^{-i\theta_1}$, x_3, $r_2e^{i\theta_2}$, $r_2e^{-i\theta_2}$; and let the order of their magnitude be

$$|x_1| > r_1 > |x_3| > r_2.$$

Then the equation having these roots is

$$(1) \qquad (x - x_1)(x - r_1e^{i\theta_1})(x - r_1e^{-i\theta_1})$$
$$\times (x - x_3)(x - r_2e^{i\theta_2})(x - r_2e^{-i\theta_2}) = 0.$$

The equation whose roots are the mth powers of the roots of this equation is therefore

$$(2) \qquad (y - x_1{}^m)(y - r_1{}^m e^{im\theta_1})(y - r_1{}^m e^{-im\theta_1})$$
$$\times (y - x_3{}^m)(y - r_2{}^m e^{im\theta_2})(y - r_2{}^m e^{-im\theta_2}) = 0,$$

where $y = x^m$.

On performing the indicated multiplications in (2), then taking out the factors $x_1{}^m r_1{}^m$, $x_1{}^m r_1{}^{2m}$, $x_1{}^m r_1{}^{2m} x_3{}^m$, $x_1{}^m r_1{}^{2m} x_3{}^m r_2{}^m$, and neglecting the ratios

$$\frac{r_1{}^m}{x_1{}^m}, \quad \frac{x_3{}^m}{x_1{}^m}, \quad \frac{r_2{}^m}{x_1{}^m}, \quad \frac{x_3{}^m}{r_1{}^m}, \quad \frac{r_2{}^m}{r_1{}^m}, \quad \frac{r_2{}^m}{x_3{}^m},$$

since each of these is negligible in comparison with unity, we finally get

$$(3) \quad y^6 - x_1{}^m y^5 + 2x_1{}^m r_1{}^m \cos m\theta_1 y^4 - x_1{}^m r_1{}^{2m} y^3 + x_1{}^m r_1{}^{2m} x_3{}^m y^2$$
$$- 2x_1{}^m r_1{}^{2m} x_3{}^m r_2{}^m \cos m\theta_2 y + x_1{}^m r_1{}^{2m} x_3{}^m r_2{}^{2m} = 0.$$

The roots of the original equation have now been separated as much as they can ever be (since in deriving (3) we neglected such ratios as $r_1{}^m/x_1{}^m$ etc.), and the given equation has been broken up into the linear and quadratic fragments

$$(4) \qquad \begin{cases} y^6 - x_1{}^m y^5 = 0, \\ - x_1{}^m y^5 + 2x_1{}^m r_1{}^m \cos m\theta_1 y^4 - x_1{}^m r_1{}^{2m} y^3 = 0, \\ - x_1{}^m r_1{}^{2m} y^3 + x_1{}^m r_1{}^{2m} x_3{}^m y^2 = 0, \\ x_1{}^m r_1{}^{2m} x_3{}^m y^2 - 2x_1{}^m r_1{}^{2m} x_3{}^m r_2{}^m \cos m\theta_2 y + x_1{}^m r_1{}^{2m} x_3{}^m r_2{}^{2m} = 0, \end{cases}$$

from which we can obtain the original roots with which we started.

Suppose, now, that we apply the root-squaring process to (3) once more, as shown below:

	y^6	y^5	y^4	y^3
mth p.	1	$-x_1{}^m$	$2x_1{}^m r_1{}^m \cos m\theta_1$	$-x_1{}^m r_1{}^{2m}$
	1	$-x_1{}^{2m}$ $+4x_1{}^m r_1{}^m \cos m\theta_1$	$+4x_1{}^{2m} r_1{}^{2m} \cos^2 m\theta_1$ $-2x_1{}^{2m} r_1{}^{2m}$ $+2x_1{}^m r_1{}^{2m} x_3{}^m$	$-x_1{}^{2m} r_1{}^{4m}$ $+4x_1{}^m r_1{}^{3m} x_3{}^m \cos m\theta_1$ $-4x_1{}^{2m} r_1{}^{2m} x_3{}^m r_2{}^m \cos m\theta_2$ $+2x_1{}^m r_1{}^{2m} x_3{}^m r_2{}^{2m}$
$2m$th p.	1	$-x_1{}^{2m}$	$+4x_1{}^{2m} r_1{}^{2m} \cos^2 m\theta_1$ $-2x_1{}^{2m} r_1{}^{2m}$	$-x_1{}^{2m} r_1{}^{4m}$

	y^2	y^1	y^0
mth p.	$x_1{}^m r_1{}^{2m} x_3{}^m$	$-2x_1{}^m r_1{}^{2m} x_3{}^m r_2{}^m \cos m\theta_2$	$x_1{}^m r_1{}^{2m} x_3{}^m r_2{}^{2m}$
	$+x_1{}^{2m} r_1{}^{4m} x_3{}^{2m}$ $-4x_1{}^{2m} r_1{}^{4m} x_3{}^m r_2{}^m \cos m\theta_2$ $+4x_1{}^{2m} r_1{}^{3m} x_3{}^m r_2{}^{2m} \cos m\theta_1$	$-4x_1{}^{2m} r_1{}^{4m} x_3{}^{2m} r_2{}^{2m} \cos^2 m\theta_2$ $+2x_1{}^{2m} r_1{}^{4m} x_3{}^{2m} r_2{}^{2m}$	$+x_1{}^{2m} r_1{}^{4m} x_3{}^{2m} r_2{}^{4m}$
$2m$th p.	$+x_1{}^{2m} r_1{}^{4m} x_3{}^{2m}$	$-4x_1{}^{2m} r_1{}^{4m} x_3{}^{2m} r_2{}^{2m} \cos^2 m\theta_2$ $+2x_1{}^{2m} r_1{}^{4m} x_3{}^{2m} r_2{}^{2m}$	$+x_1{}^{2m} r_1{}^{4m} x_3{}^{2m} r_2{}^{4m}$

It is readily seen on dividing the doubled products in each column by the squared term at the top that all these products are negligible except two in the first row. Hence the sums of the several columns are as given above. This result shows why the doubled products in the first row do not all disappear when the complex roots are present.

Furthermore, since $2\cos^2 \phi - 1 = \cos 2\phi$, we can write the coefficients of y^4 and y in the forms $2x_1{}^{2m} r_1{}^{2m} \cos 2m\theta_1$ and $-2x_1{}^{2m} r_1{}^{4m} x_3{}^{2m} r_2{}^{2m} \cos 2m\theta_2$, respectively. Hence the coefficients in the last transformed equation are simply

(5) $2m$th p. $1 - x_1{}^{2m} + 2x_1{}^{2m} r_1{}^{2m} \cos 2m\theta_1 - x_1{}^{2m} r_1{}^{4m} + x_1{}^{2m} r_1{}^{4m} x_3{}^{2m}$

$- 2x_1{}^{2m} r_1{}^{4m} x_3{}^{2m} r_2{}^{2m} \cos 2m\theta_2 + x_1{}^{2m} r_1{}^{4m} x_3{}^{2m} r_2{}^{4m}.$

On comparing this last equation with the one for the mth powers of the roots we see at once that each application of the root-squaring process doubles the amplitudes of the complex roots. Hence the cosines of these amplitudes must frequently change signs as the amplitudes are continually doubled. This explains the fluctuation in the signs of some of the coefficients when complex roots are present.

After the original equation has been broken up into linear and quadratic fragments by the root-squaring process, we can find the complex roots by solving the resulting quadratic equations for x^m and then extracting the mth root of the results by means of De Moivre's theorem. But by proceeding in this manner we would have ambiguities of sign in the computed roots, and such ambiguities are not easily removed. To obtain the complex roots without ambiguity as to signs we derive some further relations between roots and coefficients.

81b). Relations between the Coefficients of an Algebraic Equation and the Reciprocals of Its Roots. In the general equation

$$a_0 x^n + a_1 x^{n-1} + a_2 x^{n-2} + \cdots + a_{n-1} x + a_n = 0$$

let us put $x = 1/y$. The result, after clearing of fractions, is

$$a_n y^n + a_{n-1} y^{n-1} + a_{n-2} y^{n-2} + \cdots + a_3 y^3 + a_2 y^2 + a_1 y + a_0 = 0.$$

Hence from the well-known relations between roots and coefficients (p. 216) we have

$$\frac{a_{n-1}}{a_n} = -(y_1 + y_2 + \cdots + y_n),$$

$$\frac{a_{n-2}}{a_n} = y_1 y_2 + y_1 y_3 + \cdots + y_2 y_3 + \cdots,$$

$$\cdots \cdots \cdots \cdots \cdots \cdots \cdots \cdots$$

$$\frac{a_0}{a_n} = (-1)^n y_1 y_2 \cdots y_n;$$

or, since $y = 1/x$,

$$(6) \quad \begin{cases} \dfrac{1}{x_1} + \dfrac{1}{x_2} + \cdots + \dfrac{1}{x_n} = -\dfrac{a_{n-1}}{a_n}, \\[2mm] \dfrac{1}{x_1 x_2} + \dfrac{1}{x_1 x_3} + \cdots + \dfrac{1}{x_2 x_3} + \cdots + \dfrac{1}{x_{n-1} x_n} = \dfrac{a_{n-2}}{a_n}, \\[2mm] \cdots \cdots \cdots \cdots \cdots \cdots \cdots \cdots \\[2mm] \dfrac{1}{x_1 x_2 x_3 \cdots x_n} = (-1)^n \dfrac{a_0}{a_n}. \end{cases}$$

These relations between the coefficients and reciprocals of the roots will help us to avoid ambiguities of sign in the computation of complex roots.

Example 2. Find all the roots of the equation

$$x^7 - 2x^5 - 3x^3 + 4x^2 - 5x + 6 = 0.$$

Solution. The preliminary work of separating the roots is shown on pages 226-227 and should be self-explanatory.

It is evident from the last application of the root-squaring process that another application would effect no further separation of the roots. Hence we stop with the 256th powers of the roots.

The given equation has now been broken up into three linear and two quadratic fragments. We first compute the real roots from the linear fragments.

For the first real root we have by (79.1)

$$x_1{}^{256} = 9.084 \times 10^{74},$$

	x^7	x^6	x^5	x^4	x^3	x^2	x^1	x^0
Given equa.	1	0	-2	0	-3	4	-5	6
	1	0	4	0	9	-16	25	-36
		$-4n$	$0c$	$12n$	$0c$	$30n$	$-48c$	
			$-6n$	$0c$	$20n$	$0c$		
				$-10n$	$0c$			
2d p.	1	-4	-2	2	29	14	-23	-36
		-16	4	-4	$8.41 \cdot 10^2$	$-1.96 \cdot 10^2$	$5.29 \cdot 10^2$	$-1.296 \cdot 10^3$
		$-4n$	$16c$	$-116n$	$-0.56c$	$-13.34n$	$10.08c$	
			$58n$	$+112c$	$+0.92n$	$+1.44c$		
				$-46n$	$-2.88c$			
4th p.	1	-20	$7.8 \cdot 10$	$-5.4 \cdot 10$	$+5.89 \cdot 10^2$	$-1.386 \cdot 10^3$	$+1.537 \cdot 10^3$	$-1.296 \cdot 10^3$
		$-4.00 \cdot 10^2$	$+6.084 \cdot 10^3$	$-0.2916 \cdot 10^4$	$+3.4692 \cdot 10^5$	$-1.9210 \cdot 10^6$	$+2.3624 \cdot 10^6$	$-1.680 \cdot 10^6$
		$+1.56n$	$-2.160c$	$+9.1884n$	$-1.4969c$	$+1.8106n$	$-3.5925c$	
			$+1.178n$	$-5.5440c$	$+2.3977n$	$-0.1400c$		
				$+0.3074n$	$-0.5184c$			
8th p.	1	$-2.44 \cdot 10^2$	$+5.102 \cdot 10^3$	$+3.660 \cdot 10^4$	$+3.852 \cdot 10^5$	$-0.2504 \cdot 10^6$	$-1.230 \cdot 10^6$	$-1.680 \cdot 10^6$
		$-5.9536 \cdot 10^4$	$+2.6030 \cdot 10^9$	$-1.3396 \cdot 10^9$	$+1.4838 \cdot 10^{11}$	$-0.6270 \cdot 10^{11}$	$+1.5129 \cdot 10^{12}$	$-2.8224 \cdot 10^{12}$
		$+1.0204n$	$+1.7861c$	$+3.9306n$	$+0.1833c$	$-9.4759n$	$-0.8413c$	
			$+0.0770n$	$-0.1222c$	$-0.1255n$	$+1.2298c$		
				$-0.0025n$	$-0.0082c$			

	x^0	x^1	x^2	x^3	x^4	x^5	x^6	x^7
16th p.	$-2.822 \cdot 10^{12}$	$+0.6716 \cdot 10^{12}$	$-8.873 \cdot 10^{11}$	$+1.533 \cdot 10^{11}$	$+2.466 \cdot 10^{9}$	$+4.466 \cdot 10^{7}$	$-4.933 \cdot 10^{4}$	1
	$-7.964 \cdot 10^{24}$	$+0.4510 \cdot 10^{24}$	$-7.873 \cdot 10^{23}$	$+2.350 \cdot 10^{22}$	$-0.6081 \cdot 10^{19}$	$+1.9945 \cdot 10^{15}$	$-2.433 \cdot 10^{9}$	1
		$-5.0079c$	$+2.059n$	$+0.438c$	$-1.3693n$	$+0.2433c$	$+0.089n$	
			$+0.139c$	$+0.006n$	$-0.0088c$	$+0.0003n$		
				$*$	$*$			
32d p.	$-7.964 \cdot 10^{24}$	$-4.557 \cdot 10^{24}$	$-5.675 \cdot 10^{23}$	$+2.794 \cdot 10^{22}$	$+0.7524 \cdot 10^{19}$	$+2.238 \cdot 10^{15}$	$-2.344 \cdot 10^{9}$	1
	$-6.343 \cdot 10^{49}$	$+2.077 \cdot 10^{49}$	$-3.221 \cdot 10^{47}$	$+7.806 \cdot 10^{44}$	$-0.5661 \cdot 10^{38}$	$+5.009 \cdot 10^{30}$	$-5.494 \cdot 10^{18}$	1
		$-0.904c$	$-2.546n$	$+0.085c$	$+1.2502n$	$+0.035c$	$+0.004n$	
			$+0.001c$	$*$	$*$	$*$		
64th p.	$-6.343 \cdot 10^{49}$	$+1.173 \cdot 10^{49}$	$-5.766 \cdot 10^{47}$	$+7.891 \cdot 10^{44}$	$+6.841 \cdot 10^{37}$	$5.044 \cdot 10^{30}$	$-5.490 \cdot 10^{18}$	1
	$-4.023 \cdot 10^{99}$	$+1.376 \cdot 10^{98}$	$-3.325 \cdot 10^{95}$	$+6.227 \cdot 10^{89}$	$-4.680 \cdot 10^{75}$	$+2.544 \cdot 10^{61}$	$-3.014 \cdot 10^{37}$	1
		$-0.731c$	$+0.185n$	$+0.001c$	$+7.960n$	$*c$	$*n$	
128th p.	$-4.023 \cdot 10^{99}$	$0.645 \cdot 10^{98}$	$-3.140 \cdot 10^{95}$	$+6.228 \cdot 10^{89}$	$+3.280 \cdot 10^{75}$	$+2.544 \cdot 10^{61}$	$-3.014 \cdot 10^{37}$	1
	$-1.618 \cdot 10^{199}$	$+0.416 \cdot 10^{196}$	$-9.860 \cdot 10^{190}$	$+3.879 \cdot 10^{179}$	$-1.076 \cdot 10^{151}$	$+6.472 \cdot 10^{122}$	$-9.084 \cdot 10^{74}$	1
		$-0.253c$	$+0.008n$	$*c$	$+3.169n$	$*c$	$*n$	
			$*$					
256th p.	$-1.618 \cdot 10^{199}$	$+0.163 \cdot 10^{196}$	$-9.852 \cdot 10^{190}$	$+3.879 \cdot 10^{179}$	$+2.093 \cdot 10^{151}$	$+6.472 \cdot 10^{122}$	$-9.084 \cdot 10^{74}$	1

from which we find by logarithms

$$x_1 = 1.9625.$$

The second real root is found from

$$(-9.084 \cdot 10^{74}) \cdot x_2{}^{256} + 6.472 \cdot 10^{122} = 0.$$

Solving this by logarithms, we find

$$x_2 = 1.5379.$$

The next two roots are complex, but the fifth, a real root, is found from the equation

$$(3.879 \cdot 10^{179}) \cdot x_5{}^{256} - 9.852 \cdot 10^{190} = 0,$$

from which

$$x_5 = 1.1080.$$

To determine the signs of these roots we first apply Descartes's rule of signs to the original equation and find that there can not be more than one negative root. The other two real roots must therefore be positive. On substituting in the original equation the rough values ± 2, we find that -2 nearly satisfies the equation. Hence $x_1 = -1.9625$. The three real roots are therefore

$$x_1 = -1.9625, \qquad x_2 = 1.5379, \qquad x_5 = 1.1080.$$

The modulus of the first pair of complex roots is found from the quadratic equation

(a) $$(6.472 \cdot 10^{122})y^2 + (2.093 \cdot 10^{151})y + 3.879 \cdot 10^{179} = 0,$$

where $y = x^{256}$. Let r_1 denote this modulus. We find r_1 by means of a simple theorem conecting the coefficients of a quadratic equation with the modulus of its complex roots.

Let the quadratic equation

(b) $$x^2 + bx + c = 0,$$

have the complex roots $re^{i\theta}$ and $re^{-i\theta}$. Then

$$x^2 + bx + c \equiv (x - re^{i\theta})(x - re^{-i\theta})$$
$$\equiv x^2 - r(e^{i\theta} + e^{-i\theta}) + r^2$$
$$\equiv x^2 - (2r \cos \theta)x + r^2.$$

Hence $c = r^2$, $-b = 2r \cos \theta$; that is, *the absolute term in the quadratic* (b) *is equal to the square of the modulus of its complex roots.*

Let R_1 denote the modulus of the complex roots of (a). Then on dividing the equation through by 6.472×10^{122} and applying the theorem just stated, we get

$$R_1^2 = \frac{3.879 \times 10^{57}}{6.472}.$$

Since, however, $R_1 = r_1^{256}$, we have

$$r_1^{512} = \frac{3.879 \times 10^{57}}{6.472}.$$

Solving this by logarithms, we find

$$r_1 = 1.2909.$$

The modulus of the second pair of complex roots is found in like manner from the quadratic

$$(-9.852 \times 10^{190})y^2 + (0.163 \times 10^{196})y - 1.618 \times 10^{199} = 0,$$

(c)   or $$y^2 - \frac{0.163 \times 10^6}{9.852}y + \frac{1.618 \times 10^9}{9.852} = 0.$$

Denoting this modulus by r_2 and that of (c) by R_2, we have

$$R_2^2 = \frac{1.618 \times 10^9}{9.852}, \quad \text{or} \quad r_2^{512} = \frac{1.618 \times 10^9}{9.852},$$

from which

$$r_2 = 1.0618.$$

Now let the two pairs of complex roots be denoted by

$$u_1 + iv_1, \; u_1 - iv_1 \quad \text{and} \quad u_2 + iv_2, \; u_2 - iv_2,$$

respectively. Then since the sum of the roots of the given equation is 0, we have

$$x_1 + x_2 + 2u_1 + x_5 + 2u_2 = 0,$$

or

(d) $$u_1 + u_2 = -0.3417.$$

We next apply the theorem connecting the sum of the reciprocals of the roots with the coefficients of the given equation, namely

$$\frac{1}{x_1} + \frac{1}{x_2} + \frac{1}{u_1 + iv_1} + \frac{1}{u_1 - iv_1} + \frac{1}{x_5} + \frac{1}{u_2 + iv_2} + \frac{1}{u_2 - iv_2} = \frac{5}{6}.$$

Rationalizing the denominators of the complex terms and putting $u_1{}^2 + v_1{}^2 = r_1{}^2$, $u_2{}^2 + v_2{}^2 = r_2{}^2$, we get

$$\frac{1}{x_1} + \frac{1}{x_2} + \frac{2u_1}{r_1{}^2} + \frac{1}{x_5} + \frac{2u_2}{r_2{}^2} = \frac{5}{6}.$$

Now substituting in this equation the numerical values

$$\frac{1}{x_1} = -0.508386,$$

$$\frac{1}{x_2} = 0.6502374, \quad \frac{1}{x_5} = 0.902527, \quad \frac{1}{r_1{}^2} = 0.60010, \quad \frac{1}{r_2{}^2} = 0.92875$$

and dividing through by 2, we obtain

(e) $\qquad\qquad 0.6001u_1 + 0.92875u_2 = -0.10552.$

Solving (d) and (e) simultaneously, we find

$$u_1 = -0.6445, \qquad u_2 = 0.3028.$$

v_1 and v_2 are found from the formulas $v_1 = \sqrt{r_1{}^2 - u_1{}^2} = \sqrt{(r_1 + u_1)(r_1 - u_1)}$ and $v_2 = \sqrt{r_2{}^2 - u_2{}^2} = \sqrt{(r_2 + u_2)(r_2 - u_2)}$ to be

$$v_1 = 1.1185, \qquad v_2 = 1.018.$$

Hence the two pairs of complex roots are

$$-0.6445 \pm 1.118i \quad \text{and} \quad 0.3028 \pm 1.018i.$$

We have thus obtained the complex roots without any ambiguity of signs.

The computed roots in this example can be checked by substituting the values of the real roots and moduli in the known relation

$$x_1 x_2 r_1{}^2 x_5 r_2{}^2 = -6,$$

or

$$\log(x_1 x_2 r_1{}^2 x_5 r_2{}^2) = \log 6.$$

These logarithms are found to be

$$0.77816 = 0.77815.$$

The agreement is thus as close as could be expected.

Remark. If an equation contains more than two pairs of complex roots, the moduli of the roots can be found from the quadratic fragments as in the example above. Then the real parts $u_1, u_2, u_3, \cdots$ can be found by making further use of the relations connecting the roots and the reciprocals of the roots with the coefficients of the original equation.

In some equations of high degree it might be advantageous, after finding the real roots, to depress the original equation by taking out the real roots and leaving only the complex roots. This is conveniently done by synthetic division. The relations between the roots and coefficients of the depressed equation should then be used.

82. Case III. Roots Real and Numerically Equal. If two roots of an equation are numerically equal, the root-squaring process can never break up the equation into linear fragments. One of the doubled products will always remain in the first row. This product will be just half the squared term above it, as can be seen by considering an equation of the third degree.

Let the roots of

$$(1) \qquad x^3 + a_1 x^2 + a_2 x + a_3 = 0$$

be x_1, x_2, x_3. Then the equation whose roots are the mth powers of those of (1) is

$$(y - x_1{}^m)(y - x_2{}^m)(y - x_3{}^m) = 0, \quad \text{where } y = x^m,$$

or

$$y^3 - (x_1{}^m + x_2{}^m + x_3{}^m)y^2 + (x_1{}^m x_2{}^m + x_1{}^m x_3{}^m + x_2{}^m x_3{}^m)y - x_1{}^m x_2{}^m x_3{}^m = 0,$$

or

$$(2) \quad y^3 - x_1{}^m \left(1 + \frac{x_2{}^m}{x_1{}^m} + \frac{x_3{}^m}{x_1{}^m}\right) y^2$$

$$+ x_1{}^m x_2{}^m \left(1 + \frac{x_3{}^m}{x_2{}^m} + \frac{x_3{}^m}{x_1{}^m}\right) y - x_1{}^m x_2{}^m x_3{}^m = 0.$$

Now let $x_2 = x_3$ and let $|x_1| > |x_2|$. Then for sufficiently large values of m the ratio $x_2{}^m/x_1{}^m$ is negligible in comparison with unity, and (2) reduces to

$$(3) \qquad y^3 - x_1{}^m y^2 + 2x_1{}^m x_2{}^m y - x_1{}^m x_2{}^{2m} = 0.$$

The roots of the given equation have now been separated as much as they can ever be, but we shall apply the root-squaring process to (3) to see what happens. Using only the coefficients, we have

	1		
mth p.	1	$-x_1^m$	$2x_1^m x_2^m$	$-x_1^m x_2^{2m}$
	1	$-x_1^{2m}$ $+4x_1^m x_2^m$	$+4x_1^{2m}x_2^{2m}$ $-2x_1^{2m}x_2^{2m}$	$-x_1^{2m}x_2^{4m}$
$2m$th p.	1	$-x_1^{2m}$	$+2x_1^{2m}x_2^{2m}$	$-x_1^{2m}x_2^{4m}$

It will be noticed that the first doubled product is negligible in comparison with the squared term above it, whereas the second is of the *same order of magnitude* as the squared term above and just *half as large*. Furthermore, in the equation for the $2m$th powers of the roots all the coefficients except one are the squares of those in the preceding equation. This remaining one is only *half* the square of the corresponding coefficient in the preceding equation. These peculiarities enable us to detect equal real roots immediately. We shall now show how to compute such roots.

Example 3. Solve the equation

$$5x^3 + 2x^2 - 15x - 6 = 0.$$

Solution.

	5	2	-15	-6
Given equa.	5	2	-15	-6
	25	-4 $-150n$	225 $+24c$	-36
2d p.	25	$-1.54 \cdot 10^2$	$+2.49 \cdot 10^2$	-36
	$6.25 \cdot 10^2$	$-2.3716 \cdot 10^4$ $+1.2450n$	$+6.2001 \cdot 10^4$ $-1.1008c$	$-1.296 \cdot 10^3$
4th p.	$6.25 \cdot 10^2$	$-1.1266 \cdot 10^4$	$+5.0993 \cdot 10^4$	$-1.296 \cdot 10^3$
	$3.9062 \cdot 10^5$	$-1.269 \cdot 10^8$ $+0.637n$	$+2.600 \cdot 10^9$ $-0.029c$	$-1.680 \cdot 10^6$
8th p.	$3.906 \cdot 10^5$	$-0.632 \cdot 10^8$	$+2.571 \cdot 10^9$	$-1.680 \cdot 10^6$
	$1.526 \cdot 10^{11}$	$-3.994 \cdot 10^{15}$ $+2.008$	$+6.610 \cdot 10^{18}$ $*$	$-2.822 \cdot 10^{12}$
16th p.	$1.526 \cdot 10^{11}$	$-1.986 \cdot 10^{15}$	$6.610 \cdot 10^{18}$	$-2.822 \cdot 10^{12}$

The given equation has now been broken up into the simple fragment $(6.610 \cdot 10^{18})x_3^{16} - 2.822 \cdot 10^{12} = 0$ and the quadratic fragment

$1.526 \cdot 10^{11}x_1^{32} - 1.986 \cdot 10^{15}x_1^{16} + 6.610 \cdot 10^{18} = 0.$ Solving the simple fragment by logarithms, we find

$$x_3 = 0.3999.$$

To find the roots of the quadratic fragment we write the equation in the form

$$x_1^{32} - \frac{1.986 \times 10^4}{1.526} x_1^{16} + \frac{6.61 \times 10^7}{1.526} = 0.$$

Since the roots are known to be equal and since their product is equal to the absolute term of the quadratic, we have

$$x_1^{32} = \frac{6.61 \times 10^7}{1.526}.$$

Solving by logarithms, we get

$$x_1 = 1.732.$$

We check this result by putting the sum of the roots equal to the coefficient of x_1^{16} with its sign changed. Since the roots are equal, we have

$$2x_1^{16} = \frac{1.986 \times 10^4}{1.526},$$

from which

$$x_1 = 1.731.$$

We shall next determine the signs of these roots. By Descartes's rule there can not be more than one positive root nor more than two negative roots. Hence we try ± 0.4 and find that -0.4 satisfies the given equation. The other two roots are therefore ± 1.732.

For a method of finding any number of complex roots, see the following paper:

"On Graeffe's Method for Complex Roots of Algebraic Equations," by S. Brodetsky and G. Smeal. *Proc. Camb. Phil. Soc.*, Vol 22 (1924), pp. 83-87.

There are methods for improving the values of the real and imaginary parts of complex roots found by the root-squaring process, but these methods are rather long and laborious to apply. For information concerning these methods the reader is referred to Runge and König's *Numerisches Rechnen*, p. 173; Bairstow's *Applied Aerodynamics*, p. 558; and Carvallo's *Resolution Numerique des Equations*, p. 20. Sufficiently accurate values of the roots can usually be obtained by using Barlow's Tables of squares, cubes, etc. and Crelle's Multiplication Tables, or else by means of a computing machine.

The values of the real roots can be obtained more accurately by applying the Newton-Raphson method to the values found by Graeffe's method.

Carvallo * has extended Graeffe's method to the solution of transcendental equations by expanding the equation into a Taylor series, neglecting the remainder term, and then treating the resulting polynomial as an algebraic equation.

EXERCISES X

Find to four significant figures all the roots of the following equations:

1. $\qquad 7.5x^5 + 5.44x^3 - 3.24x^2 - 1.85x + 0.2 = 0.$

2. $\qquad 3.26x^6 + 4.2x^4 + 3.08x^3 - 7.16x^2 + 1.92x - 7.76 = 0.$

3. $\qquad x^6 - 6x^5 + 3x^4 + 5x^3 - 6x + 2 = 0.$

* Loc. cit., p. 24.

CHAPTER XI

THE NUMERICAL SOLUTION OF ORDINARY DIFFERENTIAL EQUATIONS

I. EQUATIONS OF THE FIRST ORDER.

83. Introduction. Certain types of differential equations are dealt with in textbooks on calculus and differential equations, and methods are developed for solving equations of the types treated. Comparatively few differential equations, however, can be integrated in finite form. But just as there are methods for finding to any desired degree of accuracy the roots of any algebraic or transcendental equation having numerical coefficients, so likewise there are methods for finding to any desired degree of accuracy the numerical solution of any ordinary differential equation having numerical coefficients and given initial conditions. Starting with the initial values, the solutions are thence constructed by short steps ahead for equal intervals $\Delta x = h$ of x, each step usually being checked by some method before proceeding to the next step. The most important of the several methods for solving differential equations numerically will be explained in the following pages.

84. Euler's Method and Its Modification. The oldest and simplest method, but also the crudest, was devised by Euler. A differential equation of the first order may be written in the symbolic form

$$(1) \qquad \frac{dy}{dx} = f(x, y)$$

The integral of (1) gives y as a function of x, which may be written symbolically as

$$(2) \qquad y = F(x).$$

The graph of (2) is a curve in the xy-plane; and since a smooth curve is practically straight for a short distance from any point on it, we have the approximate relation (see Fig. 13).

$$\Delta y \approx \Delta x \tan \theta = \left(\frac{dy}{dx}\right)_0 \Delta x,$$

so that

$$y_1 \approx y_0 + \left(\frac{dy}{dx}\right)_0 \Delta x.$$

Then the values of y corresponding to $x_2 (= x_1 + h)$, $x_3 (= x_2 + h)$, etc.
are

$$y_2 \approx y_1 + \left(\frac{dy}{dx}\right)_1 h,$$

$$y_3 \approx y_2 + \left(\frac{dy}{dx}\right)_2 h, \text{ etc.}$$

By taking h small enough and proceeding in this manner, we could tabulate
the integral of (1) as a set of corresponding values of x and y. Such was
the method of Euler, but it is either too slow (in case h is small) or too

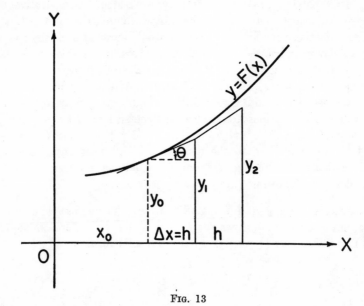

Fig. 13

inaccurate (in case h is not small) for practical use. Even if h is taken
very small for all steps, it is evident from the figure and other considerations that the computed y's will deviate farther and farther from the
true y's so long as the curvature of the graph does not change. These
considerations have led to a modification of Euler's method, as shown below.

Starting with the initial value y_0, an approximate value for y_1 is computed from the relation

$$y_1{}^{(1)} \approx y_0 + \left(\frac{dy}{dx}\right)_0 h.$$

Then this approximate value of y_1 is substituted into the given equation
(1) to get an approximate value of $\frac{dy}{dx}$ at the end of the first interval, or

$$\left(\frac{dy}{dx}\right)_1^{(1)} = f(x_1, y_1^{(1)}).$$

Then an improved value of Δy is found by multiplying h by the *average* (mean) of the values of $\frac{dy}{dx}$ at the ends of the interval x_0 to x_1, or

$$\Delta y \approx \frac{\left(\frac{dy}{dx}\right)_0 + \left(\frac{dy}{dx}\right)_1^{(1)}}{2} h.$$

That this value of Δy is more accurate than the value $\left(\frac{dy}{dx}\right)_0 h$ is evident if we think of $\frac{dy}{dx}$ as the rate of change of y with respect to x. The second approximation for y_1 is now

$$y_1^{(2)} = y_0 + \frac{\left(\frac{dy}{dx}\right)_0 + \left(\frac{dy}{dx}\right)_1^{(1)}}{2} h.$$

This improved value of $y_1^{(2)}$ is now substituted into the given equation (1) to get a second approximation for $\left(\frac{dy}{dx}\right)_1$, or

$$\left(\frac{dy}{dx}\right)_1^{(2)} = f(x_1, y_1^{(2)}).$$

The third approximation for y_1 is then

$$y_1^{(3)} = y_0 + \frac{\left(\frac{dy}{dx}\right)_0 + \left(\frac{dy}{dx}\right)_1^{(2)}}{2} h.$$

The process is repeated until no change is produced in the value of y_1 to the number of digits retained.

The computation for the next interval x_1 to $x_2(= x_1 + h)$ is carried out in exactly the same manner, by first finding an approximate value of Δy from the relation $\Delta y = \left(\frac{dy}{dx}\right)_1 h$ and then applying the averaging process until no improvement is made in y_2.

That this modification of the Euler method gives a great improvement in accuracy over the original method can be seen by a glance at Fig. 14.

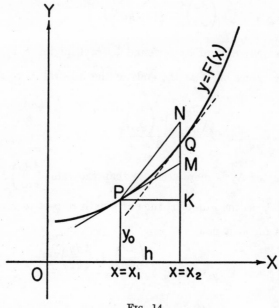

In this figure the Δy computed by the Euler method is represented by KM. If PN is drawn parallel to the tangent at Q, the Δy computed by using the slope at Q is represented by KN. On the other hand, if we take the average of the slopes we get

$$\Delta y = \frac{\left(\dfrac{dy}{dx}\right)_0 + \left(\dfrac{dy}{dx}\right)_1}{2} h = \tfrac{1}{2}\left[\, h\left(\frac{dy}{dx}\right)_0 + h\left(\frac{dy}{dx}\right)_1 \right]$$

$$= \tfrac{1}{2}(KM + KN) = \tfrac{1}{2}(KM + KM + MN) = KM + \tfrac{1}{2}MN,$$

which is very close to its true value KQ. The attainable accuracy in any case is limited by the length of the step h.

Although the modified Euler method is slow and of limited accuracy, its simplicity and applicability make it a method of great value; for it enables one to start the solution of problems where no other method will work.

As an example of the use of the modified Euler method, we compute a few values of y for the differential equation

$$\frac{dy}{dx} = x + y,$$

with the initial conditions $x_0 = 0$, $y_0 = 1$.

Substituting these values of x and y in the given equation, we have

$$\left(\frac{dy}{dx}\right)_0 = x_0 + y_0 = 0 + 1 = 1.$$

Taking $h = 0.05$, we then have

$$y_1^{(1)} = y_0 + \left(\frac{dy}{dx}\right)_0 h = 1 + 0.05 = 1.05.$$

Then

$$\left(\frac{dy}{dx}\right)_1^{(1)} = x_1 + y_1^{(1)} = 0.05 + 1.05 = 1.10.$$

The second approximation to y_1 is therefore

$$y_1^{(2)} = y_0 + \frac{\left(\frac{dy}{dx}\right)_0 + \left(\frac{dy}{dx}\right)_1^{(1)}}{2} h = 1 + \frac{1 + 1.10}{2} \times 0.05 = 1.0525.$$

The second approximation for $\left(\frac{dy}{dx}\right)_1$ is then

$$\left(\frac{dy}{dx}\right)_1^{(2)} = 0.05 + 1.0525 = 1.1025.$$

Then the third approximation to y_1 is

$$y_1^{(3)} = 1 + \frac{1 + 1.1025}{2} \times 0.05 = 1.05256.$$

Continuing the approximation, we have

$$\left(\frac{dy}{dx}\right)_1^{(3)} = 0.05 + 1.05256 = 1.10256,$$

$$y_1^{(4)} = 1 + \frac{1 + 1.10256}{2} \times 0.05 = 1.05256.$$

Since this is the same as $y_1^{(3)}$, we can get no further change in y by continuing the approximations. We therefore take

$$y_1 = 1.0526, \quad \left(\frac{dy}{dx}\right)_1 = 1.1026.$$

As a first approximation to y_2 we have

$$y_2^{(1)} = y_1 + \left(\frac{dy}{dx}\right)_1 h = 1.0526 + 1.1026 \times 0.05 = 1.1077.$$

Hence

$$\left(\frac{dy}{dx}\right)_2^{(1)} = x_2 + y_2^{(1)} = 0.1 + 1.1077 = 1.2077.$$

Then

$$y_2{}^{(2)} = 1.0526 + \frac{1.1026 + 1.2077}{2} \times 0.05 = 1.1104,$$

and

$$\left(\frac{dy}{dx}\right)_2^{(2)} = 0.1 + 1.1104 = 1.2104.$$

Hence

$$y_2{}^{(3)} = 1.0526 + \frac{1.1026 + 1.2104}{2} \times 0.05 = 1.1104,$$

which is the same as $y_2{}^{(2)}$. We therefore take

$$y_2 = 1.1104, \quad \left(\frac{dy}{dx}\right)_2 = 1.2104.$$

Collecting our results in tabular form, we have the following table:

x	y	dy/dx
0.00	1.0000	1.0000
0.05	1.0526	1.1026
0.10	1.1104	1.2104

The question now arises as to the accuracy of the results found above. Fortunately, the exact analytical solution of the given equation, with the stated initial conditions, is easily found to be

$$y = 2e^x - x - 1.$$

For $x = 0$, 0.05, 0.10, the corresponding values of y are 1, 1.05254, and 1.11034. The values in the table above can be improved only by taking a smaller value for h.

85. Picard's Method of Successive Approximations. From the equation

$$\frac{dy}{dx} = f(x, y),$$

we have

$$dy = f(x, y)\,dx = \left(\frac{dy}{dx}\right)dx.$$

Integrating this between corresponding limits for x and y, we have

$$\int_{y_0}^{y} dy = \int_{x_0}^{x} f(x, y)\,dx = \int_{x_0}^{x} \left(\frac{dy}{dx}\right)dx,$$

from which

(1) $$y = y_0 + \int_{x_0}^{x} f(x, y)\,dx = y_0 + \int_{x_0}^{x} \left(\frac{dy}{dx}\right)dx.$$

Here the integral term in the right-hand member represents the increment in y produced by an increment $x - x_0$ in x.

Confining our attention for the moment to the first form in (1), namely,

$$y = y_0 + \int_{x_0}^{x} f(x, y) \, dx,$$

we notice that the equation is complicated by the presence of y under the integral sign as well as outside it. An equation of this kind is called an *integral equation* and can be solved by a process of successive approximations, or iteration, if the indicated integrations can be performed in the successive steps.

To solve the differential equation

$$\frac{dy}{dx} = f(x, y)$$

by Picard's method of successive approximations, we get a first approximation for y by putting y_0 for y in the integrand of (1). Then

$$y^{(1)} = y_0 + \int_{x_0}^{x} f(x, y_0) \, dx.$$

The integrand is now a function of x alone and the indicated integration can be performed, in theory at least. Having now a first approximation to y, we substitute it for y in the integrand of (1) and integrate again, thus obtaining a second approximation

$$y^{(2)} = y_0 + \int_{x_0}^{x} f(x, y^{(1)}) \, dx.$$

The process is repeated in this way as many times as may be necessary or desirable, the nth approximation being given by the equation

$$y^{(n)} = y_0 + \int_{x_0}^{x} f(x, y^{(n-1)}) \, dx.$$

We now apply this method to the simple example

$$\frac{dy}{dx} = x + y,$$

with the initial conditions $x_0 = 0$, $y_0 = 1$.

To get a first approximation we substitute $y = 1$ in the right-hand member · of the given equation, thus obtaining

$$y^{(1)} = 1 + \int_{0}^{x} \left(\frac{dy}{dx}\right) dx = 1 + \int_{0}^{x} (x + 1) \, dx = \frac{x^2}{2} + x + 1.$$

For second and third approximations we have

$$y^{(2)} = 1 + \int_0^x \left(x + \frac{x^2}{2} + x + 1 \right) dx = \frac{x^3}{6} + x^2 + x + 1,$$

$$y^{(3)} = 1 + \int_0^x \left(x + \frac{x^3}{6} + x^2 + x + 1 \right) dx = \frac{x^4}{24} + \frac{x^3}{3} + x^2 + x + 1.$$

We have thus found y as a power series in x. For $x = 0.1$ we have

$$y = \frac{0.0001}{24} + \frac{0.001}{3} + 0.01 + 0.1 + 1 = 1.1103.$$

This value of y is correct to four decimal places, as shown on page 250. For $x = 0.2$ the corresponding value of $y^{(3)}$ is 1.2427, whereas the true value is 1.2428. We could get a better value by continuing the approximations to $y^{(4)}$, $y^{(5)}$, etc.; but it is better to move up to the point $x = 0.1$ and start all over again.

The graphs of $y^{(1)}$, $y^{(2)}$, $y^{(3)}$, and $y = F(x)$ are shown in Fig. 15. It will be seen that the approximating curves approach the curve $y = F(x)$ more closely with each successive approximation.

Now taking $x = 0.1$ and $y = 1.1103$ as initial values, we have

$$y^{(1)} = 1.1103 + \int_{0.1}^x (x + 1.1103) dx$$

$$= \frac{x^2}{2} + 1.1103x + 0.9943.$$

Then for second and third approximations we get

$$y^{(2)} = 1.1103 + \int_{0.1}^x \left(x + \frac{x^2}{2} + 1.1103x + 0.9943 \right) dx$$

$$= \frac{x^3}{6} + 1.0552x^2 + 0.9943x + 1.0001.$$

$$y^{(3)} = 1.1103 + \int_{0.1}^x \left(x + \frac{x^3}{6} + 1.0552x^2 + 0.9943x + 1.0001 \right) dx$$

$$= \frac{x^4}{24} + 0.3517x^3 + 0.9972x^2 + 1.0001x + 1.0000.$$

For $x = 0.2$ we get $y = 1.2428$, which is correct to four decimal places.

We could now move up to the point $x = 0.2$ and start over again; but since this method is not much used in practice, we shall not continue the computation by this method.

The practical difficulties associated with the method as outlined above lie mostly in the difficult and sometimes impossible integrations which would often have to be performed many times over. For example, if we wished

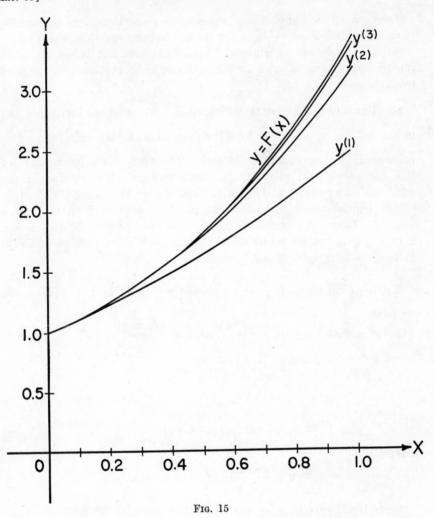

to solve the equation $dy/dx = (y - x)/(y + x)$ with the initial conditions $x_0 = 0$, $y_0 = 1$, we should have

$$y^{(1)} = 1 + \int_0^x \frac{1 - x}{1 + x}\, dx = 1 + \int_0^x \left(\frac{2}{1 + x} - 1 \right) dx$$

$$1 + 2 \ln (1 + x) - x,$$

$$y^{(2)} = 1 + \int_0^x \frac{1 + 2 \ln (1 + x) - x - x}{1 + 2 \ln (1 + x) - x + x}\, dx$$

$$= 1 + \int_0^x \left(1 - \frac{2x}{1 + 2 \ln (1 + x)} \right) dx;$$

and our troubles would continue to pile up as we continued the approximations. The difficulties would be far greater in other examples which might come up for solution. Fortunately, such difficulties, and indeed all direct integrations, can be avoided by the methods to be explained in the next two articles.

86. Use of Approximating Polynomials. We avoid the difficulties just mentioned by replacing $\dfrac{dy}{dx}$ by a polynomial and then integrating this polynomial over any desired interval. The appropriate polynomial for this purpose is that given by Newton's formula (II), because in the numerical integration of differential equations we always start with given values (initial conditions) and construct the solution from that point onward. Hence the values of the function immediately behind us are always known, but the values ahead are unknown. The problem is always to find the next value ahead.

Writing y' in place of $\dfrac{dy}{dx}$ and replacing y by y' in formula (II), p. 65, we have

$$(1) \quad y' = y'_n + u\Delta_1 y'_n + \frac{u(u+1)}{2}\Delta_2 y'_n + \frac{u(u+1)(u+2)}{6}\Delta_3 y'_n$$

$$+ \frac{u(u+1)(u+2)(u+3)}{24}\Delta_4 y'_n$$

$$= y'_n + \Delta_1 y'_n u + \frac{\Delta_2 y'_n}{2}(u^2 + u) + \frac{\Delta_3 y'_n}{6}(u^3 + 3u^2 + 2u)$$

$$+ \frac{\Delta_4 y'_n}{24}(u^4 + 6u^3 + 11u^2 + 6u),$$

where

$$u = \frac{x - x_n}{h} \quad \text{or} \quad x = x_n + hu.$$

Since the change in y for any interval is given by the formula

$$\Delta y = \int_{x_k}^{x_{k+1}} \left(\frac{dy}{dx}\right) dx = \int_{x_k}^{x_{k+1}} y' \, dx,$$

we can find by means of (1) the change in y over any interval where dy/dx is continuous. We therefore have for any interval $x_{k+1} - x_k$

$$\Delta y = \int_{x_k}^{x_{k+1}} \left[y'_n + \Delta_1 y'_n u + \frac{\Delta_2 y'_n}{2}(u^2 + u) \right.$$

$$\left. + \frac{\Delta_3 y'_n}{6}(u^3 + 3u^2 + 2u) + \frac{\Delta_4 y'_n}{24}(u^4 + 6u^3 + 11u^2 + 6u) \right] dx.$$

Since $x = x_n + hu$, we have $dx = h\,du$. Substituting this value for dx above and changing limits, we get

$$\Delta y = h \int_{u_k}^{u_{k+1}} \left[y'_n + \Delta_1 y'_n u + \frac{\Delta_2 y'_n}{2}(u^2 + u) + \frac{\Delta_3 y'_n}{6}(u^3 + 3u^2 + 2u) \right.$$
$$\left. + \frac{\Delta_4 y'_n}{24}(u^4 + 6u^3 + 11u^2 + 6u) \right]\,du,$$

or

$$(2) \quad \Delta y = h \left[y'_n u + \Delta_1 y'_n \frac{u^2}{2} + \frac{\Delta_2 y'_n}{2}\left(\frac{u^3}{3} + \frac{u^2}{2}\right) + \frac{\Delta_3 y'_n}{6}\left(\frac{u^4}{4} + u^3 + u^2\right) \right.$$
$$\left. + \frac{\Delta_4 y'_n}{24}\left(\frac{u^5}{5} + \frac{3u^4}{2} + \frac{11u^3}{3} + 3u^2\right) \right]_{u_k}^{u_{k+1}}$$

Let us now compute the value of Δy for the intervals $x_{n+1} - x_n$, $x_n - x_{n-1}$, $x_{n-1} - x_{n-2}$, etc. by substituting in (2) the proper limits for u. For the interval $x_{n+1} - x_n$ the limits for u are

$$u_{k+1} = (x_{n+1} - x_n)/h = h/h = 1, \qquad u_k = (x_n - x_n)/h = 0.$$

On substituting these in (2) and simplifying, we get

$$\Delta y = I_n^{n+1} = h \left[y'_n + \frac{1}{2} \Delta_1 y'_n + \frac{5}{12} \Delta_2 y'_n + \frac{3}{8} \Delta_3 y'_n + \frac{251}{720} \Delta_4 y'_n \right].$$

For the interval $x_n - x_{n-1}$ the limits for u are

$$u_{k+1} = \frac{x_n - x_n}{h} = 0, \qquad u_k = \frac{x_{n-1} - x_n}{h} = \frac{-h}{h} = -1;$$

and therefore

$$\Delta y = I_{n-1}^{n} = h \left[y'_n - \frac{1}{2} \Delta_1 y'_n - \frac{1}{12} \Delta_2 y'_n - \frac{1}{24} \Delta_3 y'_n - \frac{19}{720} \Delta_4 y'_n \right].$$

Proceeding in the same way for the other intervals, we get formulas for the changes in y in those intervals. The results for the several intervals are:

$$(86.\,1) \quad I_n^{n+1} = h \left[y'_n + \frac{1}{2} \Delta_1 y'_n + \frac{5}{12} \Delta_2 y'_n + \frac{3}{8} \Delta_3 y'_n + \frac{251}{720} \Delta_4 y'_n \right],$$

$$(86.\,2) \quad I_{n-1}^{n} = h \left[y'_n - \frac{1}{2} \Delta_1 y'_n - \frac{1}{12} \Delta_2 y'_n - \frac{1}{24} \Delta_3 y'_n - \frac{19}{720} \Delta_4 y'_n \right],$$

$$(86.\,3) \quad I_{n-2}^{n-1} = h \left[y'_n - \frac{3}{2} \Delta_1 y'_n + \frac{5}{12} \Delta_2 y'_n + \frac{1}{24} \Delta_3 y'_n + \frac{11}{720} \Delta_4 y'_n \right],$$

$$(86.\,4) \quad I_{n-3}^{n-2} = h \left[y'_n - \frac{5}{2} \Delta_1 y'_n + \frac{23}{12} \Delta_2 y'_n - \frac{3}{8} \Delta_3 y'_n - \frac{19}{720} \Delta_4 y'_n \right],$$

$$(86.\,5) \quad I_{n-4}^{n-3} = h \left[y'_n - \frac{7}{2} \Delta_1 y'_n + \frac{53}{12} \Delta_2 y'_n - \frac{55}{24} \Delta_3 y'_n + \frac{251}{720} \Delta_4 y'_n \right].$$

In the application of formulas (86.1) and (86.2) the coefficients $\dfrac{251}{720}$ and $\dfrac{19}{720}$ may be replaced by $\dfrac{1}{3}$ and $\dfrac{1}{38}$, respectively.

By adding (86.1) and (86.2) and then (86.2) and (86.3), we get the following additional formulas:

$$(86.6) \quad I_{n-1}^{n+1} = h \left[2y'_n + \frac{1}{3} \Delta_2 y'_n + \frac{1}{3} \Delta_3 y'_n + \frac{232}{720} \Delta_4 y'_n \right]$$

$$= 2h \left[y'_n + \frac{1}{6}(\Delta_2 y'_n + \Delta_3 y'_n + \Delta_4 y'_n) - \frac{1}{180} \Delta_4 y'_n \right]$$

$$(86.7) \quad I_{n-2}^{n} = 2h \left[y'_n - \Delta_1 y'_n + \frac{1}{6} \Delta_2 y'_n - \frac{1}{180} \Delta_4 y'_n \right].$$

Replacing the first and second differences in (86.7) by their values in tems of the y''s, namely

$$\Delta_1 y'_n = y'_n - y'_{n-1}, \qquad \Delta_2 y'_n = y'_n - 2y'_{n-1} + y'_{n-2},$$

and simplifying, we may write (86.7) in the equivalent form

$$(86.8) \quad I_{n-2}^{n} = \frac{h}{3} (y'_n + 4y'_{n-1} + y'_{n-2}) - \frac{h}{90} \Delta_4 y'_n,$$

which we recognize at once as Simpson's Rule with its remainder term.

Now a word as to the use of the foregoing formulas. Formula (86.1) is the formula for *integrating ahead*. It gives by extrapolation the change in y for the next step ahead. This change in y added to the last y already found will therefore give the new y at the end of the next step. The formula is therefore used for finding the approximate change in y in the next interval ahead of us, thereby enabling us to find the approximate value of y at the end of that interval. When a line in the table of corresponding values of x and y has been finished, the first entry in the next line is computed by (86.1).

Formula (86.2) is used for checking and improving the approximate values found by (86.1). It is not used for starting a new line in the table but for finishing the lines started by (86.1).

Formulas (86.3), (86.4), and (86.5) are used for checking the starting values in a solution when those values were found by the modified Euler method.

Formula (86.6) is another formula for integrating ahead. It covers two intervals at a time, but only one interval by extrapolation. The second form of this formula is particularly simple when the negligible quantity $-\frac{h}{90}\Delta_4 y'$ is omitted. For this reason (86.6) is a favorite formula with some computers. If $2h$ is numerically simpler than h, the formula will save time and labor in the computation. This would be the case when $h = 0.05$, $\frac{1}{2}$, etc.

Since (86.6) gives the increment in y for *two* intervals, the increments computed from this formula are to be added not to the last values found but to those *next to the last*. This fact makes the formula somewhat awkward to use.

Formulas (86.7) and (86.8) are simple and accurate formulas for checking and improving the extrapolated values found by (86.6).

The intervals covered by these formulas are shown graphically in Figure 16.

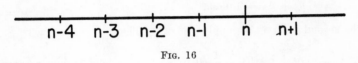

FIG. 16

Formulas (86.1) and (86.2) are the main tools which we shall use in the numerical integration of ordinary differential equations. It is needless to say that all the foregoing formulas apply equally well when the variables are any quantities whatever—time and acceleration, time and velocity, etc. Their use will be illustrated by several examples in the pages ahead.

Historical Note. The method of replacing the derivative of a function by a polynomial and integrating that polynomial over an interval was used by J. C. Adams as early as 1855.* Adams derived formulas (86.1) and (86.2), but he did not use (86.1). He used (86.2) in the manner indicated on page 251 and then applied a correction formula.

Example. We return once more to the differential equation

$$\frac{dy}{dx} = x + y.$$

In Art. 84 we computed the entries in the following table, except that now we have added on the columns of differences.

---

* *An Attempt to Test the Theories of Capillary Attraction*, by F. Bashforth and J. C. Adams, Cambridge University Press, 1883. See the Introduction and Chapter III.

x	y	y'	$\Delta_1 y'$	$\Delta_2 y'$
0.00	1.0000	1.0000		
0.05	1.0526	1.1026	$+0.1026$	
0.10	1.1104	1.2104	$+0.1078$	$+52$

Before proceeding further with the computation we had better check the values already found. If x_n denotes the third value of x in the table, then the second and first values will be x_{n-1} and x_{n-2}, respectively. (See Fig. 16.) To compute the increment in y for the first interval and thereby find y_1 we apply formula (86. 3), since it covers the interval $x_{n-1} - x_{n-2}$. We therefore have

$$\Delta y = 0.05 \left[1.2104 - \frac{3}{2}(0.1078) + \frac{5}{12}(0.0052) \right] = 0.05254.$$

$$\therefore \quad y_1 = y_0 + \Delta y = 1.0525.$$

For the second interval we apply (86. 2). Then

$$\Delta y = 0.05 \left[1.2104 - \frac{1}{2}(0.1078) - \frac{1}{12}(0.0052) \right] = 0.05780.$$

The corrected values of y are therefore $y_1 = 1.0525$,

$$y_2 = 1.0525 + 0.0578 = 1.1103.$$

We now make a new table containing the corrected values for y, y', and the first and second differences of y'. We also insert in this table a column for Δy as a matter of convenience.

x	y	Δy	y'	$\Delta_1 y'$	$\Delta_2 y'$	$\Delta_3 y'$
0.00	1.000		1.000			
0.05	1.0525	$+0.0525$	1.1025	$+0.1025$		
0.10	1.1103	$+0.0578$	1.2103	$+0.1078$	$+53$	
0.15	1.1736	$+0.0633$	1.3236	$+0.1133$	$+55$	$+2$
0.20	1.2427	$+0.0691$	1.4427	$+0.1191$	$+56$	$+1$

The computation is continued by adding a new line to the above table, the line for $x = 0.15$. The first step is to compute a new Δy by means of formula (86. 1), using the data of the third line:

$$\Delta y = 0.05 \left[1.2103 + \frac{1}{2}(0.1078) + \frac{5}{12}(0.0053) \right] = 0.0633.$$

$$\therefore \quad y_3{}^{(1)} = 1.1103 + 0.0633 = 1.1736.$$

Then

$$(y')_3{}^{(1)} = 0.15 + 1.1736 = 1.3236.$$

The next step is to enter these values of y and y' in the fourth line of the table and then compute the differences of y', as shown in the table. The entries in this line must now be checked and improved upon if possible by means of formula (86.2). Thus,

$$\Delta y = 0.05 \left[1.3236 - \frac{1}{2}(0.1133) - \frac{1}{12}(0.0055) \right] = 0.0633.$$

Since this is the same value for y as previously found, there is no possibility of improving upon the results in the fourth line and we therefore take them to be correct to four decimal places.

The fifth line in the table is computed in exactly the same way and is found to be correct at the first trial.

The fact that the correct values of y were found at the first trial in lines four and five suggests that it may be expedient to double the interval of integration, in order to progress more rapidly. We therefore take $h = 0.10$ and make a new table with differences to correspond to the longer interval.

x	y	Δy	y'	$\Delta_1 y'$	$\Delta_2 y'$	$\Delta_3 y'$	$\Delta_4 y'$
0.0	1.0000		1.0000				
0.1	1.1103	+0.1103	1.2103	+0.2103			
0.2	1.2427	0.1324	1.4427	+0.2324	+221		
0.3	1.3995	0.1568	1.6995	+0.2568	+244	+23	
0.3	1.3996	0.1569	1.6996	+0.2569	+245	+24	
0.4	1.5835	0.1839	1.9835	+0.2839	+270	+25	1
0.5	1.7973	0.2138	2.2973	+0.3138	299	+29	4
0.6	2.0441	0.2468	2.6441	+0.3468	330	+31	2
0.7	2.3274	0.2833	3.0274	+0.3833	365	+35	4
0.8	2.6510	0.3236	3.4510	0.4236	403	38	3
0.9	3.0191	0.3681	3.9191	0.4681	445	42	4
1.0	3.4364	0.4173	4.4364	0.5173	492	47	5
1.0	3.4365	0.4174	4.4365	0.5174	493	48	6

To start the line for $x = 0.3$, we first compute Δy by means of (86.1), using the data in the line for $x = 0.2$. We have

$$\Delta y = 0.1[1.4427 + 0.1162 + 0.0092] = 0.1568.$$

Hence $y_{0.3}^{(1)} = 1.2427 + 0.1568 = 1.3995$, and $(y')_{0.3}^{(1)} = 1.6995$. We now enter these values in the table and compute the differences for that line. Checking these values by means of (86.2), we get

$$\Delta y = 0.1\,(1.6995 - 0.1284 - 0.0020 - 0.0001) = 0.1569.$$

Since this value of Δy is different from that previously found, we repeat the line for $x = 0.3$ and write this value of Δy in the new line. The second approximations for $y_{0.3}$ and $(y')_{0.3}$ are then

$$y_{0.3}^{(2)} = 1.2427 + 0.1569 = 1.3996,$$

$$(y')_{0.3}^{(2)} = 1.6996.$$

Entering these values in the new line, computing the corresponding differences, and then applying formula (86.2) to the data of this line, we have

$$\Delta y = 0.1\,(1.6996 - 0.1284 - 0.0020 - 0.0002) = 0.1569.$$

Since this is the same value for Δy as previously found, we consider the results in this second line for $x = 0.3$ to be correct.

The computations are continued up to $x = 1$, as shown in the table. It so happens that formula (86.1) gives the correct result for every line except the last. Fourth differences were used in formula (86.1), but not in (86.2).

Since the exact solution of the differential equation $dy/dx = x + y$, with the initial conditions $x_0 = 0$, $y_0 = 1$, is

$$y = 2e^x - x - 1,$$

we can compute the exact value of y corresponding to any value of x. The following table gives the correct values of y for values of x differing by one tenth.

x	y	x	y
0	1	0.6	2.0442
0.1	1.1103	0.7	2.3275
0.2	1.2428	0.8	2.6511
0.3	1.3997	0.9	3.0192
0.4	1.5836	1.0	3.4366
0.5	1.7974		

It will be noticed that the values found by numerical integration are in error by one unit in the last decimal place, beginning with the value for $x = 0.2$. The truth is that the source of these errors is in the value 1.2427, which is in error by one unit in the last figure. This error was simply carried on by addition throughout the table. To avoid such errors it is necessary to have the first two or three lines in the table correct.

Note. There is another method for starting a new line in the table without the use of formula (86. 1). It consists in assuming that the highest difference in the next line will be the same as in the line just finished, and then working backwards by adding the new differences to the values in the previous line. For example, suppose we take the line for $x = 0.8$ and try to find the next line. We have

x	y	Δy	y'	$\Delta_1 y'$	$\Delta_2 y'$	$\Delta_3 y'$
0.8	2.6510	0.3236	3.4510	0.4236	403	38
0.9	3.0191	0.3681	(3.9187)	(0.4677)	(441)	(38)
0.9	3.0191	0.3681	3.9191	0.4681	445	42

The first step in this procedure was to assume that the third difference in the line for $x = 0.9$ was 0.0038, the same value as given in the line above. Then we added this 0.0038 to the second difference 0.0403 in the line above. This gave us a second difference for the new line. We added this 0.0441 to the first difference in the line above and obtained a new first difference 0.4677. This was then added to the previous y' to get the value 3.9187 for y' in the new line.

The next step is to apply formula (86. 2) to this new line, using the quantities enclosed in parentheses (these quantities are enclosed in parentheses to indicate that they are trial or assumed values). We thus get

$$\Delta y = 0.1(3.9187 - 0.2338 - 0.0037 - 0.0002) = 0.3681.$$

This value of Δy happens to be correct. We now add this to the previous y to get the new value of y and thus complete the line. But now the new y' must be computed by adding the value of x to this new y. We therefore repeat the line for $x = 0.9$ and insert the correct values of all the quantities. In some instances it would be necessary to correct this second line.

The method just outlined in this note is the one used by J. C. Adams and F. R. Moulton. It is not as much trouble to apply as it may seem from the description above, but nevertheless it requires more labor than the method of integrating ahead by (86. 1) and will therefore not be used in this book.

87. Methods of Starting the Solution. The determination of the first few values of the function is the most important and usually the most laborious part in the numerical solution of a differential equation. It is the most important part because the first few values must be *accurate to the number of significant figures desired in the solution,* and it is the most laborious because the first few values are sometimes not easily found to the desired accuracy.

Formulas (86.1) and (86.2) involve the first four differences of the function y'. These differences can be constructed only when five consecutive values of y' are known. The first value of y' can be found from the given equation and the initial values of x and y; the remaining four can be found by one or more of several methods, the most important of which are the following:

1. By *Taylor's Series.* If $y = f(x)$, the familiar Taylor formula

(1) $f(x) = f(x_0) + f'(x_0)(x - x_0) + \dfrac{f''(x_0)}{2}(x - x_0)^2$

$+ \dfrac{f'''(x_0)}{3!}(x - x_0)^3 + \cdots$

may be written in the less familiar form

(2) $y = y_0 + y'_0(x - x_0) + \dfrac{y''_0}{2}(x - x_0)^2 + \dfrac{y'''_0}{3!}(x - x_0)^3$

$+ \dfrac{y^{\text{iv}}_0}{4!}(x - x_0)^4 + \cdots$

where x_0 and y_0 denote the initial values of x and y. In finding y's by formula (2), it is desirable to keep $|x - x_0|$ numerically small in order to have rapid convergence of the series and therefore high accuracy in the y's. Hence in general we should work on both sides of the point x_0; that is, we should compute y's both to the right and to the left of the point $x = x_0$. Using the notation $y_1 = f(x_0 + h)$, $y_2 = f(x_0 + 2h)$, $y_{-1} = f(x_0 - h)$, $y_{-2} = f(x_0 - 2h)$, etc., we have from (2):

(3) $y_1 = y_0 + y'_0 h + \dfrac{y''_0 h^2}{2} + \dfrac{y'''_0 h^3}{3!} + \dfrac{y^{\text{iv}}_0 h^4}{4!} + \dfrac{y^{\text{v}}_0 h^5}{5!} + \cdots$

(4) $y_2 = y_0 + y'_0(2h) + \dfrac{y''_0(2h)^2}{2} + \dfrac{y'''_0(2h)^3}{3!} + \dfrac{y^{\text{iv}}_0(2h)^4}{4!} + \dfrac{y^{\text{v}}_0(2h)^5}{5!} + \cdots$

(5) $y_{-1} = y_0 - y'_0 h + \dfrac{y''_0 h^2}{2} - \dfrac{y'''_0 h^3}{3!} + \dfrac{y^{\text{iv}}_0 h^4}{4!} - \dfrac{y^{\text{v}}_0 h^5}{5!} + \cdots$

(6) $y_{-2} = y_0 - y'_0(2h) + \dfrac{y''_0(2h)^2}{2} - \dfrac{y'''_0(2h)^3}{3!} + \dfrac{y^{\text{iv}}_0(2h)^4}{4!} - \dfrac{y^{\text{v}}_0(2h)^5}{5!} + \cdots$

where h denotes the interval between the equidistant values of x.

If the successive derivatives of the given differential equation $y' = f(x, y)$ are easily found, the five needed consecutive values of y' can be found from the initial conditions, the given equation, and the formulas (3)-(6) above.

Example 1. Let the given differential equation be

$$\frac{dx}{dy} = y' = x + y, \quad \text{with } x_0 = 0, \ y_0 = 1.$$

Here

$$y' = x + y, \quad y'' = 1 + y', \quad y''' = y'', \quad y^{iv} = y''', \quad y^{v} = y^{iv}$$

Hence

$$y'_0 = x_0 + y_0 = 1, \ y''_0 = 1 + y_0 = 2, \ y''' = y'' = 2, \ y^{iv} = y''' = 2, \ y^{v} = 2.$$

Now taking $h = 0.1$ and substituting in (3), (4), (5), (6), we get

$$y_1 = 1.1103, \quad y_2 = 1.2428, \quad y_{-1} = 0.9097, \quad y_{-2} = 0.8375.$$

These values are all correct to four decimal places. The five desired consecutive values of y' are now found from the given equation to be:

$$y'_{-2} = x_{-2} + y_{-2} = -0.2 + 0.8375 = 0.6375$$

$$y'_{-1} = x_{-1} + y_{-1} = -0.1 + 0.9097 = 0.8097$$

$$y'_0 = x_0 + y_0 = 1$$

$$y'_1 = x_1 + y_1 = 0.1 + 1.1103 = 1.2103$$

$$y'_2 = x_2 + y_2 = 0.2 + 1.2428 = 1.4428.$$

If the function y should be non-existent for values of x less than x_0, then we compute y's only to the right of x_0 by substituting in (2) the proper values of h.

2. By *Milne's Formulas.* It frequently happens that the higher derivatives of $y' = f(x, y)$ cannot be found without excessive labor, or hardly at all. In such cases the above method cannot be used for starting the computation. If, however, the first derivative of $y' = f(x, y)$, or y'', can be found without difficulty, the five starting values of y' can be found by certain formulas first used by W. E. Milne.* To derive these formulas we need two additional Taylor series similar to (3) and (5).

Representing the function y', or $\dfrac{dy}{dx}$, in the neighborhood of $x = x_0$ by Taylor's series, we have

$$(7) \qquad y'_1 = y'_0 + y''_0 h + \frac{y'''_0 h^2}{2} + \frac{y^{iv}_0 h^3}{3!} + \frac{y^{v}_0 h^4}{4!} + \cdots$$

$$(8) \qquad y'_{-1} = y'_0 - y''_0 h + \frac{y'''_0 h^2}{2} - \frac{y^{iv}_0 h^3}{3!} + \frac{y^{v}_0 h^4}{4!} - \cdots.$$

* *American Mathematical Monthly*, Vol. 48 (1941), p. 52.

Adding (7) and (8) and then subtracting (8) from (7), we get

(9) $$y'_1 + y'_{-1} = 2y'_0 + y'''_0 h^2 + \frac{y^v_0 h^4}{12} + \cdots$$

(10) $$y'_1 - y'_{-1} = 2y''_0 h + \frac{y^{iv}_0 h^3}{3} + \cdots.$$

Now solve (9) for y'''_0, (10) for y^{iv}_0, and then substitute these values in (3) and (5). The results are

(A) $$y_1 = y_0 + \frac{h}{24}(y'_{-1} + 16y'_0 + 7y'_1) + \frac{y''_0 h^2}{4} - \frac{y^v_0 h^5}{180}$$

(B) $$y_{-1} = y_0 - \frac{h}{24}(7y'_{-1} + 16y'_0 + y'_1) + \frac{y''_0 h^2}{4} + \frac{y^v_0 h^5}{180}$$

These formulas give y_1 and y_{-1} as soon as y'_{-1} and y'_1 are known.

To find formulas giving y_2 and y_{-2}, substitute in (4) and (6) the values of y'''_0 and y^{iv}_0 found from (9) and (10). The results are

(C) $$y_2 = y_0 + \frac{2h}{3}(5y'_1 - y'_0 - y'_{-1}) - 2y''_0 h^2 + \frac{7}{45}y^v_0 h^5,$$

(D) $$y_{-2} = y_0 - \frac{2h}{3}(5y'_{-1} - y'_0 - y'_1) - 2y''_0 h^2 - \frac{7}{45}y^v_0 h^5.$$

These formulas will give y_2 and y_{-2} as soon as y'_{-1} and y'_1 are known.

An additional formula is desirable for checking y_2 and y_{-2} when found from (C) and (D). Subtracting (B) from (A), we get

$$y_1 - y_{-1} = \frac{h}{3}(y'_{-1} + 4y'_0 + y'_1) - \frac{y^v_0 h^5}{90},$$

or

$$y_1 = y_{-1} + \frac{h}{3}(y'_{-1} + 4y'_0 + y'_1) - \frac{y^v_0 h^5}{90}.$$

Since this formula holds for any interval of width $2h$, we may write it as a general formula

(E) $$y_{n+1} = y_{n-1} + \frac{h}{3}(y'_{n-1} + 4y'_n + y'_{n+1}) - \frac{y^v_n h^5}{90}.$$

The quantity $\frac{h}{3}(y'_{n-1} + 4y'_n + y'_{n+1})$ is evidently Simpson's Rule and is an approximation to the definite integral $\int_{-h}^{h} y' dx$, which represents the increment in y for the two intervals from $x_n - h$ to $x_n + h$.

In the application of formulas (A)-(E) the terms in y^v_0 are omitted. The formulas as used are thus accurate up to and including fourth differences.

It is to be noted that the second derivative y'' is to be evaluated only at the one point (x_0, y_0).

Concerning the use of the foregoing formulas, the first step is to compute trial values of y'_1 and y'_{-1} from the relations

(F) $y'_1 = y'_0 + hy''_0, \qquad y'_{-1} = y'_0 - hy''_0$ (Euler method).

Then substitute these in (A) and (B) to get first approximations to y_1 and y_{-1}. These approximate values of y_1 and y_{-1}, with the corresponding x_1 and x_{-1}, are then substituted into the given differential equation $y' = f(x, y)$ to get improved values for y'_1 and y'_{-1}, which in turn are substituted back into (A) and (B) to get better values for y_1 and y_{-1}. This iteration process is continued until no change is produced in y'_1 and y'_{-1}. To obtain high accuracy in y'_{-1} and y'_1 the value of h must be small.

Now having the three consecutive values y'_{-1}, y'_0, y'_1 to the desired degree of accuracy, we substitute them in (C) and (D) to get approximate values of y_2 and y_{-2} by extrapolation. Then these, together with x_2 and x_{-2}, are substituted into the given equation to get approximate values of y'_2 and y'_{-2}. These latter are then substituted into formula (E) to get improved values of y_2 and y_{-2}. If these agree with the previous values found by extrapolation, we take them as correct. Then these values when substituted into the given equation will give correct values for y'_2 and y'_{-2}. We thus obtain the five needed consecutive values of y' to give us the various orders of differences to use in (86.1).

Note. After having found y'_{-1}, y'_0, and y'_1 to the desired degree of accuracy, we could form first and second differences from these and then proceed with formulas (86.1) and (86.2).

Example 2. To find five consecutive values of y' for starting the solution of the equation

$$y' = \frac{xy}{x^2 + y^2}, \quad \text{with } y_0 = 1, \quad x_0 = 0,$$

we have

$$y'' = \frac{(x^2 + y^2)(xy' + y) - xy(2x + 2yy')}{(x^2 + y^2)^2}.$$

Hence

$$y'_0 = 0, \quad y''_0 = 1.$$

Taking $h = 0.1$, we have from formulas (F)

$$y'_1 = 0 + 0.1(1) = 0.1, \quad y'_{-1} = 0 - 0.1 = -0.1.$$

Then by (A) and (B),

$$y_1^{(1)} = 1 + \frac{0.1}{24}(-0.1 + 0.7) + \frac{0.01}{4} = 1.0050,$$

$$y_{-1}^{(1)} = 1 - \frac{0.1}{24}(-0.7 + 0.1) = 1.0050.$$

Now substituting these y's and the corresponding x's into the given equation, we have

$$y'_1 = \frac{(0.1)(1.005)}{(0.1)^2 + (1.005)^2} = \frac{0.1005}{0.01 + 1.010025} = 0.09853,$$

$$y'_{-1} = -0.09853.$$

On substituting these into (A) and (B), we get

$$y_1^{(2)} = 1 + \frac{0.1}{24}(-0.09853 + 0.68971) + 0.0025 = 1.00496,$$

$$y_{-1}^{(2)} = 1.00496.$$

Now substituting these into the given equation, we have

$$y'_1 = \frac{(0.1)(1.00496)}{(0.1)^2 + (1.00496)^2} = \frac{0.100496}{1.01994} = 0.09853,$$

$$y'_1 = -0.09853.$$

As these are the same values as previously found for y'_1 and y'_{-1}, we take them to be correct.

Having " dug in," as it were, about the point (x_0, y_0) and found three consecutive values of y' to the desired degree of accuracy, we next find y_{-2} and y_2 by extrapolating backward and forward by means of formulas (C) and (D). From (C) and (D) we have

$$y_2 = 1 + \frac{0.2}{3}(0.59118) - 0.02 = 1.0194,$$

$$y_{-2} = 1 - \frac{0.2}{3}(-0.59118) - 0.02 = 1.0194.$$

These values must now be checked by formula (E) after first finding y'_2 and y'_{-2} from the giving equation. Substituting in the given equation the value of $x_2 (= 2h = 0.2)$ and the value of y_2 found above, we have

$$y'_2 = \frac{0.2(1.0194)}{(0.2)^2 + (1.0194)^2} = \frac{0.20388}{1.07918} = 0.18892.$$

Likewise, for $x_{-2} (= -2h = -0.2)$ and the value of y_{-2} found above, we get

$$y'_{-2} = \frac{-0.2(1.0194)}{(-0.2)^2 + (1.0194)^2} = -0.18892.$$

Then from formula (E),

$$y_2 = y_0 + \frac{h}{3} (y'_0 + 4y'_1 + y'_2)$$

$$= 1 + \frac{0.1}{3} (0 + 4 \times 0.09853 + 0.18892) = 1.0194.$$

For checking the backward value y_{-2} we write formula (E) in the transposed form

$$y_{n-1} = y_{n+1} - \frac{h}{3} (y'_{n-1} + 4y'_n + y'_{n+1}).$$

Hence we have

$$y_{-2} = y_0 - \frac{h}{3} (y'_{-2} + 4y'_{-1} + y'_0)$$

$$= 1 - \frac{0.1}{3} (- 0.18892 - 4 \times 0.09853) = 1.0194.$$

Since these values are the same as those found by extrapolation, we consider them to be correct.

Now having five correct consecutive values for y and y', we can form differences up to and including the fourth for these quantities and proceed with the numerical solution by means of formulas (86.1) and (86.2).

At this point it is instructive to compare these computed values of y and y' with their exact values. The homogeneous equation $y' = \dfrac{xy}{x^2 + y^2}$ can readily be solved by the usual artifice of putting $y = vx$. The solution, with the given initial conditions, is found to be

$$x^2 = y^2 \ln y^2.$$

The Newton-Raphson method, when applied to this equation, shows that y_1 should be corrected by the amount 0.000003 and y_2 by the amount 0.00003. The values previously found are thus true to the number of significant figures retained in the computation.

3. By the *Runge-Kutta Method*. The use of this method will be explained in a subsequent article.

4. By the *Modified Euler Method*. This method has been explained in Article 84. It can be used for starting the numerical solution of any ordinary differential equation and is used when the previously-explained methods cannot be used to advantage.

After the five consecutive starting values have been found, the numerical solution of a differential equation is continued as far as desired by means of formulas (86.1) and (86.2). This part of the solution is mostly smooth sailing. If the differences higher than the second become negligible, it will be well to double the interval h. When this is done, a new table of differences must be constructed for the wider interval, using the previously-computed values of y' for this purpose.

If, on the other hand, the fourth differences should become large, or if several trial computations should be required to obtain the correct result, or if the term $\dfrac{h}{3}\Delta_4 y'$ should equal or exceed half a unit in the last decimal place (or in the last significant figure retained in the computation), then the interval h should be reduced by half and the computation continued with the shorter interval as far as may seem necessary. The best way of reducing the interval is explained below.

88. Halving the Interval for h. Since the process of reducing the interval is the same as beginning a new solution of the given equation, it is absolutely necessary that five consecutive values of y' be known *accurately* in the region where the new computation is to begin. The best way to find accurate values at the midpoints of old intervals is to use Bessel's formula for interpolating to halves, namely:

$$(88.1) \quad y'_{1/2} = \frac{y'_0 + y'_1}{2} - \frac{1}{8}\frac{\Delta^2 y'_{-1} + \Delta^2 y'_0}{2} + \frac{3}{128}\frac{\Delta^4 y'_{-2} + \Delta^4 y'_{-1}}{2},$$

where $y'_{1/2}$ is the value of y' halfway between y'_0 and y'_1. Note that the differences used in this formula are ordinary *diagonal differences*. It will be necessary to find the value of y' at two midintervals in order to have five consecutive values for starting the computation with halved intervals.

Example. The numerical solution of the equation $y' = x + y$ is tabulated on page 249 from $x = 0$ to $x = 1$. Suppose it were desired to reduce the interval by half from the point $x = 0.6$ onward.

Solution. We take $x = 0.6$ as the zero point and then rewrite the differences of the y''s in diagonal-difference form, as shown below:

	x	y'	$\Delta y'$	$\Delta^2 y'$	$\Delta^3 y'$	$\Delta^4 y'$
-2	0.4	1.9835				
			$+0.3138$			
-1	0.5	2.2973		330		
			0.3468		35	
0	0.6	2.6441		365		3
			0.3833		38	
1	0.7	3.0274		403		4
			0.4236		42	
2	0.8	3.4510		445		6
			0.4681		48	
3	0.9	3.9191		493		
			0.5174			
4	1.0	4.4365				

Then for $x = 0.65$, we have

$$y'_{0.65} = \frac{2.6441 + 3.0274}{2} - \frac{1}{8} \frac{0.0365 + 0.0403}{2}$$

$$+ \frac{3}{128} \frac{0.0003 + 0.0004}{2} = 2.8358 - 0.0048 = 2.8310,$$

and

$$y'_{0.75} = \frac{3.0274 + 3.4510}{2} - \frac{1}{8} \frac{0.0403 + 0.0445}{2} = 3.2339.$$

The five starting values for the new table, considering only y', would be as shown below:

x	y'	$\Delta_1 y'$	$\Delta_2 y'$	$\Delta_3 y'$	$\Delta_4 y'$
0.60	2.6441				
0.65	2.8310	+0.1869			
0.70	3.0274	0.1964	95		
0.75	3.2339	0.2065	101	6	
0.80	3.4510	0.2171	106	5	−1
0.85	3.6792	0.2282	111	5	0
0.90	3.9191	0.2399	117	6	1

Continuing the computations, we apply (86.1) to the line for $x = 0.80$ and get

$$\Delta y = 0.05[3.4510 + 0.1086 + 0.0044 + 0.0002] = 0.1782.$$

Then

$$y_{0.85} = 2.6510 + 0.1782 = 2.8292.$$

Hence

$$y'_{0.85} = 0.85 + 2.8292 = 3.6792.$$

We next fill in the line for $x = 0.85$ and apply (86.2) to this line as a check. We have

$$\Delta y = 0.05[3.6792 - 0.1141 - 0.0009] = 0.1782,$$

which is the same as before.

We continue the table through the line $x = 0.90$ to see if the new schedule with halved intervals gives the values previously found. Applying (86.1) to the line for $x = 0.85$, we have

$$\Delta y = 0.05[3.6792 + 0.1141 + 0.0046 + 0.0002] = 0.1899.$$

Hence

$$y_{0.90} = 2.8292 + 0.1899 = 3.0191.$$

Then

$$y'_{0.90} = 0.90 + 3.0191 = 3.9191.$$

These are the same values as previously found before the interval was halved, and they indicate that no error was introduced in changing to the shorter interval. It is to be noted that the shorter interval reduces the fourth differences to insignificance.

EXERCISES XI

1. Obtain by the modified Euler method five consecutive starting values for the numerical solution of

$$\frac{dy}{dx} = \log_{10} \frac{x}{y},$$

with $x_0 = 20$, $y_0 = 5$. Check the starting values by formulas (86.2) to (86.5) and then add two more lines to your table.

2. Obtain by Taylor's series five consecutive starting values for the numerical solution of

$$\frac{dy}{dx} = 2x - y,$$

with $x_0 = 1$, $y_0 = 3$. Check the values and then add three more lines to the table.

Compare your results with those obtained from the exact analytical solution $y = 2x + 3e^{1-x} - 2$.

3. Tabulate the numerical solution of

$$\frac{dy}{dx} = \sin x + \cos y$$

from $x_0 = 30°$, $y_0 = 45°$ to $x = 60°$.

4. Use the Taylor-series method to start the numerical solution of

$$\frac{dy}{dx} = x^2 + y^2,$$

with $x_0 = 1$, $y_0 = 0$.

Then solve the equation analytically and compute accurate values of y for comparison with the computed starting values.

5. Given the equation

$$\frac{dy}{dx} = -\frac{x}{2y} + \sqrt{\left(\frac{x}{2y}\right)^2 - 1},$$

with $x_0 = 1$, $y_0 = 1/4$; find $(d^2y/dx^2)_0$ and then find five consecutive starting values by means of the Euler method and the Milne formulas. Note that a solution exists only in the regions where $|x/2y| > 1$.

6. Integrate the equation of Ex. 2 by Picard's method of successive approximations.

II. EQUATIONS OF THE SECOND ORDER AND SYSTEMS OF SIMULTANEOUS EQUATIONS.

89. Equations of the Second Order. Any differential equation of the second or higher order can be reduced to a system of first-order equations by the introduction of auxiliary variables. Thus, the second-order equation

$$\frac{d^2y}{dx^2} + P\,\frac{dy}{dx} + Qy = 0$$

can be reduced to two first-order equations by putting $y' = dy/dx$. The resulting equations are

$$\frac{dy}{dx} = y', \ \frac{dy'}{dx} = -Py' - Qy.$$

In like manner, any equation higher than the second order or any system of equations of the second or higher order can be reduced to a system of equations of the first order. These first-order equations can then be solved by the methods already given.

Example. When a pendulum swings in a resisting medium, its equation of motion is of the form

$$\frac{d^2\theta}{dt^2} + a\frac{d\theta}{dt} + b\sin\theta = 0,$$

where a and b are constants. Assuming $a = 0.2$, $b = 10$, start the solution of the above equation, taking as initial conditions $\theta = 0.3$ radian and $d\theta/dt = 0$ when $t = 0$.

Solution. The substitutions $d\theta/dt = \dot{\theta}$, $d^2\theta/dt^2 = d\dot{\theta}/dt = \ddot{\theta}$ reduce the given equation to the two first-order equations

$$\begin{cases} \dfrac{d\theta}{dt} = \dot{\theta}, \\[2ex] \dfrac{d\dot{\theta}}{dt} = \ddot{\theta} = -0.2\dot{\theta} - 10\sin\theta. \end{cases}$$

Since the second equation involves θ directly, it is necessary to compute this angle at every step throughout the computation. Also, since θ in this problem is always expressed in radians, it is practically necessary to use a table of sines in which the argument is given directly in radians.*

* The best table of this kind is *Tables of Circular and Hyperbolic Sines and Cosines for Radian Arguments.* New York, 1939.

The formulas to be used in the solution of this example are:

(1) $\qquad \ddot{\theta} = -0.2\dot{\theta} - 10 \sin \theta$, the given equation;

(2) $\Delta\dot{\theta} = \int_{t_n}^{t_{n+1}} \ddot{\theta}\, dt = \Delta t (\ddot{\theta}_n + \frac{1}{2}\Delta_1\ddot{\theta}_n + \frac{5}{12}\Delta_2\ddot{\theta}_n + \frac{3}{8}\Delta_3\ddot{\theta}_n + \frac{1}{3}\Delta_4\ddot{\theta}_n)$,

for starting a new line;

(3) $\Delta\dot{\theta} = \int_{t_{n-1}}^{t_n} \ddot{\theta}\, dt = \Delta t (\ddot{\theta}_n - \frac{1}{2}\Delta_1\ddot{\theta}_n - \frac{1}{12}\Delta_2\ddot{\theta}_n - \frac{1}{24}\Delta_3\ddot{\theta}_n - \frac{1}{38}\Delta_4\ddot{\theta})$,

for checking and correcting the value of $\Delta\dot{\theta}$ found by (2);

(4) $\Delta\theta = \int_{t_{n-1}}^{t_n} \dot{\theta}\, dt = \Delta t (\dot{\theta}_n - \frac{1}{2}\Delta_1\dot{\theta}_n - \frac{1}{12}\Delta_2\dot{\theta}_n - \frac{1}{24}\Delta_3\dot{\theta}_n - \frac{1}{38}\Delta_4\dot{\theta})$,

for finding θ in the new line, where t_{n+1} in (2) denotes the same instant as t_n in (3) and (4). After the starting values are found, the above formulas are applied in the following order: (2), (4), (1); (3), (4), (1); (3), (4), (1) until the new line is finished.

The starting values for this problem can be found by any of the methods mentioned in Art. 87. We shall find them by the Taylor-series method.

The Taylor series for θ is

(5) $\theta = \theta_0 + \dot{\theta}_0 t + \dfrac{\ddot{\theta}_0 t^2}{2} + \dfrac{\dddot{\theta}_0 t^3}{3!} + \dfrac{\theta^{iv}{}_0 t^4}{4!} + \dfrac{\theta^v{}_0 t^5}{5!} + \dfrac{\theta^{vi}{}_0 t^6}{6!} + \cdots$.

From the given equation $\ddot{\theta} = -0.2\dot{\theta} - 10 \sin \theta$ we get

$\dddot{\theta} = -0.2\ddot{\theta} - 10\dot{\theta}\cos\theta$

$\theta^{iv} = -0.2\dddot{\theta} + 10(\dot{\theta}^2 \sin\theta - \ddot{\theta}\cos\theta)$

$\theta^v = 0.2\theta^{iv} + 10[(\dot{\theta}^3 - \dddot{\theta})\cos\theta + 3\dot{\theta}\ddot{\theta}\sin\theta]$

$\theta^{vi} = -0.2\theta^v + 10[(3\dot{\theta}^2\ddot{\theta} - \theta^{iv})\cos\theta - (\dot{\theta}^4 - \dot{\theta}\dddot{\theta})\sin\theta$
$\qquad + 3(\dot{\theta}^2\ddot{\theta}\cos\theta + \ddot{\theta}^2\sin\theta + \dot{\theta}\ddot{\theta}\sin\theta)]$.

For $\theta = 0.3$ radian, $\dot{\theta} = 0$ when $t = 0$, the above equations give

$\ddot{\theta}_0 = -10 \sin 0.3 = -2.9552$,

$\dddot{\theta}_0 = -0.2\ddot{\theta}_0 = 0.2 \times 2.9552 = 0.59104$,

$\theta^{iv}{}_0 = -0.2\dddot{\theta}_0 - 10\ddot{\theta}_0 \cos 0.3 = -0.1182 + 28.2321 = 28.1139$,

$\theta^v{}_0 = -0.2\theta^{iv}{}_0 - 10\dddot{\theta}_0 \cos 0.3 = -5.6228 - 5.6464 = -11.2692$,

$\theta^{vi}{}_0 = -0.2\theta^v{}_0 - 10\theta^{iv}{}_0 \cos 0.3 + 30\dot{\theta}^2 \sin 0.3 = 2.254 - 268.582 + 77.425$
$\qquad = -188.903$.

Substituting in (5) these values and the initial conditions, we get

(6) $\theta = 0.3 - \dfrac{2.9552}{2} t^2 + \dfrac{0.59104}{6} t^3 + \dfrac{28.114}{24} t^4 - \dfrac{11.269}{120} t^5$

   $- \dfrac{188.90}{720} t^6 \cdots$.

Differentiating (6) with respect to t, we have

(7) $\dot\theta = -2.9552t + \dfrac{0.59104}{2} t^2 + \dfrac{28.114}{6} t^3 - \dfrac{11.269}{24} t^4 - \dfrac{188.90}{120} t^5$.

We are now ready to find starting values of θ, $\dot\theta$, and $\ddot\theta$ for values of t near zero and at steps of $\dfrac{1}{20}$ sec. Putting $t = -\dfrac{1}{10}, -\dfrac{1}{20}, 0, \dfrac{1}{20}, \dfrac{1}{10}$ in (6) and (7) and then computing the corresponding values of $\ddot\theta$ from (1), we get the first five values of these quantities as given in the table on page 264.

After forming the various orders of differences for these quantities, we are ready to extend the table by applying formulas (2), (4), (1), (3), etc. Two additional lines computed in this manner are given in the table. The actual computation of the line for $t = 0.15$ was as follows:

Applying formula (2) to the acceleration quantities in the line for $t = 0.10$, we have

$$\Delta\dot\theta = \frac{1}{20} [-2.758 + 0.066 + 0.029] = -0.1332.$$

This is the first entry in the new line for $t = 0.15$. Adding this $\Delta\dot\theta$ to the previous value of $\dot\theta$, we get -0.4211 for the new $\dot\theta$. Now compute the various orders of differences for the new $\dot\theta$.

We next compute $\Delta\theta$ for this line by applying (4) to the $\dot\theta$ quantities. We thus have

$$\Delta\theta = \frac{1}{20} [-0.4211 + 0.0666 - 0.0007 - 0.0001] = -0.0178.$$

Adding this to the previous value of θ, we have

$$\theta_{0.15} = 0.2854 - 0.0178 = 0.2676.$$

We next substitute in the given equation (1) the values of θ and $\dot\theta$ for the new line, in order to get the acceleration when $t = 0.15$. We thus have

$$\ddot\theta = -0.2(-0.4211) - 10 \sin 0.2676 = -2.560.$$

Then we compute the several orders of differences for this acceleration.

t	θ	$\Delta\theta$	$\dot\theta$	$\Delta_1\dot\theta$	$\Delta_2\dot\theta$	$\Delta_3\dot\theta$	$\Delta_4\dot\theta$	$\ddot\theta$	$\Delta_1\ddot\theta$	$\Delta_2\ddot\theta$	$\Delta_3\ddot\theta$	$\Delta_4\ddot\theta$
-0.10	0.2852		0.2938					-2.872				
		+111		-0.1459					-77			
-0.05	0.2963		0.1479		-20			-2.949		+71		
		+37		-0.1479		+35			-6		-1	
0	0.3000		0.0000		+15		-1	-2.955		+70		0
		-37		-0.1464		+34			+64		-1	
+0.05	0.2963		-0.1464		+49		0	-2.891		+69		-3
		-109		-0.1415		+34			+133		-4	
0.10	0.2854		-0.2879		+83		-3	-2.758		+65		0
		-178		-0.1332		+31			+198		-4	
0.15	0.2676		-0.4211		+114			-2.560		+61		
		-242		-0.1218					+259			
0.20	0.2434		-0.5429					-2.301				

The line for $t = 0.15$ is now completely filled, but it must be checked. Hence we apply formula (3) to the acceleration data last filled in and have

$$\Delta\dot\theta = \frac{1}{20}\,[-2.560 - 0.099 - 0.005] = -0.1332.$$

Since this is the same value of $\Delta\dot\theta$ as previously found, there is no possibility of improving any of the entries in the line for $t = 0.15$ and we therefore regard them as correct.

Succeeding lines are added to the table in exactly the same manner as above described.

In this example the time interval Δt must be taken short, because θ, $\dot\theta$, and $\ddot\theta$ are all changing rapidly. To obtain results accurate to four significant figures Δt should be kept at $\frac{1}{20}$ second.

Space does not permit the higher differences of θ to be shown in the table, but these differences should always be computed as a check on the accuracy of the computed values of θ.

Another check formula for second-order differential equations is the following: *

(5) $$y_{n+1} = 2y_n - y_{n-1} + h^2(y''_n + \tfrac{1}{12}\Delta_2 y''_{n+1}),$$

in which the first error term (the principal part of the inherent error) is $\frac{h^6}{240}\,y^{vi}{}_n$, which is practically $\frac{\Delta^6 y_n}{240}$.

Let us check the value of $\theta_{0.20}$ in the above table by formula (5). We have

$$\theta_{0.20} = 2(0.2676) - 0.2854 + \frac{1}{400}\,[-2.560 + \tfrac{1}{12}(0.061)] = 0.2434,$$

which is the value already found and checked by (4) and (3).

90. Special Differential Equations of the Second Order. When a second-order differential equation does not contain the first derivative, its numerical solution can be found rapidly and accurately by a shorter and simpler procedure than that employed in the preceding article. In this case we replace the *second derivative* by a polynomial and integrate twice to find the desired formulas for numerical integration.

We consider first the single equation

(1) $$\frac{d^2y}{dx^2} = f(x, y),$$

---

* Levy and Baggott, *Numerical Studies in Differential Equations*, p. 145.

which we write in the form

(2) $$y'' = f(x, y).$$

Replacing y_n by y''_n in Newton's formula (II), we have

(3) $$y'' = y''_n + u\Delta_1 y''_n + \frac{u(u+1)}{2}\Delta_2 y''_n + \frac{u(u+1)(u+2)}{3!}\Delta_3 y''_n$$
$$+ \frac{u(u+1)(u+2)(u+3)}{4!}\Delta_4 y''_n + \cdots,$$

where $u = \dfrac{x - x_n}{h}$ or $x = x_n + hu$. Integrating this with respect to x and remembering that $dx = h\,du$, we have

$$y' = h\left[\, y''_n u + \Delta_1 y''_n \frac{u^2}{2} + \frac{\Delta_2 y''_n}{2}\left(\frac{u^3}{3} + \frac{u^2}{2}\right) + \frac{\Delta_3 y''_n}{6}\left(\frac{u^4}{4} + u^3 + u^2\right)\right.$$
$$\left. + \frac{\Delta_4 y''_n}{24}\left(\frac{u^5}{5} + \frac{3u^4}{2} + \frac{11u^3}{3} + 3u^2\right)\right] + C_1.$$

We determine C_1 from the condition that $y' = y'_n$ when $x = x_n$. But when $x = x_n$, $u = 0$. Hence on putting $u = 0$ and $y' = y'_n$, we get $C_1 = y'_n$. Then y' becomes

$$y' = y'_n + h\left[\, y''_n u + \Delta_1 y''_n \frac{u^2}{2} + \frac{\Delta_2 y''_n}{2}\left(\frac{u^3}{3} + \frac{u^2}{2}\right)\right.$$
$$\left. + \frac{\Delta_3 y''_n}{6}\left(\frac{u^4}{4} + u^3 + u^2\right) + \frac{\Delta_4 y''_n}{24}\left(\frac{u^5}{5} + \frac{3u^4}{2} + \frac{11u^3}{3} + 3u^2\right)\right].$$

Now integrating again with respect to x and determining the constant of integration C_2 from the condition that $y = y_n$ when $x = x_n$ or $u = 0$, we get $C_2 = y_n$ and

(4) $$y = y_n + h\,y'_n u + h^2\left[\, y''_n \frac{u^2}{2} + \Delta_1 y''_n \frac{u^3}{6} + \frac{\Delta_2 y''_n}{2}\left(\frac{u^4}{12} + \frac{u^3}{6}\right)\right.$$
$$\left. + \frac{\Delta_3 y''_n}{6}\left(\frac{u^5}{20} + \frac{u^4}{4} + \frac{u^3}{3}\right) + \frac{\Delta_4 y''_n}{24}\left(\frac{u^6}{30} + \frac{3u^5}{10} + \frac{11u^4}{12} + u^3\right)\right].$$

The values of y for $x = x_{n+1}$, $x = x_{n-1}$, $x = x_{n-2}$ can be found from (4) by putting $u = 1$, $u = -1$, $u = -2$ (obtained from the relation $u = \dfrac{x - x_n}{h}$). We thus find

(5) $$y_{n+1} = y_n + h\,y'_n + h^2\left[\frac{1}{2}y''_n + \frac{1}{6}\Delta_1 y''_n + \frac{1}{8}\Delta_2 y''_n + \frac{19}{180}\Delta_3 y''_n\right.$$
$$\left. + \frac{3}{32}\Delta_4 y''_n\right],$$

(6) $y_{n-1} = y_n - h\, y'_n + h^2 \left[\frac{1}{2} y''_n - \frac{1}{6} \Delta_1 y''_n - \frac{1}{24} \Delta_2 y''_n - \frac{1}{45} \Delta_3 y''_n \right.$

$$\left. - \frac{7}{480} \Delta_4 y''_n \right],$$

(7) $y_{n-2} = y_n - 2h\, y'_n + h^2 \left[2y''_n - \frac{4}{3} \Delta_1 y''_n - \frac{2}{45} \Delta_3 y''_n - \frac{1}{30} \Delta_4 y''_n \right].$

We now eliminate y'_n from these three equations to get the two desired formulas. Adding (5) and (6) and transposing y_{n-1} to the right-hand member, we get

(8) $y_{n+1} = 2y_n - y_{n-1} + h^2 \left[y''_n + \frac{1}{12} \Delta_2 y''_n + \frac{1}{12} \Delta_3 y''_n + \frac{19}{240} \Delta_4 y''_n \right].$

Multiplying (6) by 2 and subtracting the result from (7), we get

(9) $y_n = 2y_{n-1} - y_{n-2} + h^2 \left[y''_n - \Delta_1 y''_n + \frac{1}{12} \Delta_2 y''_n - \frac{1}{240} \Delta_4 y''_n \right].$

Now since

$$\frac{19}{240} \Delta_4 y''_n = \left(\frac{20}{240} - \frac{1}{240} \right) \Delta_4 y''_n = \frac{1}{12} \Delta_4 y''_n - \frac{1}{240} \Delta_4 y''_n, \text{ and since}$$

$\frac{1}{240} \Delta_4 y''_n$ is practically negligible, formulas (8) and (9) may be written in the simpler forms *

(90. 1) $y_{n+1} = 2y_n - y_{n-1} + h^2 [y''_n + \frac{1}{12}(\Delta_2 y''_n + \Delta_3 y''_n + \Delta_4 y''_n)]$

(90. 2) $y_n = 2y_{n-1} - y_{n-2} + h^2 (y''_n - \Delta_1 y''_n + \frac{1}{12} \Delta_2 y''_n).$

Formulas (90. 1) and (90. 2) give a step-by-step solution of the equation $\frac{d^2y}{dx^2} = f(x, y)$ with given initial conditions. The first is a formula for integrating ahead and finding the approximate value of y_{n+1} by extrapolation. The extrapolated value is checked and corrected by (90. 2), the y_n is this formula denoting the same ordinate as y_{n+1} in (90. 1). The starting values of y and y'' are to be found by the methods given in Art. 87.

Example. Tabulate the solution of

$$\frac{d^2y}{dx^2} - \sin y + 1 = 0, \text{ or } y'' = \sin y - 1,$$

with the initial conditions $y = 0.1132$ and $y' = 0$ when $x = 0$.

---

* The equivalent of formula (90. 1) was first used by Carl Störmer in 1907. *Archives des Sciences physiques et naturelles*, Genève, juillet-octobre 1907, p. 63 ff.

Formula (90. 2) is due to W. E. Milne. *American Mathematical Monthly*, Vol. XL (1933), p. 324.

Solution. We find the first few values of y from its Taylor expansion about the point $x = 0$. Starting with the given equation $y'' = \sin y - 1$, we have

$$y''' = \cos y \, \frac{dy}{dx} = y' \cos y$$

$$y^{\text{iv}} = -y'^2 \sin y + y'' \cos y$$

$$y^{\text{v}} = y''' \cos y - 3y'y'' \sin y - y'^3 \cos y.$$

Substituting in the above equations the initial values $y = 0.1132$, $y' = 0$ when $x = 0$, we get

$$y''_0 = \sin(0.1132) - 1 = 0.112958 - 1 = -0.88704$$

$$y'''_0 = 0$$

$$y^{\text{iv}}_0 = -0.88704 \cos(0.1132) = -0.88704 \times 0.99360 = -0.88136$$

$$y^{\text{v}}_0 = 0.$$

Substituting these values in the Taylor formula

$$y = y_0 + y'_0 x + \frac{y''_0}{2} x^2 + \frac{y'''_0}{3!} x^3 + \frac{y^{\text{iv}}_0}{4!} x^4 + \frac{y^{\text{v}}_0}{5!} x^5,$$

we get

(a) $$y = 0.1132 - 0.4435 x^2 - 0.03672 x^4.$$

By means of this equation (a) we compute the y's in the first five rows of the following table. Then we substitute these y's in the given equation to find the corresponding values of y'' in the seventh column of the table. The differences $\Delta_1 y''$, $\Delta_2 y''$, $\Delta_3 y''$ are then computed.

From this point onward we continue the computation with $h = \frac{1}{20} = 0.05$ by means of formulas (90.1) and (90.2), always applying (90.1) first and then checking and correcting the new row by (90.2). Hence to get started on the sixth row we apply (90.1) to the last row found by Taylor's series and get

$$y_6 = 2(0.1088) - 0.1121 + \frac{1}{400} \left[-0.8914 + \frac{1}{12} (-0.0022) \right]$$

$$= 0.1033.$$

Then we substitute this value of y_6 in the given equation and find $y''_6 = -0.8969$. The sixth row is completed by filling in the new differences.

We now apply (90.2) to the new sixth row as a check on its correctness.

x	y	$\Delta_1 y$	$\Delta_2 y$	$\Delta_3 y$	Δy_4	y''	$\Delta_1 y''$	$\Delta_2 y''$	$\Delta_3 y''$	$\Delta y_4''$
-0.10	0.1088					-0.8914				
		0.0033					0.0033			
-0.05	0.1121		-22			-0.8881		-22		
		0.0011		0			0.0011		0	
0	0.1132		-22		0	-0.8870		-22		0
		-0.0011		0			-0.0011		0	
0.05	0.1121		-22		0	-0.8881		-22		0
		-0.0033		0			-0.0033		0	
0.10	0.1088		-22		0	-0.8914		-22		1
		-0.0055		0			-0.0055		1	
0.15	0.1033		-22		-1	-0.8969		-21		-4
		-0.0077		-1			-0.0076		-3	
0.20	0.0956		-23		1	-0.9045		-24		4
		-0.0100		0			-0.0100		1	
0.25	0.0856		-23			-0.9145		-23		
		-0.0123					-0.0123			
0.30	0.0733					-0.9268				

We have

$$y_6 = 2(0.1088) - 0.1121 + \frac{1}{400} \left[-0.8969 + 0.0055 + \frac{1}{12}(-22) \right]$$
$$= 0.1033,$$

as before. Hence we consider the sixth line to be correct. The succeeding lines are computed in the same way.

The differences of the y's are not used in the computation, but they should be computed as a check on the accuracy of the work. Irregularities in the higher differences would indicate that a mistake had been made in the computation.

Systems of two, three, or any number of simultaneous equations of the second order in which first derivatives are absent can be solved numerically by formulas similar to (90.1) and (90.2). Thus for a system of three equations

(90.3)
$$\begin{cases} \dfrac{d^2x}{dt^2} = x'' = f_1(x, y, z, t) \\[2mm] \dfrac{d^2y}{dt^2} = y'' = f_2(x, y, z, t) \\[2mm] \dfrac{d^2z}{dt^2} = z'' = f_3(x, y, z, t), \end{cases}$$

each equation is integrated separately by means of its own formula analogous to (90.1). Then the extrapolated values of x, y, z are substituted into the right-hand members of (90.3) to get x'', y'', z'' at the new point ahead. Then new differences are computed, and formulas analogous to (90.2) are applied to the new rows as checks.

The necessary formulas for the three equations (90.3), for example, are

(90.4)
$$\begin{cases} x_{n+1} = 2x_n - x_{n-1} + h^2[x''_n + \frac{1}{12}(\Delta_2 x''_n + \Delta_3 x''_n + \Delta_4 x''_n)] \\[2mm] y_{n+1} = 2y_n - y_{n-1} + h^2[y''_n + \frac{1}{12}(\Delta_2 y''_n + \Delta_3 y''_n + \Delta_4 y''_n)] \\[2mm] z_{n+1} = 2z_n - z_{n-1} + h^2[z''_n + \frac{1}{12}(\Delta_2 z''_n + \Delta_3 z''_n + \Delta_4 z''_n)] \end{cases}$$

for finding approximate values at the next point ahead, and

(90.5)
$$\begin{cases} x_n = 2x_{n-1} - x_{n-2} + h^2(x''_n - \Delta_1 x''_n + \frac{1}{12}\Delta_2 x''_n) \\[2mm] y_n = 2y_{n-1} - y_{n-2} + h^2(y''_n - \Delta_1 y''_n + \frac{1}{12}\Delta_2 y''_n) \\[2mm] z_n = 2z_{n-1} - z_{n-2} + h^2(z''_n - \Delta_1 z''_n + \frac{1}{12}\Delta_2 z''_n) \end{cases}$$

for checking and correcting the new values given by (90.4). Here $h = t_{n+1} - t_n$.

Of course t may be absent from the functions f_1, f_2, f_3, in the right-hand members of (90.3) just as x was absent from the right-hand member of the equation $y'' = \sin y - 1$.

If the functions f_1, f_2, f_3 are easy to differentiate, the first five values of x, y, z needed to start the computation can be found from the initial conditions and from the Taylor expansions of x, y, z, each as a function of t; if the three functions are not easy to differentiate, the beginning values must be found by the Milne method or by the modified Euler method, using short intervals of t.

91. Systems of Simultaneous Equations. We have already dealt with certain systems of simultaneous equations in reducing a second-order equation to two first-order equations. In the present article we consider more general types of simultaneous equations.

Example. Required the numerical solution of the simultaneous equations

(1)
$$\begin{cases} \dfrac{dx}{dt} - 2\,\dfrac{dy}{dt} + x = \sin t \\[2mm] \dfrac{d^2x}{dt^2} - \dfrac{dy}{dt} + 2x - y = \ln \cos t, \end{cases}$$

with the initial conditions $x = 1$, $y = 2$, $\dfrac{dx}{dt} = 0$, when $t = 0$.

Solution. To integrate these equations numerically, we first write them in the forms

(2) $$\dot{y} = \tfrac{1}{2}(x + \dot{x} - \sin t),$$

(3) $$\ddot{x} = y - 2x + \dot{y} + \ln \cos t.$$

To get the starting values we use the Taylor-series method. Assume

(4) $x = x_0 + \dot{x}_0 t + \dfrac{\ddot{x}_0 t^2}{2} + \dfrac{\dddot{x}_0 t^3}{3!} + \dfrac{x^{iv}_0 t^4}{4!} + \dfrac{x^v_0 t^5}{5!} + \dfrac{x^{vi}_0 t^6}{6!} + \cdots$

(5) $y = y_0 + \dot{y}_0 t + \dfrac{\ddot{y}_0 t^2}{2} + \dfrac{\dddot{y}_0 t^3}{3!} + \dfrac{y^{iv}_0 t^4}{4!} + \dfrac{y^v_0 t^5}{5!} + \dfrac{y^{vi}_0 t^6}{6!} + \cdots.$

From (2) we get

$$\ddot{y} = \tfrac{1}{2}(\dot{x} + \ddot{x} - \cos t), \qquad \dddot{y} = \tfrac{1}{2}(\ddot{x} + \dddot{x} + \sin t), \text{ etc.};$$

and similarly from (3),

$$\dddot{x} = \dot{y} - 2\dot{x} + \ddot{y} - \tan t, \qquad x^{iv} = \ddot{y} - 2\ddot{x} + \dddot{y} - \sec^2 t, \text{ etc.}$$

Using the initial values and putting $t = 0$ in the above equations, we have

$$\dot{y}_0 = 1/2$$

$$\ddot{y}_0 = \tfrac{1}{2}(\tfrac{1}{2} - 1) = -1/4$$

$$\dddot{y}_0 = \tfrac{1}{2}(\tfrac{1}{2} + \tfrac{1}{4}) = 3/8$$

$$y^{iv}_0 = -\frac{5}{16}, y^v_0 = -\frac{37}{32}, y^{vi}_0 = -\frac{37}{64}$$

$$\ddot{x}_0 = 2 - 2 + \tfrac{1}{2} = 1/2$$

$$\dddot{x}_0 = 1/2 - 1/4 = 1/4$$

$$x^{iv}_0 = -1/4 - 1 + 3/8 - 1 = -15$$

$$x^v_0 = -7/16, \quad x^{vi}_0 = 9/32.$$

Note that these successive coefficients are found alternately by a zigzag procedure, starting with $\dot{y}$, then going to $\ddot{x}$, then back to $\dddot{y}$, etc.

On substituting in (4) and (5) the coefficients just found, we get

(6) $$x = 1 + \frac{1}{4} t^2 + \frac{1}{24} t^3 - \frac{5}{64} t^4 - \frac{7}{1920} t^5 + \frac{1}{2560} t^6,$$

(7) $$y = 2 + \frac{1}{2} t - \frac{1}{8} t^2 + \frac{1}{16} t^3 - \frac{5}{384} t^4 - \frac{37}{3840} t^5 - \frac{37}{46080} t^6.$$

Also, from (6),

(8) $$\dot{x} = \frac{1}{2} t + \frac{1}{8} t^2 - \frac{5}{16} t^3 - \frac{7}{384} t^4 + \frac{3}{1280} t^5.$$

On putting $t = -0.10, -0.05, 0.05, 0.10$ in (6), (7), (8), and using the initial values, we get the values of x, y, and $\dot{x}$ given in the first five lines of the following table. The corresponding values of $\dot{y}$ and $\ddot{x}$ are found from the given equations (2) and (3), by using the proper values of x, y, $\dot{x}$, and t.

The computation is continued by means of the following formulas:

(9) $$\Delta\dot{x} = h[\ddot{x} + \frac{1}{2} \Delta_1\ddot{x} + \frac{5}{12} \Delta_2\ddot{x} + \frac{3}{8} \Delta_3\ddot{x} + \frac{1}{3}\Delta_4\ddot{x}],$$

for starting a new line;

(10) $$\Delta x = h[\dot{x} - \frac{1}{2} \Delta_1\dot{x} - \frac{1}{12} \Delta_2\dot{x} - \frac{1}{24} \Delta_3\dot{x} - \frac{1}{38} \Delta_4\dot{x}],$$

for finding Δx in the new line:

(11) $\dot{y} = \tfrac{1}{2}(x + \dot{x} - \sin t)$, for finding $\dot{y}$ in the new line;

(12) $\ddot{x} = y - 2x + \dot{y} + \ln \cos t$, for finding $\ddot{x}$ in the new line;

(13) $$\Delta\dot{x} = h[\ddot{x} - \frac{1}{2} \Delta_1\ddot{x} - \frac{1}{12} \Delta_2\ddot{x} - \frac{1}{24} \Delta_3\ddot{x} - \frac{1}{38} \Delta_4\ddot{x}],$$

for checking $\Delta\dot{x}$ in the new line; all formulas to be used in the order given.

t	x	Δx	y	Δy	$\dot{x}$	$\Delta_1\dot{x}$	$\Delta_2\dot{x}$	$\Delta_3\dot{x}$	$\Delta_4\dot{x}$	$\dot{y}$	$\Delta_1\dot{y}$	$\Delta_2\dot{y}$	$\Delta_3\dot{y}$	$\Delta_4\dot{y}$	$\ddot{x}$	$\Delta_1\ddot{x}$	$\Delta_2\ddot{x}$	$\Delta_3\ddot{x}$	$\Delta_4\ddot{x}$
−0.10	1.0024		1.9487		−0.0484					0.5269					0.4657				
		−18		260		238					−139					+195			
−0.05	1.0006		1.9747		−0.0246		+8			0.5130		+9			0.4852		−47		
		−6		253		246		−1			−130		1			148		1	
0	1.0000		2.0000		0.0000		7		−3	0.5000		10		−3	0.5000		−46		−3
		−6		247		253		−4			−120		−2			102		−2	
+0.05	1.0006		2.0247		0.0253		3		3	0.4880		8		3	0.5102		−48		2
		+6		241		256		−1			−112		1			54		0	
0.10	1.0025		2.0488		0.0509		2		−2	0.4768		9		−2	0.5156		−48		0
		+19		236		258		−3			−103		−1			6		0	
0.15	1.0057		2.0724		0.0767		−1			0.4665		8			0.5162		−48		
		+32		231		257					−95					−42			
0.20	1.0102		2.0955		0.1024					0.4570					0.5120				

92. Conditions for Convergence. The conditions for the convergence of the numerical solution by approximating polynomials can be arrived at most easily by means of the Picard process.

For the simple equation

$$\frac{dy}{dx} = y' = f(x, y)$$

the Picard process converges to the true solution provided

$$h < \frac{1}{\left|\dfrac{\partial f}{\partial y}\right|_{\max}}$$

in the region of integration *; and in the case of the two simultaneous equations

$$\frac{dx}{dt} = f_1(x, y, t)$$

$$\frac{dy}{dt} = f_2(x, y, t)$$

the conditions for convergence are

$$\Delta t < \frac{1}{\left|\dfrac{\partial f_1}{\partial x}\right|_{\max} + \left|\dfrac{\partial f_2}{\partial x}\right|_{\max}} \quad \text{and} \quad \Delta t < \frac{1}{\left|\dfrac{\partial f_1}{\partial y}\right|_{\max} + \left|\dfrac{\partial f_2}{\partial y}\right|_{\max}}$$

in the region considered.*

Now since a polynomial can be made to approximate any continuous function to any required degree of accuracy, it follows that the approximating polynomial used for the numerical solution of a differential equation can be made to approach the Picard solution by taking h sufficiently small. Then since the polynomial solution can be made to coincide with the Picard solution as closely as desired, it is evident from the geometric significance of partial derivatives that the conditions for the convergence of the polynomial solution are the same as for the Picard solution when h is sufficiently small.

In the simple equation

$$y' = f(x, y)$$

the numerical process of solution will fail in a region where

$$\frac{\partial y'}{\partial y} \longrightarrow \infty \; ;$$

---

* The proof of these conditions will be found in the first edition of this book.

and in the case of simultaneous equations the process will fail in a region where any one of the partial derivatives

$$\frac{\partial f_1}{\partial x}, \frac{\partial f_2}{\partial x}, \frac{\partial f_1}{\partial y}, \frac{\partial f_2}{\partial y}$$

becomes infinite. Before starting the numerical solution of a differential equation, it is well to examine the partial derivatives for the range or region to be covered.

III. THE DIFFERENTIAL EQUATIONS OF EXTERIOR BALLISTICS.

93. The Simplest Case—Flat Earth with Constant Acceleration of Gravity. This book is not primarily concerned with the derivations of differential equations, but inasmuch as one of the main fields of application of numerical integration to the solution of differential equations is that of exterior ballistics—the science which deals with the motion of a projectile after it leaves the gun—, it seems not amiss to sketch briefly the derivation of the fundamental differential equations of the motion of projectiles. The projectile will be considered as a material particle acted on by the force of gravity and by a tangential retarding force due to the resistance of the air. In the present article the acceleration of gravity will be assumed constant in magnitude and direction, which means that we are assuming a flat earth and that the projectile does not reach a great height. The air resistance is proportional to some (variable) power of the velocity, which power itself depends on the velocity. The equations will be derived first by taking θ as the independent variable and then by taking time (t) as the independent variable.

Case I. Taking θ as the Independent Variable. Let a projectile of weight W be fired with an initial velocity v_0 at an angle of elevation ϕ; let v denote the velocity of the projectile at any point in its path and let θ denote the inclination of the velocity vector at that point; and, finally, let ρ denote the radius of curvature of the trajectory (path) at the point in question and let kv^n denote the air resistance at that point. Then resolving forces along the tangent and the normal at P (see Fig. 17),

we have by the fundamental law of dynamics:

$$(1) \qquad\qquad - kv^n - W \sin \theta = \frac{W}{g} \frac{dv}{dt},$$

$$(2) \qquad\qquad - W \cos \theta = \frac{W}{g} \frac{v^2}{\rho}.$$

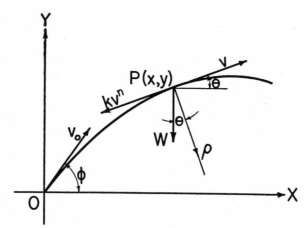

FIG. 17

From (2), $\rho = -\dfrac{v^2}{g \cos \theta}$; and since $\rho = \dfrac{ds}{d\theta}$ we have $\dfrac{ds}{d\theta} = -\dfrac{v^2}{g \cos \theta}$, or

(3)
$$ds = -\frac{v^2}{g \cos \theta} \, d\theta.$$

Then from (1),

$$\frac{dv}{dt} = -g \left(\frac{k}{W} v^n + \sin \theta \right);$$

and since

$$\frac{dv}{dt} = \frac{dv}{ds} \cdot \frac{ds}{dt} = v \frac{dv}{ds},$$

we have

$$v \frac{dv}{ds} = -g \left(\frac{k}{W} v^n + \sin \theta \right),$$

or

(4)
$$ds = -\frac{v\,dv}{g \left(\dfrac{k}{W} v^n + \sin \theta \right)}.$$

Equating the values of ds from (3) and (4) and simplifying slightly, we obtain

(5)
$$\frac{dv}{d\theta} - v \tan \theta = c \, v^{n+1} \sec \theta,$$

where $c = k/W$.

This equation (5) is frequently called the fundamental equation of exterior ballistics. When n is an *integer*, the equation becomes the well-known Bernoulli type of linear differential equation and can be solved for v as a function of θ.

The values of the exponent n for various velocities are as given below:

$$0 < v < 790 \text{ ft./sec.,} \quad n = 2$$
$$790 < v < 970 \text{ ft./sec.,} \quad n = 3$$
$$970 < v < 1230 \text{ ft./sec.,} \quad n = 5$$
$$1230 < v < 1370 \text{ ft./sec.,} \quad n = 3$$
$$1370 < v < 1800 \text{ ft./sec.,} \quad n = 2$$
$$1800 < v < 2600 \text{ ft./sec.,} \quad n = 1.7$$
$$2600 < v < 3600 \text{ ft./sec.,} \quad n = 1.55.$$

For $n = 2$ and the initial conditions $\theta = \phi$, $v = v_0$, the solution of (5) is

$$(93.1) \quad \frac{1}{v^2} = c \cos^2 \theta \left[\sec \phi \tan \phi - \sec \theta \tan \theta + \ln \frac{\sec \phi + \tan \phi}{\sec \theta + \tan \theta} \right] + \frac{\cos^2 \theta}{v_0^2 \cos^2 \phi}.$$

To find in terms of θ the rectangular coordinates of any point on the trajectory and the time of flight of the projectile, we have

$$\frac{dx}{d\theta} = \frac{dx}{ds} \cdot \frac{ds}{d\theta} = -\rho \cos \theta = -\frac{v^2}{g}.$$

$$\frac{dy}{d\theta} = \frac{dy}{ds} \cdot \frac{ds}{d\theta} = -\rho \sin \theta = -\rho \cos \theta \cdot \frac{\sin \theta}{\cos \theta} = -\frac{v^2}{g} \tan \theta.$$

$$\frac{dt}{d\theta} = \frac{dt}{ds} \cdot \frac{ds}{d\theta} = \frac{1}{v} (-\rho) = -\frac{\rho}{v} = -\frac{v}{g} \sec \theta.$$

Integrating these three expressions from $\theta = \phi$ to $\theta = \theta$, we get

$$(93.2) \quad \begin{cases} x = -\dfrac{1}{g} \displaystyle\int_\phi^\theta v^2 \, d\theta \\[2mm] y = -\dfrac{1}{g} \displaystyle\int_\phi^\theta v^2 \tan \theta \, d\theta \\[2mm] t = -\dfrac{1}{g} \displaystyle\int_\phi^\theta v \sec \theta \, d\theta. \end{cases}$$

These integrals can be computed by Simpson's Rule as soon as the values of the integrands are known for equidistant values of θ. In the case $n = 2$ the values of v can be found from (93.1).

Case II. Taking Time (t) as the Independent Variable. In most ballistic calculations it is better to take time as the independent variable. To find the differential equations of motion for this case, we resolve forces in the horizontal and vertical directions. Then (see Fig. 17)

$$- kv^n \cos \theta = \frac{W}{g} \ddot{x}$$

$$- kv^n \sin \theta - W = \frac{W}{g} \ddot{y},$$

or

$$\ddot{x} = - \frac{kg}{W} v^n \cos \theta = - R \cos \theta = - \frac{R}{v} \cdot v \cos \theta = - \frac{R}{v} \dot{x}$$

$$\ddot{y} = - \frac{kg}{W} v^n \sin \theta - g = - R \sin \theta - g = - \frac{R}{v} \cdot v \sin \theta - g$$

$$= - \frac{R}{v} \dot{y} - g,$$

where $R = \frac{kg}{W} v^n$. Hence the fundamental differential equations in rectangular form are

$$(93.3) \quad \begin{cases} \ddot{x} = - \dfrac{R}{v} \dot{x} \\[2mm] \ddot{y} = - \dfrac{R}{v} \dot{y} - g. \end{cases}$$

These equations are connected by the velocity $v = \sqrt{\dot{x}^2 + \dot{y}^2}$ and must therefore be integrated simultaneously.

94. The General Case, Allowing for Variation in Air Density with Altitude. The ballistic equations thus far given do not permit the decrease in air resistance and gravity with altitude to be taken into account and are therefore inadequate for modern gunnery. To allow for variation in air density with altitude it has been the practice in this country to write the fundamental differential equations in the forms: *

$$(94.1) \quad \begin{cases} \ddot{x} = - E\dot{x} \\ \ddot{y} = - E\dot{y} - g, \end{cases}$$

where

$$E = \frac{G(v) H(y)}{C}.$$

Here $G(v)$ is a function of the velocity alone, $H(y)$ is a function of the

---

* The reduction of the ballistic equations to the form (94.1) and the integration of them numerically was first done by F. R. Moulton.

altitude alone, and C is a constant whose value depends on the weight and shape of the projectile. The function $H(y)$ is

$$H(y) = 10^{-0.000045y} = e^{-0.0001036y},$$

when the altitude y is in meters. The function $G(v)$ is much more complicated. These functions $G(v)$ and $H(y)$ have been tabulated for a wide range of values of v and y.‡

95. Methods of Finding the Starting Values. The use of Taylor's series in starting the computation of a trajectory by numerical integration is out of the question, because of the difficulty in finding successive derivatives of the given differential equations. The Runge-Kutta method is likewise unsuitable for obtaining the necessary starting values. The Milne method can be used for the simple problems not requiring the E-function, but in the general case of projectiles fired with high velocities and reaching considerable heights, the starting values must be found by one of the following methods:

(a). *The Modified Euler Method.* This method, as previously stated, will give starting values in any problem, provided short steps (intervals) are taken. In starting the computation of a trajectory, two consecutive values of the required functions, in addition to the initial values, are computed by taking very short intervals of time. From these three values first and second differences are formed. Then the computation is continued by means of formulas (86.1) and (86.2). After the first five values are found, they are checked by formulas (86.3), (86.4), and (86.5).

(b). *Barker's Hyperbolic-Arc Method.* In recent years a new and entirely different method of starting the computation of trajectories has been devised by J. E. Barker.* Having in mind the fact that the path of a projectile fired through the air has a vertical asymptote at no great distance from the gun (usually at a distance of two to three times the horizontal range), Barker conceived the idea of replacing the trajectory near the origin by the arc of a hyperbola passing through the origin and having a vertical asymptote at a horizontal distance c from the origin. The equation of such a hyperbola is of the form

$$(1) \qquad\qquad y = \frac{x(ax + b)}{c - x}$$

‡ See Tables Ia and Ic in *Exterior Ballistic Tables Based on Numerical Integration*, Vol. I, Washington, 1924.

* Mathematician at the U. S. Naval Proving Grounds, Dahlgren, Va.

where a, b, and c are undetermined parameters. These parameters are to be determined by the condition that the hyperbola shall have third-order contact with the trajectory at the origin. This means that $\dfrac{dy}{dx}$, $\dfrac{d^2y}{dx^2}$, and $\dfrac{d^3y}{dx^3}$ for the hyperbola must equal the same three derivatives of the trajectory at the origin. The hyperbola will then approximate the trajectory extremely closely in the neighborhood of the origin and may therefore be used for computing starting values for the trajectory in that region. From (1) we get by differentiation

$$(2) \qquad \begin{cases} \dfrac{dy}{dx} = \dfrac{2acx + bc - ax^2}{(c - x)^2}, \\[2mm] \dfrac{d^2y}{dx^2} = \dfrac{2ac^2 + 2bc}{(c - x)^3}, \\[2mm] \dfrac{d^3y}{dx^3} = \dfrac{6c(ac + b)}{(c - x)^4}. \end{cases}$$

To find the corresponding derivatives of the trajectory, we have

$$\frac{dy}{dx} = \tan \theta$$

$$\frac{d^2y}{dx^2} = \sec^2 \theta \, \frac{d\theta}{dx} = \sec^2 \theta \, \frac{d\theta/dt}{dx/dt} = \sec^2 \theta \, \frac{\dot\theta}{\dot x}$$

$$= \dot\theta \sec \theta \cdot \frac{\sec \theta}{\dot x} = \dot\theta \sec \theta \cdot \frac{1}{\dot x \cos \theta}.$$

But since $\rho = \dfrac{ds}{d\theta} = \dfrac{ds/dt}{d\theta/dt} = \dfrac{v}{\dot\theta}$, and $\rho = -\dfrac{v^2}{g \cos \theta}$ by Art. 93, we have $\dfrac{v}{\dot\theta} = -\dfrac{v^2}{g \cos \theta}$, from which $\dot\theta \sec \theta = -\dfrac{g}{v}$. Hence

$$\frac{d^2y}{dx^2} = -\frac{g}{v} \cdot \frac{1}{\dot x \cos \theta} = -\frac{g}{\dot x v \cos \theta} = -\frac{g}{\dot x v_x} = -\frac{g}{\dot x^2}.$$

Also,

$$\frac{d^3y}{dx^3} = \frac{d}{dx}\left(-\frac{g}{\dot x^2}\right) = \frac{d}{dt}(-g\dot x^{-2})\frac{dt}{dx} = 2g\dot x^{-3} \cdot \ddot x \cdot \frac{1}{\dot x}$$

$$= 2g \, \frac{\ddot x}{\dot x^4} = \frac{2g(-E\dot x)}{\dot x^4} = -\frac{2gE}{\dot x^3}.$$

Now equating these three derivatives to the corresponding derivatives in (2), putting $x = 0$, $\dot x = \dot x_0$, $\theta = \phi$, $E = E_0$, and then solving the resulting equations for a, b, and c, we get

$$c = \frac{3}{2} \frac{\dot{x}_0}{E_0}, \qquad b = \frac{3}{2} \frac{\dot{x}_0}{E_0} \tan \phi,$$

and

$$a = - \left(\frac{3g}{4 E_0 \dot{x}_0} \right) - \tan \phi.$$

On substituting these values in (1) we get y in terms of x.

But since the independent variable in the ballistic equations is t, we must have x and y in terms of t. To get the required relations we go back to the relations

$$\frac{d^2 y}{dx^2} = \frac{2c(ac+b)}{(c-x)^3} = - \frac{g}{\dot{x}^2}$$

Solving for $\dot{x}$, separating the variables, and integrating, we have

$$\sqrt{-2c(ac+b)} \int_0^x (d-x)^{-3/2} \, dx = \sqrt{g} \int_0^t dt.$$

From this we find

$$x = c \left[1 - \left(\frac{2\sqrt{-2(ac+b)}}{\sqrt{g}t + 2\sqrt{-2(ac+b)}} \right)^2 \right]$$

Reducing the right-hand member to its simplest form and then replacing a, b, and c by their values as previously found, we get

$$(3) \qquad x = \frac{3\dot{x}_0}{2} \cdot \frac{t(E_0 t + 6)}{(E_0 t + 3)^2} = \frac{3\dot{x}_0}{2} \left[\frac{t}{E_0 t + 3} + \frac{3t}{(E_0 t + 3)^2} \right]$$

When this value of x is substituted in (1), the value of y becomes

$$y = \frac{t}{24} \frac{(E_0 t + 6)}{(E_0 t + 3)^2} (36\dot{y}_0 - 3gE_0 t^2 - 18gt),$$

which is equivalent to

$$(4) \qquad y = - \frac{g}{8 E^2{}_0} (E_0 t + 3)^2 + \frac{9g + 6 E_0 \dot{y}_0}{4 E^2{}_0} - \frac{27(3g + 4 E_0 \dot{y}_0)}{8 E^2{}_0 (E_0 t + 3)^2} .$$

Differentiating (3) with respect to t and simplifying, we get

$$(95.1) \qquad \dot{x} = \dot{x}_0 \left(1 + \frac{E_0 t}{3} \right)^{-3},$$

which may be written as the binomial series

$$(95.2) \qquad \dot{x} = \dot{x}_0 \left[1 - (E_0 t) + \frac{2}{3} (E_0 t)^2 - \frac{10}{27} (E_0 t)^3 + \frac{5}{27} (E_0 t)^4 \cdots \right]$$

On differentiating (4) with respect to t, we find

$$\dot{y} = -\frac{3g}{4E_0}\left(1 + \frac{E_0t}{3}\right) + \frac{3g}{4E_0}\left(1 + \frac{E_0t}{3}\right)^{-3} + \dot{y}_0\left(1 + \frac{E_0t}{3}\right)^{-3}.$$

In view of (95.1) and the fact that $\dot{y}_0/\dot{x}_0 = \tan\phi$, the third term on the right is equal to $\dot{x}\tan\phi$. Then on replacing the middle term by its binomial expansion and reducing the right-hand member to its simplest form, we get

(95.3) $\dot{y} = \dot{x}\tan\phi - gt[1 - (1/2)(E_0t) + (5/18)(E_0t)^2 - (5/36)(E_0t)^3$
$$+ \cdots].$$

From (95.1) or (95.2), $\dot{x}$ is readily found. Then this value of $\dot{x}$ is used in (95.3) to find $\dot{y}$. Formula (4) is not convenient for finding y. When the values of $\dot{y}_{-1}$, $\dot{y}_1$, and $\dot{y}_2$ have been computed by means of (95.3), the values of y are more easily found from the quadrature formulas

(95.4)
$$\begin{cases} u_{-1} = u_0 - \dfrac{\Delta t}{24}\left(9\dot{u}_{-1} + 19\dot{u}_0 - 5\dot{u}_1 + \dot{u}_2\right) \\[2mm] u_1 = u_0 + \dfrac{\Delta t}{24}\left[-\dot{u}_{-1} + 13(\dot{u}_0 + \dot{u}_1) - \dot{u}_2\right] \\[2mm] u_2 = u_0 + \dfrac{\Delta t}{3}\left(\dot{u}_0 + 4\dot{u}_1 + \dot{u}_2\right), \end{cases}$$

where u stands for any variable, $\dot{u}$ its time derivative, and $\Delta t (= h)$ is the interval between equidistant values of t. Note that t in (95.1), (95.2), and (95.3) may be either positive or negative, but Δt in (95.4) is always positive.

The values of $\dot{x}$ and $\dot{y}$ found from (95.1), (95.2), and (95.3) are extremely accurate, but they can usually be slightly improved by iteration by means of formulas (95.4). The computation of a trajectory is started by the Barker method as follows:

Close approximations to $\dot{x}_{-1}$, $\dot{x}_1$, $\dot{x}_2$ and $\dot{y}_{-1}$, $\dot{y}_1$, $\dot{y}_2$ are first found by means of (95.1) and (95.3), using $t = -\Delta t$, $t = \Delta t$, $t = 2\Delta t$. These $\dot{x}$'s and $\dot{y}$'s are then substituted in the given differential equations (94.1) to get $\ddot{x}_{-1}$, $\ddot{x}_1$, $\ddot{x}_2$, and $\ddot{y}_{-1}$, $\ddot{y}_1$, $\ddot{y}_2$. Then these $\ddot{x}$'s and $\ddot{y}$'s are substituted in the right-hand members of (95.4) to get improved values of $\dot{x}_{-1}$, $\dot{x}_1$, $\dot{x}_2$, and $\dot{y}_{-1}$, $\dot{y}_1$, $\dot{y}_2$. If there is any reason for thinking that these last values can be improved, the iteration process through (94.1) and (95.4) is repeated.

When the final values of $\dot{y}_{-1}$, $\dot{y}_1$, and $\dot{y}_2$ have been found, they are substituted in the right-hand members of (95.4) to get the values of y_{-1},

y_1, y_2. If the values of x_{-1}, x_1, x_2 are desired, they can be found in a similar manner.

When two or three sets of values of the several quantities mentioned above have been found by the process outlined, differences up to the second or third order will.be available. The computation is then continued by means of the difference formulas (86.1) and (86.2). The application of the Barker method to a simple trajectory will be shown below.

The actual computation of a modern high-altitude trajectory cannot be given here, because of lack of space for the necessary tables. The reader will find such a problem worked out completely in the *Encyclopedia Britannica*, Twelfth Edition (1922), Vol. XXX, p. 390. A simple trajectory will be worked out below.

Note. Since the advent of high-altitude rockets of the V-2 type, the motion of projectiles in a vacuum has become of practical importance. A simple and direct treatment of this astro-ballistic problem will be found in the following paper: "The Actual Path of a Projectile in a Vacuum," *American Journal of Physics,* Vol. 13, No. 4 (August, 1945), pp. 253-255.

A thorough and masterly treatment of the motion of projectiles and rockets under all conditions will be found in *Ballistics of the Future,* by Kooy and Uytenbogaart, 1946.

Example. A bullet is fired at an angle of 38° 30′ with the horizon and with an initial velocity of 780 feet per second. Assuming that the air resistance varies as the square of the velocity of the bullet and that the resistance coefficient is — 0.00005, find the range, time of flight, and angle of fall of the bullet.

Solution. Let θ denote the angle which the velocity vector makes with the horizontal at any instant. Then the equations of motion are

$$\frac{d^2x}{dt^2} = - R \cos \theta = - 0.00005v^2 \cos \theta,$$

$$\frac{d^2y}{dt^2} = - R \sin \theta - g = - 0.00005v^2 \sin \theta - g,$$

where $R(= 0.00005v^2)$ denotes the tangential retardation. Since $v \cos \theta = v_x = dx/dt$ and $v \sin \theta = v_y = dy/dt$, the equations of motion can be written in the form

$$\frac{x_z p}{dt^2} = - 0.00005v \frac{dx}{dt},$$

$$\frac{d^2y}{dt^2} = - 0.00005v \frac{dy}{dt} - g.$$

These can be reduced to a system of first-order equations by putting

$$\dot{x} = \frac{dx}{dt}, \quad \dot{y} = \frac{dy}{dt}, \quad \ddot{x} = \frac{d\dot{x}}{dt} = \frac{d^2x}{dt^2}, \quad \ddot{y} = \frac{d\dot{y}}{dt} = \frac{d^2y}{dt^2}.$$

Taking $g = 32.16$ ft./sec.^{2}, we then have the system

$$\begin{cases} \dfrac{dx}{dt} = \dot{x}, \\[2mm] \dfrac{d\dot{x}}{dt} = \ddot{x} = -0.00005v\dot{x}, \\[2mm] \dfrac{dy}{dt} = \dot{y} \\[2mm] \dfrac{d\dot{y}}{dt} = \ddot{y} = -0.00005v\dot{y} - 32.16. \end{cases}$$

To start the numerical solution of this system of equations we first find the initial values of the velocities and accelerations. Thus,

$$v_0 = 780,$$
$$\dot{x}_0 = v_0 \cos 38° \, 30' = 610.44,$$
$$\dot{y}_0 = v_0 \sin 38° \, 30' = 485.56,$$
$$\ddot{x}_0 = -0.00005v_0\dot{x}_0 = -23.81,$$
$$\ddot{y}_0 = -0.00005v_0\dot{y}_0 - 32.16 = -51.10.$$

These quantities give the first line in the table to be computed (page 291).

To find additional starting values in this example by the Taylor-series method is out of the question, because of the difficulty in finding the higher derivatives of the given equations. But since the derivative of

$$\ddot{x} = -0.00005x\sqrt{\dot{x}^2 + \dot{y}^2} \quad \text{is}$$
$$\dddot{x} = -0.00005 \left(\frac{\ddot{x}\dot{y}^2 + 2\ddot{x}\dot{x}^2 + \dot{x}\dot{y}\ddot{y}}{\sqrt{\dot{x}^2 + \dot{y}^2}} \right),$$

and a similar expression for $\dddot{y}$, the starting values could be found by the Milne method. However, for the purpose of illustrating the methods, we shall find the second and third lines of the table first by the modified Euler method and then by the Barker method.

(a). *Modified Euler Method.* To find the second line of the table on page 291 by the modified Euler method, we assume that the initial accelerations will remain practically constant for the next 1/4 second. Hence

$$\Delta\dot{y} = \tfrac{1}{4}(-51.10) = -12.78,$$
$$\Delta\dot{x} = \tfrac{1}{4}(-23.81) = -5.95;$$

and therefore

$$\dot{y}_{1/4}{}^{(1)} = \dot{y}_0 + \Delta\dot{y} = 485.56 - 12.78 = 472.78,$$
$$\dot{x}_{1/4}{}^{(1)} = \dot{x}_0 + \Delta\dot{x} = 610.44 - 5.95 = 604.49.$$

Since $v = \sqrt{\dot{x}^2 + \dot{y}^2}$, we have

$$v_{1/4}{}^{(1)} = \sqrt{(604.49)^2 + (472.78)^2} = 767.42.$$

Then

$$\ddot{y}_{1/4}{}^{(2)} = -0.00005 \times 767.42 \times 472.78 - 32.16 = -50.30.$$
$$\ddot{x}_{1/4}{}^{(2)} = -0.00005 \times 767.42 \times 604.49 = -23.19.$$

Better values for $\Delta\dot{y}$ and $\Delta\dot{x}$ are therefore

$$\Delta\dot{y} = \frac{1}{4}\left(\frac{-51.10 - 50.30}{2}\right) = -12.68,$$

$$\Delta\dot{x} = \frac{1}{4}\left(\frac{-23.81 - 23.19}{2}\right) = -5.88.$$

$$\therefore \quad \dot{y}_{1/4}{}^{(2)} = 485.56 - 12.68 = 472.88,$$
$$\dot{x}_{1/4}{}^{(2)} = 610.44 - 5.88 = 604.56,$$
$$v_{1/4}{}^{(2)} = \sqrt{(604.56)^2 + (472.88)^2} = 767.53.$$

The third approximations for the accelerations at the end of the interval are then

$$\ddot{y}_{1/4}{}^{(3)} = -50.31,$$
$$\ddot{x}_{1/4}{}^{(3)} = -23.20.$$

These values differ from the preceding values by only one unit in the last digit and will give the same values of $\dot{x}$ and $\dot{y}$ as before. Hence we take them as correct for the present.

To find the value of y when $t = \frac{1}{4}$, we have

$$\Delta y = \frac{1}{4}\left(\frac{485.56 + 472.88}{2}\right) = 119.80 \text{ ft.}$$

$$\therefore \quad y_{1/4} = 0 + 119.80 = 119.80$$

The values are now known for the second line in the table.

To find the third line we assume that the acceleration at the end of the first $\frac{1}{4}$ second will remain practically constant for the next $\frac{1}{4}$ second. Hence we have

$$(\Delta\dot{x})_{1/2}{}^{(1)} = \tfrac{1}{4}(-23.20) = -5.80$$
$$(\Delta\dot{y})_{1/2}{}^{(1)} = \tfrac{1}{4}(-50.31) = -12.58.$$

Then

$$(\dot{x})_{1/2}{}^{(1)} = 604.56 - 5.80 = 598.76$$
$$(\dot{y})_{1/2}{}^{(1)} = 472.88 - 12.58 = 460.30$$
$$(v)_{1/2}{}^{(1)} = \sqrt{(598.76)^2 + (460.30)^2} = 755.24,$$
$$(\ddot{x})_{1/2}{}^{(2)} = -0.00005(598.76 \times 755.24) = -22.61$$
$$(\ddot{y})_{1/2}{}^{(2)} = -0.00005(460.30 \times 755.24) - 32.16 = -49.54.$$

Better values for $\Delta\dot{x}$ and $\Delta\dot{y}$ are now

$$(\Delta\dot{x})_{1/2}{}^{(2)} = \frac{1}{4}\left(\frac{-23.20 - 22.61}{2}\right) = -5.73$$

$$(\Delta\dot{y})_{1/2}{}^{(2)} = \frac{1}{4}\left(\frac{-50.31 - 49.54}{2}\right) = -12.48.$$

Hence

$$(\dot{x})_{1/2}{}^{(2)} = 604.56 - 5.73 = 598.83$$
$$(\dot{y})_{1/2}{}^{(2)} = 472.88 - 12.48 = 460.40$$
$$(v)_{1/2}{}^{(2)} = \sqrt{(598.83)^2 + (460.40)^2} = 755.36$$

Then

$$(\ddot{x})_{1/2}{}^{(3)} = -0.00005(598.83 \times 755.36) = -22.62$$
$$(\ddot{y})_{1/2}{}^{(3)} = -0.00005(460.40 \times 755.36) = -49.55.$$

These values differ from the preceding values by only one unit in the last figure, and they give the same new values for $\Delta\dot{x}$ and $\Delta\dot{y}$. Hence we consider them correct for the present. The increment in y for the second interval is

$$\Delta y = \frac{1}{4}\left(\frac{472.88 + 460.40}{2}\right) = 116.66.$$

Hence the new value of y is

$$y_{1/2} = 119.80 + 116.66 = 236.46.$$

(b). *Barker Method.* To find the second and third lines of the table by the Barker method we first note that

$$E_0 = 0.00005 \times 780 = 0.039$$

and

$$\tan \phi = 0.79544$$

Then on substituting $t = -\frac{1}{4}$ in (95.1) or (95.2) we get $\dot{x}_{-1} = 616.43$. Now substituting in (95.3) this value of $\dot{x}_{-1}$ and $t = -\frac{1}{4}$, we get $\dot{y}_{-1} = 498.41$. The value of v_{-1} is then

$$v_{-1} = \sqrt{(616.43)^2 + (498.41)^2} = 792.72.$$

These values are now substituted in the given equations to get the corresponding accelerations. Thus,

$$\ddot{x}_{-1} = -\frac{792.72 \times 616.43}{20,000} = -24.43,$$

$$\ddot{y}_{-1} = -\frac{792.72 \times 498.41}{20,000} - 32.16 = -51.91.$$

These quantities are placed in the first line of the trial table (Table A, p. 288). The quantities in the third and fourth lines of Table A are found in exactly the same manner by substituting $t = \frac{1}{4}$ and $t = \frac{1}{2}$, respectively, in formulas (95.1) and (95.3) or in (95.2) and (95.3).

We next check these computed trial values by substituting the accelerations in the right-hand members of (95.4). Thus, taking $\Delta t = \frac{1}{4}$,

$$(\dot{x}_{-1})^{(2)} = 610.44 - \frac{1}{96}[9(-24.43) + 19(-23.81) - 5(-23.20) - 22.61]$$
$$= 616.47,$$

$$(\dot{y}_{-1})^{(2)} = 485.56 - \frac{1}{96}[9(-51.91) + 19(-51.10) - 5(-50.30) - 49.54]$$
$$= 498.44,$$

and similarly for the other values of $\dot{x}$ and $\dot{y}$. The corresponding v's are then computed and then new accelerations are found from the given differential equations.

It will be observed that the improved values in the second table (Table B) differ very little from the first computed values. A second iteration by formulas (95.4) makes no improvement whatever except in the case of $y_{1/2}$, which it changes from 460.41 to 460.40. We therefore take the values in Table B to be correct.

We are now ready to find y for $t = \frac{1}{4}$ and $t = \frac{1}{2}$. These are found from (95.4) as follows:

$$y_1 = 0 + \frac{1}{96}[-498.44 + 13(485.56 + 472.88) - 460.40] = 119.80 \text{ ft.}$$

$$y_2 = 0 + \frac{1}{12}(485.56 + 1891.52 + 460.40) = 236.46 \text{ ft.}$$

It will be noted that nearly all these values in Table B are identical with those found by the modified Euler method.

Now having three complete lines of the table, we can form first and second differences of the quantities $\ddot{x}$, $\ddot{y}$, $\dot{x}$, $\dot{y}$. Then we can continue the computation by integrating ahead and back-checking. For this purpose the following formulas are applied in the order in which they are written:

$$(1) \quad \Delta y = \int_{t_n}^{t_{n+1}} \dot{y}\,dt = \Delta t\left[\dot{y}_n + \frac{1}{2}\Delta_1\dot{y}_n + \frac{5}{12}\Delta_2\dot{y}_n + \frac{3}{8}\Delta_3\dot{y}_n + \frac{1}{3}\Delta_4\dot{y}_n\right],$$

Table A—First Computed Values

t	v	y	Δy	$\dot{x}$	$\Delta_1\dot{x}$	$\Delta_2\dot{x}$	$\Delta_3\dot{x}$	$\dot{y}$	$\Delta_1\dot{y}$	$\Delta_2\dot{y}$	$\Delta_3\dot{y}$	$\ddot{x}$	$\Delta_1\ddot{x}$	$\ddot{y}$	$\Delta_1\ddot{y}$
$-1/4$	792.72			616.43				498.41				-24.43		-51.91	
0	780	0		610.44				485.56				-23.81		-51.10	
$1/4$	767.50			604.53				472.86				-23.20		-50.30	
$1/2$	755.18			598.69				460.30				-22.61		-49.54	

Table B—First Iteration Values

t	v	y	Δy	$\dot{x}$	$\Delta_1\dot{x}$	$\Delta_2\dot{x}$	$\Delta_3\dot{x}$	$\dot{y}$	$\Delta_1\dot{y}$	$\Delta_2\dot{y}$	$\Delta_3\dot{y}$	$\ddot{x}$	$\Delta_1\ddot{x}$	$\ddot{y}$	$\Delta_1\ddot{y}$
$-1/4$	792.78			616.47				498.44				-24.44		-51.92	
0	780			610.44				485.56				-23.81		-51.10	
$1/4$	767.53	119.80		604.56				472.88				-23.20		-50.31	
$1/2$	755.37	236.46		598.84				460.40				-22.62		-49.55	

for finding $\dot{y}$ in a new line;

(2) $\quad \Delta\dot{x} = \int_{t_n}^{t_{n+1}} \ddot{x}\,dt = \Delta t\left[\ddot{x}_n + \frac{1}{2}\Delta_1\ddot{x}_n + \frac{5}{12}\Delta_2\ddot{x}_n + \frac{3}{8}\Delta_3\ddot{x}_n + \frac{1}{3}\Delta_4\ddot{x}_n\right],$

for finding $\dot{x}$ in the new line;

(3) $\quad v = \sqrt{\dot{x}^2 + \dot{y}^2}\;;$

(4) $\quad \ddot{y} = -\,0.00005v\dot{y} - 32.16\,;$

(5) $\quad \ddot{x} = -\,0.00005v\dot{x}\,;$

(6) $\quad \Delta\dot{y} = \int_{t_{n-1}}^{t_n} \ddot{y}\,dt = \Delta t\left[\ddot{y}_n - \frac{1}{2}\Delta_1\ddot{y}_n - \frac{1}{12}\Delta_2\ddot{y}_n - \frac{1}{24}\Delta_3\ddot{y}_n\right],$

for checking and correcting the value of $\dot{y}$ found by (1);

(7) $\quad \Delta\dot{x} = \int_{t_{n-1}}^{t_n} \ddot{x}\,dt = \Delta t\left[\ddot{x}_n - \frac{1}{2}\Delta_1\ddot{x}_n - \frac{1}{12}\Delta_2\ddot{x}_n - \frac{1}{24}\Delta_3\ddot{x}_n\right],$

for checking and correcting the value of $\dot{x}$ found by (2);

(8) $\quad \Delta y = \int_{t_{n-1}}^{t_n} \dot{y}\,dt = \Delta t\left[\dot{y}_n - \frac{1}{2}\Delta_1\dot{y}_n - \frac{1}{12}\Delta_2\dot{y}_n - \frac{1}{24}\Delta_3\dot{y}_n - \frac{1}{38}\Delta_4\dot{y}_n\right],$

for finding the new y after the correct value of $\dot{y}$ has been obtained. In these formulas the instant t_{n+1} in (1) and (2) is the same as t_n in (6), (7), and (8).

The increments in x for the several intervals can be found by means of the formula

(9) $\quad \Delta x = \int_{t_{n-1}}^{t_n} \dot{x}\,dt = \Delta t\left[\dot{x}_n - \frac{1}{2}\Delta_1\dot{x}_n - \frac{1}{12}\Delta_2\dot{x}_n - \frac{1}{24}\Delta_3\dot{x}_n - \frac{1}{38}\Delta_4\dot{x}_n\right],$

after the correct value of $\dot{x}$ has been found for the interval considered. Since only the range is called for in this problem, however, it is not necessary to find x at the end of each interval. The range is more easily found by means of Simpson's Rule, as follows:

$$x = \int_0^T \dot{x}\,dt = \frac{\Delta t}{3}\,[\dot{x}_0 + 4(\dot{x}_1 + \dot{x}_3 + \cdots + \dot{x}_{n-1})$$
$$+ 2(\dot{x}_2 + \dot{x}_4 + \cdots + \dot{x}_{n-2}) + \dot{x}_n],$$

where T denotes the time of flight.

The table is continued with the time interval $\Delta t = \frac{1}{4}$ sec. until five lines have been computed.

The computed values of $\Delta\dot{y}$ and $\Delta\dot{x}$ are then checked by applying formulas (86.5), (86.4), and (86.3) to the acceleration values in the fifth line, checking the interval $t = 0$ to $t = 1/4$ by (86.5), the second interval by (86.4), etc. The checks show that all computed values are correct.

Since the correct values are given at the first trial for $t = \frac{1}{2}$, $t = \frac{3}{4}$, and $t = 1$, we start a new table with $\Delta t = \frac{1}{2}$ sec., using the previously computed values of $\dot{x}$, $\dot{y}$, $\ddot{x}$, $\ddot{y}$, and v for the lines $t = 0$, $t = \frac{1}{2}$, $t = 1$. Here, again, the correct values of the several quantities are given at the first trial in the fourth and fifth lines of the table. So we double the interval again and start a new table with $\Delta t = 1$ sec., using the previously computed values for lines $t = 0$, $t = 1$, $t = 2$. This new table is continued up to the line $t = 8$. Then the interval is doubled once more and a new table started. The computation is continued with this interval until the problem is finished. In most cases only one correction is necessary for $\dot{x}$, $\dot{y}$, and v, and none for $\ddot{y}$ and $\ddot{x}$.

When using formulas (1), (2), (6), (7), (8), with $\Delta t = 2$ the student should not round off the numbers within the brackets before multiplying through by the factor 2; for by so doing he would double the error due to rounding. He should also be careful not to discard fractional quantities of less than half a unit in the second decimal place until he is sure that the algebraic sum of these quantities is less than half a unit in the second decimal place. Attention to these matters, instead of being a waste of time, will frequently save the time and labor of recomputing a whole line in the table. For example, let us check the value of Δy in the line for $t = 26$. We have

$$\Delta y = 2 \left[-376.89 + \frac{1}{2} (47.27) - \frac{1}{12} (3.04) - \frac{1}{24} (0.15) \right]$$

$$= -753.78 + 47.27 - \frac{1}{6} (3.04) - \frac{1}{12} (0.15)$$

$$= -753.78 + 47.27 - 0.507 - 0.012 = -707.03.$$

By rounding off before multiplying by 2 we have

$$\Delta y = 2[-376.89 + 23.64 - 0.25 - 0.01] = -707.02,$$

which differs from the previous value by a unit in the last figure.

The preceding remarks apply with even greater force when $\Delta t = 4$.

The final results of the computation for this problem are given on the following page.

This page is a numerical difference table for the integration of the exterior-ballistic equations. It is divided into four sub-tables corresponding to the integration step used ($\Delta t = \tfrac14,\ \tfrac12,\ 1,\ 2$). In each sub-table the columns (left to right in the original) are the successive differences of the acceleration and velocity components. Difference columns are printed staggered between the data rows in the original; here each difference value is aligned to the upper endpoint of its interval.

Step $\Delta t = \tfrac14$ ($t = 0$ to 1)

$\Delta^4\ddot{x}$	$\Delta^3\ddot{x}$	$\Delta^2\ddot{x}$	$\Delta\ddot{x}$	$\ddot{x}$	$\Delta\dot{x}$	$\dot{x}$	$\Delta^4\ddot{y}$	$\Delta^3\ddot{y}$	$\Delta^2\ddot{y}$	$\Delta\ddot{y}$	$\ddot{y}$	$\Delta^3\dot{y}$	$\Delta^2\dot{y}$	$\Delta\dot{y}$	$\dot{y}$	Δy	y	v	t
−0.04	0.02	−0.03	0.61	−23.81	−5.88	610.44	0.01	0.00	−0.03	0.79	−51.10	−0.02	0.20	−12.68	485.56	119.80	0	780.00	0
	−0.02	−0.01	0.58	−23.20	−5.73	604.56		0.01	−0.03	0.76	−50.31	0.00	0.18	−12.48	472.88	116.66	119.80	767.53	¼
		−0.03	0.57	−22.62	−5.58	598.83			−0.02	0.73	−49.55		0.18	−12.30	460.40	113.56	236.46	755.36	½
			0.54	−22.05	−5.44	593.25				0.71	−48.82			−12.12	448.10	110.50	350.02	743.46	¾
				−21.51		587.81					−48.11				435.98		460.52	731.85	1

Step $\Delta t = \tfrac12$ ($t = 0$ to 2)

$\Delta^4\ddot{x}$	$\Delta^3\ddot{x}$	$\Delta^2\ddot{x}$	$\Delta\ddot{x}$	$\ddot{x}$	$\Delta\dot{x}$	$\dot{x}$	$\Delta^4\ddot{y}$	$\Delta^3\ddot{y}$	$\Delta^2\ddot{y}$	$\Delta\ddot{y}$	$\ddot{y}$	$\Delta^3\dot{y}$	$\Delta^2\dot{y}$	$\Delta\dot{y}$	$\dot{y}$	Δy	y	v	t
0.01	0.00	−0.08	1.19	−23.81	−11.60	610.44	0.01	0.00	−0.11	1.55	−51.10	−0.04	0.74	−25.16	485.56	236.44	0	780.00	0
	0.01	−0.08	1.11	−22.62	−11.02	598.84		0.01	−0.11	1.44	−49.55	−0.06	0.70	−24.42	460.40	224.06	236.44	755.35	½
		−0.07	1.03	−21.51	−10.50	587.82			−0.10	1.33	−48.11		0.64	−23.72	435.98	212.03	460.50	731.85	1
			0.96	−20.48	−10.00	577.32				1.23	−46.78			−23.08	412.26	200.32	672.53	709.42	1½
				−19.52		567.32					−45.55				389.18		872.85	687.98	2

Step $\Delta t = 1$ ($t = 0$ to 8)

$\Delta^4\ddot{x}$	$\Delta^3\ddot{x}$	$\Delta^2\ddot{x}$	$\Delta\ddot{x}$	$\ddot{x}$	$\Delta\dot{x}$	$\dot{x}$	$\Delta^4\ddot{y}$	$\Delta^3\ddot{y}$	$\Delta^2\ddot{y}$	$\Delta\ddot{y}$	$\ddot{y}$	$\Delta^3\dot{y}$	$\Delta^2\dot{y}$	$\Delta\dot{y}$	$\dot{y}$	Δy	y	v	t
−0.03	0.06	−0.31	2.30	−23.81	−22.62	610.44	−0.05	0.09	−0.43	2.99	−51.10	−0.39	2.78	−49.58	485.56	460.50	0	780.00	0
0.00	0.03	−0.25	1.99	−21.51	−20.50	587.82	0.01	0.04	−0.34	2.56	−48.11	−0.33	2.39	−46.80	435.98	412.35	460.50	731.85	1
−0.01	0.03	−0.22	1.74	−19.52	−18.63	567.32	−0.01	0.05	−0.30	2.22	−45.55	−0.28	2.06	−44.41	389.18	366.79	872.85	687.98	2
0.00	0.02	−0.19	1.52	−17.78	−17.00	548.69	−0.01	0.04	−0.25	1.92	−43.33	−0.20	1.78	−42.35	344.77	323.44	1239.64	648.00	3
0.00	0.02	−0.17	1.33	−16.26	−15.58	531.69	0.00	0.03	−0.21	1.67	−41.41	−0.21	1.58	−40.57	302.42	281.99	1563.08	611.67	4
	0.02	−0.15	1.16	−14.93	−14.34	516.11		0.03	−0.18	1.46	−39.74	−0.17	1.37	−38.99	261.85	242.24	1845.07	578.74	5
		−0.13	1.01	−13.77	−13.25	501.77			−0.15	1.28	−38.28		1.20	−37.62	222.86	203.95	2087.31	549.04	6
			0.88	−12.76	−12.31	488.52				1.13	−37.00			−36.42	185.24	166.94	2291.26	522.46	7
				−11.88		476.21					−35.87				148.82		2458.20	498.93	8

Step $\Delta t = 2$ ($t = 0$ to 26)

$\Delta^4\ddot{x}$	$\Delta^3\ddot{x}$	$\Delta^2\ddot{x}$	$\Delta\ddot{x}$	$\ddot{x}$	$\Delta\dot{x}$	$\dot{x}$	$\Delta^4\ddot{y}$	$\Delta^3\ddot{y}$	$\Delta^2\ddot{y}$	$\Delta\ddot{y}$	$\ddot{y}$	$\Delta^3\dot{y}$	$\Delta^2\dot{y}$	$\Delta\dot{y}$	$\dot{y}$	Δy	y	v	t
−0.09	0.26	−1.03	4.29	−23.81	−43.12	610.44	−0.11	0.40	−1.41	5.55	−51.10	−2.42	9.62	−96.38	485.56	872.85	0	780.00	0
−0.04	0.17	−0.77	3.26	−19.52	−35.63	567.32	−0.09	0.29	−1.01	4.14	−45.55	−1.68	7.20	−86.76	389.18	690.23	872.85	687.98	2
−0.05	0.13	−0.60	2.49	−16.26	−29.92	531.69	−0.02	0.20	−0.72	3.13	−41.41	−1.26	5.52	−79.56	302.42	524.23	1563.08	611.67	4
−0.01	0.08	−0.47	1.89	−13.77	−25.56	501.77	−0.06	0.18	−0.52	2.41	−38.28	−0.86	4.26	−74.04	222.86	370.89	2087.31	549.04	6
−0.01	0.07	−0.39	1.42	−11.88	−22.28	476.21	0.03	0.12	−0.34	1.89	−35.87	−0.51	3.40	−69.78	148.82	227.22	2458.20	498.93	8
0.00	0.06	−0.32	1.03	−10.46	−19.84	453.93	−0.09	0.15	−0.22	1.55	−33.98	−0.34	2.89	−66.38	79.04	91.20	2685.42	460.77	10
0.00	0.06	−0.26	0.71	−9.43	−18.09	434.09	0.00	0.06	−0.07	1.33	−32.43	−0.05	2.55	−63.49	12.66	−38.63	2776.62	434.27	12
0.00	0.06	−0.20	0.45	−8.72	−16.93	416.00	−0.01	0.06	−0.01	1.26	−31.10	0.04	2.50	−60.94	−50.83	−163.00	2737.99	419.05	14
0.00	0.06	−0.14	0.25	−8.27	−16.26	399.07	−0.07	0.05	0.05	1.25	−29.84	0.16	2.54	−58.44	−111.77	−282.39	2574.99	414.43	16
−0.01	0.05	−0.08	0.11	−8.02	−15.91	382.81	0.02	−0.02	0.10	1.30	−28.59	0.19	2.70	−55.90	−170.21	−396.74	2292.60	418.95	18
−0.04	0.01	−0.03	0.03	−7.91	−15.78	366.90		0.00	0.08	1.40	−27.29	0.15	2.89	−53.20	−226.11	−505.89	1895.86	430.96	20
		−0.02	0.00	−7.88	−15.76	351.12			0.08	1.48	−25.89		3.04	−50.31	−279.31	−609.43	1389.97	448.66	22
			−0.02	−7.88	−15.78	335.36				1.56	−24.41			−47.27	−329.62	−707.03	780.54	470.23	24
				−7.90		319.58					−22.85				−376.89		73.51	494.14	26

To find the time of flight we replace the terminal part of the trajectory by a parabola through the points corresponding to $t = 22$, $t = 24$, and $t = 26$. Hence y is to be a quadratic function of t, and we find this function by constructing a table of differences and employing Newton's interpolation formula (II) of Art. 21.

t	y	$\Delta_1 y$	$\Delta_2 y$
· 22	1389.97		
24	780.54	-609.43	
26	73.51	-707.03	-97.60

Putting $y = 0$ in that formula, we have

$$y_n + \Delta_1 y_n u + \frac{\Delta_2 y_n}{2}\, (u^2 + u) = 0.$$

$$\therefore\quad 73.51 - 707.03u - 48.8\,(u^2 + u) = 0,$$

or

$$48.8u^2 + 755.83u = 73.51.$$

$$\therefore\quad u = \frac{-755.83 + 765.26}{97.6} = \frac{9.43}{97.6} = 0.0966,$$

and

$$\therefore\quad t = t_n + hu = 26 + 2 \times 0.0966 = 26.19 \text{ sec.}$$

We next compute the range by means of Simpson's Rule. The horizontal distance covered during the first two seconds is, taking $h = \Delta t = \frac{1}{2}$ sec.,

$$x = \tfrac{1}{6}[610.44 + 4(598.84 + 577.32) + 2 \times 587.82 + 567.32]$$
$$= 1176.3 \text{ ft.}$$

For the interval from $t = 2$ to $t = 26$, taking $h = 2$, we have

$$x = \tfrac{2}{3}[567.32 + 4(531.69 + 476.21 + 434.09 + 399.07$$
$$+\, 366.90 + 335.36) + 2(501.77 + 453.93 + 416.00$$
$$+\, 382.81 + 351.12) + 319.58] = 10{,}181 \text{ ft.}$$

Hence the horizontal distance covered in the first 26 seconds is $10181 + 1176 = 11{,}357$ ft.

To find the distance covered in the remaining 0.19 second we assume that the horizontal acceleration will remain at -7.90 for 0.19 sec. Then the change in velocity during this time will be $(-7.90) \times 0.19 = -1.5$. The horizontal velocity at the *end* of 26.19 seconds with therefore be $319.6 - 1.5$ or 318.1 ft./sec., and the average velocity during this fraction of a second is $(319.6 + 318.1)/2 = 318.8$ ft./sec. Hence the horizontal distance covered in the last 0.19 sec., is $318.8 \times 0.19 = 61$ ft. The total range is therefore

$$X = 11357 + 61 = \underline{11{,}418 \text{ ft.}}$$

If we compute the increments in x for the several time intervals and add them as we go along, as was done in the case of y, we shall find the same value for the range as found by Simpson's Rule.

If ω denote the angle of fall, then

$$\tan \omega = \frac{\dot{y}}{\dot{x}}.$$

We have already found the value of $\dot{x}$ for $t = 26.19$. To find $\dot{y}$ we assume that the second difference in $\ddot{y}$ will be the same for the interval $t = 26$ to $t = 28$ as for the preceding interval. Then for the next two seconds we shall have $\Delta_1 \ddot{y} = 1.64$. Hence for one second the change in $\ddot{y}$ will be 0.82, and for 0.19 second it will be $0.82 \times 0.19 = 0.16$. The vertical acceleration when $t = 26.19$ will therefore be $-22.85 + 0.16 = -22.69$. The change in the vertical velocity during the last 0.19 second is then

$$\frac{-22.85 - 22.69}{2} \times 0.19 = -4.3.$$

Hence $\dot{y} = -376.9 - 4.3 = -381.2$.

$$\therefore \quad \tan \omega = \frac{-381.2}{318.1} = -1.198,$$

and $\omega = -50° 9'$.

The terminal velocity is

$$v = \sqrt{\dot{x}^2 + \dot{y}^2} = \sqrt{(318.1)^2 + (381.2)^2} = 496.5 \text{ ft./sec.}$$

The value given by formula (93. 1) is also 496.5.

IV. OTHER METHODS OF SOLVING DIFFERENTIAL EQUATIONS NUMERICALLY.

96. Milne's Method. A simple and reasonably accurate method of solving differential equations numerically has been devised by W. E. Milne.* It does not employ differences, but uses two quadrature formulas instead— one for integrating ahead by extrapolation and the other for checking the extrapolated value. These formulas are derived from Newton's formula (I), p. 63.

* "Numerical Integration of Ordinary Differential Equations," *American Mathematical Monthly*, vol. 33 (1926), pp. 455-460. Also, *Numerical Calculus*, pp. 135-139.

That formula in terms of y' and u is

$$(1) \quad y' = y'_0 + u\Delta y'_0 + \frac{u(u-1)}{2}\Delta^2 y'_0 + \frac{u(u-1)(n-2)}{6}\Delta^3 y'_0$$
$$+ \frac{u(u-1)(u-2)(u-3)}{24}\Delta^4 y'_0 + \cdots,$$

where $u = \dfrac{x - x_0}{h}$, or $x = x_0 + hu$. Integrating this formula over the interval x_0 to $x_0 + 4h$, or $u = 0$ to $u = 4$, we have, since $dx = h\,du$,

$$\Delta y = \int_{x_0}^{x_0+4h} y'\,dx = h\int_0^4 \left(y'_0 + u\Delta y'_0 + \frac{u(u-1)}{2}\Delta^2 y'_0\right.$$
$$\left. + \frac{u(u-1)(u-2)}{6}\Delta^3 y'_0 + \frac{u(u-1)(u-2)(u-3)}{24}\Delta^4 y'_0\right)du$$
$$= h\left(4y'_0 + 8\Delta y'_0 + \frac{20}{3}\Delta^2 y'_0 + \frac{8}{3}\Delta^3 y'_0 + \frac{28}{90}\Delta^4 y'_0\right).$$

Now replacing the first, second, and third differences by their values as given on p. 53 and simplifying, we get

$$\Delta y = \frac{4h}{3}(2y'_1 - y'_2 + 2y'_3) + \frac{28}{90}h\Delta^4 y'_0.$$

But here $\Delta y = y_4 - y_0$. Hence

$$(2) \qquad y_4 = y_0 + \frac{4h}{3}(2y'_1 - y'_2 + 2y'_3) + \frac{28}{90}h\Delta^4 y'_0.$$

This is Milne's extrapolation formula.

To get the checking formula we integrate (1) from x_0 to $x_0 + 2h$, or from $u = 0$ to $u = 2$. Then

$$\Delta y = h\left(2y'_0 + 2\Delta y'_0 + \frac{1}{3}\Delta^2 y'_0 - \frac{1}{90}\Delta^4 y'_0\right).$$

Now replacing $\Delta y'_0$ and $\Delta^2 y'_0$ by their values as given on p. 53, we have

$$\Delta y = \frac{h}{3}(y'_0 + 4y'_1 + y'_2) - \frac{h}{90}\Delta^4 y'_0.$$

But in this case $\Delta y = y_2 - y_0$. Hence

$$(3) \qquad y_2 = y_0 + \frac{h}{3}(y'_0 + 4y'_1 + y'_2) - \frac{1}{90}\Delta^4 y'_0.$$

This is the second of the Milne formulas and is seen at once to be Simpson's Rule. The terms involving $\Delta^4 y'_0$ are not used directly in the application of (2) and (3), but only as indicators of the accuracy of the results.

Since $x_0, \cdots, x_4$ may be any five consecutive values of x, formulas (2) and (3) may be written in the more general forms

(4) $$y_{n+1} = y_{n-3} + \frac{4h}{3}(2y'_{n-2} - y'_{n-1} + 2y'_n),$$

(5) $$y_{n+1} = y_{n-1} + \frac{h}{3}(y'_{n-1} + 4y'_n + y'_{n+1}),$$

which are the final forms of the Milne formulas.

The principal part of the error in the value of y computed by these formulas is easily found as follows:

Let $y_{n+1}^{(1)}$ and $y_{n+1}^{(2)}$ denote the values of y given by (4) and (5), respectively. Then if the value of h is such that the inherent error in each formula is given by its remainder term involving $\Delta^4 y'$, the true value of y at $x = x_{n+1}$ is either

$$y = y_{n+1}^{(1)} + \frac{28}{90} h \Delta^4 y'$$

or

$$y = y_{n+1}^{(2)} - \frac{h}{90} \Delta^4 y'.$$

Equating these values of y, we have

$$y_{n+1}^{(1)} + \frac{28}{90} h \Delta^4 y' = y_{n+1}^{(2)} - \frac{h}{90} \Delta^4 y',$$

or

$$y_{n+1}^{(1)} - y_{n+1}^{(2)} = -\frac{29}{90} h \Delta^4 y' = 29 \left(-\frac{h}{90} \Delta^4 y'\right) = 29 E_2,$$

where E_2 denotes the principal part of the error in (5). From this we get

(6) $$E_2 = \frac{1}{29}(y_{n+1}^{(1)} - y_{n+1}^{(2)}).$$

This simple formula enables the computer to test the accuracy of each computed result. If we write

(7) $$D = y_{n+1}^{(1)} - y_{n+1}^{(2)},$$

it is well to provide a column for D just to the right of the column of y's, or whatever quantity is being computed; and the behavior of the D's should be observed as the computation proceeds. If the D's become erratic, look at once for a mistake.

It will be observed that Milne's method requires the four starting values

y_{n-3}, y'_{n-2}, y'_{n-1}, and y'_n. These values are to be found by the starting methods previously described in this book. Milne's method will now be applied to three types of differential equations.

(*a*) *Equations of the First Order.* To tabulate the solution of the first-order equation

(a) $$\frac{dy}{dx} = y' = f(x, y),$$

we first find three consecutive values of y and y' in addition to the initial values. Then we find the next value of y by (4), substitute this in (a) for the new y', and then substitute the new y' in (5) to get the corrected value of the new y. If the corrected value agrees closely with the extrapolated value, proceed to the next interval.

If the corrected value differs appreciably from the extrapolated value and no error can be found in the work, compute E_2 by (6). If E_2 is too small to affect the last digit to be retained, all is well; proceed to the next interval. But if E_2 is large enough to affect the last figure to be retained, the value of h is too large and must be reduced.

Example 1. Tabulate by Milne's method the numerical solution of

$$\frac{dy}{dx} = x + y,$$

with

$$x_0 = 0, \quad y_0 = 1.$$

Solution. On page 250 we found the starting values given in the first four lines of the accompanying table. To start the fifth line we have by (4)

x	y	y'
0	1.0000	1.0000
0.1	1.1103	1.2103
0.2	1.2428	1.4428
0.3	1.3997	1.6997
0.4	1.5836	1.9836
0.5	1.7974	2.2974

$$y_{0.4} = 1 + \frac{0.4}{3}\left[2(1.2103) - 1.4428 + 2(1.6997)\right]$$
$$= 1.5836.$$

Then

$$y'_{0.4} = 0.4 + 1.5836 = 1.9836.$$

Now checking $y_{0.4}$ by (5), we have

$$y_{0.4} = 1.2428 + \frac{0.1}{3}\left[1.4428 + 4(1.6997) + 1.9836\right] = 1.5836,$$

which is the same value of $y_{0.4}$ as found by (4). Hence we consider it correct.

Proceeding now to the next line, we have by (4)

$$y_{0.5} = 1.1103 + \frac{0.4}{3}\,[2(1.4428) - 1.6997 + 2(1.9836)] = 1.7974.$$

Then

$$y'_{0.5} = 1.7974 + 0.5 = 2.2974.$$

Now checking by (5),

$$y_{0.5} = 1.3997 + \frac{0.1}{3}\,[1.6997 + 4(1.9836) + 2.2974] = 1.7974,$$

which is the same value of $y_{0.5}$ as previously found.

(b) *Equations of the Second Order.* Since formulas (4) and (5) are merely relations between a function and its derivative, similar formulas hold when the function is y'. Hence we may write

(8) $$y'_{n+1} = y'_{n-3} + \frac{4h}{3}\,(2y''_{n-2} - y''_{n-1} + 2y''_n)$$

(9) $$y'_{n+1} = y'_{n-1} + \frac{h}{3}(y''_{n-1} + 4y''_n + y''_{n+1}).$$

The general equation of the second order, when solved for $\dfrac{d^2y}{dx^2}$, may be written in the symbolic form

(b) $$y'' = f(x, y, y').$$

When four starting values of y and y' have been found by some method, the solution is continued as follows:

1. Use (8) to find a first approximation to the new y'.

2. Substitute this new y' in (5) to get a new y.

3. Substitute in the given equation (b) the new y and new y' to get an approximation to y''.

4. Check the new y' by (9), using the new y'' just found.

5. If the y' just found by (9) does not agree with that first found by (8), substitute the corrected y' in (5) to get a corrected y.

6. Then substitute in (b) the corrected y and y' to find a corrected y''.

7. Substitute this corrected y'' in (9) to get a better y', and then substitute this last y' in (5) to get a better y.

8. As a final check, apply (6) to the last two consecutive y''s and y's. If the error is too great, decrease h.

Example. Compute by Milne's method the last line of the table on page 264.

Solution. Substituting in (8) the appropriate values of $\dot\theta$ and $\ddot\theta$, we have

$$\dot\theta_5 = 0 + \frac{1}{15}\ (-5.782 + 2.758 - 5.120) = -0.5429.$$

Now substituting this $\dot\theta_5$ in (5), we get

$$\theta_5 = 0.2854 + \frac{1}{60}\ (-0.2879 - 1.6844 - 0.5429) = 0.2435.$$

Then substituting $\dot\theta_5$ and θ_5 in the given equation $\ddot\theta = -0.2\dot\theta - 10\sin\theta$, we get

$$\ddot\theta_5 = 0.1086 - 2.4110 = -2.3024.$$

As a check on $\dot\theta_5$ we next use (9) with the $\ddot\theta_5$ just computed. We have

$$\dot\theta_5 = -0.2879 + \frac{1}{60}\ (-2.758 - 10.240 - 2.302) = -0.5429,$$

which agrees with the value previously found. We therefore take these values to be correct.

The reader will note that formula (8) was used only once, and would not have been used again even if the two values of $\dot\theta$ had not agreed on the first round.

(c) *Simultaneous Equations.* The solution of simultaneous equations by Milne's method can be explained best by an example.

Example 3. Compute by Milne's method the values of $\dot x$, x, $\dot y$, and y in the seventh line of the table on p. 273.

Solution. We first find $\dot x_7$ by means of formula (8). Thus,

$$\dot x_7 = 0 + \frac{0.2}{3}\ [2(0.5102) - 0.5156 + 2(0.5162)] = 0.1025.$$

Now using this value of $\dot x$ in (5), we get

$$x_7 = 1.0025 + \frac{0.05}{3}\ [0.0509 + 4(0.0767) + 0.1025] = 1.0102.$$

Substituting these values of $\dot x$ and x in the given equation $\dot y = \frac{1}{2}(x + \dot x - \sin t)$, with $t = 0.2$, we have

$$\dot y_7 = \frac{1}{2}(1.0102 + 0.1025 - 0.1987) = 0.4570.$$

Now using (5) to find y, we have

$$y_7 = 2.0488 + \frac{0.05}{3} [0.4768 + 4(0.4665)) + 0.4570] = 2.0955.$$

We next substitute in the given equation $\ddot{x} = y - 2x + \dot{y} + \ln \cos t$ the values of x, y, and $\dot{y}$ found above, with $t = 0.2$. Then we get $\ddot{x} = 0.5120$. Finally, we check the whole procedure by means of (9). We thus have

$$\dot{x}_7 = 0.0509 + \frac{0.05}{3} [0.5136 + 4(0.5162) + 0.5120] = 0.1024.$$

Since this value differs from the extrapolated value by only one unit in the last figure, we take it as correct.

Additional lines of the table can be computed by exactly the same procedure as employed above.

The reader will note that the values found by Milne's method are the same as those found by the difference method, formulas (86. 1) and (86. 2).

97. The Runge-Kutta Method. This method was devised by Runge * about the year 1894 and extended by Kutta † a few years later. It is unlike any of the methods explained in the preceding pages. Here the increments of the function (or functions) are calculated once for all by means of a definite set of formulas. The calculations for the first increment, for example, are exactly the same as for any other increment.

The formulas for several types of differential equations are given below.

(a) *First-Order Equations.* Let $dy/dx = f(x, y)$ represent any first-order equation, and let h denote the interval between equidistant values of x. Then if the initial values are x_0, y_0, the first increment in y is computed from the formulas

(1)
$$\begin{cases} k_1 = f(x_0, y_0)h, \\[2mm] k_2 = f\left(x_0 + \frac{h}{2}, \ y_0 + \frac{k_1}{2}\right) h, \\[2mm] k_3 = f\left(x_0 + \frac{h}{2}, \ y_0 + \frac{k_2}{2}\right) h, \\[2mm] k_4 = f(x_0 + h, \ y_0 + k_3)h, \\[2mm] \Delta y = \frac{1}{6}(k_1 + 2k_2 + 2k_3 + k_4), \end{cases}$$

taken in the order given. Then

* C. Runge, *Mathematische Annalen*, Vol. 46 (1895).
† W. Kutta, *Zeitschrift für Math. und Phys.*, Vol. 46 (1901).

$$x_1 = x_0 + h, \qquad y_1 = y_0 + \Delta y.$$

The increment in y for the second interval is computed in a similar manner by means of the formulas

$$k_1 = f(x_1, y_1) h,$$

$$k_2 = f\left(x_1 + \frac{h}{2}, \ \ y_1 + \frac{k_1}{2}\right) h,$$

$$k_3 = f\left(x_1 + \frac{h}{2}, \ \ y_1 + \frac{k_2}{2}\right) h,$$

$$k_4 = f(x_1 + h, \ \ y_1 + k_3) h,$$

$$\Delta y = \tfrac{1}{6}(k_1 + 2k_2 + 2k_3 + k_4),$$

and so on for the succeeding intervals.

It will be noticed that the only change in the formulas for the different intervals is in the values of x and y to be substituted. Thus, to find Δy in the nth interval we should have to substitute x_{n-1}, y_{n-1}, in the expressions for k_1, k_2, etc.

In the special case where dy/dx is a function of x alone the Runge-Kutta method reduces to Simpson's Rule.   For if $dy/dx = f(x)$, then

$$k_1 = f(x_0) h,$$

$$k_2 = f\left(x_0 + \frac{h}{2}\right) h,$$

$$k_3 = f\left(x_0 + \frac{h}{2}\right) h,$$

$$k_4 = f(x_0 + h) h;$$

and therefore

$$\Delta y = \frac{h}{6}\left[f(x_0) + 2f\left(x_0 + \frac{h}{2}\right) + 2f\left(x_0 + \frac{h}{2}\right) + f(x_0 + h) \right]$$

$$= \frac{\left(\dfrac{h}{2}\right)}{3}\left[f(x_0) + 4f\left(x_0 + \frac{h}{2}\right) + f(x_0 + h) \right],$$

which is the same result as would be obtained by applying Simpson's Rule to the interval from x_0 to $x_0 + h$ if we take two equal subintervals of width $h/2$.

(b) *Second-Order Equations* of the general type

$$y'' = f(x, y, y')$$

are integrated step by step by means of the following formulas, applied
in the order given:

$$(2) \quad \begin{cases} k_1 = hf(x_n, y_n, y'_n) \\[2mm] k_2 = hf(x_n + \dfrac{h}{2}, \quad y_n + \dfrac{h}{2}y'_n + \dfrac{h}{8}k_1, \quad y'_n + \dfrac{k_1}{2}), \\[2mm] k_3 = hf(x_n + \dfrac{h}{2}, \quad y_n + \dfrac{h}{2}y'_n + \dfrac{h}{8}k_1, \quad y'_n + \dfrac{k_2}{2}), \\[2mm] k_4 = hf(x_n + h, \quad y_n + hy'_n + \dfrac{h}{2}k_3, \quad y'_n + k_3), \\[2mm] \Delta y = h[y'_n + \dfrac{1}{6}(k_1 + k_2 + k_3)], \\[2mm] \Delta y' = \dfrac{1}{6}(k_1 + 2k_2 + 2k_3 + k_4), \end{cases}$$

where $n = 0, 1, 2, \cdots$.

For the special second-order equation

$$y'' = f(x, y),$$

the increments in y and y' are found from the formulas:

$$(3) \quad \begin{cases} k_1 = hf(x_n, y_n), \\[2mm] k_2 = hf(x_n + \dfrac{h}{2}, \quad y_n + \dfrac{h}{2}y'_n + \dfrac{h}{8}k_1), \\[2mm] k_3 = hf(x_n + h, \quad y_n + hy'_n + \dfrac{h}{2}k_2), \\[2mm] \Delta y = h[y'_n + \dfrac{1}{6}(k_1 + 2k_2)], \\[2mm] \Delta y' = \dfrac{1}{6}(k_1 + 4k_2 + k_3). \end{cases}$$

(c) *Simultaneous Equations.* In a pair of simple simultaneous equations
of the type

$$\frac{dx}{dt} = f_1(t, x, y)$$

$$\frac{dy}{dt} = f_2(t, x, y)$$

the increments in x and y for the first interval are found from the
following formulas:

$$\left\{ \begin{aligned} &k_1 = f_1(t_0, x_0, y_0)\Delta t, \\ &k_2 = f_1\left(t_0 + \frac{\Delta t}{2}, \quad x_0 + \frac{k_1}{2}, \quad y_0 + \frac{l_1}{2}\right)\Delta t, \\ &k_3 = f_1\left(t_0 + \frac{\Delta t}{2}, \quad x_0 + \frac{k_2}{2}, \quad y_0 + \frac{l_2}{2}\right)\Delta t, \\ &k_4 = f_1(t_0 + \Delta t, \quad x_0 + k_3, \quad y_0 + l_3)\Delta t, \\ &\Delta x = \tfrac{1}{6}(k_1 + 2k_2 + 2k_3 + k_4). \end{aligned} \right.$$

(4)

$$\left\{ \begin{aligned} &l_1 = f_2(t_0, x_0, y_0)\Delta t, \\ &l_2 = f_2\left(t_0 + \frac{\Delta t}{2}, \quad x_0 + \frac{k_1}{2}, \quad y_0 + \frac{l_1}{2}\right)\Delta t, \\ &l_3 = f_2\left(t_0 + \frac{\Delta t}{2}, \quad x_0 + \frac{k_2}{2}, \quad y_0 + \frac{l_2}{2}\right)\Delta t, \\ &l_4 = f_2(t_0 + \Delta t, \quad x_0 + k_3, \quad y_0 + l_3)\Delta t, \\ &\Delta y = \tfrac{1}{6}(l_1 + 2l_2 + 2l_3 + l_4). \end{aligned} \right.$$

The increments for the succeeding intervals are computed in exactly the same way except that t_0, x_0, y_0 are replaced by t_1, x_1, y_1, etc. as we proceed.

The simultaneous equations

$$\frac{dy}{dx} = f_1(x, y, z)$$

$$\frac{dz}{dx} = f_2(x, y, z)$$

are solved by formulas (4) by changing t to x, x to y, y to z, and putting $\Delta t = h$.

The derivation of the formulas used in the Runge-Kutta method is a somewhat lengthy process and will not be given here.*

The inherent error in the Runge-Kutta method is not easy to estimate, but is of the order h^5 † and is therefore of the same order as that in Simpson's Rule.

We shall illustrate the method by applying it to an example to which the previous methods were applied.

---

* See Kutta, *loc. cit.*, or *Numerisches Rechnen*, by C. Runge and H. König, pp. 287-294 and 311-313.

† See Kutta, *loc. cit.*, or *Numerische Integration*, by F. A. Willers, pp. 91-92.

Example. Solve the equation

$$\frac{dy}{dx} = x + y,$$

with the initial conditions $x_0 = 0$, $y_0 = 1$.

Solution. Taking $h = 0.1$, we have

$$k_1 = 0.1 \times 1 = 0.1,$$
$$k_2 = 0.1[0.05 + 1.05] = 0.11,$$
$$k_3 = 0.1[0.05 + 1.055] = 0.1105,$$
$$k_4 = 0.1[0.1 + 1.1105] = 0.12105.$$

$$\therefore \quad \Delta y = \tfrac{1}{6}[0.1 + 0.22 + 0.221 + 0.12105] = 0.11034.$$

Hence $x_1 = x_0 + h = 0.1$, $y_1 = y_0 + \Delta y = 1 + 0.1103 = 1.1103$.

Then for the second interval we have

$$k_1 = 0.1(0.1 + 1.1103) = 0.12103,$$
$$k_2 = 0.1(0.1 + 0.05 + 1.1103 + 0.06051) = 0.13208,$$
$$k_3 = 0.1(0.1 + 0.05 + 1.1103 + 0.06604) = 0.13263,$$
$$k_4 = 0.1(0.1 + 0.1 + 1.1103 + 0.13262) = 0.14429.$$

$$\therefore \quad \Delta y = \tfrac{1}{6}(0.12103 + 0.26416 + 0.26526 + 0.14429) = 0.13246,$$

and $x_2 = 0.2$, $y_2 = 1.1103 + 0.1325 = 1.2428$. These values for y_1 and y_2 are correct to four decimal places. The computation can be continued in this manner as far as desired.

98. Checks, Errors, and Accuracy. Attention has already been called to the use of formulas (86. 2), (86. 3), (86. 4), and (86. 5) for checking the computed change in a function over a single interval. A formula has also been given for checking the results found by Milne's method. Simpson's Rule furnishes a convenient and reliable means of checking the summation of any function over an even number of intervals. For example, the decrease in the horizontal velocity of the bullet in the example of Art. 95, from $t = 2$ to $t = 26$, is

$$\Delta \dot{x} = \int_{2}^{26} \ddot{x}\,dt = \frac{\Delta t}{3}\left[\ddot{x}_2 + 4(\ddot{x}_4 + \ddot{x}_8 + \ddot{x}_{12} + \ddot{x}_{16} + \ddot{x}_{20} + \ddot{x}_{24})\right.$$
$$\left. + 2(\ddot{x}_6 + \ddot{x}_{10} + \ddot{x}_{14} + \ddot{x}_{18} + \ddot{x}_{22}) + \ddot{x}_{26}\right],$$

or

$$\Delta \dot{x} = \tfrac{2}{3}[-19.52 + 4(-16.26 - 11.88 - 9.43 - 8.27 - 7.91 - 7.88)$$
$$+ 2(-13.77 - 10.46 - 8.72 - 8.02 - 7.88) - 7.90] = -247.76.$$

Hence

$$\dot{x}_{26} = 567.32 - 247.76 = 319.56,$$

which differs from the value in the table by only two units in the last digit. The fifth figure in all these numbers is uncertain, probably worthless, but the two methods certainly check within a unit in the fourth figure. The values of $\dot{y}$ and y may be checked in a similar manner.

A single error in any one of the quantities $\dot{x}$, $\dot{y}$, and y will persist throughout the computation in the column in which it occurs, but its effect will usually not increase as the computation continues. An error in the acceleration will likewise persist and will affect in some degree all the other computed quantities, but the effect may not be serious. An error in the differences of the acceleration and in the second, third, and fourth differences of the other functions will soon disappear, and its effect on the final results will usually be negligible. If several errors are made, they will probably neutralize one another to a considerable extent, but it is possible that they may accumulate sufficiently to affect seriously some of the later results.

As an example of the effect of a single error near the beginning of a computation, it may be stated that the example of Art. 89 was first computed throughout by starting with an error of two units in the last digit of $\dot{\theta}$ for $t = 0.05$ sec. The maximum error in any subsequent value of $\dot{\theta}$ up to $t = 2.1$ was five units in the last digit, whereas the greatest error in any later value of θ and $\ddot{\theta}$ was only two units in the last figure.

An error of more than a unit in the last digit of a computed result can usually be detected by inspection of the second, third, and fourth differences of that result. If these higher differences run smoothly— that is, vary in a regular fashion without sudden changes in magnitude or sign—, it is quite certain that no error has been made; but if the third and fourth differences become grossly irregular, the student had better stop and look for an error at once. The error may be located approximately by the method explained in Art. 17. The computer should watch the behavior of the higher differences as he goes along, so as to detect an error as soon as possible after it appears.

The safest plan to insure accuracy is to take h so small that fourth differences will be negligible to the number of figures desired in the final results. When fourth differences are negligible, the application of formula (86.2) as many times as it will effect improvement will usually insure that the error is less than half a unit in the last figure retained. Since these half-unit (or less) errors are as likely to be positive as negative, they are largely neutralized in the calculation process. Hence it is not worth while to consider them in estimating the accuracy of a final result.

Whatever method is used in tabulating the numerical solution of a differential equation or a system of equations, the successive differences of all computed quantities should be computed and recorded. The behavior of the differences will show at a glance whether a mistake has been made in the computation or whether the value of h is too large.

99. Some General Remarks. The methods given in the preceding pages are believed to be sufficient for the numerical solution of all ordinary differential equations having numerical coefficients and sufficient initial conditions. Equations higher than the second order have not been treated, but equations of the third and fourth orders can be handled by the methods given. All that has to be remembered is that *formulas for integrating ahead and starting a new line are to be applied to the derivative of highest order in the equation (or equations) and the various differences of that highest-order derivative.*

The most important matter in the numerical solution of a differential equation is getting correct starting values. These can be found by several methods, but in some of them there is no certain means of determining the accuracy of the results found. When the starting values are found by the modified Euler method, the value of h should be so small that one or two repetitions of the averaging process will give the final result for that value of h. Likewise, when the starting values are found by Taylor's series, h should be so small that only three or four terms of the series have any effect on the computed result.

Reliable starting values can be found by the Runge-Kutta method in many cases, but usually at a greater expenditure of labor than by other methods.

The Milne method of finding starting values is accurate and reasonably short. When the derivative of the given highest derivative can be found without difficulty, this is a good method for computing the starting values.

After correct starting values have been found, there are two good methods for continuing the computation: the method employing differences, formulas (86. 1) and (86. 2) for example, and the method of Milne. Which of these is preferable probably depends on the taste and equipment of the computer. In the difference method much of the work can be done mentally and with. very little effort. On the other hand, if the computer is equipped with a computing machine and is expert in using it, he may find the Milne method shorter and easier.

The Runge-Kutta method is too' laborious for tabulating many steps of a numerical solution.

The Picard method gives the solution theoretically when the derivative is any type of function, but the method is of limited practical value because of the difficulty frequently encountered in performing the required successive integrations.

The reader has observed that the numerical solution of a differential equation by any method involves considerable labor. But the numerical methods also have certain redeeming features in their favor; for they provide a means of obtaining solutions to problems which could not be solved otherwise, and they also give a complete record of the behavior of the functions within the regions considered. In some problems the exact analytical solution may involve more labor than the numerical method if certain information is desired. The following example will illustrate this point.

Suppose the differential equation

$$\frac{dy}{dx} = \frac{y-x}{y+x}$$

is given, with initial conditions $x_0 = 0$, $y_0 = 1$, and it is required to find several corresponding values of x and y. The given equation can be solved by putting $y = vx$, separating the variables, and integrating. The result, for the given initial conditions, is

$$\frac{1}{2} \ln (x^2 + y^2) + \tan^{-1} \left(\frac{y}{x} \right) = \frac{\pi}{2} .$$

To find pairs of corresponding values of x and y from this equation we could substitute the desired values of x and then solve the resulting equation for y. But this resulting equation will always be a complicated transcendental equation which can be solved only by trial—by Newton's method or otherwise. The labor of solving this equation for even a single value of y would probably be as great as that of computing several tabular values by numerical integration. The numerical method might therefore be the easier in this example.

The numerical solution of a differential equation, however, will give no information concerning the function outside the range of computed values, whereas the exact analytical solution will enable us to predict the behavior of the function for any values whatever of the independent variable. For this reason the solutions of differential equations expressing natural phenomena should always be obtained in analytical form if possible.

EXERCISES XII

1. Solve the simultaneous equations

$$\frac{dx}{dt} = 2x + y, \frac{dy}{dt} = x - 3y,$$

with the initial conditions $x = 0$, $y = 0.5$ when $t = 0$. Compute the first six lines of a tabular solution.

2. Compute the first six lines of a tabular solution of

$$\frac{d^2\theta}{dt^2} + 0.1\frac{d\theta}{dt} + \sin\theta = 0,$$

with the initial conditions $\theta = 30°$, $\frac{d\theta}{dt} = 0$, when $t = 0$.

3. Use the method of Art. 90 to solve the equation

$$\frac{d^2\theta}{dt^2} + 0.9\sin\theta = 0,$$

with the initial conditions $\theta = 5°$, $\frac{d\theta}{dt} = 0$, when $t = 0$. Tabulate the first six lines of the solution.

4. Use the method of Art. 89 to solve

$$\frac{d^2r}{dt^2} = -\frac{0.0002959}{r^2} + 0.01\left(\frac{dr}{dt}\right)^2,$$

with the initial conditions $r = 1$, $\frac{dr}{dt} = 0$, when $t = 0$. Compute the first six lines of a tabular solution.

5. The motion of a bullet is determined by the equations

$$\frac{d^2x}{dt^2} = -0.000035v\frac{dx}{dt}$$

$$\frac{d^2y}{dt^2} = -0.000035v\frac{dy}{dt} - 32.16.$$

If the initial conditions are $v = 800$ ft./sec., $\frac{dx}{dt} = 692.82$ ft./sec., $\frac{dy}{dt} = 400$ ft./sec. when $t = 0$, find the horizontal range and time of flight of the bullet.

6. Compute the first ten lines of a tabular solution of the simultaneous equations

$$\frac{d^2x}{dt^2} = -\frac{0.0002959x}{r^3},$$

$$\frac{d^2y}{dt^2} = -\frac{0.0002959y}{r^3},$$

with the initial conditions $x = 0.31$, $y = 0$, $\dfrac{dx}{dt} = 0$, $\dfrac{dy}{dt} = 0.034$, when $t = 0$. Here $r = \sqrt{x^2 + y^2}$.

CHAPTER XII

THE NUMERICAL SOLUTION OF PARTIAL DIFFERENTIAL EQUATIONS

100. Introduction. One of the greatest needs in applied mathematics is a general and reasonably short method of solving partial differential equations by numerical methods. Several methods have been proposed for meeting this need, but none can be called entirely satisfactory. They are all long and laborious.

Soon after Runge discovered his method of solving ordinary differential equations, Gans[1] extended the method to partial differential equations with given initial conditions. Some years later, Willers[2] extended the improved Runge-Kutta method to the solution of partial differential equations with given initial conditions. These methods are slow and laborious and have not come into general use.

Certain types of boundary-value problems can be solved by replacing the differential equation by the corresponding difference equation and then solving the latter by a process of iteration. This method of solving partial differential equations was devised and first used by L. F. Richardson.[3] It was later improved by H. Liebmann[4] and further improved more recently by Shortley and Weller.[5] The process is slow, but gives good results on boundary-value problems which satisfy Laplace's, Poisson's, and several other partial differential equations. A strong point in its favor is that the computation can be done by an automatic sequence-controlled calculating machine.

A somewhat similar method is the relaxation method devised by R. V. Southwell.[6] This method is shorter and more flexible than the iteration method, but is not adapted to automatic machine computation. In both of these methods the approximate solution of a partial differential equation, with given boundary values, is found by finding the solution of the corresponding partial difference equation.

---

[1] *Zeitschrift für Mathematik und Physik*, Vol. 48 (1902), pp. 394-399.

[2] *Numerische Integration* (1923), pp. 96-100.

[3] Transactions of the Royal Society A, 210 (1910), pp. 307-357.

[4] Sitzungsberichte der math.-phys. Klasse der Bayerische Akad, Munchen, 1918, p. 385.

[5] *Journal of Applied Physics*, Vol. 9 (1938), pp. 334-348.

[6] *Relaxation Methods in Theoretical Physics*.

I. DIFFERENCE QUOTIENTS AND DIFFERENCE EQUATIONS.

101. Difference Quotients. A difference quotient is the quotient obtained by dividing the difference between two values of a function by the difference between the two corresponding values of the independent variable. Thus for a function $f(x)$ of a single variable the difference quotient is the familiar expression $\dfrac{f(x+h)-f(x)}{h}$, whose limiting value is the derivative of $f(x)$ with respect to x. A difference quotient is thus an approximation to the derivative, the approximation becoming closer as h becomes smaller.

Partial-difference quotients of the second and higher orders are best constructed with reference to a network of points in the xy-plane for a function of two variables and in space for a function of three variables. For a function $u(x, y)$ of two variables, let the xy-plane be divided into a network or lattice of squares of side h, by drawing the two families of parallel lines

$$x = mh, \qquad m = 0, 1, 2, \cdots$$

$$y = nh, \qquad n = 0, 1, 2, \cdots$$

as indicated in Fig. 18. The points of intersection of these families of lines are called *lattice points*.

With reference to Fig. 18, the forward first-difference quotient of $u(x, y)$ with respect to x is

$$(101.1) \qquad u_x = \frac{u(x+h, y) - u(x, y)}{h},$$

and the backward first-difference quotient with respect to x is

$$(101.2) \qquad u_{\bar{x}} = \frac{u(x, y) - u(x-h, y)}{h}.$$

The second-difference quotient of $u(x, y)$ with respect to x is the difference quotient of the first-difference quotients (101.1) and (101.2). Hence we have

$$(101.3) \quad u_{\bar{x}x} = \frac{u_x - u_{\bar{x}}}{h} = \frac{\dfrac{u(x+h, y) - u(x, y)}{h} - \dfrac{u(x, y) - u(x-h, y)}{h}}{h}$$

$$= \frac{u(x+h, y) - 2u(x, y) + u(x-h, y)}{h^2}.$$

The first- and second-difference quotients of $u(x, y)$ with respect to y are found in exactly the same manner and are

(101. 4) $\quad u_y = \dfrac{u(x, y + h) - u(x, y)}{h}, \quad u_{\bar y} = \dfrac{u(x, y) - u(x, y - h)}{h},$

and

(101. 5) $\quad u_{\bar y y} = \dfrac{u(x, y + h) - 2u(x, y) + u(x, y - h)}{h^2}.$

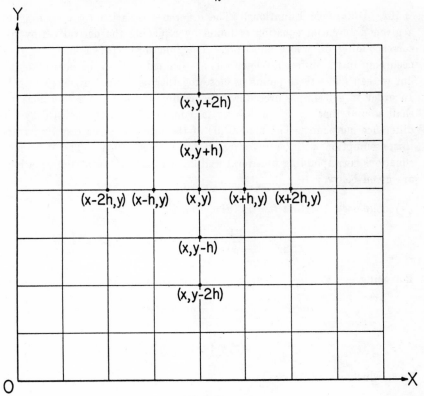

FIG. 18

Higher difference quotients are found in exactly the same manner except that additional lattice points must be used.

Difference quotients of a function $u(x, y, z)$ of three variables are found by the same process as used above. Thus for the second-difference quotient with respect to z we have

(101. 6) $\quad u_{\bar z z} = \dfrac{u(x, y, z + h) - 2u(x, y, z) + u(x, y, z - h)}{h^2}.$

The reader will note that the differences used in finding all these difference quotients are *central differences*. When central differences are used, the inherent error made by replacing a second derivative by a second-difference quotient is proportional to h^2 if h is small. This fact can be shown by replacing the terms $u(x+h, y)$ and $u(x-h, y)$ in (101. 3) by their Taylor expansions and then comparing $u_{\overline{xx}}$ with $\dfrac{\partial^2 u}{\partial x^2}$.

102. Difference Equations. The difference equation corresponding to a given differential equation is found by replacing the derivatives by the corresponding difference quotients. The functions $u(x, y)$ and $u(x, y, z)$ occurring in the difference equations are defined only at the lattice points, but we can make these points as close together as desired by decreasing h. In order to get simple procedures for solving the difference equations we shall assume that the given differential equation is exactly satisfied by the difference quotients. The magnitude of the inherent error resulting from this assumption will be investigated later (Art. 104). The difference equations corresponding to several well-known partial differential equations are given below.

(a) *Laplace's equation for two dimensions,*

$$\frac{\partial^2 V}{\partial x^2} + \frac{\partial^2 V}{\partial y^2} = 0.$$

Replacing $\dfrac{\partial^2 V}{\partial x^2}$ and $\dfrac{\partial^2 V}{\partial y^2}$ by $u_{\overline{xx}}$ and $u_{\overline{yy}}$, respectively, we get

$$\frac{u(x+h, y) - 2u(x, y) + u(x-h, y)}{h^2}$$

$$+ \frac{u(x, y+h) - 2u(x, y) + u(x, y-h)}{h^2} = 0,$$

from which

(102. 1) $u(x, y) = \tfrac{1}{4}[u(x+h, y) + u(x, y+h)$

$$+ u(x-h, y) + u(x, y-h)].$$

This equation shows that the value of u at any interior lattice point is the arithmetic mean of the values of u at the four lattice points nearest it.

(b) *Laplace's equation for three dimensions,*

$$\frac{\partial^2 V}{\partial x^2} + \frac{\partial^2 V}{\partial y^2} + \frac{\partial^2 V}{\partial z^2} = 0.$$

Replacing the second derivatives by the second-difference quotients as given by (101. 3), (101. 5), and (101. 6), and solving for $u(x, y, z)$, we get

$$(2) \quad u(x, y, z) = \tfrac{1}{6}[u(x + h, y, z) + u(x, y + h, z) + u(x, y, z + h)$$
$$+ u(x - h, y, z) + u(x, y - h, z) + u(x, y, z - h)].$$

This equation (2) shows that the value of u at any interior lattice point in space is the arithmetic mean of the values of u at the six lattice points nearest it.

(c) *Poisson's equation in two dimensions,*

$$\frac{\partial^2 V}{\partial x^2} + \frac{\partial^2 V}{\partial y^2} = - 4\pi\rho(x, y).$$

Replacing $\dfrac{\partial^2 V}{\partial x^2}$ and $\dfrac{\partial^2 V}{\partial y^2}$ by $u_{\bar{x}x}$ and $u_{\bar{y}y}$, respectively, as given by (101. 3) and (101. 5), we get

$$(102. 2) \quad u(x, y)$$
$$= \tfrac{1}{4}[u(x+h, y)+u(x, y+h)+u(x-h, y)+u(x, y-h)]+\pi h^2\rho(x, y).$$

Here the value of u at an interior lattice point depends not only on the u's of the adjacent points but also explicitly on the value of h and the function $\rho(x, y)$.

(d) *The equation of heat conduction in a plane,*

$$\frac{\partial T}{\partial t} = a^2 \left(\frac{\partial^2 T}{\partial x^2} + \frac{\partial^2 T}{\partial y^2}\right).$$

Here t denotes time and T denotes temperature at any time and place, or $T = T(x, y, t)$, and a^2 is a constant. If the temperature of the plane area has reached a steady state, so that $\dfrac{\partial T}{\partial t} = 0$, then the above equation reduces to Laplace's equation.

If the steady state has not been reached, the temperature at any point depends on the time. Hence the difference quotient at any lattice point at time t is

$$T'_t = \frac{T(x, y, t + \Delta t) - T(x, y, t)}{\Delta t}.$$

The second-difference quotients $T_{\bar{x}x}$ and $T_{\bar{y}y}$ at any instant (t fixed) are given by (101. 3) and (101. 5) if u is replaced by T. Hence on replacing the derivatives in the heat equation by the corresponding difference quotients, we get

$$\frac{T(x, y, t + \Delta t) - T(x, y, t)}{\Delta t}$$

$$= a^2 \left[\frac{T(x + h, y, t) - 2T(x, y, t) + T(x - h, y, t)}{h^2} \right.$$

$$\left. + \frac{T(x, y + h, t) - 2T(x, y, t) + T(x, y - h, t)}{h^2} \right],$$

from which

$$T(x, y, t + \Delta t)$$

$$= T(x, y, t) + \frac{a^2}{h^2} \Delta t [T(x + h, y, t) + T(x, y + h, t) + T(x - h, y, t)$$

$$+ T(x, y - h, t) - 4T(x, y, t)]$$

Since Δt is an arbitrary increment of time, we may set $\Delta t = \dfrac{h^2}{4a^2}$. Then the above equation reduces to

(4) $T(x, y, t + \Delta t)$

$$= \tfrac{1}{4}[T(x + h, y, t) + T(x, y + h, t) + T(x - h, y, t) + T(x, y - h, t)].$$

This equation gives the temperature at any interior lattice point at time $t + \Delta t$ as the arithmetic mean of the temperatures of the four adjacent lattice points at time t. If the temperature has reached the steady state, we have

(102. 3) $T(x, y, t)$

$$= \tfrac{1}{4}[T(x + h, y, t) + T(x, y + h, t) + T(x - h, y, t) + T(x, y - h, t)].$$

Other types of partial differential equations can be replaced by partial difference equations by proceeding as in the above examples.

II. THE METHOD OF ITERATION.

103. Solution of Difference Equations by Iteration. We consider a process of solving Laplace's equation in two variables and with given boundary conditions. For simplicity we assume that the function $u(x, y)$ is required over a rectangular area. We therefore cover the area with a network of squares of side h, as shown in Fig. 19.

Since the boundary values of the desired function are assumed to be known, we denote them by a's, as indicated in Fig. 19. The values of the required function at the interior lattice points are unknown, but in order to start the iteration process by equation (102. 1) we compute rough values for them as shown in the solution of Example 1 below.

We start the iteration process by computing an improved value of u_1 by means of formula (102. 1), the new or improved value of u_1 being

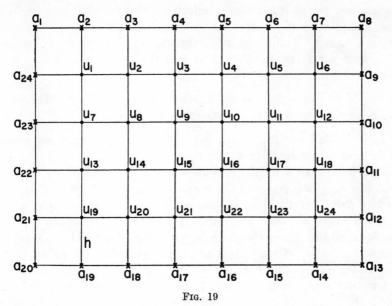

FIG. 19

denoted by u'_1. Then we proceed to improve u_2 in the same manner, and so on with all the other interior lattice points. The traverse, as it is called, proceeds over the network in the order in which the points are numbered. Thus we have

$$u'_1 = \tfrac{1}{4}(u_2 + a_2 + a_{24} + u_7)$$
$$u'_2 = \tfrac{1}{4}(u_3 + a_3 + u'_1 + u_8)$$
$$\cdot \ \cdot \ \cdot \ \cdot \ \cdot \ \cdot \ \cdot \ \cdot \ \cdot \ \cdot \ \cdot$$
$$u'_7 = \tfrac{1}{4}(u_8 + u'_1 + a_{23} + u_{13})$$
$$u'_8 = \tfrac{1}{4}(u_9 + u'_2 + u'_7 + u_{14})$$
$$\cdot \ \cdot \ \cdot \ \cdot \ \cdot \ \cdot \ \cdot \ \cdot \ \cdot \ \cdot \ \cdot$$
$$\cdot \ \cdot \ \cdot \ \cdot \ \cdot \ \cdot \ \cdot \ \cdot \ \cdot \ \cdot \ \cdot$$
$$u'_{24} = \tfrac{1}{4}(a_{12} + u'_{18} + u'_{23} + a_{14}).$$

Note that improved values are used as soon as available in computing improved values for points ahead.

The process outlined above is repeated as long as it produces any improvement in the u's. For the second traverse we would start with

$$u''_1 = \tfrac{1}{4}(u'_2 + a_2 + a_{24} + u'_7),$$

etc.

In solving partial-difference equations by the iteration process, it is advisable to start with a coarse net (large value of h). Then when iteration gives no further improvement in the u's, the whole process is repeated with a finer net (smaller value of h) and the iteration carried on until no change occurs in the u's.

Example 1. Solve the Laplace difference equation for a square region and having the boundary values shown in Fig. 20.

Solution. We start with a coarse net by dividing the given square into 16 smaller squares, as shown in the figure.

To get initial values for the interior points of the network, we first find a value for u_5 at the center of the square by taking the mean of the four boundary values at the ends of the heavy lines drawn at right angles through the center. Then we find the values for the centers of the four large squares into which the given square is divided by the heavy lines through the center. These values are found by taking the means of the values at the ends of the diagonals of the large squares.* The values for the four remaining interior points lying on the heavy central lines are found by taking the means of the four adjacent points in each case; that is, the four nearest points lying on the horizontal and vertical lines through the points considered. The computation of some of the interior values is shown at the bottom of Fig. 20.

Now having all the boundary values for the network and rough values for the interior lattice points, we are ready to start with the iteration process. Beginning with the first interior point in the upper left-hand corner of the square, we proceed to the right until the last interior point on the line is improved. Then we drop down to the next line and proceed

---

* This method of taking the mean of the values of the function at the ends of the diagonals of a square is perfectly legitimate, because if we make a transformation of coordinates by rotating the x- and y-axes through $45°$, the ends of the diagonals are on the new coordinate axes; and from the transformation equations

$$x = \frac{1}{\sqrt{2}}(x' - y'), \quad y = \frac{1}{\sqrt{2}}(x' + y') \text{ it follows that } \frac{\partial^2 u}{\partial x'^2} + \frac{\partial^2 u}{\partial y'^2} = \frac{\partial^2 u}{\partial x^2} + \frac{\partial^2 u}{\partial y^2}. \text{ (See E.}$$

B. Wilson's *Advanced Calculus*, p. 112, Ex. 25, or Vallée-Poussin's *Cours d'Analyse Infinitesimale*, I (4th Edition), p. 159, Ex. 6.) Hence u satisfies Laplace's equation in the new coordinates, and Equation (102.1) is therefore valid here.

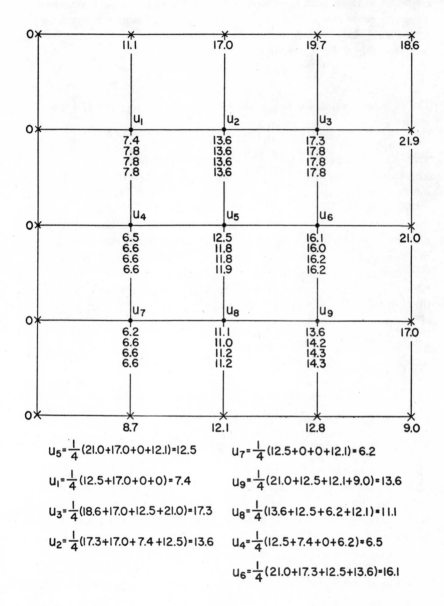

$$u_5 = \frac{1}{4}(21.0+17.0+0+12.1) = 12.5 \qquad u_7 = \frac{1}{4}(12.5+0+0+12.1) = 6.2$$

$$u_1 = \frac{1}{4}(12.5+17.0+0+0) = 7.4 \qquad u_9 = \frac{1}{4}(21.0+12.5+12.1+9.0) = 13.6$$

$$u_3 = \frac{1}{4}(18.6+17.0+12.5+21.0) = 17.3 \qquad u_8 = \frac{1}{4}(13.6+12.5+6.2+12.1) = 11.1$$

$$u_2 = \frac{1}{4}(17.3+17.0+7.4+12.5) = 13.6 \qquad u_4 = \frac{1}{4}(12.5+7.4+0+6.2) = 6.5$$

$$u_6 = \frac{1}{4}(21.0+17.3+12.5+13.6) = 16.1$$

Fig. 20

from left to right with the interior points in that line and so on, the order being the same as that followed in reading the lines of a printed page.

The first improved value in the top line of interior points is found from formula (102. 1) to be

$$u'_1 = \tfrac{1}{4}(13.6 + 11.1 + 0 + 6.5) = 7.8.$$

The improved value for the next lattice point to the right is

$$u'_2 = \tfrac{1}{4}(17.3 + 17.0 + 7.8 + 12.5) = 13.65,$$

which, for the sake of simplicity, we round off to 13.6.

The process is repeated until it produces no change in the values of the interior points.

The next step in the computation is to halve the value of h, and repeat the iteration process with the smaller squares. The initial values for the new mesh points are computed just as in the previous case, by taking the the means of the values of the corners to get the values at the centers of the previous larger squares and then finding the remaining values by taking the means of the nearest points on the horizontal and vertical lines through the point considered. Thus, for the value at the center of the first of the previous squares we have

$$u_1 = \tfrac{1}{4}(7.8 + 11.1 + 0 + 0) = 4.7.$$

For the value at the center of the next old square we have

$$u_3 = \tfrac{1}{4}(13.6 + 17.0 + 11.1 + 7.8) = 12.4.$$

Then for u_2 of the new mesh points we have

$$u_2 = \tfrac{1}{4}(12.4 + 11.1 + 4.7 + 7.8) = 9.0.$$

The remaining initial values for the new network are found in like manner.

Having initial values for all the lattice points of the new net, the computer then begins the iteration process for the new network. The first improved value for the first interior mesh point in the upper left-hand corner is (see Fig. 21)

$$u'_1 = \tfrac{1}{4}(9.0 + 7.7 + 0 + 4.0) = 5.2.$$

Two applications of the iteration process suffice to complete the solution for the new value of h. If desired, one could halve h again and get a closer approximation for the solution of the given example. For this new computation with a still smaller h, additional intermediate boundary values would have to be interpolated, estimated, or scaled from a curve plotted

from the given boundary values of Fig. 20. The computed interior points
will then be no more accurate than the new boundary points.

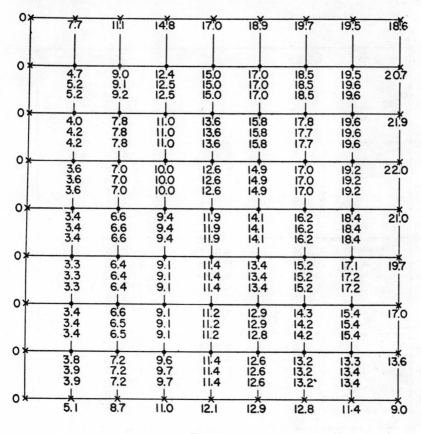

FIG. 21

Remark. The reader should keep in mind the fact that the computed
values at the mesh points in a network are determined by two things:

1). The given differential equation.

2). The set of given boundary values.

Hence if the boundary values are known to only two or three significant
figures, it is useless to compute the interior points to more figures.

Example 2. Solve the Laplace difference equation for a square region having the boundary equations shown in Fig. 24.*

Solution. Here the value of u on the boundaries is given by definite analytic expressions which may be evaluated at any point on the boundary

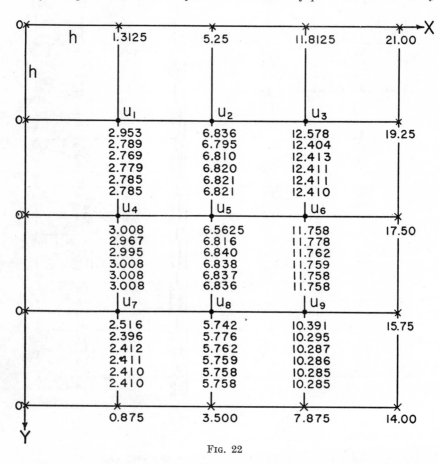

FIG. 22

to any desired degree of accuracy. Such boundaries also make it possible to express u analytically as a Fourier series and thus enable us to compare the numerical solution with the Fourier solution.

We start with a coarse net by dividing the given square region into

---

* The given boundary values in this example are quantities of zero dimensions, or pure numbers. Hence the computed values at all interior mesh points will likewise be pure numbers.

16 squares. Approximate values of u at the mesh points are found as already explained in the preceding example. Five applications of the iteration process gave the results shown in Fig. 22.

We then halve the value of h and make a new computation, as indicated in Fig. 23. The initial values at the new interior mesh points are found

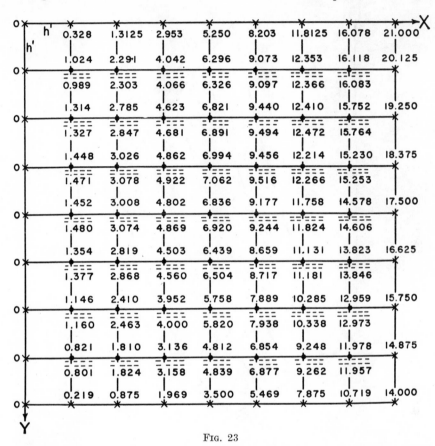

Fig. 23

as explained in the previous example. All initial values are written *above* the corresponding mesh points. The final values for the interior mesh points are written *below* the points. The iteration process was applied 20 times to get these final values. By noting the time required for one traverse, it is an easy matter to estimate the time required for solving this problem.

Additional values of the function in the region of the network can be found by the following procedure:

Find the values at the centers of the squares by applying formula (102. 1) to the final values just obtained for the net points. Then find the value of the function at the midpoints of the sides of the squares by applying (102. 1) to the new center points and the final values at the mesh points.

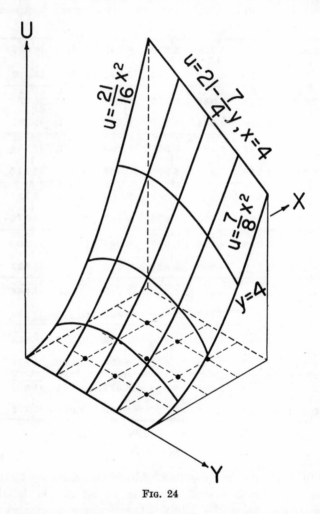

FIG. 24

The last points to reach their stationary values were those near the center of the region, and it may therefore be fairly assumed that the values at these points are the least accurate of all; that is, the differences between these computed values and the true values of the function are greatest for these points. On the other hand, a Fourier series for the function gives its *most* accurate values for these points near the center. Hence the difference between the given computed value and the value given by a Fourier series for points near the center of this region will be very close to the true error of the computed values for those points.

The Fourier series for $u_{2,2}$, or for the point $x = 2$, $y = 2$, is a rapidly converging alternating series whose value is 6.9535 correct to four decimal places. The approximate error in the difference equation is thus about $6.9535 - 6.920$, or about 0.03.

Figure 24 represents the surface $u = f(x, y)$ whose ordinates have been computed in this example.

104. The Inherent Error in the Solution by Difference Equations. The inherent error in the difference-equation solution of a differential equation can be found by expressing the difference quotients in terms of derivatives, and this can be done by means of Taylor's formula.

Taylor's formula for a function of two variables can be written symbolically in the form

$$(1) \qquad f(x + h, y + k) = \sum_{n=0}^{n=\infty} \frac{1}{n!} \left(h \frac{\partial}{\partial x} + k \frac{\partial}{\partial y} \right)^n f(x, y).$$

When $k = 0$, this becomes

$$f(x + h, y) = f(x, y) + h \frac{\partial f}{\partial x} + \frac{h^2}{2!} \frac{\partial^2 f}{\partial x^2} + \frac{h^3}{3!} \frac{\partial^3 f}{\partial x^3} + \frac{h^4}{4!} \frac{\partial^4 f}{\partial x^4} + \cdots,$$

from which

$$(2) \qquad \frac{f(x + h, y) - f(x, y)}{h} = \frac{\partial f}{\partial x} + \frac{h}{2!} \frac{\partial^2 f}{\partial x^2} + \frac{h^2}{3!} \frac{\partial^3 f}{\partial x^3} + \frac{h^3}{4!} \frac{\partial^4 f}{\partial x^4} + \cdots.$$

Changing h to $-h$ in (2), we get

$$(3) \qquad \frac{f(x, y) - f(x - h, y)}{h} = \frac{\partial f}{\partial x} - \frac{h}{2!} \frac{\partial^2 f}{\partial x^2} + \frac{h^2}{3!} \frac{\partial^3 f}{\partial x^3} - \frac{h^3}{4!} \frac{\partial^4 f}{\partial x^4} + \cdots.$$

Forming the second-difference quotient by subtracting (3) from (2) and then dividing throughout by h, we have

$$(4) \qquad \frac{f(x + h, y) - 2f(x, y) + f(x - h, y)}{h^2} = \frac{\partial^2 f}{\partial x^2} + \frac{2h^2}{4!} \frac{\partial^4 f}{\partial x^4}$$

$$+ \text{ terms in } h^4, h^6, \text{ etc.}$$

Likewise, on putting $h = 0$ in (1) and proceeding exactly as above, we get

$$(5) \qquad \frac{f(x, y + k) - 2f(x, y) + f(x, y - k)}{k^2} = \frac{\partial^2 f}{\partial y^2} + \frac{2k^2}{4!} \frac{\partial^4 f}{\partial y^4}$$

$$+ \text{ terms in } k^4, k^6, \text{ etc.}$$

Putting $k = h$ for a square net, using the notation of Art. 101 for second differences, and then adding (4) and (5), we get

$$(6) \quad u_{\bar{x}x} + u_{\bar{y}y} = \frac{\partial^2 u}{\partial x^2} + \frac{\partial^2 u}{\partial y^2} + \frac{2h^2}{4!} \frac{\partial^4 u}{\partial x^4} + \frac{2h^2}{4!} \frac{\partial^4 u}{\partial y^4} + \text{terms in } h^4, h^6, \text{etc.,}$$

$$= 0 + \frac{2h^2}{4!} \left(\frac{\partial^4 u}{\partial x^4} + \frac{\partial^4 u}{\partial y^4} \right) + \text{terms in } h^4, h^6, \text{etc.,}$$

since $\dfrac{\partial^2 u}{\partial x^2} + \dfrac{\partial^2 u}{\partial y^2} = 0$ by hypothesis. The error committed in writing $u_{\bar{x}x} + u_{\bar{y}y} = 0$ is thus a power series in even powers of h, the principal part of the error being the first term of this series.

Now if we solve the equation $u_{\bar{x}x} + u_{\bar{y}y} = 0$ and thereby neglect the error terms, the error in the solution will be the integral of these error terms; and since h is independent of x and y (has a *fixed value* throughout the integration), the integral of the error terms will be a power series in h^2, h^4, etc. Hence when h is small the principal error in the solution will be the first or h^2 term. We are therefore justified in assuming that the inherent error in the difference-equation solution of a partial differential equation of the second order is proportional to h^2.

To find a simple formula for the inherent error, we have by hypothesis

$$E = ch^2,$$

where E denotes the error and c is a constant of proportionality. Then for any two values h_1 and h_2 of h, the corresponding errors are $E_1 = ch_1^2$ and $E_2 = ch_2^2$, from which $\dfrac{E_2}{E_1} = \dfrac{h_2^2}{h_1^2}$ or $E_2 = \left(\dfrac{h_2}{h_1}\right)^2 E_1$. If $h_2 = \frac{1}{2}h_1$, then

$$(7) \qquad\qquad\qquad E_2 = \tfrac{1}{4}E_1.$$

Let a_1 and a_2 denote the final approximate values of the function u at any interior mesh point, corresponding to h_1 and h_2 respectively. Then

$$u = a_1 + E_1, \qquad u = a_2 + E_2.$$

Eliminating u and taking account of (7), we get

$$(8) \qquad\qquad\qquad E_2 = \tfrac{1}{3}(a_2 - a_1).$$

This formula gives the approximate value of the inherent error at each intersection point of the network after two values of h have been used, the second value of h being half the first value.

Since $u = a_2 + E_2$, we can substitute the value of E_2 from (8) and get

$$(9) \qquad\qquad\qquad u = a_2 + \tfrac{1}{3}(a_2 - a_1),$$

which gives a close approximation to the true value of u at any net point.

As an application of formulas (8) and (9), let us consider the error in u at the point $x = 2$, $y = 2$ of Example 2, Art. 103. There $a_1 = 6.836$, $a_2 = 6.920$. Hence

$$E_2 = \tfrac{1}{3}(6.920 - 6.836) = 0.028$$
$$u = 6.920 + 0.028 = 6.948.$$

This value agrees closely with the extremely accurate value given by Fourier's series.

Note. Although the Fourier series solution gives very accurate values near the center of the region of Example 2, it gives very poor values on and near the boundaries even when 12 terms of the series are used. On the whole, the solution by difference equations is preferable in that example and is obtained by much less work.

105. Application of Conformal Transformation to Certain Problems. In the determination of stresses in thin plates by photo-elastic methods, it is sometimes desirable to transform an area bounded by circular arcs into a rectangular area which can be divided into a network of squares. The appropriate transformation is

$$w = \ln z,$$

where $z = x + iy = r(\cos \theta + i \sin \theta) = re^{i\theta}$ and $w = u + iv$. On replacing w and z by their values in terms of u, v, r, θ, we have

$$u + iv = \ln re^{i\theta} = \ln r + i\theta.$$

Hence, on equating real and imaginary parts,

$$(1) \qquad\qquad u = \ln r, \qquad v = \theta.$$

In order to transform the area bounded by two concentric circles and any two radii, denote the inner and outer radii by r_1 and r_2, respectively, and take one boundary as the line $\theta = 0$ (see Fig. 25). Then from the first of equations (1) we have

$$u_1 = \ln r_1, \qquad u_2 = \ln r_2.$$

The width of the transformed rectangle is $u_2 - u_1$ (see Fig. 26) ; and if the rectangular area is to be divided into squares of side h, the side of one of these squares is

$$(2) \qquad\qquad h = \frac{u_2 - u_1}{n} = \frac{\ln r_2 - \ln r_1}{n},$$

where n denotes the number of subdivisions of $u_2 - u_1$.

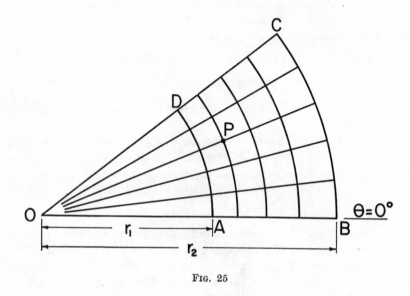

Fig. 25

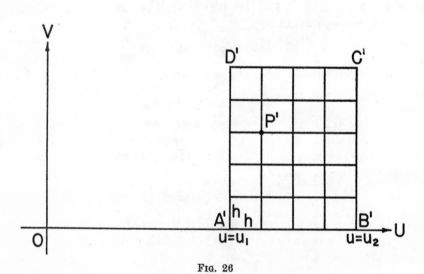

Fig. 26

To find the subdivision points in AB corresponding to those of $u_2 - u_1$, we write the equation $u_1 = \ln r_1$ in the form $r_1 = e^{u_1}$, give u_1 an increment Δu, and compute the corresponding increment in r. Thus,

$$r_1 = e^{u_1}$$
$$\underline{r_1 + \Delta r = e^{u_1 + \Delta u}}$$
$$\Delta r = e^{u_1 + \Delta u} - e^{u_1} = e^{u_1}(e^{\Delta u} - 1),$$

or

(3) $$\Delta r = r_1(e^{\Delta u} - 1).$$

On putting $\Delta u = h, 2h, \cdots (n-1)h$ we get the subdivision points along AB. Note that Δr is measured from the point A on the circle $r = r_1$.

To find the subdivisions of the angle from $\theta = 0$ to $\theta = \theta_2$ we consider the second of Equations (1), from which

$$\Delta v = \Delta \theta.$$

Since the area in Fig. 26 is divided into squares of side h we must have $\Delta v = h$. Hence

(4) $$\Delta \theta = h = \frac{\ln r_2 - \ln r_1}{n},$$

where $\Delta \theta$ is in radians.

Having decided on the size of the squares in the transformed area $A'B'C'D'$ in Fig. 26, one can compute the corresponding mesh points of Fig. 25 by means of Equations (2), (3), and (4). Note that the boundary $ABCD$ of Fig. 25 is transformed into the boundary $A'B'C'D'$ of Fig. 26, that a point P of Fig. 25 goes into P' of Fig. 26, etc. Note also that the transformation gives values of the function closer together on the concave side of the given curved area than on the convex side—a desirable circumstance in stress problems.

Example. If $r_1 = 2.2$, $r_2 = 3.8$, $n = 4$, find the subdivision intervals for r and θ.

Solution. From (2) we have

$$h = \frac{\ln 3.8 - \ln 2.2}{4} = \frac{1.3350 - 0.7885}{4} = 0.1366.$$

Hence $\Delta \theta = 0.1366$ radian $= 7° \, 50'$.

$$(\Delta r)_1 = 2.2(e^{0.1366} - 1) = 0.322$$
$$(\Delta r)_2 = 2.2(e^{0.2732} - 1) = 0.691$$
$$(\Delta r)_3 = 2.2(e^{0.4098} - 1) = 1.114.$$

These Δr's are to be measured outward from the point where $r = 2.2$ on the line $\theta = 0$.

III. THE METHOD OF RELAXATION.

106. Solution of Difference Equations by Relaxation. In solving the Laplace difference equation by iteration, we employed the relation

$$u_0 = \tfrac{1}{4}(u_1 + u_2 + u_3 + u_4),$$

or

$$u_1 + u_2 + u_3 + u_4 - 4u_0 = 0$$

until the equation was satisfied at any interior lattice point of the network. Except in the final stages of the process this equation is only approximately satisfied, the approximation becoming closer as the iteration process continues. Let Q_0 denote the *residual*, or discrepancy, at the lattice point u_0, so that

(106. 1) $$Q_0 = u_1 + u_2 + u_3 + u_4 - 4u_0.$$

A similar residual equation holds for any other interior lattice point.

To solve the Laplace difference equation by the method of relaxation we divide the region into a network of squares, write down the known values of the function at the net points on the boundary, and then compute, estimate, or assign values for the function at all interior net points, just as was done in Example 1 of Art. 103. The next step is to compute the residuals at all interior net points by means of equation (106. 1). *The object of the relaxation process is to reduce all residuals to zero*, as nearly as possible, by continued alteration ("relaxation") of the values of the function at the interior lattice points.

But when the value of the function u is changed at a lattice point, the values of the residuals at the adjacent interior points must be changed by exactly the same amount. Furthermore, the residual at the given point must be changed by -4 times the change in the function at that point. These facts will become clear from a consideration of equation (106. 1) and an appropriate figure.

Let Fig. 27 represent a portion of a lattice network. Consider the point $C3$. The residual at this point is

(2) $$Q_m = n + h + l + r - 4m.$$

If m is altered by an amount Δm, Q_m is necessarily altered by some amount ΔQ_m. Hence

$$Q_m + \Delta Q_m = n + h + l + r - 4(m + \Delta m).$$

Subtracting (2) from this equation, we get

(106. 2) $$\Delta Q_m = -4\Delta m.$$

The change in the residual at $C3$ is thus -4 times the change in the function at that point.

Let us now see what happens to the residual at $C2$ when m is changed. The residual at $C2$ is given by

(4) $$Q_l = m + g + k + q - 4l.$$

A change in m necessarily changes Q_l according to the relation

$$Q_l + \Delta Q_l = m + \Delta m + g + k + q - 4l.$$

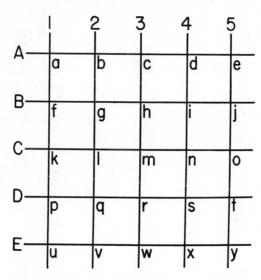

FIG. 27

Substracting (4) from this equation, we get

(106. 3) $$\Delta Q_l = \Delta m.$$

It is thus apparent that when any functional value is altered (relaxed), the residuals of the adjacent interior points must be changed by an equal amount. The relations (106. 2) and (106. 3) must be strictly observed every time a functional value is changed. When the residuals are changed as required by (106. 2) and (106. 3), their resultant values will always be the same as those computed by formula (106. 1).

Arithmetical mistakes are exceedingly apt to occur in working a problem by the relaxation process, due mainly to the fact that the computer will forget to correct some of the residuals at the adjacent points or else will make mistakes in combining the new alterations with the previous residuals.

Hence *the computer must be extremely careful to make all required corrections arising from a given point before he goes on to the next point.* We shall explain the relaxation method further by applying it to the two examples worked in Art. 103.

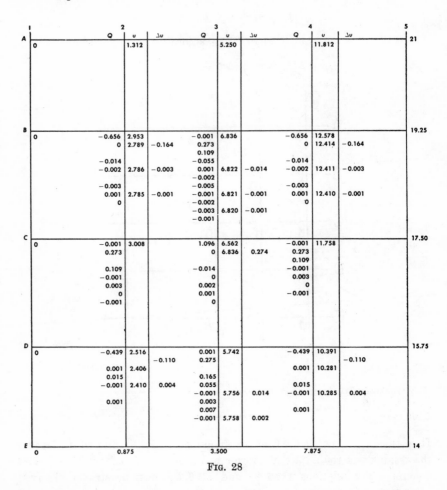

FIG. 28

Example 1. Solve Example 2 of Art. 103 by the method of relaxation.

Solution. We take from Fig. 22 the boundary values and the approximate values of the function at the interior lattice points, as shown in Fig. 28. Then we compute the residuals for all interior points by formula (106. 1). The relaxation process may be started at any point, but it is advisable and customary to begin near the center of the lattice area and at the point having the largest residual. Then proceed to the point having the next largest residual, and so on. Furthermore, in order to "liquidate" a residual at any point, the increment of the function at that point must have the same algebraic sign as the residual and must be one-fourth as large. Hence to find the required magnitude of the relaxation at any point we divide the residual at that point by 4.

The largest residual in Fig. 28 is at the point $C3$. Hence we relax u at that point by the amount $\dfrac{1.096}{4} = 0.274$. Then according to equations (106. 2) and (106. 3) we must add -4×0.274 to the residual at $C3$ and add 0.274 to the residuals at the four adjacent lattice points as indicated in the figure, the results of these additions being recorded as the new residuals at the affected points.

The next largest residuals are at $B2$ and $B4$. Hence we relax at these points by the amount -0.164 and correct all affected residuals according to equations (106. 2) and (106. 3). Note that we record the new value of the function at the relaxed point as soon as the relaxation is made.

The greatest remaining residuals are at $D2$ and $D4$. So we relax at these points by -0.110. Then we relax at $B3$ by the amount -0.014 and at $D3$ by 0.014. $D2$ and $D4$ are next relaxed by 0.004, and then $B2$ and $B4$ are relaxed by -0.003. Then relax $D3$ by 0.002 and $B3$ by -0.001. Now relax $B2$ and $B4$ by -0.001. Finally, relax $B3$ by 0.001. No further improvement is possible without decreasing the size of the mesh squares. It will be noted that the final residuals satisfy equation (106. 1), and that the final values of the function at the interior mesh points are the same (with one exception) as those found by the iteration process in Fig. 22. No computation by the relaxation method is finished until the final residuals are checked by (106. 1) and found to satisfy that equation.

The reader who is studying the relaxation method for the first time should work the above problem for himself by carrying out the computation as outlined above.

Example 2. Continue the solution of the above example by the relaxation process when the value of h is halved.

Solution. We take from Fig. 23 the values of the function u on the boundaries and at all interior mesh points, and enter them in Fig. 29 as shown. Then we compute by formula (106. 1), the residuals at the interior points. The relaxation is started at $B2$ and $B8$ by relaxing at these points by -0.041. The mesh-point values having the next largest residuals are then relaxed and the process continued until no residual exceeds 0.002 in magnitude. It is not possible to reduce all residuals to a smaller magnitude. The final values of the function at the interior mesh points, and their corresponding residuals, are recorded below the dotted lines in Fig. 29, the

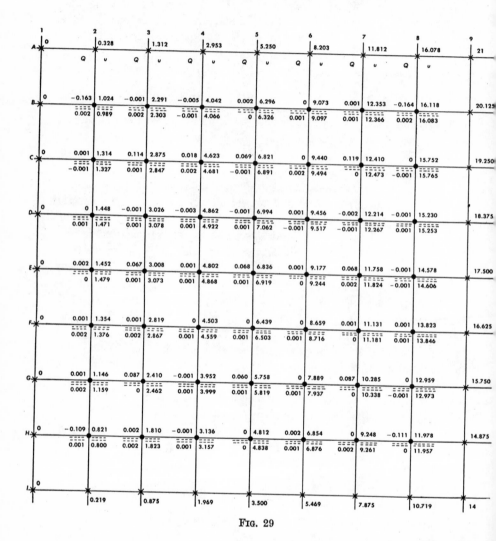

FIG. 29

corresponding initial values being written above the horizontal lines through the mesh points. It will be seen that the final values agree within a unit in the last digit with the values found by iteration in Fig. 23.

The trend of the functional values in lines D to H enabled us to speed up the convergence of the relaxation process to some extent, as it soon became evident that these functional values were continually increasing. Hence it was safe to *overrelax* in this area; that is, instead of changing the functional values by amounts just sufficient to liquidate their residuals, we change the functional values enough to produce residuals with changed signs and as large as they were before. The new residuals will soon be wiped out by increments added when adjacent points are relaxed. Such over-relaxation is always advisable when the residuals adjacent to a given point have the same sign as the residual at that point.

In carrying out the computation for this problem some of the functional values had to be relaxed 14 times, by amounts varying from 0.017 at first down to 0.001 at the end. The number of relaxations could have been decreased by drastic overrelaxation in the central region of the network. But drastic overrelaxation should not be resorted to unless the computer knows about what the functional values should be in the end.

107. Triangular Networks. Although the square network is the simplest and the one most commonly used, a network of equilateral triangles is sometimes more suitable for a particular problem. This is likely to be the case in a region having an irregular or angular boundary. Fig. 30 represents a portion of a triangular network.

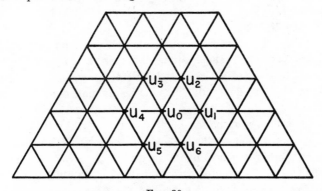

FIG. 30

In this case the fundamental relation which must be satisfied in the case of Laplace's equation is

$$(1) \qquad u_0 = \tfrac{1}{6}(u_1 + u_2 + u_3 + u_4 + u_5 + u_6),$$

and the residuals are given by

$$(2) \qquad Q_0 = u_1 + u_2 + u_3 + u_4 + u_5 + u_6 - 6u_0.$$

Formula (1) is derived on pages 21-23 of Southwell's book mentioned above. Incidentally, Southwell points out, p. 24, that formula (1) is more accurate than (102. 1).

Formulas (1) and (2) are applied to triangular networks in exactly the same manner as (102. 1) and (106. 1) are applied to networks of square meshes. Formula (106. 3) applies unchanged to triangular networks, but (106. 2) must be replaced by

$$(3) \qquad\qquad \Delta Q_m = - 6\Delta m.$$

Hence to liquidate a residual at any point, we must relax by one-sixth the residual at that point and then add the increment to the residuals at the six adjacent points.

108. Block Relaxation. Up to this point we have been altering or relaxing one functional value at a time. It sometimes saves time and labor to relax a whole group of functional values at a time. This procedure is advisable when the residuals at adjacent points in a region are nearly equal. In this case the functional values are relaxed as a block by changing them all by the same amount. We now consider the effect of such block relaxation on the residuals within the block and on those outside it.

In Fig. 31 the group in the region surrounded by the heavy border are to be relaxed as a block by relaxing all functional values in the block (including those on the border) by an amount ϵ. It is clearly evident that the residuals at interior points such as P are not altered by block relaxation; for although the residual at such a point is immediately changed by $- 4\epsilon$, each of the four adjacent points a, b, c, d contributes a quantity ϵ to this residual and thus leaves it unchanged by the block relaxation.

Such is not the case at points on the border. The residual at each of these is immediately changed by $- 4\epsilon$, but the compensating contributions from adjacent points depend on how many of the adjacent points are in the relaxed block. The residual at point M, for example, is not changed, because the four adjacent points are all in the relaxed block. The same is true at Q and S. At the point N, three of the adjacent points are in the block and one outside it; so the residual at N is changed by $- \epsilon$. At R, two of the adjacent points are in the block and two outside it. Hence at R the residual is changed by $- 2\epsilon$.

The amount of change in the residual at any border point on a square network is evidently $- n\epsilon$, where n denotes the number of adjacent points which lie *outside* the relaxed block.

Similar considerations apply to a triangular network. At all interior points such as P in Fig. 32 the residuals are not changed, whereas at all

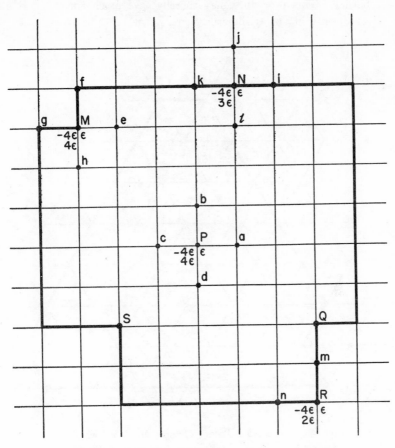

Residuals at Border Points Changed by $-n\epsilon$, where
$n =$ Number of Adjacent Points *Outside* the Relaxed Block.

FIG. 31

border points the residuals are changed by the amount $-n\epsilon$, where n denotes the number of adjacent points lying *outside* the relaxed area. At B, for example, the residual is changed by $-\epsilon$, whereas at A the change is -4ϵ.

When the functional values in a block are relaxed by an amount ϵ, the residuals of all adjacent points just *outside* the block must also be changed by an amount ϵ as required by formula (106.3).

In block relaxation all functional values in the block are changed by the same amount, but no residuals are changed except those at the points on the border. This procedure may thereby save much time, and it also reduces the possibility of arithmetical errors.

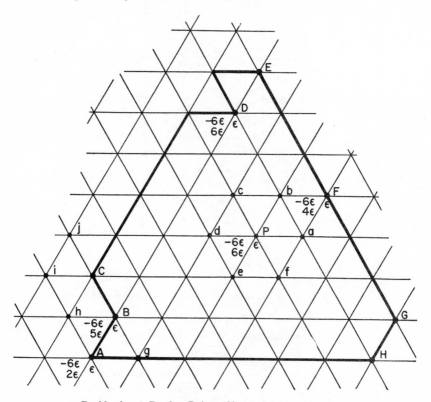

Residuals at Border Points Changed by — $n\epsilon$, where
$n =$ Number of Adjacent Points *Outside* the Relaxed Block.

FIG. 32

The amount by which all functional values in a block are relaxed may be anything desired. Southwell relaxes a block of values in accordance with the formula

$$\epsilon = \frac{\Sigma Q}{m},$$

where ΣQ denotes the algebraic sum of the residuals in the block and m denotes the number of *adjacent points just outside the block*. (The outside adjacent points should be thought of as outside *connections* to the block points. Sometimes an outside point is connected to two block points and is then to be counted as two adjacent points outside the block. See Fig. 33.)

Example. Let it be required to relax as a block the functional values within the bordered area of Fig. 33, only the residuals being shown.

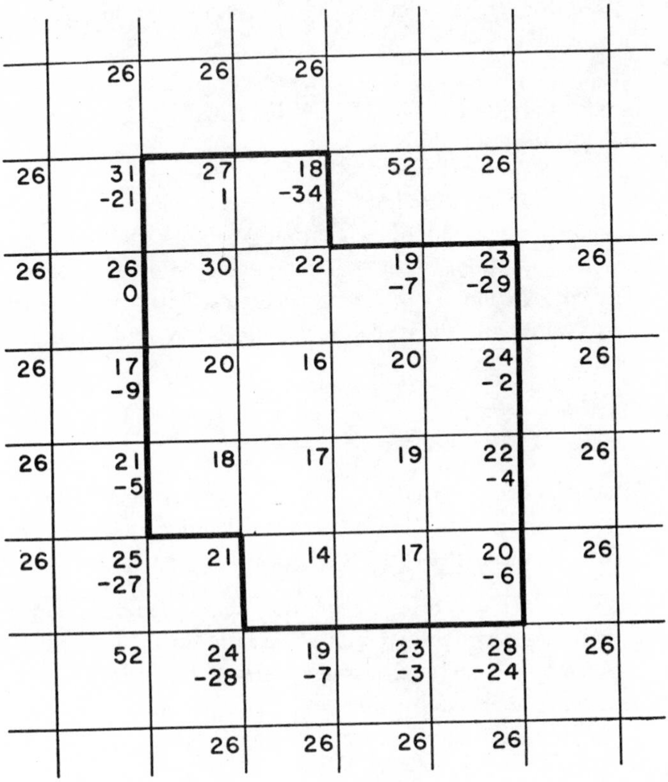

	26	26	26				
26	31 -21	27 1	18 -34	52	26		
26	26 0	30	22	19 -7	23 -29	26	
26	17 -9	20	16	20	24 -2	26	
26	21 -5	18	17	19	22 -4	26	
26	25 -27	21	14	17	20 -6	26	
	52	24 -28	19 -7	23 -3	28 -24	26	
		26	26	26	26		

Fig. 33

Here
$$\Sigma Q = 31 + 27 + 18 + \cdots = 581$$

and
$$n = 22$$

Hence

$$\epsilon = \frac{581}{22} = 26.4.$$

Using round numbers, we relax all functional values of the block by 26 and change the border residuals by $-26n$, the results being indicated in Fig. 33. Note that the residuals of the outside points adjacent to the border have been changed as required by formula (106. 3).

One may also relax a block within a larger block that is to be relaxed. In that case the inner block should be relaxed first and the residuals at outside points adjacent to its border changed in accordance with formula (106. 3). Then the larger block (including the relaxed inner one) can be relaxed as desired.

After a group of values has been relaxed as a block, the whole network (both inside and outside the block) may be relaxed point by point in any manner until all residuals have been liquidated.

109. The Iteration and Relaxation Methods Compared. The method of iteration and the method of relaxation are both methods for solving partial difference equations with given boundary values. Although they reach the desired solution by different processes, both methods are of the same inherent accuracy. Their points of similarity and dissimilarity are listed below.

1. Both methods require that the bounded region be divided into a network of squares or other similar polygons.

2. Both methods require that the boundary values be written down and that rough values of the function be computed, estimated, or assumed for all interior points of the network.

3. In order to start a computation, the iteration method assumes that a functional value at any mesh point satifies the given difference equation (Laplace's, Poisson's, etc.) and thereby derives the relation which must exist between that functional value and the adjacent functional values. The process of iteration is then applied until the required relation is satisfied.

4. The method of relaxation, on the other hand, recognizes at the start that an assumed functional value at any mesh point will *not* satisfy the given difference equation, but that there will be a *residual* at that point. The residuals are computed for all points before the relaxations process is started.

5. The method of iteration starts with the upper left-hand corner of the network and proceeds to correct all net-work values by means of formula (102. 1) (in the case of Laplace's equation), using the latest computed

values available. The process is carried out in a systematic and definite order by going from left to right until the end of a line is reached and then dropping down to the next line, just as in reading the consecutive lines of a printed page. This method of correcting the netpoint values is continued until no further improvements can be effected by the iteration process. The iteration process can be performed mechanically by an automatic sequence-controlled calculating machine.

6. The method of relaxation requires that the residuals at every interior netpoint be computed by formula (106.1). Then these residuals are liquidated or reduced to zero (or nearly so) as quickly as possible by altering (relaxing) the netpoint values to any extent that seems advisable, always observing that the increment of the function must be of the same sign as the residual at that point and being careful to correct all affected residuals in accordance with formulas (106.2) and (106.3). The revised values of the function should also be recorded at the time of alteration. The relaxation process may start at any interior netpoint and jump around all over the bounded region, usually beginning with the numerically largest residuals and then proceeding to the next largest wherever they may be found. Because of the perfectly arbitrary manner in which the relaxations are made, the relaxation process cannot be carried out by an automatic calculating machine. ' It is an individual, hand method just as the slide rule is a hand device.

7. The iteration process is slow, sure, and frequently long. The relaxation process is more rapid, less certain, and usually reasonably short. The convergence is rapid by both methods at first, but becomes slow with both methods long before the end is reached.

8. The arithmetic operations are easier and shorter with the method of relaxation. The mental effort necessary to avoid mistakes, however, is much greater than with the iteration method.

9. The greatest drawback to the method of iteration is its length; the greatest drawback to the method of relaxation is its liability to errors of computation. Such errors can be kept out only by extreme care and unceasing vigilance on the part of the computer.

10. Computational errors in the method of iteration are immediately evident and are self-correcting. In the method of relaxation any errors in the functional values remain hidden and can be brought to light only by application of formula (106.1). For this reason, all interior netpoint values should be checked by (106.1) several times during a long compu-

tation. Such checking takes time and keeps the relaxation process from being as short as it might at first appear.

11. In the iteration process, attention is always fixed on the functional values at the lattice points; in the relaxation process attention is always centered on the residuals at those points.

When a computer discovers that a mistake has occurred somewhere in the relaxation solution, he should not spend much time in looking for its origin. Instead, he should compute all residuals by formula (106. 1) and continue the solution with the new residuals.

The reader should solve a problem of moderate length by both iteration and relaxation. Then he can decide for himself which method is preferable in his case.

Further information concerning short cuts, etc. in the iteration method can be found in the papers by Shortley and Weller; and additional information concerning the method of relaxation can be found in a valuable paper by Howard W. Emmons, entitled "The Numerical Solution of Partial Differential Equations" (*Quarterly of Applied Mathematics,* Vol. II, No. 3, pp. 173-195, Oct., 1944), and in R. V. Southwell's *Relaxation Methods in Theoretical Physics,* 1946.

IV. THE RAYLEIGH-RITZ METHOD.

110. Introduction. The Rayleigh-Ritz method of solving boundary-value problems is entirely different from either of the two methods considered in the preceding pages. It is not based on difference equations and does not employ them. In finding the solution of a physical problem by this method, one assumes that the solution can be represented by a linear combination of simple and easily calculated functions each of which satisfies the given boundary conditions. After the problem has been formulated as the definite integral of the algebraic sum of two or more homogeneous, positive, and definite quadratic forms, or as the quotient of two such integrals, the desired unknown function is replaced in the integrals by the assumed linear combination. Then the integral, or the quotient of the integrals, is minimized with respect to each of the arbitrary constants occurring in the linear combination.

This method is direct and short if only approximate results are desired; but if results of high accuracy are required, the method is quite laborious and the labor cannot be appreciably lessened by mechanical aids. The labor involved is mostly in long and tedious algebraic manipulations.

A special and simple form of the Rayleigh-Ritz method was first used by Lord Rayleigh [1] (J. W. Strutt) for finding the fundamental vibration period of an elastic body. It was later extended, generalized, and its convergence proved by W. Ritz.[2] We shall attempt to explain it to some extent by applying it to two examples.

111. The Vibrating String. Consider a tightly stretched elastic string or wire of length l and fixed at the ends, and assume that it vibrates in a vacuum. Let P denote the tension in the string and let ρ denote the mass of unit length of the string. With coordinate axes as shown in Fig. 34, let y denote the displacement of any point along the x-axis.

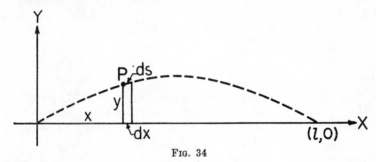

Fig. 34

Then y is evidently a function of both the distance x and the time t. The differential equation for the motion of a point of the string is thus a *partial* differential equation and is easily shown to be *

(1) $\dfrac{\partial^2 y}{\partial x^2} = \dfrac{\rho}{P} \dfrac{\partial^2 y}{\partial t^2}$, with the boundary conditions $y(0) = 0$, $y(l) = 0$.

If we also impose the *initial* condition that $\dfrac{\partial y}{\partial t} = 0$ when $t = 0$, we find by the method of separation of variables that the solution of (1) is

(2) $y = C \sin \dfrac{n\pi}{l} x \cos \sqrt{\dfrac{P}{\rho}} \dfrac{n\pi}{l} t, \quad n = 1, 2, 3, \cdots .$

The vibration frequency is therefore

(3) $f = \dfrac{1}{2\pi} \sqrt{\dfrac{P}{\rho}} \dfrac{n\pi}{l} = \dfrac{n}{2l} \sqrt{\dfrac{P}{\rho}} .$

---

[1] *Theory of Sound*, §§ 88, 89.

[2] *Journal für die reine und angewandte Mathematik*, Bd. CXXXV, pp. 1-61; *Göttinger Nachrichten, math.-physik. Klasse*, 1908, pp. 236-248; *Annalen der Physik*, Vierte Folge, Bd. XXVIII (1909), pp. 737-786; also Gesammelte Werke Walther Ritz, pp. 192-316.

* See any standard work on partial differential equations; for example, Miller's *Partial Differential Equations*, pp. 69-70.

For $n = 1$ we get the natural or fundamental frequency. Hence for this frequency we have

$$(4) \qquad\qquad f = \frac{1}{2l} \sqrt{\frac{P}{\rho}}.$$

The higher frequencies or overtones are found from (3) by putting $n = 2, 3, \cdots$ etc.

To find the vibration frequencies of the cord by the Rayleigh-Ritz method, we neither set up a partial differential equation nor solve one. On the contrary, we assume that the cord is vibrating in a vacuum and utilize the fact that under this condition the total energy of the vibrating cord remains constant. Hence the maximum kinetic energy must be equal to the maximum potential energy.

The potential energy at any instant is the stored-up elastic energy due to stretching. It is equal to the work done in stretching the string to its longer form in the bowed position. Since the total energy of the string is constant, the potential energy at the end of a swing when the string comes momentarily to rest is equal to the kinetic energy when the string coincides with the x-axis and is at that instant unstretched.

Because of the elasticity of the material of the string, the deflection y at any point is, by Hooke's law, proportional to the force in the y-direction. Hence the motion is necessarily harmonic and can be represented by the equation

$$(5) \qquad\qquad y = X \sin \omega t,$$

where X is a function of x alone and ω is a constant.

From Fig. 34 it is evident that the increase in length of an initially unstretched segment dx is $ds - dx$, or

$$\sqrt{1 + \left(\frac{dy}{dx}\right)^2}\, dx - dx = \left(\sqrt{1 + \left(\frac{dy}{dx}\right)^2} - 1\right) dx;$$

and the work done in producing this stretch is $P\left(\sqrt{1 + \left(\frac{dy}{dx}\right)^2} - 1\right) dx$. Hence the work done in stretching the whole string is

$$U = P \int_0^l \left(\sqrt{1 + \left(\frac{dy}{dx}\right)^2} - 1\right) dx.$$

On expanding the radical into a binomial series and neglecting $\left(\frac{dy}{dx}\right)^4$, $\left(\frac{dy}{dx}\right)^6$, etc., since the slope of the string is small, we have

$$U = \frac{P}{2} \int_0^l \left(\frac{dy}{dx} \right)^2 dx.$$

Now replacing $\left(\dfrac{dy}{dx} \right)^2$ by its value found from (5), we have

$$U = \left[\frac{P}{2} \int_0^l \left(\frac{dX}{dx} \right)^2 dx \right] \sin \omega t.$$

This is the potential energy of the string at any time. Its maximum value is when $\sin \omega t = 1$. Hence

$$U_{\max} = \frac{P}{2} \int_0^l \left(\frac{dX}{dx} \right)^2 dx.$$

The kinetic energy of a segment dx of the vibrating string is $\frac{1}{2}\rho dx \left(\dfrac{\partial y}{\partial t} \right)^2$, and therefore for the whole string it is

$$T = \frac{\rho}{2} \int_0^l \left(\frac{\partial y}{\partial t} \right)^2 dx.$$

Replacing $\dfrac{\partial y}{\partial t}$ by its value from (5), we have

$$T = \left[\frac{\rho \omega^2}{2} \int_0^l X^2 dx \right] \cos^2 \omega t.$$

This has its maximum value when $\cos^2 \omega t = 1$. Hence the maximum kinetic energy is

$$T_{\max} = \frac{\rho \omega^2}{2} \int_0^l X^2 dx.$$

Since $U_{\max} = T_{\max}$, we get

$$\frac{P}{2} \int_0^l \left(\frac{dX}{dx} \right)^2 dx = \frac{\rho}{2} \omega^2 \int_0^l X^2 dx,$$

from which

(6)
$$\omega^2 = \frac{P}{\rho} \frac{\displaystyle\int_0^l \left(\frac{dX}{dx} \right)^2 dx}{\displaystyle\int_0^l X^2 dx}.$$

The next step in solving this problem by the Ritz method is to choose for X a simple function which satisfies the boundary conditions and contains several parameters. These parameters are to be chosen or determined so as to make the right member of (6) a minimum. A suitable expression for X in the vibrating string problem is

(7) $X = x(l - x)(a_1 + a_2 x + a_3 x^2 + \cdots).$

This is substituted for X in (6) and then the partial derivative of the right member with respect to each parameter is placed equal to zero. The result is a system of homogeneous linear equations in the unknown parameters.

In order to reduce the labor of finding the partial derivatives of the right member of (6), we differentiate it with respect to a typical parameter and derive a formula from which the linear equations are easily obtained. Bearing in mind that X, as expressed by (7), contains the independent parameters $a_1, a_2, \cdots a_n$, we have by (6) and by using the rule for differentiating a quotient,

$$\frac{\partial}{\partial a_i}\left(\frac{P}{\rho}\frac{\int_0^l \left(\frac{dX}{dx}\right)^2 dx}{\int_0^l X^2 dx}\right)$$

$$= \frac{P}{\rho}\frac{\int_0^l X^2 dx \frac{\partial}{\partial a_i}\int_0^l \left(\frac{dX}{dx}\right)^2 dx - \int_0^l \left(\frac{dX}{dx}\right)^2 dx \frac{\partial}{\partial a_i}\int_0^l X^2 dx}{\left[\int_0^l X^2 dx\right]^2} = 0,$$

or

$$\int_0^l X^2 dx \frac{\partial}{\partial a_i}\int_0^l \left(\frac{dX}{dx}\right)^2 dx - \int_0^l \left(\frac{dX}{dx}\right)^2 dx \frac{\partial}{\partial a_i}\int_0^l X^2 dx = 0.$$

But, by (6), $\int_0^l \left(\frac{dX}{dx}\right)^2 dx = \frac{\omega^2\rho}{P}\int_0^l X^2 dx.$ Making this substitution in the second term of the equation above, we get

$$\int_0^l X^2 dx \frac{\partial}{\partial a_i}\int_0^l \left(\frac{dX}{dx}\right)^2 dx - \frac{\omega^2\rho}{P}\int_0^l X^2 dx \frac{\partial}{\partial a_i}\int_0^l X^2 dx = 0.$$

Taking out the common factor $\int_0^l X^2 dx$, which is not zero, we have

$$\frac{\partial}{\partial a_i}\left(\int_0^l \left(\frac{dX}{dx}\right)^2 dx - \frac{\omega^2\rho}{P}\int_0^l X^2 dx\right) = 0,$$

or

(8) $$\frac{\partial}{\partial a_i}\left(\int_0^l \left(\frac{dX}{dx}\right)^2 dx - k\int_0^l X^2 dx\right) = 0, \quad i = 1, 2, \cdots n,$$

where $k = \frac{\omega^2\rho}{P}.$

In order to increase the rapidity of convergence of the Ritz process, we shall move the origin of space coordinates to the midpoint of the string. Then the boundary conditions will be $y(-l/2) = y(l/2) = 0$, and the appropriate polynomial to meet these conditions will be

$$(9) \qquad X = (c^2 - x^2)(a_1 + a_2 x^2 + a_3 x^4 + \cdots),$$

where $c = l/2$. It is to be noted that (9) gives only the modes of vibration which are symmetric to the position of the y-axis.

Taking only the first term of (9) as a first approximation for X, we have

$$X = a_1(c^2 - x^2), \qquad \frac{dX}{dx} = -2a_1 x.$$

Then

$$\int_{-c}^{c} \left(\frac{dX}{dx}\right)^2 dx = 4a_1^2 \int_{-c}^{c} x^2 dx = \frac{8a_1^2 c^3}{3},$$

$$\int_{-c}^{c} X^2 dx = a_1^2 \int_{-c}^{c} (c^4 - 2c^2 x^2 + x^4) dx = \frac{16}{15} a_1^2 c^5.$$

Substituting these in (8), we get

$$\frac{d}{da_1}\left(\frac{8a_1^2 c^3}{3} - k\frac{16}{15} a_1^2 c^5\right) = \frac{16a_1 c^3}{3} - \frac{32ka_1 c^5}{15} = 0.$$

Hence $k = \dfrac{5}{2c^2} = \dfrac{10}{l^2}$. The exact value of k as previously found is

$k = \dfrac{\pi^2}{l^2} = \dfrac{9.8696}{l^2}$. The agreement is thus fairly close.

To get a better approximation, we take the first two terms of (9). Then

$$X = (c^2 - x^2)(a_1 + a_2 x^2),$$

and

$$\frac{dX}{dx} = -2a_1 x + 2a_2 c^2 x - 4a_2 x^3.$$

Hence

$$\int_{-c}^{c} \left(\frac{dX}{dx}\right)^2 dx = \frac{8a_1^2 c^3}{3} + \frac{16}{15} a_1 a_2 c^5 + \frac{88}{105} a_2^2 c^7,$$

and

$$\int_{-c}^{c} X^2 dx = \frac{16}{15} a_1^2 c^5 + \frac{32}{105} a_1 a_2 c^7 + \frac{16}{315} a_2^2 c^9.$$

Substituting these in (8), taking the partial derivatives with respect to a_1 and a_2 in turn, and then reducing slightly, we get

$$\left(1 - \frac{2kc^2}{5}\right)a_1 + \frac{c^2}{5}\left(1 - \frac{2kc^2}{7}\right)a_2 = 0.$$

$$\left(1 - \frac{2kc^2}{7}\right)a_1 + \frac{c^2}{7}\left(11 - \frac{2kc^2}{3}\right)a_2 = 0.$$

These two homogeneous equations will have a common non-trivial solution only if the determinant of their coefficients is zero, or

$$\begin{vmatrix} 1 - \dfrac{2kc^2}{5} & \dfrac{c^2}{5}\left(1 - \dfrac{2kc^2}{7}\right) \\ 1 - \dfrac{2kc^2}{7} & \dfrac{c^2}{7}\left(11 - \dfrac{2kc^2}{3}\right) \end{vmatrix} = 0,$$

from which we get

$$c^4 k^2 - 28 c^2 k + 63 = 0.$$

Solving this equation for k, we find

$$k = \frac{25.53256}{c^2}, \quad \frac{2.46744}{c^2}.$$

In the exact case we found

$$\frac{\rho \omega^2}{P} = k = \frac{n^2 \pi^2}{l^2} = \frac{n^2 \pi^2}{4c^2}.$$

Hence

for $n = 1$, $k = \dfrac{\pi^2}{4c^2} = \dfrac{9.869604}{4c^2} = \dfrac{2.467401}{c^2}$;

for $n = 3$, $k = \dfrac{9\pi^2}{4c^2} = \dfrac{22.20661}{c^2}$.

On comparing the above Ritz values of k with these exact values, we see that for the fundamental mode the Ritz value agrees with the exact value to five significant figures.

Values of still greater accuracy can be found by taking the first three terms of the second parenthesis of (9):

$$X = (c^2 - x^2)(a_1 + a_2 x^2 + a_3 x^4).$$

On evaluating $\displaystyle\int_{-c}^{c} \left(\frac{dX}{dx}\right)^2 dx$ and $\displaystyle\int_{-c}^{c} X^2 dx$, differentiating them with respect to a_1, a_2, a_3 in turn, and substituting the results in (8), we get

$$\frac{1}{3}\left(1 - \frac{2kc^2}{5}\right)a_1 + \frac{c^2}{15}\left(1 - \frac{2kc^2}{7}\right)a_2 + \frac{c^4}{35}\left(1 - \frac{2kc^2}{9}\right)a_3 = 0.$$

$$\frac{1}{5}\left(1 - \frac{2kc^2}{7}\right)a_1 + \frac{c^2}{35}\left(11 - \frac{2kc^2}{3}\right)a_2 + c^4\left(\frac{1}{5} - \frac{2kc^2}{231}\right)a_3 = 0.$$

$$\frac{1}{35}\left(1 - \frac{2kc^2}{9}\right)a_1 + \frac{c^2}{3}\left(\frac{1}{5} - \frac{2kc^2}{231}\right)a_2 + \frac{c^4}{33}\left(\frac{13}{7} - \frac{2kc^2}{39}\right)a_3 = 0.$$

These homogeneous equations will have a common, non-trivial solution if and only if

$$
\begin{vmatrix}
\dfrac{1}{3}\left(1-\dfrac{2kc^2}{5}\right) & \dfrac{c^2}{15}\left(1-\dfrac{2kc^2}{7}\right) & \dfrac{c^4}{35}\left(1-\dfrac{2kc^2}{9}\right) \\[3mm]
\dfrac{1}{5}\left(1-\dfrac{2kc^2}{7}\right) & \dfrac{c^2}{35}\left(11-\dfrac{2kc^2}{231}\right) & c^4\left(\dfrac{1}{5}-\dfrac{2kc^2}{231}\right) \\[3mm]
\dfrac{1}{35}\left(1-\dfrac{2kc^2}{9}\right) & \dfrac{c^2}{3}\left(\dfrac{1}{5}-\dfrac{2kc^2}{231}\right) & \dfrac{c^4}{33}\left(\dfrac{13}{7}-\dfrac{2kc^2}{39}\right)
\end{vmatrix}
= 0.
$$

Putting $2kc^2 = \lambda$, expanding the determinant, and simplifying, we get

$$\lambda^3 - 225\lambda^2 + 8910\lambda - 38610 = 0,$$

where all the coefficients are *exact* numbers (not rounded).

The smallest root of the above cubic equation is easily found by the Newton-Raphson method, starting with the approximate value 4.93488 (or preferably 4.935) found in the previous calculation. The new value is thus found to be

$$\lambda_1 = 4.934802217,$$

correct to the last digit given.

The other two roots are best found by taking the root λ_1 out of the given equation, by synthetic division, and then solving the resulting quadratic equation. The depressed equation is

$$\lambda^2 - 220.065197783\lambda + 7824.02177410 = 0,$$

the roots of which (found by the quadratic formula) are

$$\lambda_2 = 44.586811825, \qquad \lambda_3 = 175.478385958.$$

As a check on these values it may be noted that

$$\lambda_1 + \lambda_2 + \lambda_3 = 225.000,000,000,$$

as required by theory.

We will now compare these Ritz values with the exact values. Since

$$\lambda = 2kc^2, \quad k = \frac{\omega^2 \rho}{P}, \quad \text{and} \quad \omega^2 = \frac{P}{\rho}\,\frac{n^2\pi^2}{l^2} = \frac{P}{\rho}\,\frac{n^2\pi^2}{4c^2},$$

we find

$$\lambda = \frac{n^2\pi^2}{2}.$$

Hence

$$\lambda_1 = \frac{\pi^2}{2} = \frac{9.869604401089}{2} = 4.934802200545,$$

$$\lambda_2 = \frac{9\pi^2}{2} = 44.4132198,$$

$$\lambda_3 = \frac{25\pi^2}{2} = 123.37.$$

It will be noted that the Ritz value for λ_1 is correct to eight significant figures, that the value for λ_2 is hardly correct to two figures, and that the value of λ_3, although of the proper order of magnitude, is so inaccurate as to be almost worthless.

The reader will observe that all the Ritz values are larger than the corresponding exact values. This is usually the case. The reader should also note that more accurate Ritz values were found by taking additional terms in (9) and not by correcting previous values. As more terms of (9) are taken, the labor of computation increases enormously, so that more than three terms will involve an almost prohibitive amount of labor.

112. Vibration of a Rectangular Membrane. Consider a thin elastic membrane of rectangular form with sides a and b (Fig. 35), such as a very thin sheet of rubber, and assume that the membrane is made fast at the edges while tightly stretched. Take a set of three mutually perpendicular axes, with the xy-plane coinciding with the membrane and the z-axis perpendicular to it. Then if an interior region of the membrane be pulled or pushed in a direction at right angles to its plane of equilibrium (the xy-plane), it becomes distorted into a curved surface, the area of which is

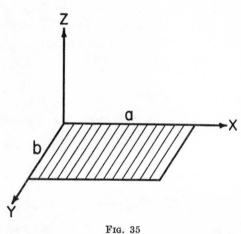

FIG. 35

$$S = \int_0^a \int_0^b \sqrt{1 + \left(\frac{\partial z}{\partial x}\right)^2 + \left(\frac{\partial z}{\partial y}\right)^2} \, dy \, dx$$

$$= \int_0^a \int_0^b \left[1 + \tfrac{1}{2}\left(\frac{\partial z}{\partial x}\right)^2 + \tfrac{1}{2}\left(\frac{\partial z}{\partial y}\right)^2\right] dy \, dx,$$

approximately, since the distortion is small. The increase in area of the membrane due to the distortion is therefore

$$\Delta S = \int_0^a \int_0^b \left[1 + \tfrac{1}{2}\left(\frac{\partial z}{\partial x}\right)^2 + \tfrac{1}{2}\left(\frac{\partial z}{\partial y}\right)^2 \right] dy\, dx - ab$$

$$= \tfrac{1}{2}\int_0^a \int_0^b \left[\left(\frac{\partial z}{\partial x}\right)^2 + \left(\frac{\partial z}{\partial y}\right)^2 \right] dy\, dx.$$

Let T denote the tension on a unit length of boundary of the membrane, the direction of T being perpendicular to the edge of the boundary. Then the work done in deflecting the membrane until its area is increased by an amount ΔS is $T\Delta S$; * and the potential energy in the deflected position is equal to the work done in producing the deflection. Since the deflection is small, the tension T remains practically constant. Hence the potential energy of the membrane in a deflected position is

$$\text{P. E.} = \frac{T}{2}\int_0^a \int_0^b \left[\left(\frac{\partial z}{\partial x}\right)^2 + \left(\frac{\partial z}{\partial y}\right)^2 \right] dy\, dx.$$

Because of the elasticity of the membrane, the deflection at any point is proportional to the force applied, and the motion is thus simple harmonic. Hence the deflection is a periodic function of the time, or

$$z = Z(x, y) \sin \omega t.$$

* Consider a rectangular region of dimensions u and v (Fig. 36). First let the side AB be fixed and let the membrane be pulled to the right with a force of T pounds per unit of width, or Tv for the whole side. The force Tv will stretch the membrane an amount Δu and do $Tv \cdot \Delta u$ units of work in doing so.

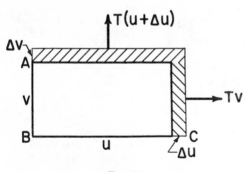

Fig. 36

Now let the side BC be fixed and let the membrane be pulled in the direction of the side AB by a force of T pounds per unit length of border, or $T(u + \Delta u)$ for the whole side. The force $T(u + \Delta u)$ will stretch the membrane by an amount Δv in that direction and do $T(u + \Delta u) \cdot \Delta v$ units of work in doing so.

Hence the total work done is

$$Tv \cdot \Delta u + T(u + \Delta u) \cdot \Delta v = T(v\Delta u + u\Delta v + \Delta u\Delta v)$$
$$= T \text{ times area of shaded border}$$
$$= T \text{ times increase in area of membrane.}$$

On substituting this value of z in the above expression for the potential energy, we get

$$\text{P. E.} = \left(\frac{T}{2} \int_0^a \int_0^b \left[\left(\frac{\partial Z}{\partial x} \right)^2 + \left(\frac{\partial Z}{\partial y} \right)^2 \right] dy\, dx \right) \sin^2 \omega t.$$

The maximum value of this is

$$(\text{P. E.})_{\max} = \frac{T}{2} \int_0^a \int_0^b \left[\left(\frac{\partial Z}{\partial x} \right)^2 + \left(\frac{\partial Z}{\partial y} \right)^2 \right] dy\, dx.$$

The kinetic energy of an element $dm = \rho\, dy\, dx$ of the membrane is

$$\tfrac{1}{2}\rho dy\, dx \cdot \left(\frac{dz}{dt} \right)^2 = \tfrac{1}{2}\rho dy\, dx \cdot Z^2(x,y)\omega^2 \cos^2 \omega t,$$

where ρ denotes the mass of unit area of the membrane.

The kinetic energy of the entire vibrating membrane is therefore

$$\text{K. E.} = (\tfrac{1}{2}\omega^2\rho \int_0^a \int_0^b Z^2 dy\, dx) \cos^2 \omega t,$$

and the maximum value of this is

$$(\text{K. E.})_{\max} = \frac{\omega^2\rho}{2} \int_0^a \int_0^b Z^2 dy\, dx.$$

Since there is assumed to be no loss of energy due to vibration, the maximum potential energy is equal to the maximum kinetic energy and we thus have

$$\frac{\omega^2\rho}{2} \int_0^a \int_0^b Z^2 dy\, dx = \frac{T}{2} \int_0^a \int_0^b \left[\left(\frac{\partial Z}{\partial x} \right)^2 + \left(\frac{\partial Z}{\partial y} \right)^2 \right] dy\, dx,$$

or

(1)
$$\omega^2 = \frac{T}{\rho} \frac{\int_0^a \int_0^b \left[\left(\frac{\partial Z}{\partial x} \right)^2 + \left(\frac{\partial Z}{\partial y} \right)^2 \right] dy\, dx}{\int_0^a \int_0^b Z^2 dy\, dx}.$$

We must now assume for Z a linear combination of simple functions which will satisfy the boundary conditions of the problem. Such a function is

(2) $Z = (a - x)(b - y)(a_1 + a_2 x + a_3 y + a_4 x^2 + a_5 y^2 + a_6 xy + \cdots).$

In order to make the convergence as rapid as possible, however, we move the origin to the center of the rectangle. Then because of symmetry we may write

(3) $Z = (p^2 - x^2)(q^2 - y^2)(a_1 + a_2 x^2 + a_3 y^2 + a_4 x^2 y^2 + \cdots)$,

where $p = a/2$, $q = b/2$.

Assuming that Z in (1) has been replaced by (2) or (3) above, we must determine the a's so as to make ω^2 a minimum. Hence the derivative of the right member of (1) with respect to each of the a's must be zero. Then by the rule for differentiating a quotient we have

$$\int_0^a \int_0^b Z^2 dy \, dx \cdot \frac{\partial}{\partial a_i} \left(\int_0^a \int_0^b \left\{ \left(\frac{\partial Z}{\partial x}\right)^2 + \left(\frac{\partial Z}{\partial y}\right)^2 \right\} dy \, dx \right)$$

$$- \int_0^a \int_0^b \left\{ \left(\frac{\partial Z}{\partial x}\right)^2 + \left(\frac{\partial Z}{\partial y}\right)^2 \right\} dy \, dx \cdot \frac{\partial}{\partial a_i} \int_0^a \int_0^b Z^2 dy \, dx = 0.$$

Replacing

$$\int_0^a \int_0^b \left\{ \left(\frac{\partial Z}{\partial x}\right)^2 + \left(\frac{\partial Z}{\partial y}\right)^2 \right\} dy \, dx$$

in the second term by its value

$$\frac{\rho}{T} \omega^2 \int_0^a \int_0^b Z^2 \, dy \, dx$$

as found from (1), we have

$$\int_0^a \int_0^b Z^2 \, dy \, dx \cdot \frac{\partial}{\partial a_i} \int_0^a \int_0^b \left\{ \left(\frac{\partial Z}{\partial x}\right)^2 + \left(\frac{\partial Z}{\partial y}\right)^2 \right\} dy \, dx$$

$$- \frac{\rho \omega^2}{T} \int_0^a \int_0^b Z^2 \, dy \, dx \cdot \frac{\partial}{\partial a_i} \int_0^a \int_0^b Z^2 \, dy \, dx = 0.$$

Now taking out the common factor $\int_0^a \int_0^b Z^2 dy \, dx$, we get

$$\frac{\partial}{\partial a_i} \int_0^a \int_0^b \left\{ \left(\frac{\partial Z}{\partial x}\right)^2 + \left(\frac{\partial Z}{\partial y}\right)^2 \right\} dy \, dx - \frac{\rho \omega^2}{T} \frac{\partial}{\partial a_i} \int_0^a \int_0^b Z^2 \, dy \, dx = 0,$$

or

(4) $\dfrac{\partial}{\partial a_i} \left[\int_0^a \int_0^b \left\{ \left(\dfrac{\partial Z}{\partial x}\right)^2 + \left(\dfrac{\partial Z}{\partial y}\right)^2 \right\} dy \, dx - k \int_0^a \int_0^b Z^2 \, dy \, dx \right] = 0$,

where $k = \rho \omega^2 / T$ and $i = 1, 2, \cdots n$. Formula (4) will give n homogeneous equations for determining n values of k.

If the form (3) is used for Z, the limits of integration in (4) will be from $-p$ to p for x and $-q$ to q for y.

To get a first approximation to the vibration frequency of the membrane, we take only the first term of the parenthetic polynomial in (3). Then

$$Z = a_1(p^2 - x^2)(q^2 - y^2)$$

$$\frac{\partial Z}{\partial x} = -2a_1 x(q^2 - y^2)$$

$$\frac{\partial Z}{\partial y} = -2a_1 y(p^2 - x^2).$$

Hence

$$\int_{-p}^{p}\int_{-q}^{q} \left\{ \left(\frac{\partial Z}{\partial x}\right)^2 + \left(\frac{\partial Z}{\partial y}\right)^2 \right\} \, dy \, dx$$

$$= 4a_1^2 \int_{-p}^{p}\int_{-q}^{q} \{x^2(q^2 - y^2)^2 + y^2(p^2 - x^2)^2\} dy \, dx$$

$$= 4a_1^2 \int_{-p}^{p} \left(\frac{16}{15} q^5 x^2 + \frac{2}{3} q^3(p^2 - x^2)^2\right) dx = \frac{8}{3}\left(\frac{16}{15}\right) p^3 q^3(p^2 + q^2)a_1^2,$$

and

$$\int_{-p}^{p}\int_{-q}^{q} Z^2 \, dy \, dx = a_1^2 \int_{-p}^{p}\int_{-q}^{q} (p^2 - x^2)^2(q^2 - y^2)^2 \, dy \, dx = \left(\frac{16}{15}\right)^2 p^5 q^5 a_1^2.$$

On substituting these in (4), we get

$$\frac{\partial}{\partial a_1} \left\{ \frac{8}{3}\left(\frac{16}{15}\right) a_1^2 p^3 q^3(p^2 + q^2) - k\left(\frac{16}{15}\right)^2 a_1^2 p^5 q^5 \right\} = 0,$$

or

$$\frac{8}{3}(p^2 + q^2) - \frac{16}{15} kp^2 q^2 = 0,$$

from which

$$k = \frac{5}{2}\left(\frac{p^2 + q^2}{p^2 q^2}\right) = \frac{5}{2}\left(\frac{1}{p^2} + \frac{1}{q^2}\right).$$

Replacing p by $a/2$ and q by $b/2$, we get

$$k = 10\left(\frac{1}{a^2} + \frac{1}{b^2}\right).$$

Since $k = \rho\omega^2/T$, we finally get

$$\omega = \sqrt{10} \sqrt{\frac{T}{\rho}\left(\frac{1}{a^2} + \frac{1}{b^2}\right)}.$$

The frequency is therefore

$$f = \frac{\omega}{2\pi} = \frac{\sqrt{10}}{2\pi} \sqrt{\frac{T}{\rho}\left(\frac{1}{a^2} + \frac{1}{b^2}\right)}.$$

This is the lowest or natural vibration frequency of the membrane.

The vibration frequencies found by the classical method of separating the variables are given by the formula

$$f_{m,n} = \tfrac{1}{2} \sqrt{\frac{T}{\rho} \left(\frac{m^2}{a^2} + \frac{n^2}{b^2} \right)}.$$

For $m = 1$, $n = 1$, this formula becomes

$$f = \tfrac{1}{2} \sqrt{\frac{T}{\rho} \left(\frac{1}{a^2} + \frac{1}{b^2} \right)}.$$

Since $\sqrt{10}/2\pi = 0.5033$, it is evident that the Ritz method gives a close approximation to the exact value. A more accurate value could be obtained by taking the first three terms of the parenthetical polynomial in (3), but the increased accuracy would be obtained at considerable expense in time and labor.

113. Comments on the Three Methods. Three numerical methods for solving boundary-value problems in two dimensions have been considered in the present chapter. Each method has its advantages and disadvantages. The iteration method is slow, self-correcting, and well adapted to use with an automatic sequence-controlled calculating machine. The arithmetical operations are short and simple.

The relaxation method is faster and more flexible than the iteration method. The arithmetical operations are simple, but mistakes are easy to make and are not self-correcting. It requires constant vigilance and alertness on the part of the computer. It is not adapted to use by an automatic calculating machine.

The Rayleigh-Ritz method is of considerable value in handling problems of equilibrium and elastic vibrations. It does not require a partial differential equation to start with, but it does require that a physical problem be reduced to the definite integral of a sum, difference, or quotient of two or more homogeneous positive and definite quadratic forms. The method furnishes a short and easy way of finding a good approximation to the natural vibration period of an elastic body, deflection of a membrane, etc. The chief disadvantage of the method is the laborious algebra involved in getting results of high accuracy.

It is an easy matter to estimate the accuracy of results obtained by the iteration and relaxation methods, but this is not the case with the Raleigh-Ritz method. No simple and useful formula for estimating the inherent error involved in this method has yet been devised.

A choice between the iteration and relaxation methods would depend upon the mechanical aids at the disposal of the computer. If an automatic sequence-controlled calculator is at hand, the iteration method would be used. If an automatic calculator is not at hand, the relaxation will give the desired solution in the shortest time and with the least work.

Finally, it must be realized that not all three methods may be applicable to a given problem. To use the iteration and relaxation methods, a physical problem must first be set up as a partial differential equation and this must then be converted to a partial' difference equation. The Rayleigh-Ritz method will give an approximate solution of a problem without setting up a partial differential equation, as was done in the cases of the vibrating string and vibrating membrane. In problems where all three methods are applicable, the Rayleigh-Ritz method would probably be the third choice.

It is needless to say that all these methods are inferior to the classical method of separating the variables, but they will give approximate solutions to problems in which the variables cannot be separated.

CHAPTER XIII

THE NUMERICAL SOLUTION OF INTEGRAL EQUATIONS

114. Integral Equations—Definitions. An integral equation is a functional equation in which the unknown function occurs under the integral sign as well as outside it. The simplest type imaginable arises from the integration of the simple differential equation $dy/dx = f(x, y)$, with the initial condition $y = y_0$ when $x = x_0$. The result is

$$y = \int_{x_0}^{x} f(x, y)\, dx + C = \int_{x_0}^{x} f(x, y)\, dx + y_0,$$

as stated on page 240. Two important types of integral equations are

$$(1) \qquad\qquad \phi(x) = \int_{a}^{b} K(x, t)\phi(t)\, dt$$

and

$$(2) \qquad\qquad \phi(x) = f(x) + \int_{a}^{b} K(x, t)\phi(t)\, dt.$$

Here the functions $K(x, t)$ and $f(x)$ are known and $\phi(x)$ is the unknown. $K(x, t)$ is called the *kernel* or nucleus and is assumed to be a continuous function of x and t throughout the interval (a, b); that is, $a \leqq x \leqq b$, $a \leqq t \leqq b$. In physical problems the kernel is usually Green's function.

Equations (1) and (2) are called *linear* integral equations because the unknown function ϕ occurs to the first degree. Also, (1) is called a homogeneous equation and (2) is called a non-homogeneous equation.

An integral equation of the form

$$(3) \qquad\qquad \phi(x) = f(x) + \int_{a}^{b} K(x, t)F[t, \phi(t)]\, dt$$

is called a *non-linear* integral equation because the unknown function ϕ does not occur in a linear fashion.

To solve an integral equation of any type is to find the unknown function $\phi(x)$. In some cases this can be done by the method of iteration, by starting with an approximate value for $\phi(x)$, substituting it in the integrand, and performing the integration. The new value of $\phi(x)$ is then substituted in the integrand as before and the process is repeated until no improvement is found in $\phi(x)$. In general, however, the solution of integral equations by exact analytical methods is not easy. Hence it is necessary to fall back on approximate solutions by numerical methods.

Several methods have been proposed for finding numerical solutions of integral equations. One of the simplest and most direct is the method suggested by Goursat [1] and later developed and extended in various directions by Nyström.[2] The method explained in the following pages is a modification and amplification of Nyström's method. The method consists essentially in replacing the unknown function under the integral sign by a polynomial of some form, integrating this polynomial over an interval, and then evaluating the integral at certain specified points within the interval of integration.

Before proceeding to the numerical solution of integral equations, we make a short digression to indicate how integral equations can arise from simple problems, and particularly how the kernel gets into the equation.

115. Boundary-Value Problems of Ordinary Differential Equations. Green's Functions. In the elementary treatment of differential equations the function and all its derivatives are assumed to be continuous throughout the interval of integration. The general solution based on these assumptions is not as general as one might suppose. A few simple examples will suffice to show this fact.

Example 1. Suppose a solution of the differential equation $d^2y/dx^2 = 0$ is required such that $y = 0$ for $x = 0$ and $x = 1$. Proceeding by the usual method, we have

$$\frac{dy}{dx} = c_1, \quad y = c_1 x + c_2.$$

Substituting the conditions given above, we find $c_2 = 0$ and $c_1 = 0$. Hence the solution is

$$y = 0,$$

the equation of a straight line through the points $(0, 0)$ and $(1, 0)$.

This solution is trivial and is not the only solution which will satisfy the given equation and the given conditions. Since the solution must be of the form $y = Ax + B$, the graph of which is a straight line, it is evident that a solution might consist of two linear functions whose graphs would pass through the respective end points and intersect at some point $x = s$, as shown in Fig. 37. We therefore attempt to find such a solution.

Let the two linear functions be

$$(1) \qquad\qquad y_1 = Ax$$

[1] *Cours d'Analyse Mathematique*, Tome III (3rd edition, 1923), pp. 368-369.
[2] *Acta Mathematica*, Vol. 54 (1930), pp. 185-204.

and

(2) $y_2 = C(1 - x),$

which evidently satisfy the respective end conditions. A third condition is
that $y_1 = y_2$ at $x = s$. Hence from (1) and (2)

(3) $As = C(1 - s).$

A fourth condition becomes evident when we look at the graphs in Fig. 37.

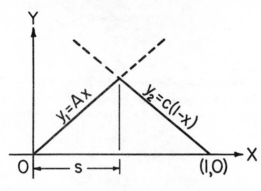

Fig. 37

The slopes of the two lines are different at the point of intersection, or for
$x = s$. Hence the first derivative of the required function is discontinuous
at $x = s$, the amount of the discontinuity (difference of slopes) being anything we please but evidently depending on s. Call it $k(s)$. Then

(4) $$\frac{dy_1}{dx} - \frac{dy_2}{dx} = A + C = k(s).$$

Solving (3) and (4) simultaneously, we get

$$A = (1 - s)k(s), \quad C = sk(s),$$

the arbitrary "constants" A and C thus depending on s. Substituting in
(1) and (2) these values of A and C respectively, we get

(5) $y_1 = k(s)(1 - s)x, \quad y_2 = k(s)s(1 - x).$

In this and similar problems it is customary to put $k(s) = 1$. Hence
the final solution is

(6) $\begin{cases} y = (1 - s)x & \text{for} \quad 0 \leqq x \leqq s \\ y = s(1 - x) & \text{for} \quad s \leqq x \leqq 1. \end{cases}$

The reader will note that by discarding the usual assumption of continuous derivatives in this example we have been able to find a worth-while solution which is everywhere continuous and satisfies the given boundary conditions. On putting $k(s) = 0$ in (5) we get the trivial solution first found. The solution (5) is thus more general than the usual " general " solution.

The solution (6) may be written as the single equation

$$y = K(x, s),$$

where

$$K(x, s) = (1 - s)x \quad \text{for} \quad 0 \leqq x \leqq s$$
$$K(x, s) = s(1 - x) \quad \text{for} \quad s \leqq x \leqq 1.$$

The function $K(s, x)$ is called *Green's Function* for this example. It is a function of the two independent variables x and s in the interval $(0, 1)$ and is evidently symmetrical in those variables. Green's function in this case is thus the solution of the differential equation $y''(x) = 0$, with the given boundary conditions.

Example 2. Required the solution of

(1) $$y''(x) - a^2y = 0,$$

with the boundary conditions $y = 0$ when $x = 0$ and $x = 1$.

Solution. By the usual elementary method of solving such equations, we have

$$r^2 = a^2, \quad \text{or} \quad r = \pm a.$$

Hence the general solution is

(2) $$y = c_1e^{ax} + c_2e^{-ax}$$
$$= A \cosh ax + B \sinh ax.$$

Substituting in (2) the values $y = 0$, $x = 0$ and $y = 0$, $x = 1$, respectively, we get

$$0 = A$$
$$0 = A \cosh a + B \sinh a$$

$\therefore$ $B \sinh a = 0$, or $B = 0$ (since we assume $a \neq 0$).

Hence (2) becomes

$$y = 0,$$

another trivial solution.

To get a worth-while solution of this example we assume a function of the form (2) for each end point of the interval $x = 0$ to $x = 1$. However, since $\cosh 0 \neq 0$, it is plain that the assumed functions need not contain $\cosh ax$. Hence we take

(3) $$y_1 = A \sinh ax \quad \text{and} \quad y_2 = B \sinh a(1 - x),$$

where we have now utilized the boundary conditions in writing down these functions. See Fig. 38. The graphs of these functions will evidently

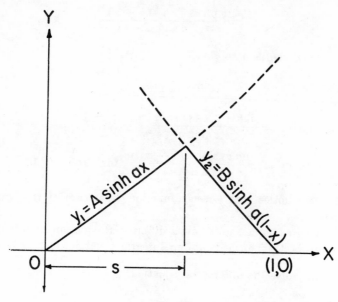

FIG. 38

intersect at some point where $x = s$, and at that point the functions will be equal and their first derivatives will be unequal. Hence for $x = s$ we have from (3),

(4) $$A \sinh as = B \sinh a(1 - s)$$

(5) $$\frac{dy_1}{dx} - \frac{dy_2}{dx} = Aa \cosh as + Ba \cosh a(1 - s) = 1, \text{ say.}$$

From (4),

(6) $$A = \frac{B \sinh a(1 - s)}{\sinh as}.$$

Substituting this value of A in (5), we find

$$B = \frac{\sinh as}{a \sinh a}.$$

Hence from (6),

$$A = \frac{\sinh a(1-s)}{a \sinh a}.$$

Substituting in (3) these values of A and B, we get

$$y_1 = \frac{\sinh a(1-s) \sinh ax}{a \sinh a},$$

$$y_2 = \frac{\sinh as \sinh a(1-x)}{a \sinh a}.$$

These can be written as a single solution in the form

$$y = K(s, x),$$

where

$$K(s, x) = \frac{\sinh a(1-s) \sinh ax}{a \sinh a} \quad \text{for} \quad 0 \leqq x \leqq s$$

$$K(s, x) = \frac{\sinh as \sinh a(1-x)}{a \sinh a} \quad \text{for} \quad s \leqq x \leqq 1.$$

The reader will notice that Green's function takes care of the boundary conditions.

The following example shows how a differential equation with boundary conditions can be transformed into an integral equation.

Example 3. Solve the differential equation

(1) $$\frac{d^2y}{dx^2} = f(x),$$

subject to the conditions that $y = 0$ when $x = a$ and $y = 0$ when $x = b$.

Solution. From (1) we have

$$\frac{dy}{dx} = \int_a^x f(x)\,dx + C_1 = \int_a^x f(s)\,ds + C_1$$

and

(2) $$y = \int_a^x \left(\int_a^x f(s)\,ds \right) dx + C_1 x + C_2.$$

At this point it is well to look at this double integral from a geometric standpoint.

The double integral $\int_a^x \left(\int_a^x f(s)\,ds \right) dx$ may be looked upon as the evaluation of the function $f(s)$ over the region (area) ALP of Fig. 39, by first integrating over the vertical strip MN with respect to s and then finding the limit of the sum of such strips by integrating with respect to x. Since x and s are both continuous throughout the region ALP, however, the double integral may equally well be evaluated over this region by

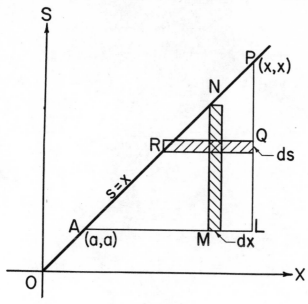

FIG. 39

integrating first over the horizontal strip RQ with respect to x and then finding the limit of the sum of these strips by integrating with respect to s.

In this latter case the double integral would be $\int_a^x \left(\int_s^x f(s)\,dx \right) ds$. Hence we have

(3)
$$\int_a^x \left(\int_a^x f(s)\,ds \right) dx = \int_a^x \left(\int_s^x f(s)\,dx \right) ds$$
$$= \int_a^x \left[f(s)x \right]_s^x ds = \int_a^x (x-s)f(s)\,ds.$$

It is thus seen that the substitution of an equivalent integral for the given one enabled us to perform one integration and thereby reduce a double integral to a single integral.

Now replacing the integral in (2) by the single integral given in (3), we have

$$(4) \qquad y = \int_a^x (x-s) f(s)\, ds + C_1 x + C_2.$$

To find C_1 and C_2 we substitute in (4) the given boundary conditions $x = a$, $y = 0$ and $x = b$, $y = 0$. Hence we have

$$0 = 0 + C_1 a + C_2$$

$$0 = \int_a^b (b-s) f(s)\, ds + C_1 b + C_2.$$

Solving these equations for C_1 and C_2, we get

$$C_1 = - \frac{\int_a^b (b-s) f(s)\, ds}{b-a}, \qquad C_2 = \frac{a \int_a^b (b-s) f(s)\, ds}{b-a}.$$

Hence (4) now becomes

$$(5) \quad y = \int_a^x (x-s) f(s)\, ds - \frac{x \int_a^b (b-s) f(s)\, ds}{b-a} + \frac{a \int_a^b (b-s) f(s)\, ds}{b-a}$$

$$= \int_a^x (x-s) f(s)\, ds + \frac{a-x}{b-a} \int_a^b (b-s) f(s)\, ds.$$

For the purpose of this example we transform the second integral by the well-known relation $\int_a^b = \int_a^x + \int_x^b$. Then we have

$$y(x) = \int_a^x (x-s) f(s)\, ds + \frac{a-x}{b-a} \int_a^x (b-s) f(s)\, ds$$

$$+ \frac{a-x}{b-a} \int_x^b (b-s) f(s)\, ds$$

$$= \int_a^x \left(x - s + \frac{a-x}{b-a}(b-s) \right) f(s)\, ds + \int_x^b \frac{(x-a)(s-b)}{b-a} f(s)\, ds,$$

or

$$(6) \quad y(x) = \int_a^x \frac{(x-b)(s-a)}{b-a} f(s)\, ds + \int_x^b \frac{(x-a)(s-b)}{b-a} f(s)\, ds,$$

which may be written

$$(7) \qquad y(x) = \int_a^b K(x, s) f(s)\, ds,$$

where

$$K(x, s) = \frac{(x-b)(s-a)}{b-a} \quad \text{for} \quad a \leqq x \leqq s$$

$$K(x, s) = \frac{(x-a)(s-b)}{b-a} \quad \text{for} \quad s \leqq x \leqq b.$$

Here, again, we note that $K(x, s)$ is symmetrical in x and s.

The final result (7) is a simple integral equation, and we have thus transformed a simple differential equation with boundary conditions into a simple integral equation. But we still have not found y; for in (7) y is expressed in terms of itself, the $f(s)$ under the integral sign.

It is instructive to check the correctness of (6) by differentiation. To do this we must use the formula for differentiating under the sign of integration. If

$$I(\alpha) = \int_{x_1(\alpha)}^{x_2(\alpha)} f(x, \alpha)\,dx,$$

then

$$\frac{dI}{d\alpha} = \int_{x_1(\alpha)}^{x_2(\alpha)} \frac{\partial f(x, \alpha)}{\partial \alpha}\,dx + f(x_2, \alpha)\,\frac{dx_2}{d\alpha} - f(x_1, \alpha)\,\frac{dx_1}{d\alpha}.$$

Applying this formula to (6) and treating x as α, we have

$$\frac{dy}{dx} = \int_a^x \frac{s-a}{b-a} f(s)\,ds + \frac{(x-b)(x-a)}{b-a}\,f(x)$$
$$+ \int_x^b \frac{s-b}{b-a} f(s)\,ds - \frac{(x-a)(x-b)}{b-a}\,f(x),$$

the second and fourth terms canceling each other, and

$$\frac{d^2y}{dx^2} = 0 + \frac{x-a}{b-a}\,f(x) + 0 - \frac{x-b}{b-a}\,f(x)$$
$$= \frac{x-a-x+b}{b-a}\,f(x) = \frac{b-a}{b-a}\,f(x) = f(x),$$

which shows that (6) is correct.

116. Linear Integral Equations. We shall first consider the linear equation

$$(1) \qquad \phi(x) = f(x) + \int_a^b K(x, t)\phi(t)\,dt.$$

Since a definite integral can be closely approximated by any one of several quadrature formulas (each of which was derived by integrating a polynomial over an interval), it is evident that the definite integral in (1) can be replaced by a quadrature formula, so that (1) may be written in the form

$$(2) \qquad \phi(x) = f(x) + (b-a)[C_1K(x, t_1)\phi(t_1) + C_2K(x, t_2)\phi(t_2) \cdots$$
$$+ C_nK(x, t_n)\phi(t_n)],$$

where $t_1, t_2, \cdots t_n$ are subdivision points of the interval (a, b) and the C's are weighting coefficients whose values depend on the type of quadrature formula used. And since (2) must hold for all values of x in the interval

(a, b), it must hold for $x = t_1$, $x = t_2, \cdots$, $x = t_n$. Hence from (2) we get n equations of the type

$$(3) \quad \phi(t_i) = f(t_i) + (b - a)[C_1 K(t_i, t_1)\phi(t_1) + C_2 K(t_i, t_2)\phi(t_2)$$
$$+ \cdots + C_n K(t_i, t_n)\phi(t_n)], \quad i = 1, 2, \cdots n.$$

For brevity let us put $\phi(t_i) = \phi_i$ and $f(t_i) = f_i$. Then the system (3) becomes

$$(4) \quad \begin{cases} \phi_1 = f_1 + (b - a)[C_1 K(t_1, t_1)\phi_1 + C_2 K(t_1, t_2)\phi_2 + \cdots + C_n K(t_1, t_n)\phi_n] \\ \phi_2 = f_2 + (b - a)[C_1 K(t_2, t_1)\phi_1 + C_2 K(t_2, t_2)\phi_2 + \cdots + C_n K(t_2, t_n)\phi_n] \\ \cdots \cdots \cdots \cdots \cdots \cdots \cdots \cdots \cdots \cdots \cdots \cdots \cdots \cdots \cdots \cdots \\ \phi_n = f_n + (b - a)[C_1 K(t_n, t_1)\phi_1 + C_2 K(t_n, t_2)\phi_2 + \cdots + C_n K(t_n, t_n)\phi_n \end{cases}$$

Equations (4) are a system of n linear equations in the n unknowns $\phi_1, \phi_2, \cdots \phi_n$ and can be solved for these unknowns by the usual methods for solving systems of linear equations. After the ϕ's have been found, they are substituted in the right-hand member of equation (2). The result is the desired solution of the given equation (1), since (2) will then give $\phi(x)$ for any value of x.

The reader will note that in a quadrature formula the functional values $\phi_1, \phi_2, \cdots \phi_n$ at the points of subdivision are given, whereas in integral equations these values must be found as part of the process of solving the equation. We get the equations for finding them by putting $x = t_1, t_2$, etc.

Because of the difficulty of solving a large number of simultaneous linear equations, it is highly desirable that only a small number of functional values (ϕ's) be computed. In important problems the formulas of Gauss and Lobatto should therefore be used.

Example 1. Solve the integral equation

$$u(x) = \frac{5x}{6} - \frac{1}{9} + \frac{1}{3} \int_0^1 (t + x)u(t)\,dt.$$

Solution. In this simple example we evaluate the integral by Simpson's Rule, taking $n = 3$ or $h = \frac{1}{2}$. Then

$$(5) \quad u(x) = \frac{5x}{6} - \frac{1}{9} + \frac{1}{3} \cdot \frac{1}{3} \cdot \frac{1}{2} \, [(t_1 + x)u(t_1) + 4(t_2 + x)u(t_2)$$
$$+ (t_3 + x)u(t_3)].$$

Since (5) must hold for all values of x from 0 to 1, it holds for $x = t_1, t_2, t_3$. Hence from (5) we get

$$u(t_1) = \frac{5t_1}{6} - \frac{1}{9} + \frac{1}{18}[2t_1u(t_1) + 4(t_2 + t_1)u(t_2) + (t_3 + t_1)u(t_3)],$$

$$u(t_2) = \frac{5t_2}{6} - \frac{1}{9} + \frac{1}{18}[(t_1 + t_2)u(t_1) + 4(2t_2)u(t_2) + (t_3 + t_2)u(t_3)],$$

$$u(t_3) = \frac{5t_3}{6} - \frac{1}{9} + \frac{1}{18}[(t_1 + t_3)u(t_1) + 4(t_2 + t_3)u(t_2) + 2t_3u(t_3)].$$

Now putting $t_1 = 0$, $t_2 = \frac{1}{2}$, $t_3 = 1$ and writing $u(t_i) = u_i$, we get

$$u_1 = -\frac{1}{9} + \frac{1}{18}[2u_2 + u_3]$$

$$u_2 = \frac{5}{12} + \frac{1}{18}[\tfrac{1}{2}u_1 + 4u_2 + \tfrac{3}{2}u_3]$$

$$u_3 = \frac{5}{6} + \frac{1}{18}[u_1 + 6u_2 + 2u_3].$$

Clearing of fractions and transposing the u's to the left side of the equations, we have

$$36u_1 - 4u_2 - 2u_3 = -4$$
$$-u_1 + 28u_2 - 3u_3 = 11$$
$$-2u_1 - 12u_2 + 32u_3 = 26.$$

On solving these equations by determinants (Cramer's Rule) or otherwise, we find $u_1 = 0$, $u_2 = \frac{1}{2}$, $u_3 = 1$. Then substituting in (5) these values of the u's and putting $t_1 = 0$, $t_2 = \frac{1}{2}$, $t_3 = 1$, we get

$$u(x) = \frac{5x}{6} - \frac{1}{9} + \frac{1}{18}[0 + 4(\tfrac{1}{2} + x)(\tfrac{1}{2}) + (1 + x)(1)] = x.$$

This result can be checked by substituting it in the integrand of the original equation and performing the integration. Thus, putting $u(t) = t$, we have

$$w(x) = \frac{5x}{6} - \frac{1}{9} + \frac{1}{3}\int_0^1 (t + x)t \, dt = \frac{5x}{6} - \frac{1}{9} + \frac{1}{3}\left[\frac{t^3}{3} + \frac{xt^2}{2}\right]_0^1$$

$$= \frac{5x}{6} - \frac{1}{9} + \frac{1}{9} + \frac{x}{6} = x.$$

Simpson's Rule gives the exact result in this example because the integrand is a second-degree polynomial in t.

Example 2. Solve the integral equation

$$(6) \qquad\qquad u(x) = 2x + \frac{1}{5}\int_{-2}^3 (x - t)u(t) \, dt$$

by Gauss's formula, using three points of subdivision.

Solution. We must first transform the equation so that the new limits of integration will be from $-\frac{1}{2}$ to $\frac{1}{2}$. Hence we put

$$t = a + bv, \qquad x = c + dw.$$

Substituting in the first of these equations the corresponding limits $t = -2$, $v = -\frac{1}{2}$ and $t = 3$, $v = \frac{1}{2}$, we get $a = \frac{1}{2}$, $b = 5$. Hence the equation of transformation is

$$t = \frac{1}{2} + 5v.$$

Likewise,

$$x = \frac{1}{2} + 5w.$$

Substituting in (6) these values of t and x, we have

$$u(\tfrac{1}{2} + 5w) = 1 + 10w + \int_{-\frac{1}{2}}^{\frac{1}{2}} (w - v)u(\tfrac{1}{2} + 5v)5dv.$$

Now put $u(\frac{1}{2} + 5w) = \phi(w)$, $u(\frac{1}{2} + 5v) = \phi(v)$. Then

$$\phi(w) = 1 + 10w + 5\int_{-\frac{1}{2}}^{\frac{1}{2}} (w - v)\phi(v)\,dv.$$

Replacing the integral by Gauss's formula, we have

(7) $\phi(w) = 1 + 10w$

$$+ 5[R_1(w - v_1)\phi(v_1) + R_2(w - v_2)\phi(v_2) + R_3(w - v_3)\phi(v_3)].$$

Now since (7) must hold for all values of w from $-\frac{1}{2}$ to $\frac{1}{2}$, it must hold for $w = v_1$, $w = v_2$, $w = v_3$. Hence on substituting in (7) these values for w we get the equations

$$\phi(v_1) = 1 + 10v_1 + 5[R_2(v_1 - v_2)\phi(v_2) + R_3(v_1 - v_3)\phi(v_3)]$$
$$\phi(v_2) = 1 + 10v_2 + 5[R_1(v_2 - v_1)\phi(v_1) + R_3(v_2 - v_3)\phi(v_3)]$$
$$\phi(v_3) = 1 + 10v_3 + 5[R_1(v_3 - v_1)\phi(v_1) + R_2(v_3 - v_2)\phi(v_2)].$$

For the Gauss formula with three points of subdivision we have

$$v_1 = -\tfrac{1}{2}\sqrt{\tfrac{3}{5}}, \quad v_2 = 0, \quad v_3 = \tfrac{1}{2}\sqrt{\tfrac{3}{5}}, \qquad R_1 = \frac{5}{18}, \; R_2 = \frac{4}{9}, \; R_3 = \frac{5}{18}.$$

On substituting these values in the equations above and writing ϕ_1 for $\phi(v_1)$ etc., we get

(8)
$$\begin{cases}
\phi_1 = 1 - \sqrt{15} + 5\left[\dfrac{4}{9}\left(-\tfrac{1}{2}\sqrt{\tfrac{3}{5}}\right)\phi_2 + \dfrac{5}{18}\left(-\sqrt{\tfrac{3}{5}}\right)\phi_3\right] \\[2ex]
\phi_2 = 1 + 5\left[\dfrac{5}{18}\left(\tfrac{1}{2}\sqrt{\tfrac{3}{5}}\right)\phi_1 + \dfrac{5}{18}\left(-\tfrac{1}{2}\sqrt{\tfrac{3}{5}}\right)\phi_3\right] \\[2ex]
\phi_3 = 1 + \sqrt{15} + 5\left[\dfrac{5}{18}\left(\sqrt{\tfrac{3}{5}}\right)\phi_1 + \dfrac{4}{9}\left(\tfrac{1}{2}\sqrt{\tfrac{3}{5}}\right)\phi_2\right],
\end{cases}$$

or

$$(9) \quad \begin{cases} \phi_1 + \dfrac{2}{9}\sqrt{15}\ \phi_2 + \dfrac{5}{18}\sqrt{15}\ \phi_3 = 1 - \sqrt{15} \\[2mm] -\dfrac{5}{36}\sqrt{15}\ \phi_1 + \phi_2 + \dfrac{5}{36}\sqrt{15}\ \phi_3 = 1 \\[2mm] \dfrac{5}{18}\sqrt{15}\ \phi_1 + \dfrac{2}{9}\sqrt{15}\ \phi_2 - \phi_3 = -1 - \sqrt{15}. \end{cases}$$

Solving these equations by determinants, we find

$$\phi_1 = -\frac{2}{37}(19 + 9\sqrt{15})$$

$$\phi_2 = -\frac{38}{37}$$

$$\phi_3 = -\frac{2}{37}(19 - 9\sqrt{15}).$$

As a partial check on the correctness of these results we notice that by adding the first and third of equations (8) and comparing the sum with the second equation we get $\phi_1 + \phi_3 = 2\phi_2$, and this is true of the values found above.

Now substituting in (7) these values of the ϕ's, and the numerical values of the R's and v's, we get

$$(10) \qquad\qquad \phi(w) = \frac{180w}{37} - \frac{38}{37}.$$

Since $w = \dfrac{x - \frac{1}{2}}{5}$, the final solution of (6) is

$$u(x) = \frac{180}{37}\ \frac{(x - \frac{1}{2})}{5} - \frac{38}{37} = \frac{36x}{37} - \frac{56}{37} = \frac{4}{37}(9x - 14).$$

This solution can be checked by substituting it in the original equation (6), as shown below:

$$u(x) = 2x + \frac{1}{5}\int_{-2}^{3}(x - t)\,\frac{4}{37}(9t - 14)\,dt$$

$$= 2x + \frac{4}{185}\int_{-2}^{3}(9xt - 14x - 9t^2 + 14t)\,dt$$

$$= 2x + \frac{4}{185}\left[\frac{9xt^2}{2} - 14xt - 3t^3 + 7t^2\right]_{-2}^{3}$$

$$= 2x - \frac{38}{37}\,x - \frac{56}{37} = \frac{36x}{37} - \frac{56}{37} = \frac{4}{37}(9x - 14).$$

117. Non-Linear Integral Equations and Boundary-Value Problems.
Many boundary-value problems lead to non-linear integral equations of the
type (3), Art. 114. The unknown function $F[t, \phi(t)]$ may be any function of $\phi(t)$, such as $[\phi(t)]^n$, $\sin \phi(t)$, etc. In such problems the ϕ's
cannot be found by solving a system of simple linear equations as was done
in the examples worked in Art. 116. It is possible, however, to find a
system of equations which give the ϕ's in terms of the functions $F[t, \phi(t)]$.
The ϕ's can then be found by the process of iteration as was explained in
Art. 74.

Before proceeding with the solution of such non-linear integral equations
we return to a further discussion of boundary-value problems. We consider first the second-order differential equation

$$(1) \qquad y''(x) = \frac{d^2y}{dx^2} = \lambda A(x)y + f(x),$$

with the boundary conditions $y = 0$ when $x = a$ and $y = 0$ when $x = b$.
These conditions are usually written $y(a) = y(b) = 0$. The functions
$A(x)$ and $f(x)$ are assumed to be continuous in the interval (a, b), and
λ is an arbitrary constant or parameter.

Equation (1) can be reduced by direct integration[1] to the integral
equation

$$(2) \qquad y(x) = \lambda \int_a^b K(x, s)A(s)y(s)ds + \int_a^b K(x, s)f(s)ds,$$

where

$$K(x, s) = \frac{(x - b)(s - a)}{b - a} \quad \text{for} \quad a \leqq s \leqq x$$

$$K(x, s) = \frac{(x - a)(s - b)}{b - a} \quad \text{for} \quad x \leqq s \leqq b,$$

but we shall here simply verify by differentiation that (2) is the solution
of (1). Since $K(x, s)$ has two different values, we write (2) in the
equivalent and extended form

$$y(x) = \lambda \int_a^x \frac{(x - b)(s - a)}{b - a} A(s)y(s)ds + \lambda \int_x^b \frac{(x - a)(s - b)}{b - a} A(s)y(s)ds$$

$$+ \int_a^x \frac{(x - b)(s - a)}{b - a} f(s)ds + \int_x^b \frac{(x - a)(s - b)}{b - a} f(s)ds$$

$$= \int_a^x \frac{(x - b)(s - a)}{b - a} [\lambda A(s)y(s) + f(s)]ds$$

$$+ \int_x^b \frac{(x - a)(s - b)}{b - a} [\lambda A(s)y(s) + f(s)]ds.$$

[1] Lovett's *Linear Integral Equations*, p. 82; Goursat's *Cours d'Analyse*, III, p. 494.

Now applying the formula for differentiating under the sign, we have

$$y'(x) = \int_a^x \frac{s-a}{b-a}[\lambda A(s)y(s) + f(s)]ds + \frac{(x-b)(x-a)}{b-a}[\lambda A(x)y(x) + f(x)]$$

$$+ \int_x^b \frac{s-b}{b-a}[\lambda A(s)y(s) + f(s)]ds - \frac{(x-a)(x-b)}{b-a}[\lambda A(x)y(x) + f(x)],$$

the integrated terms canceling each other, and

$$y''(x) = 0 + \frac{x-a}{b-a}[\lambda A(x)y(x) + f(x)] + 0 - \frac{x-b}{b-a}[\lambda A(x)y(x) + f(x)]$$

$$= [\lambda A(x)y(x) + f(x)]\left(\frac{x-a}{b-a} - \frac{x-b}{b-a}\right)$$

$$= [\lambda A(x)y(x) + f(x)]\left(\frac{x-a-x+b}{b-a}\right),$$

or

$$y''(x) = \lambda A(x)y(x) + f(x),$$

which is Equation (1).

Let us now consider a more general boundary problem defined by the differential equation

(3) $$\frac{d^2\phi}{dx^2} = \phi''(x) = F[x, \phi(x)] + g(x),$$

where $F[x, \phi(x)]$ represents any continuous function, $g(x)$ is a given function, and the boundary conditions are $\phi(a) = \phi(b) = 0$. This differential equation with the given boundary conditions is equivalent to the integral equation

(4) $$\phi(x) = \int_a^b K(x, s)F[s, \phi(s)]ds + \int_a^b K(x, s)g(s)ds,$$

where

$$K(x, s) = \frac{(x-b)(s-a)}{b-a} \quad \text{for} \quad a \leqq s \leqq x$$

$$K(x, s) = \frac{(x-a)(s-b)}{b-a} \quad \text{for} \quad x \leqq s \leqq b.$$

We shall verify this fact by direct differentiation of (4).

Writing (4) in the equivalent form

$$\phi(x) = \int_a^x \frac{(x-b)(s-a)}{b-a} F[s, \phi(s)]ds + \int_x^b \frac{(x-a)(s-b)}{b-a} F[s, \phi(s)]ds$$

$$+ \int_a^x \frac{(x-b)(s-a)}{b-a} g(s)ds + \int_x^b \frac{(x-a)(s-b)}{b-a} g(s)ds$$

$$= \int_a^x \frac{(x-b)(s-a)}{b-a} \{F[s, \phi(s)] + g(s)\}ds$$

$$+ \int_x^b \frac{(x-a)(s-b)}{b-a} \{F[s, \phi(s)] + g(s)\}ds,$$

we differentiate the equation with respect to x, as in the preceding example. Thus

$$\phi'(x) = \int_a^x \frac{s-a}{b-a} \{F[s, \phi(s)] + g(s)\}ds + \frac{(x-b)(x-a)}{b-a} \{F[x, \phi(x)] + g(x)\}$$

$$+ \int_x^b \frac{s-b}{b-a} \{F[s, \phi(s)] + g(s)\}ds - \frac{(x-a)(x-b)}{b-a} \{F[x, \phi(x)] + g(x)\},$$

the integrated terms canceling each other, and

$$\phi''(x) = 0 + \frac{x-a}{b-a} (F[x, \phi(x)] + g(x)) + 0 - \frac{x-b}{b-a} (F[x, \phi(x)] + g(x))$$

$$= \{F[x, \phi(x)] + g(x)\} \left(\frac{x-a}{b-a} - \frac{x-b}{b-a} \right)$$

$$= \{F[x, \phi(x)] + g(x)\} \left(\frac{b-a}{b-a} \right) = F[x, \phi(x)] + g(x),$$

as was to be shown. We therefore solve the differential equation (3) by solving the equivalent integral equation (4).

Since it is desirable to have a small number of equations for determining the ϕ's, and yet a high degree of accuracy is desirable, we restrict the function $F[x, \phi(x)]$ to the cases where $F[a, \phi(a)] = 0$ and $F[b, \phi(b)] = 0$. This restriction enables us to employ the subdivision points called for in Lobatto's formula for five functional values, thus giving a high degree of accuracy and yet causing the two end values to drop out. We thus have only three interior points to consider and therefore only three equations for determining the ϕ's. Although we can use the subdivision points required by Lobatto's formula, we cannot use the quadrature formula itself, because that formula was derived by integrating a single function throughout the interval from $x = a$ to $x = b$, whereas in the problem before us there are two different functions. We therefore replace the function $F[x, \phi(x)]$ over the interval (a, b) by a fourth-degree polynomial given by Lagrange's interpolation formula.

To adapt the interval of integration as required for Lobatto's points of subdivision, we must change the limits of integration to $-\frac{1}{2}$ and $\frac{1}{2}$, as was done in Ex. 2, Art. 116. We assume that the interval has thus been changed. The subdivision points for Lobatto's formula are then $s_1 = 0$, $s_2 = -\frac{1}{2}\sqrt{3/7}$, $s_3 = \frac{1}{2}\sqrt{3/7}$, $s_4 = -\frac{1}{2}$, $s_5 = \frac{1}{2}$.

$$|\text{------------}|\text{----------}|\text{----------}|\text{----------}|$$
$$s_4 = -\tfrac{1}{2} \quad s_2 = -\tfrac{1}{2}\sqrt{3/7} \qquad s_1 = 0 \qquad\quad s_3 = \tfrac{1}{2}\sqrt{3/7} \qquad s_5 = \tfrac{1}{2}$$

Lagrange's formula for $F[s, \phi(s)]$ for these five functional values is therefore

$$(5)\quad F[s, \phi(s)] = \frac{\left(s + \tfrac{1}{2}\sqrt{\tfrac{3}{7}}\right)\left(s - \tfrac{1}{2}\sqrt{\tfrac{3}{7}}\right)(s + \tfrac{1}{2})(s - \tfrac{1}{2})}{\left(\tfrac{1}{2}\sqrt{\tfrac{3}{7}}\right)\left(-\tfrac{1}{2}\sqrt{\tfrac{3}{7}}\right)(\tfrac{1}{2})(-\tfrac{1}{2})} F[0, \phi_1]$$

$$+ \frac{(s)\left(s - \tfrac{1}{2}\sqrt{\tfrac{3}{7}}\right)(s + \tfrac{1}{2})(s - \tfrac{1}{2})}{\left(-\tfrac{1}{2}\sqrt{\tfrac{3}{7}}\right)\left(-\tfrac{1}{2}\sqrt{\tfrac{3}{7}} - \tfrac{1}{2}\sqrt{\tfrac{3}{7}}\right)\left(-\tfrac{1}{2}\sqrt{\tfrac{3}{7}} + \tfrac{1}{2}\right)\left(-\tfrac{1}{2}\sqrt{\tfrac{3}{7}} - \tfrac{1}{2}\right)}$$

$$\times F[-\tfrac{1}{2}\sqrt{\tfrac{3}{7}}, \phi_2]$$

$$+ \frac{(s)\left(s - \tfrac{1}{2}\sqrt{\tfrac{3}{7}}\right)(s + \tfrac{1}{2})(s - \tfrac{1}{2})}{\left(\tfrac{1}{2}\sqrt{\tfrac{3}{7}}\right)\left(\tfrac{1}{2}\sqrt{\tfrac{3}{7}} + \tfrac{1}{2}\sqrt{\tfrac{3}{7}}\right)\left(\tfrac{1}{2}\sqrt{\tfrac{3}{7}} + \tfrac{1}{2}\right)\left(\tfrac{1}{2}\sqrt{\tfrac{3}{7}} - \tfrac{1}{2}\right)} F[\tfrac{1}{2}\sqrt{\tfrac{3}{7}}, \phi_3],$$

the terms in $F[-\frac{1}{2}, \phi(-\frac{1}{2})]$ and $F[\frac{1}{2}, \phi(\frac{1}{2})]$ not being written because they are zero. When the terms in (5) are multiplied out, we get

$$(6)\quad F[s, \phi(s)] = \frac{112}{3}\left(s^4 - \frac{5}{14}s^2 + \frac{3}{112}\right)F(0, \phi_1)$$

$$- \frac{98}{3}\left(s^4 - \frac{s^3}{2}\sqrt{\frac{3}{7}} - \frac{s^2}{4} + \frac{s}{8}\sqrt{\frac{3}{7}}\right)F(-\tfrac{1}{2}\sqrt{\tfrac{3}{7}}, \phi_2)$$

$$- \frac{98}{3}\left(s^4 + \frac{s^3}{2}\sqrt{\frac{3}{7}} - \frac{s^2}{4} - \frac{s}{8}\sqrt{\frac{3}{7}}\right)F(\tfrac{1}{2}\sqrt{\tfrac{3}{7}}, \phi_3).$$

Equation (6) gives $F[-\frac{1}{2}, \phi(-\frac{1}{2})] = 0$ and $F[\frac{1}{2}, \phi(\frac{1}{2})] = 0$ as it should.

The next step is to substitute (6) in (4) and then integrate over the intervals $-\frac{1}{2}$ to x and x to $\frac{1}{2}$, using the appropriate value of $K(x, s)$ in each case. Thus, since a is now $-\frac{1}{2}$ and b is $\frac{1}{2}$ we have

(7) $\phi(x) = \int_{-\frac{1}{2}}^{x} (x - \tfrac{1}{2})(s + \tfrac{1}{2})F[s, \phi(s)]ds$

$$+ \int_{x}^{\frac{1}{2}} (x + \tfrac{1}{2})(s - \tfrac{1}{2})F[s, \phi(s)]ds + f(x),$$

where $f(x)$ stands for $\int_{-\frac{1}{2}}^{\frac{1}{2}} K(x,s)g(s)ds$ and $F[s, \phi(s)]$ stands for the right-hand member of (6).

In carrying out the integration in (7), x is treated as a constant; and although the integration is perfectly straightforward, it is long and tedious. The result is

(8) $\phi(x) = \dfrac{112}{3} F(0, \phi_1)\left(\dfrac{x^6}{30} - \dfrac{5x^4}{168} + \dfrac{3x^2}{224} - \dfrac{9}{\cdot 4480}\right)$

$-\dfrac{98}{3} F(-\tfrac{1}{2}\sqrt{\tfrac{3}{7}}, \phi_2)\left(\dfrac{x^6}{30} - \dfrac{x^5}{40}\sqrt{\tfrac{3}{7}} - \dfrac{x^4}{48} + \dfrac{x^3}{48}\sqrt{\tfrac{3}{7}} - \dfrac{7x}{1920}\sqrt{\tfrac{3}{7}} + \dfrac{1}{1280}\right)$

$-\dfrac{98}{3} F(\tfrac{1}{2}\sqrt{\tfrac{3}{7}}, \phi_3)\left(\dfrac{x^6}{30} + \dfrac{x^5}{40}\sqrt{\tfrac{3}{7}} - \dfrac{x^4}{48} - \dfrac{x^3}{48}\sqrt{\tfrac{3}{7}} + \dfrac{7x}{1920}\sqrt{\tfrac{3}{7}} + \dfrac{1}{1280}\right)$

$+ f(x).$

This formula (8) gives the complete solution of the integral equation (4), or the differential equation (3), for any function $F[x, \phi(x)]$ as soon as ϕ_1, ϕ_2, ϕ_3 are known.

To find these ϕ's, we evaluate (8) for $x = 0$, $x = -\tfrac{1}{2}\sqrt{\tfrac{3}{7}}$, and $x = \tfrac{1}{2}\sqrt{\tfrac{3}{7}}$. Denoting $\phi(x_1)$ by ϕ_1, $f(x_1)$ by f_1, etc., and doing some tedious arithmetic, we get

(9) $\begin{cases} \phi_1 = -\dfrac{3}{40} F(0, \phi_1) - \dfrac{49}{1920} F(-\tfrac{1}{2}\sqrt{\tfrac{3}{7}}, \phi_2) - \dfrac{49}{1920} F(\tfrac{1}{2}\sqrt{\tfrac{3}{7}}, \phi_3) + f_1 \\[3mm] \phi_2 = -\dfrac{16}{490} F(0, \phi_1) - \dfrac{13}{420} F(-\tfrac{1}{2}\sqrt{\tfrac{3}{7}}, \phi_2) - \dfrac{1}{140} F(\tfrac{1}{2}\sqrt{\tfrac{3}{7}}, \phi_3) + f_2 \\[3mm] \phi_3 = -\dfrac{16}{490} F(0, \phi_1) - \dfrac{1}{140} F(-\tfrac{1}{2}\sqrt{\tfrac{3}{7}}, \phi_2) - \dfrac{13}{420} F(\tfrac{1}{2}\sqrt{\tfrac{3}{7}}, \phi_3) + f_3 ; \end{cases}$

or, with decimal coefficients,

$$(10) \begin{cases} \phi_1 = -0.075000000 \ F(0, \phi_1) - 0.025520833 \ F(-\tfrac{1}{2}\sqrt{\tfrac{3}{\gamma}}, \phi_2) \\ \qquad - 0.025520833 \ F(\tfrac{1}{2}\sqrt{\tfrac{3}{\gamma}}, \phi_3) + f_1 \\ \\ \phi_2 = -0.032653061 \ F(0, \phi_1) - 0.030952381 \ F(-\tfrac{1}{2}\sqrt{\tfrac{3}{\gamma}}, \phi_2) \\ \qquad - 0.007142857 \ F(\tfrac{1}{2}\sqrt{\tfrac{3}{\gamma}}, \phi_3) + f_2 \\ \\ \phi_3 = -0.032653061 \ F(0, \phi_1) - 0.007142857 \ F(-\tfrac{1}{2}\sqrt{\tfrac{3}{\gamma}}, \phi_2) \\ \qquad = -0.030952381 \ F(\tfrac{1}{2}\sqrt{\tfrac{3}{\gamma}}, \phi_3) + f_3. \end{cases}$$

Since $f(x)$ can be easily found in any given problem, the ϕ's can be found from (9) or (10) by the process of iteration if approximate values are known at the start. Then the desired solution of (4) is found by substituting the ϕ's in (8).

The reader should observe that in the special case where $F[x, \phi(x)] = \phi(x)$, equations (9) and (10) will give the ϕ's in a system of linear equations as in Art. 116. A differential equation of the form

$$\phi''(x) = \phi(x) + f(x),$$

with $\phi(a) = \phi(b) = 0$, can thus be solved by means of (9) or (10).

Example. Solve the differential equation

$$(11) \qquad \phi''(x) = \sin \phi(x) - 1,$$

with the boundary conditions $\phi(-\tfrac{1}{2}) = \phi(\tfrac{1}{2}) = 0$.

Solution. Here $F[x, \phi(x)] = \sin \phi(x)$ and $g(x) = -1$. Since $\phi(\pm \tfrac{1}{2}) = 0$, $\sin \phi(\pm \tfrac{1}{2}) = 0$ and we may therefore utilize equations (9) or (10).

To get approximate values for ϕ we assume that the solution of (11) is not very different from the solution of the similar equation

$$(12) \qquad \phi''(x) = \phi(x) - 1,$$

or

$$(13) \qquad \phi'' - \phi = -1.$$

Solving this by the usual elementary method, we have

$$r^2 - 1 = 0 \quad \text{or} \quad r = \pm 1.$$

Hence the complementary function is

$$\phi_c = A \cosh x + B \sinh x.$$

To find a particular integral we assume $\phi_p = C$. Hence $\phi''_p = 0$. Substituting these in (13), we get

$$-C = -1 \quad \text{or} \quad C = 1.$$

Hence the general solution of (12) is

(14) $$\phi = A \cosh x + B \sinh x + 1.$$

Now substituting in (14) the given boundary conditions $\phi(\pm \tfrac{1}{2}) = 0$, we have

$$0 = A \cosh \tfrac{1}{2} - B \sinh \tfrac{1}{2} + 1$$
$$0 = A \cosh \tfrac{1}{2} + B \sinh \tfrac{1}{2} + 1.$$

Solving these for A and B, we get

$$A = -\frac{1}{\cosh \tfrac{1}{2}}, \quad B = 0.$$

Then (14) becomes

(15) $$\phi = 1 - \frac{\cosh x}{\cosh \tfrac{1}{2}}.$$

We now find ϕ_1, ϕ_2, ϕ_3 by putting $x_1 = 0$, $x_2 = -\tfrac{1}{2}\sqrt{\tfrac{3}{7}}$, and $x_3 = \tfrac{1}{2}\sqrt{\tfrac{3}{7}}$ in (15). Then

$$\phi_1 = 1 - \frac{\cosh 0}{\cosh 0.5} = 0.11318.$$

$$\phi_2 = 1 - \frac{\cosh \left(-\tfrac{1}{2}\sqrt{\tfrac{3}{7}}\right)}{\cosh 0.5} \doteq 1 - \frac{\cosh 0.3273268}{\cosh 0.5}$$

$$= 1 - \frac{1.054051446}{1.127625965} = 0.065247.$$

$$\phi_3 = 1 - \frac{\cosh \left(\tfrac{1}{2}\sqrt{\tfrac{3}{7}}\right)}{\cosh 0.5} = 0.065247.$$

The next step is to evaluate the integral giving $f(x)$. We have

$$f(x) = \int_{-\frac{1}{2}}^{\frac{1}{2}} K(x, s) g(s)\, ds.$$

Since $g(x) = -1$, we have

$$f(x) = -\left\{ \int_{-\frac{1}{2}}^{x} (x - \tfrac{1}{2})(s + \tfrac{1}{2})\,ds + \int_{x}^{\frac{1}{2}} (x + \tfrac{1}{2})(s - \tfrac{1}{2})\,ds \right\}$$

$$= -\left\{ (x - \tfrac{1}{2})\left[\frac{s^2}{2} + \frac{s}{2}\right]_{-\frac{1}{2}}^{x} + (x + \tfrac{1}{2})\left[\frac{s^2}{2} - \frac{s}{2}\right]_{x}^{\frac{1}{2}} \right\}$$

$$= \frac{1}{8} - \frac{x^2}{2}.$$

Hence

$$f(x_1) = \frac{1}{8}, \quad f(x_2) = \frac{1}{8} - \frac{1}{8}\left(\frac{3}{7}\right) = \frac{1}{14}, \quad f(x_3) = \frac{1}{8} - \frac{1}{8}\left(\frac{3}{7}\right) = \frac{1}{14}.$$

Since $F[x, \phi(x)] = \sin \phi(x)$, equations (9) become

(16)
$$\begin{cases} \phi_1 = -\dfrac{3}{40} \sin \phi_1 - \dfrac{49}{1920} \sin \phi_2 - \dfrac{49}{1920} \sin \phi_3 + f_1 \\[2mm] \phi_2 = -\dfrac{16}{490} \sin \phi_1 - \dfrac{13}{420} \sin \phi_2 - \dfrac{1}{140} \sin \phi_3 + f_2 \\[2mm] \phi_3 = -\dfrac{16}{490} \sin \phi_1 - \dfrac{1}{140} \sin \phi_2 - \dfrac{13}{420} \sin \phi_3 + f_3. \end{cases}$$

We now substitute in the right-hand member of the first equation of (16) the numerical value of f_1 and the approximate values of ϕ_1, ϕ_2, ϕ_3 found above. Then we have

$$\phi_1^{(1)} = -\frac{3}{40} \sin(0.11318) - \frac{49}{1920} \sin(0.065247)$$

$$- \frac{49}{1920} \sin(0.065247) + 0.125000$$

$$= -0.0084704 - 0.0033279 + 0.1250000$$

$$= 0.11320.$$

Now substituting this value $\phi_1^{(1)}$ in the second equation of (16), we get

$$\phi_2^{(1)} = -\frac{16}{490} \sin(0.11320) - \frac{13}{420} \sin(0.065247)$$

$$- \frac{1}{140} \sin(0.065247) + 0.07142857$$

$$= -0.0036884 - 0.0020181 - 0.0004657 + 0.07142857$$

$$= 0.065256.$$

Also,

$$\phi_3^{(1)} = 0.065256.$$

We now repeat the above process by substituting $\phi_1^{(1)}$, $\phi_2^{(1)}$, $\phi_3^{(1)}$ in the right-hand member of the first of equations (16). Then

$$\phi_1^{(2)} = -\frac{3}{40}\sin(0.11320) - \frac{49}{1920}\sin(0.065256)$$

$$-\frac{49}{1920}\sin(0.065256) + 0.125000$$

$$= -0.0084719 - 0.0033284 + 0.1250000$$

$$= 0.11320.$$

Now substituting this value $\phi_1^{(2)}$ in the second of equations (16), we have

$$\phi_2^{(2)} = -\frac{16}{490}\sin(0.11320) - \frac{13}{420}\sin(0.065256)$$

$$-\frac{1}{140}\sin(0.065256) + 0.07142857,$$

or

$$\phi_2^{(2)} = -0.0036884 - 0.0020184 - 0.0004658 + 0.07142857$$

$$= 0.065256;$$

and

$$\phi_3^{(2)} = 0.065256.$$

Since these values of the ϕ's are the same as the preceding set of values, we take them to be correct.

The required solution of equation (11) is now obtained by substituting in (8) the values of ϕ and $f(x)$ found above. Thus, since $f(x) = \frac{1}{8} - \frac{x^2}{2}$ and $F[0, \phi_1]$, $F\left[-\frac{1}{2}\sqrt{\frac{3}{7}}, \phi_2\right]$, $F\left[\frac{1}{2}\sqrt{\frac{3}{7}}, \phi_3\right]$ are to be replaced by $\sin\phi_1$, $\sin\phi_2$, and $\sin\phi_3$, respectively, we have

$$\phi(x) = \frac{112}{3}(0.112958)\left(\frac{x^6}{30} - \frac{5x^4}{168} + \frac{3x^2}{224} - \frac{9}{4480}\right)$$

$$-\frac{98}{3}(0.065210)\left(\frac{x^6}{30} - \frac{x^5}{40}\sqrt{\frac{3}{7}} - \frac{x^4}{48} + \frac{x^3}{48}\sqrt{\frac{3}{7}} - \frac{7x}{1920}\sqrt{\frac{3}{7}} + \frac{1}{1280}\right)$$

$$-\frac{98}{3}(0.065210)\left(\frac{x^6}{30} + \frac{x^5}{40}\sqrt{\frac{3}{7}} - \frac{x^4}{48} - \frac{x^3}{48}\sqrt{\frac{3}{7}} + \frac{7x}{1920}\sqrt{\frac{3}{7}} + \frac{1}{1280}\right)$$

$$+\frac{1}{8} - \frac{x^2}{2},$$

or

$$(17) \quad \phi(x) = 0.11320 - 0.44352x^2 - 0.03675x^4 - 0.001443x^6.$$

As a partial check on this result we find by substituting $x = -\frac{1}{2}$ and $x = \frac{1}{2}$ in (17) that $\phi(\pm \frac{1}{2}) = 0$, as it should be. To check the result completely, it is necessary to go back to equation (6) and replace $F(0, \phi_1)$, $F(-\frac{1}{2}\sqrt{\frac{3}{7}}, \phi_2)$, and $F(\frac{1}{2}\sqrt{\frac{3}{7}}, \phi_3)$ by $\sin \phi_1$, $\sin \phi_2$, and $\sin \phi_3$, respectively. The result is then substituted in equation (4). The integration is then carried out over the intervals $-\frac{1}{2}$ to x and x to $\frac{1}{2}$, the appropriate value of $K(x, s)$ being used in each case. Note that the second integral in (4) is $f(x) = \frac{1}{8} - \frac{x^2}{2}$, which has already been found. This complete check has been carried out for this problem, the right-hand member of (4) giving the right-hand member of (17) above.

CHAPTER XIV

THE NORMAL LAW OF ERROR AND THE
PRINCIPLE OF LEAST SQUARES

118. Errors of Observation and Measurement. All measurements are subject to three kinds of errors: constant or systematic errors, mistakes, and accidental errors. *Systematic errors* are those which affect all measurements alike. They are mostly due to imperfections in the construction or adjustment of instruments, the "personal equation" of the observer, etc. Such errors are usually determinate and can be remedied by applying the proper corrections.

Mistakes or blunders are large errors due to careless reading of measuring instruments or faulty recording of the readings. They consist mostly in reading the wrong scale, reading a vernier backward, making a miscount in observations which involve counting, putting down the wrong number when recording the readings, etc. Mistakes do not follow any law and can be avoided or remedied only by constant vigilance and careful checking on the part of the observer.

Accidental errors are those whose causes are unknown and indeterminate. They are usually small, and they follow the laws of chance. The mathematical theory of errors deals with accidental errors only.

119. The Law of Accidental Errors. In order to get a better understanding of the behavior of accidental errors the reader should try the following experiment:

Take a sheet of ruled paper and draw with pen or pencil a line bisecting the space between two rulings near the middle of the sheet, as shown in Fig. 40. Lay the sheet flat on a table or floor, with the rulings upward. Now take a sharp-pointed pencil, hold it lightly by the top between the finger tips of both hands, and about two feet above the paper. Take good aim at the line on the paper and try to hit it by dropping the pencil on it. Drop the pencil in this way at least 100 times, making an honest effort to hit the line every time. The shots will be self-recorded as dots on the paper. Count the dots in the compartment (space between the rulings) containing the target line, and the number in each of the other compartments on each side of the central one. Plot a curve by using as abscissas the distances from the target line to the midpoints of the several compartments containing dots, and as ordinates the number of dots in the corresponding compartments.

378

An experiment of this kind gave the results recorded in the table below. These results are plotted in Fig. 41.

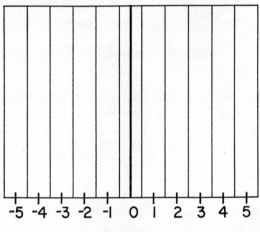

FIG. 40

Compartment	No. of dots
3	1
2	6
1	31
0	53
−1	32
−2	6
−3	1
Total	130

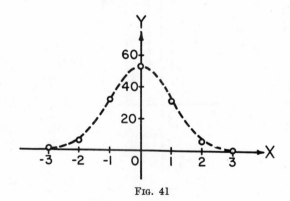

FIG. 41

If the pencil had been dropped 10,000 or more times instead of 130 and the width of the compartments correspondingly decreased, the plotted points would have followed the curve shown in Fig. 41. This curve is known as the *Normal Probability Currve*. Its equation will be derived in Art. 121.

All kinds of accidental errors follow the same law as the pencil shots in this experiment.

120. The Probability of Errors Lying between Given Limits. In many applications of the theory of probability it is necessary to find the chance that a given error will lie within certain specified limits. In such cases we utilize the fact that *the probability that an error lies within given limits is equal to the area under the probability curve between those limits.* The following proof, while not altogether rigorous, is sufficient to show the truth of this statement.

Going back for a moment to the target experiment of Art. 119, we recall that in plotting the results we erected ordinates at equal distances apart along the x-axis. The height of each ordinate was made proportional to the number of dots falling within the corresponding interval on the target. If we imagine rectangles constructed with the equal intervals along the x-axis as bases and the corresponding ordinates as altitudes (see Fig. 42),

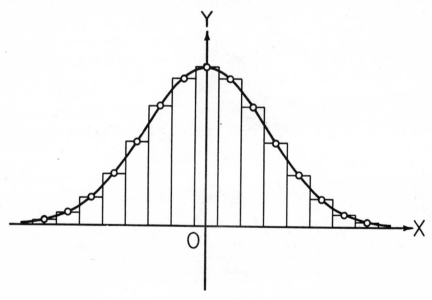

FIG. 42

we readily see that the area of each rectangle is proportional to the number
of dots falling within the corresponding compartment. Thus, if N_i is the
number of dots in any compartment and A_i is the area of the corresponding
rectangle, we have

$$(1) \qquad A_i = k_1 N_i .$$

Now if we make one more attempt to hit the target line in the experiment of Art. 119, the chance of hitting within the central compartment
is about 53/130, that of hitting within the next compartment to the right
is about 31/130, etc. The chance of hitting within *some one* of these
compartments is therefore

$$\frac{53}{130} + \frac{31}{130} + \frac{6}{130} + \frac{1}{130} + \frac{32}{130} + \frac{6}{130} + \frac{1}{130} = \frac{130}{130} = 1.$$

Since the chance of hitting within any compartment is proportional to
the number of hits made in a large number of shots, we have for any
compartment

$$(2) \qquad p_i = k_2 N_i ,$$

where p_i is the probability that a single additional shot will fall in any
compartment in which N_i shots fell in a previous experiment. Eliminating
N_i between equations (1) and (2), we get

$$(3) \qquad p_i = \frac{k_2}{k_1} A_i ,$$

which shows that the chance of making a hit in any compartment is
proportional to the area of the corresponding rectangle. The chance of
hitting within *some* compartment is therefore

$$(4) \qquad p = 1 = p_1 + p_2 + \cdots = \frac{k_2}{k_1} (A_1 + A_2 + \cdots) = \frac{k_2}{k_1} \Sigma A.$$

Now when the number of shots is increased indefinitely and the width
of each compartment on the target is correspondingly decreased, it is
plain that the bases of the corresponding rectangles will likewise decrease
and that the sum of the areas of these rectangles will approach the area
under the probability curve as a limit. The area under this curve is
always finite, and since it represents the probability that a shot will fall
somewhere, it (the area) represents certainty and therefore may be taken
as 1; or $\lim \Sigma A = 1$. Hence by (4) we have

$$1 = \frac{k_2}{k_1} (1), \quad \text{or} \quad k_2 = k_1 .$$

Equation (3) now becomes

(5) $p_i = A_i$,

which shows that the chance of making a hit in any compartment is *equal* to the area of the corresponding rectangle.

From equation (5) we have the important result that the chance of making an error whose magnitude lies between x and $x + \Delta x$ is *

(6) $p = y\Delta x$,

where y is the ordinate to the probability curve. The chance of making an error whose magnitude is between x_1 and x_2 is therefore

(7) $$p = \lim_{\Delta x \to 0} \sum_{x=x_1}^{x=x_2} y\Delta x = \int_{x_1}^{x_2} y \, dx \ .$$

121. The Probability Equation. To derive the equation of the Probability Curve we make use of the following facts as to the distribution of accidental errors, as indicated by the table of Art. 119 and the corresponding curve:

1. Small errors are more frequent than large ones, which shows that the probability of an error depends upon its size.

2. Positive and negative errors of the same size are about equal in number, thus making the probability curve symmetrical about the y-axis.

3. Very large accidental errors do not occur.

These three fundamental facts are so self-evident that they may be taken as axioms.

From axioms 1 and 2 it is plain that the ordinate to the probability curve must be a function of the square of the abscissa, or

$$y = f(x^2).$$

Here the function $f(x^2)$ is called the *error function*. Our problem now is to determine the form of this function.

Referring once more to the target experiment, we can readily see that if we had aimed at a particular *point* on the target line the distribution of shots *with respect to the line* would not have been different from that found in this experiment. Suppose, then, that we try another experiment of this kind and aim at some *point* O in the plane of the paper. The shots will be distributed about O in such a manner that if we draw *any*

---

* Except for differentials of higher order.

line through O the probability that any shot hits at a distance ϵ *from this line* will be

$$p = f(\epsilon^2)\, d\epsilon.$$

Let us therefore draw through O any two lines at right angles to each other. We shall take these as axes of coordinates for two variables x and y. Let us consider any shot that falls at a point $P(x, y)$. The chance that P lies in a strip of width dx at distance x from the y-axis is

$$p_x = f(x^2)\, dx;$$

and the chance that P lies in a strip of width dy at a distance y from the x-axis is

$$p_y = f(y^2)\, dy.$$

The chance that P lies in *both* of these strips and hence in the small rectangle $dxdy$ is therefore

(1) $$p = p_x p_y = f(x^2) f(y^2)\, dxdy.$$

If we draw any other set of rectangular axes through O, so that the coordinates of P referred to these axes are x' and y', we evidently have

$$p_{x'} = f(x'^2)\, dx',$$
$$p_{y'} = f(y'^2)\, dy'.$$

Hence the chance that P lies in the rectangle $dx'dy'$ is

(2) $$p' = f(x'^2) f(y'^2)\, dx'dy'.$$

But the chance that this particular shot falls within a small area A is the same regardless of the orientation of the axes through O. Hence if we take dx' and dy' such that

$$dx'dy' = dxdy = A,$$

we have

$$p = f(x^2) f(y^2) A = f(x'^2) f(y'^2) A,$$

or

(3) $$f(x^2) f(y^2) = f(x'^2) f(y'^2).$$

Suppose now that the axes OX' and OY' are oriented so that OX' passes through P. Then

$$x' = \sqrt{x^2 + y^2}, \qquad y' = 0.$$

Hence (3) becomes

(4) $$f(x^2)f(y^2) = f(x^2 + y^2)f(0) = Cf(x^2 + y^2),$$

since $f(0)$ is a constant.

Equation (4) is a *functional equation* and can be solved by first differentiating and then integrating.

Differentiating (4) partially with respect to x^2 and y^2 in turn, we have

$$f'(x^2)f(y^2) = C\,\frac{\partial f(x^2 + y^2)}{\partial(x^2)},$$

$$f'(y^2)f(x^2) = C\,\frac{\partial f(x^2 + y^2)}{\partial(y^2)}.$$

Now since $\partial f(u + v)/\partial u = \partial f(u + v)/\partial v$, the right-hand members of these equations are equal. Hence

$$f'(x^2)f(y^2) = f'(y^2)f(x^2),$$

or

$$\frac{f'(x^2)}{f(x^2)} = \frac{f'(y^2)}{f(y^2)} = k,\ \text{say.}$$

Multiplying the equation $f'(x^2)/f(x^2) = k$ through by $d(x^2)$ and integrating with respect to x^2, we have

$$\log_e f(x^2) = kx^2 + \log_e c,$$

or

(5) $$f(x^2) = ce^{kx^2}.$$

Now since the probability of an error decreases as the size of the error increases, it is plain that k must be negative. Putting $k = -h^2$, we have

(6) $$f(x^2) = ce^{-h^2x^2}.$$

Hence

(7) $$y = ce^{-h^2x^2}$$

is the equation of the probability curve.

To determine the constant c we utilize the fact that the area under the probability curve is equal to 1. Hence we have

(8) $$1 = \int_{-\infty}^{\infty} ce^{-h^2x^2}dx = \frac{2c}{h}\int_{0}^{\infty} e^{-(hx)^2}d(hx).$$

This integral must be evaluated by an indirect method. To effect the evaluation let us consider the volume of the solid of revolution (Fig. 43) included between the xy-plane and the surface generated by revolving the curve $z = e^{-x^2}$ about the z-axis. Since this is a surface of revolution, its equation is

(9) $$z = e^{-(x^2+y^2)}.$$

In cylindrical coordinates this equation becomes

(10) $$z = e^{-r^2}, \quad \text{where} \quad x^2 + y^2 = r^2.$$

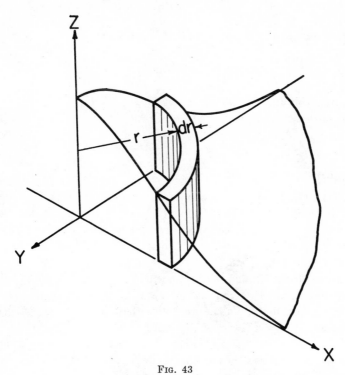

FIG. 43

Taking as the element of volume a cylindrical shell of radius r, thickness dr, and height z, we have

$$dV = 2\pi r \cdot dr \cdot z = 2\pi r e^{-r^2} dr.$$

(11) $$\therefore \ V = 2\pi \int_0^\infty e^{-r^2} r \, dr = -\pi \int_0^\infty e^{-r^2}(-2r \, dr) = -\pi (e^{-r^2}\Big]_0^\infty = \pi.$$

Using rectangular cordinates, we take as the element of volume a prism of base $dx \, dy$ and altitude z. Hence we have from (9)

$$(12) \qquad V = 4 \int zdxdy = 4 \int_0^\infty \int_0^\infty e^{-(x^2+y^2)} dxdy$$

$$= 4 \int_0^\infty e^{-x^2} dx \int_0^\infty e^{-y^2} dy.$$

Now since the value of a definite integral depends only on its limits and not on the variable of integration, we may replace y by x in the second integral. We then have

$$(13) \qquad V = 4 \int_0^\infty e^{-x^2} dx \int_0^\infty e^{-x^2} dx = \left[2 \int_0^\infty e^{-x^2} dx \right]^2.$$

Since we have already found $V = \pi$ above, we have

$$(14) \qquad \left[2 \int_0^\infty e^{-x^2} dx \right]^2 = \pi, \quad \text{or} \quad \int_0^\infty e^{-x^2} dx = \frac{\sqrt{\pi}}{2}.$$

Substituting this in (8), we get $c = h/\sqrt{\pi}$. Now putting this value of c in (7), we have finally

$$(121. 1) \qquad y = \frac{h}{\sqrt{\pi}} e^{-h^2 x^2}$$

as the equation of the probability curve.

Equation (121. 1) is of *fundamental importance*; for it is the foundation of the Theory of Errors, the Principle of Least Squares, and the Precision of Measurements. It is known as the Probability Equation, Error Equation, etc.; and its graph is known as the Normal Probability Curve, the Error Curve, Gaussian Curve, etc.

It will be observed that this important equation contains only one arbitrary constant. This constant h is called the "index of precision." To see the reason for this name we notice that the larger h is the higher the probability curve will rise in the middle and the more rapidly it will fall on each side of the "hump." This fact, when considered in connection with the target problem, means that a large percentage of the shots hit near the target and very few hit far from it. In other words, it means accurate shooting.

122. The Law of Error of a Linear Function of Independent Quantities.
We shall next prove a fundamental theorem of great importance, namely:

If $M_1, M_2, \cdots M_n$ are *independent* observed quantities whose laws of error are

$$y = \frac{h_1}{\sqrt{\pi}} e^{-h_1^2 x^2}, \; y = \frac{h_2}{\sqrt{\pi}} e^{-h_2^2 x^2}, \cdots y = \frac{h_n}{\sqrt{\pi}} e^{-h_n^2 x^2},$$

then any linear function of these quantities obeys a similar law of error.

Proof: Let the linear function be

$$(1) \qquad F = a_1 M_1 + a_2 M_2 + \cdots a_n M_n,$$

where $a_1, a_2, \cdots a_n$ are arbitrary constants. If $x_1, x_2, \cdots x_n$ denote the errors of $M_1, M_2, \cdots M_n$, respectively, and ξ denote the corresponding error in F, we have

$$F + \xi = a_1 (M_1 + x_1) + a_2 (M_2 + x_2) + \cdots + a_n (M_n + x_n)$$
$$= a_1 M_1 + a_1 x_1 + a_2 M_2 + a_2 x_2 + \cdots + a_n M_n + a_n x_n.$$

Subtracting (1),

$$(2) \qquad \xi = a_1 x_1 + a_2 x_2 + \cdots a_n x_n.$$

The error ξ in F is thus a linear function of the errors in M_1, M_2, etc. We are now to show that the law of error for ξ is the same as the laws for x_1, x_2, etc.

To simplify the proof we first take a linear function of two independent quantities,

$$F = a_1 M_1 + a_2 M_2.$$

Then

$$(3) \qquad \xi = a_1 x_1 + a_2 x_2.$$

Hence

$$\xi + \Delta \xi = a_1 (x_1 + \Delta x_1) + a_2 (x_2 + \Delta x_2).$$

An error of magnitude x_1 to $x_1 + \Delta x_1$ in M_1 combined with an error of magnitude x_2 to $x_2 + \Delta x_2$ in M_2 will therefore produce an error of magnitude ξ to $\xi + \Delta \xi$ in F.

The probability of the occurrence of an error lying between x_1 and $x_1 + \Delta x_1$ in M_1 is

$$p_1 = \frac{h_1}{\sqrt{\pi}} e^{-h_1^2 x_1^2} \Delta x_1,$$

and similarly the chance of an error lying between x_2 and $x_2 + \Delta x_2$ in M_2 is

$$p_2 = \frac{h_2}{\sqrt{\pi}} e^{-h_2^2 x_2^2} \Delta x_2.$$

The probability that these two independent errors will occur simultaneously and thereby cause an error lying between ξ and $\xi + \Delta \xi$ in F is therefore the product of their separate probabilities, or

$$(4) \qquad P = p_1 p_2 = \frac{h_1 h_2}{\pi} e^{-h_1^2 x_1^2 - h_2^2 x_2^2} \Delta x_1 \Delta x_2.$$

This is the probability that any single error in M_1 combined with any single error in M_2 will produce a single error in F. But equation (3) shows that an error in F may be produced by combining any value of x_2 (that is, any error in M_2) with all possible values of x_1 from $-\infty$ to $+\infty$. Hence the total probability of an error between ξ and $\xi + \Delta\xi$ is the sum of these mutually exclusive events, or

$$(5) \qquad \phi(\xi)\Delta\xi = \frac{h_1 h_2}{\pi} \Delta x_2 \int_{-\infty}^{\infty} e^{-h_1^2 x_1^2 - h_2^2 x_2^2} dx_1 \,,$$

where $\phi(\xi)$ denotes the error function for ξ.

Let us now consider a single definite error ξ in F. This means that ξ in (3) is to be considered constant for the time being. Hence from (3) we have

$$x_2 = \frac{\xi - a_1 x_1}{a_2} \,.$$

Substituting this value of x_2 in (5), we get

$$(6) \qquad \phi(\xi)\Delta\xi = \frac{h_1 h_2}{\pi} \Delta x_2 \int_{-\infty}^{\infty} e^{-h_1^2 x_1^2 - h_2^2 [(\xi - a_1 x_1)/a_2]^2} dx_1 \,.$$

To simplify the integration, we transform and simplify the exponent of e as follows:

For convenience we write

$$E = - h_1^2 x_1^2 - h_2^2 \left(\frac{\xi - a_1 x_1}{a_2}\right)^2 .$$

Now expand the squared term and reduce the whole right-hand member to a common denominator. The result is

$$E = \frac{- a_2^2 x_1^2 h_1^2 - h_2^2 \xi^2 + 2 a_1 x_1 h_2^2 \xi - a_1^2 x_1^2 h_2^2}{a_2^2} \,,$$

or

$$E = - \frac{h_2^2 \xi^2}{a_2^2} - \frac{a_1^2 x_1^2 h_2^2 + a_2^2 x_1^2 h_1^2}{a_2^2} + \frac{2 a_1 x_1 h_2^2 \xi}{a_2^2} \,.$$

Now multiply numerator and denominator of the first fraction on the right by $a_1^2 h_2^2 + a_2^2 h_1^2$. We then have

$$E = - \frac{h_2^2 \xi^2 (a_1^2 h_2^2 + a_2^2 h_1^2)}{a_2^2 (a_1^2 h_2^2 + a_2^2 h_1^2)} - \frac{(a_1^2 h_2^2 + a_2^2 h_1^2) x_1^2}{a_2^2} + \frac{2 a_1 x_1 h_2^2 \xi}{a_2^2} \,,$$

which can be written in the form

$$E = -\frac{a_2{}^2 h_1{}^2 h_2{}^2 \xi^2}{a_2{}^2(a_1{}^2 h_2{}^2 + a_2{}^2 h_1{}^2)} - \frac{(a_1{}^2 h_2{}^2 + a_2{}^2 h_1{}^2) x_1{}^2}{a_2{}^2}$$
$$+ \frac{2 a_1 x_1 \xi h_2{}^2}{a_2{}^2} - \frac{a_1{}^2 h_2{}^4 \xi^2}{a_2{}^2(a_1{}^2 h_2{}^2 + a_2{}^2 h_1{}^2)},$$

or

$$E = -\frac{h_1{}^2 h_2{}^2 \xi^2}{a_1{}^2 h_2{}^2 + a_2{}^2 h_1{}^2} - \frac{a_1{}^2 h_2{}^2 + a_2{}^2 h_1{}^2}{a_2{}^2}$$
$$\times \left(x_1{}^2 - \frac{2 a_1 x_1 \xi h_2{}^2}{a_1{}^2 h_2{}^2 + a_2{}^2 h_1{}^2} + \frac{a_1{}^2 h_2{}^4 \xi^2}{(a_1{}^2 h_2{}^2 + a_2{}^2 h_1{}^2)^2} \right)$$
$$= -\frac{h_1{}^2 h_2{}^2 \xi^2}{a_1{}^2 h_2{}^2 + a_2{}^2 h_1{}^2} - \frac{a_1{}^2 h_2{}^2 + a_2{}^2 h_1{}^2}{a_2{}^2} \left(x_1 - \frac{a_1 h_2{}^2 \xi}{a_1{}^2 h_2{}^2 + a_2{}^2 h_1{}^2} \right)^2.$$

We now simplify this by putting $C^2 = a_1{}^2 h_2{}^2 + a_2{}^2 h_1{}^2$. Then

$$E = -\frac{h_1{}^2 h_2{}^2 \xi^2}{C^2} - \frac{C^2}{a_2{}^2} \left(x_1 - \frac{a_1 h_2{}^2 \xi}{C^2} \right)^2.$$

The integrand in (6) now becomes

$$e^{-h_1{}^2 h_2{}^2 \xi^2 / C^2 - (C^2 / a_2{}^2)(x_1 - a_1 h_2{}^2 \xi / C^2)^2},$$

which can be written in the form

$$e^{-h_1{}^2 h_2{}^2 \xi^2 / C^2} \cdot e^{-(C^2 / a_2{}^2)(x_1 - a_1 h_2{}^2 \xi / C^2)^2}.$$

Since the first factor is independent of x_1, it may be removed from under the integral sign. Then (6) becomes

$$\phi(\xi)\Delta\xi = \frac{h_1 h_2}{\pi} \Delta x_2 \cdot e^{-h_1{}^2 h_2{}^2 \xi^2 / C^2} \int_{-\infty}^{\infty} e^{-(C^2 / a_2{}^2)(x_1 - a_1 h_2{}^2 \xi / C^2)^2} dx_1.$$

Now put

$$u = \frac{C}{a_2} \left(x_1 - \frac{a_1 h_2{}^2 \xi}{C^2} \right).$$

Then $du = (C/a_2)\,dx_1$, or $dx_1 = (a_2/C)\,du$, since ξ is constant. Hence

$$\phi(\xi)\Delta\xi = \frac{h_1 h_2}{\pi} \Delta x_2 e^{-h_1{}^2 h_2{}^2 \xi^2 / C^2} \cdot \frac{a_2}{C} \int_{-\infty}^{\infty} e^{-u^2} du.$$

But

$$\int_{-\infty}^{\infty} e^{-u^2} du = 2 \int_{0}^{\infty} e^{-u^2} du = 2 \cdot \frac{\sqrt{\pi}}{2} = \sqrt{\pi},$$

by Art. 121.

(7) $$\therefore \quad \phi(\xi)\Delta\xi = \frac{h_1 h_2}{\sqrt{\pi}} \Delta x_2 e^{-h_1{}^2 h_2{}^2 \xi^2 / C^2} \cdot \frac{a_2}{C}.$$

We have now taken account of the effect of the errors x_1 in M_1 in causing a particular error ξ in F, so that ξ is now a function of x_2 alone. Hence from (3), regarding x_1 as a constant, we get $\Delta\xi = a_2\Delta x_2$. Substituting this value for $\Delta\xi$ in (7) and replacing C by its value $\sqrt{a_1{}^2h_2{}^2 + a_2{}^2h_1{}^2}$, we get

(8)
$$\phi(\xi) = \frac{\dfrac{h_1 h_2}{\sqrt{a_1{}^2h_2{}^2 + a_2{}^2h_1{}^2}}}{\sqrt{\pi}} \, e^{-[h_1{}^2h_2{}^2/(a_1{}^2h_2{}^2+a_2{}^2h_1{}^2)]\xi^2},$$

or

(9)
$$\phi(\xi) = \frac{H_1}{\sqrt{\pi}} \, e^{-H_1{}^2\xi^2},$$

where

(10)
$$H_1{}^2 = \frac{h_1{}^2h_2{}^2}{a_1{}^2h_2{}^2 + a_2{}^2h_1{}^2}.$$

The law of error for ξ, the error in F, is thus of the same form as the laws of error for x_1 and x_2, the errors in M_1 and M_2.

From (10) we have

(11)
$$\frac{1}{H_1{}^2} = \frac{a_1{}^2h_2{}^2 + a_2{}^2h_1{}^2}{h_1{}^2h_2{}^2} = \frac{a_1{}^2}{h_1{}^2} + \frac{a_2{}^2}{h_2{}^2}.$$

To extend this relation to a linear function of any number of independent quantities, take

$$F = a_1M_1 + a_2M_2 + a_3M_3 = (a_1M_1 + a_2M_2) + a_3M_3.$$

If h_3 denote the precision index of the errors in M_3, and H_2 the precision index for F, then by (11)

$$\frac{1}{H_2{}^2} = \frac{1}{H_1{}^2} + \frac{a_3{}^2}{h_3{}^2} = \frac{a_1{}^2}{h_1{}^2} + \frac{a_2{}^2}{h_2{}^2} + \frac{a_3{}^2}{h_3{}^2}.$$

In the same way, we can extend the formula to a linear function of 4, 5, or any number of quantities. We therefore arrive at the following result:

If F be a linear function of n independent quantities which have been determined by observation, the function F follows an error law which is of the same form as the error laws of the independent unknowns. If the function is

$$F = a_1M_1 + a_2M_2 + a_3M_3 \cdots + a_nM_n,$$

the index of precision, H, of F is given by

(122. 1)
$$\frac{1}{H^2} = \frac{a_1{}^2}{h_1{}^2} + \frac{a_2{}^2}{h_2{}^2} + \frac{a_3{}^2}{h_3{}^2} + \cdots + \frac{a_n{}^2}{h_n{}^2} = \Sigma\left(\frac{a^2}{h^2}\right).$$

Even when F is not a linear function of the independent quantities $M_1, M_2, \cdots M_n$, the error ξ in F will follow the Normal Law approximately if the errors $x_1, x_2, \cdots x_n$ are relatively small. For let

$$(12) \qquad\qquad F = f(M_1, M_2, \cdots M_n)$$

represent any function of M_1, M_2, etc. Then errors in the M's will cause an error in F according to the relation

$$F + \xi = f(M_1 + x_1, M_2 + x_2, \cdots M_n + x_n).$$

Expanding the right-hand member by Taylor's theorem, as in Art. 6, we have

$$(13) \quad F + \xi = f(M_1, M_2, \cdots M_n) + \frac{\partial f}{\partial M_1} x_1 + \frac{\partial f}{\partial M_2} x_2 + \cdots + \frac{\partial f}{\partial M_n} x_n$$
$$+ \text{ terms in } x_1{}^2, x_1 x_2, \text{ etc.}$$

Now if x_1, x_2, etc. are so small that their squares, products, and higher powers may be neglected, we have after subtracting (12) from (13)

$$(14) \qquad\qquad \xi = \frac{\partial F}{\partial M_1} x_1 + \frac{\partial F}{\partial M_2} x_2 + \cdots + \frac{\partial F}{\partial M_n} x_n,$$

which is a linear function of x_1, x_2, etc. Hence by (122.1) we have

$$(122.2) \qquad \frac{1}{H^2} = \frac{\left(\dfrac{\partial F}{\partial M_1}\right)^2}{h_1{}^2} + \frac{\left(\dfrac{\partial F}{\partial M_2}\right)^2}{h_2{}^2} + \cdots + \frac{\left(\dfrac{\partial F}{\partial M_n}\right)^2}{h_n{}^2},$$

where H denotes the index of precision for the errors ξ.

123. The Probability Integral and Its Evaluation. To find the probability that an error of a given series will lie between the limits x_1 and x_2 we merely find the area under the probability curve from $x = x_1$ to $x = x_2$, as shown in Art. 120. This means that we must evaluate the integral

$$(1) \qquad P = \frac{h}{\sqrt{\pi}} \int_{x_1}^{x_2} e^{-h^2 x^2} dx = \frac{h}{\sqrt{\pi}} \left\{ \int_0^{x_2} e^{-h^2 x^2} dx - \int_0^{x_1} e^{-h^2 x^2} dx \right\}.$$

The integral

$$I = h \int_0^x e^{-h^2 x^2} dx = \int_0^x e^{-(hx)^2} d(hx)$$

can not be evaluated in finite form, but we can expand the integrand into a power series and then integrate as many terms as we need. Since

$$e^x = 1 + x + \frac{x^2}{2!} + \frac{x^3}{3!} + \cdots + \frac{x^n}{n!} + \cdots,$$

we have

$$e^{-t^2} = 1 - t^2 + \frac{t^4}{2!} - \frac{t^6}{3!} + \frac{t^8}{4!} - \cdots.$$

Hence

$$(2) \qquad I = \int_0^t e^{-t^2} dt = t - \frac{t^3}{3} + \frac{t^5}{5 \times 2!} - \frac{t^7}{7 \times 3!} + \frac{t^9}{9 \times 4!}.$$

This series converges rapidly for small values of t, and the error committed by stopping at any term is less than the first term omitted (Art. 12). For example, if $t = \frac{1}{2}$ we have

$$\int_0^{\frac{1}{2}} e^{-t^2} dt = \frac{1}{2} - \frac{1}{24} + \frac{1}{320} - \frac{1}{5376} + \frac{1}{110592}$$

$$= 0.5 - 0.04167 + 0.00313 - 0.00019 + 0.00001$$

$$= 0.46128.$$

This result is correct to the last figure, since the error is less than

$$\frac{(\frac{1}{2})^{11}}{11 \times 5!} + \frac{1}{2703360} = 0.00000037.$$

For large values of t the series (2) is not convenient for purposes of computation, because too many terms are needed to give the desired degree of accuracy. We shall therefore derive an expansion in descending powers of t, which may be used when t is large.

Since

$$\int_0^\infty e^{-t^2} dt = \int_0^t e^{-t^2} dt + \int_t^\infty e^{-t^2} dt,$$

we have

$$(3) \qquad \int_0^t e^{-t^2} dt = \int_0^\infty e^{-t^2} dt - \int_t^\infty e^{-t^2} dt.$$

The value of the first integral on the right-hand side has already been found to be $\sqrt{\pi}/2$. Hence (3) becomes

$$(4) \qquad \int_0^t e^{-t^2} dt = \frac{\sqrt{\pi}}{2} - \int_t^\infty e^{-t^2} dt.$$

The remaining integral on the right-hand side can be written in the form

$$\int_t^\infty e^{-t^2} dt = -\frac{1}{2} \int_t^\infty \frac{1}{t} \; e^{-t^2} (-2t\,dt) = -\frac{1}{2} \int_t^\infty \frac{1}{t} \; d(e^{-t^2}).$$

Integrating this last expression by parts, by putting $u = 1/t$, $dv = d(e^{-t^2})$, we get

$$\int_t^\infty e^{-t^2}dt = -\frac{1}{2}\left[\frac{e^{-t^2}}{t}\right]_t^\infty + \frac{1}{2}\int_t^\infty \left(-\frac{1}{t^2}e^{-t^2}\right)dt$$

$$= \frac{1}{2}\frac{e^{-t^2}}{t} + \frac{1}{4}\int_t^\infty \frac{1}{t^3}e^{-t^2}(2tdt)$$

$$= \frac{1}{2}\frac{e^{-t^2}}{t} + \frac{1}{4}\int_t^\infty \frac{1}{t^3}d(e^{-t^2})$$

$$= \frac{1}{2}\frac{e^{-t^2}}{t} + \frac{1}{4}\left[\frac{e^{-t^2}}{t^3}\right]_t^\infty - \frac{1}{4}\int_t^\infty \left(-\frac{3}{t^4}e^{-t^2}\right)dt,$$

or

$$\int_t^\infty e^{-t^2}dt = \frac{1}{2}\frac{e^{-t^2}}{t} - \frac{1}{4}\frac{e^{-t^2}}{t^3} + \frac{3}{4}\int_t^\infty \frac{e^{-t^2}}{t^4}dt.$$

By continuing this process of integrating by parts and substituting limits, we get the following expansion:

(5) $$\int_t^\infty e^{-t^2}dt = \frac{e^{-t^2}}{2t}\left(1 - \frac{1}{2t^2} + \frac{1\cdot 3}{(2t^2)^2} - \frac{1\cdot 3\cdot 5}{(2t^2)^3} + \cdots\right).$$

Substituting this in (4), we get

(6) $$\int_0^t e^{-t^2}dt = \frac{\sqrt{\pi}}{2} - \frac{e^{-t^2}}{2t}\left(1 - \frac{1}{2t^2} + \frac{1\cdot 3}{(2t^2)^2} - \frac{1\cdot 3\cdot 5}{(2t^2)^3} + \cdots\right).$$

This series (6) is called an *asymptotic series*. It is divergent, but the terms in parenthesis decrease in numerical value so long as the number of terms does not exceed $t^2 + 1$. This is the maximum number of terms ever used in computations with this series. The error committed in using (6) is less than the last term retained.*

As an example of the use of (6) we shall compute

$$\int_0^2 e^{-t^2}dt.$$

We have

$$\int_0^2 e^{-t^2}dt = \frac{\sqrt{\pi}}{2} - \frac{e^{-4}}{4}\left(1 - \frac{1}{8} + \frac{3}{64} - \frac{15}{512} + \cdots\right)$$

$$= 0.8862 - 0.004579(1 - 0.125 + 0.046875 - 0.029297)$$

$$= 0.8862 - 0.0041 = 0.8821.$$

* See Chauvent's *Spherical and Practical Astronomy*, Vol. I, p. 156.

The error committed is less than

$$0.004579 \times 0.029297 = 0.00013.$$

As a matter of fact, the number 0.8821 is correct to its last figure.

By means of formulas (2) and (6) one could compute a table giving the value of the probability integral for any value of t. Such tables were computed long ago, and a table of this kind is given at the end of this book. This table gives the probability of an error lying between $-t$ and $+t$, where $t = hx$. Since the probability curve is symmetrical with respect to the y-axis, the chance that an error lies between $-t$ and $+t$ is twice the chance that it lies between 0 and $+t$. Hence the probability of such an error is

$$P = \frac{1}{\sqrt{\pi}} \int_{-t}^{t} e^{-t^2} dt = \frac{2}{\sqrt{\pi}} \int_{0}^{t} e^{-t^2} dt,$$

where $t = hx$. The use of the table will be explained in working the examples in the next article.

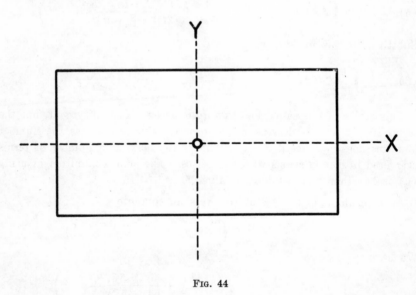

Fig. 44

124. The Probability of Hitting a Target. Suppose we take a rectangular target and draw through its geometric center two lines at right angles to each other and parallel to the sides of the target, as indicated in Fig. 44. Suppose, further, that we set up this target in a vertical plane at a convenient distance away and shoot at it 100 times with a good rifle. If the rifle is accurately aimed at the intersection of the dotted lines, the hits will be distributed symmetrically above and below the horizontal dotted line and to the right and left of the vertical dotted line, just as in the case of the pencil hits described in Art. 119.

If we take the horizontal line as x-axis, the vertical line as y-axis, and a line through the intersection of these and perpendicular to the plane of the target as z-axis, the hits will be distributed on each side of the vertical line according to the formula

$$(1) \qquad z = \frac{h_x}{\sqrt{\pi}} e^{-h_x^2 x^2} \; ;$$

and they will be distributed above and below the horizontal line according to the equation

$$(2) \qquad z = \frac{h_y}{\sqrt{\pi}} e^{-h_y^2 y^2} \, .$$

The indices of precision h_x and h_y in the two directions may or may not be equal.

Before we can apply formulas (1) and (2) to problems in target practice we must know the values of h_x and h_y for the particular gun at the given range. The precision of a gun is indicated by its probable error or its mean error (see Art. 133), and these are determined from firings at the proving grounds.

If r and η denote the probable error and the mean error, respectively, we have (see Art. 133)

$$h = \frac{0.4769}{r} = \frac{0.5642}{\eta} \, .$$

Hence

$$(3) \qquad hx = \frac{0.4769x}{r} = \frac{0.5642x}{\eta} \, .$$

Note. When using the probability table for the solution of target problems the student must keep in mind the fact that the argument for this table is hx, where x is the given or allowable error; but since $hx = 0.4769x/r = 0.5642x/\eta$, it is evident that the proper argument for entering the table is

$$(a) \qquad \frac{0.4769x}{r}$$

when the *probable* error of the gun is given, and

(b) $$\frac{0.5642x}{\eta}$$

when the *mean* error of the gun is given.

Example 1. For a certain 3-inch gun at a range of 4000 yards the probable errors were $r_x = 10.4$ yards and $r_y = 5.8$ yards. Find the probability of hitting at the first shot a rectangular target 18 ft. high and 30 ft. long.

Solution. The probability that the shot will land in a vertical strip 10 yds. wide is

$$P_x = \frac{h_x}{\sqrt{\pi}} \int_{-5}^{5} e^{-h_x^2 x^2} dx = \frac{2}{\sqrt{\pi}} \int_{0}^{5} e^{-(h_x x)^2} d(h_x x) ;$$

and the probability that the same shot will land in a horizontal strip 6 yds. wide is

$$P_y = \frac{h_y}{\sqrt{\pi}} \int_{-3}^{3} e^{-h_y^2 y^2} dy = \frac{2}{\sqrt{\pi}} \int_{0}^{3} e^{-(h_y y)^2} d(h_y y).$$

The chance that the shot will land in both of these strips and therefore hit the target is

$$P = P_x P_y = \frac{2}{\sqrt{\pi}} \int_{0}^{5} e^{-(h_x x)^2} d(h_x x) \times \frac{2}{\sqrt{\pi}} \int_{0}^{3} e^{-(h_y y)^2} d(h_y y).$$

But

$$h_x x = \frac{0.4769x}{r_x} = \frac{0.4769 \times 5}{10.4} = 0.229,$$

by (3), and

$$h_y y = \frac{0.4769y}{r_y} = \frac{0.4769 \times 3}{5.8} = 0.247.$$

Entering the probability table with these values of hx as arguments, we find

$$P_x = 0.254, \quad P_y = 0.273.$$

Hence

$$P = P_x P_y = 0.254 \times 0.273 = 0.0693.$$

It would therefore require on the average about $1/0.0693 = 15$ shots to get a single hit.

Example 2. The mean errors for a certain gun at a range of 3000 yards are

$$\eta_x = 8.3 \text{ yds.}, \quad \eta_y = 4.6 \text{ yds.}$$

If 30 shots are fired at the side of a house 12 yds. wide and 6 yds. high at a distance of 3000 yards,

(a) How many hits may be expected?

(b) What is the chance of hitting a door 6 ft. × 3 ft. in the lower right-hand corner of the side of the house?

Solution. (a) If the gun is accurately aimed at the geometric center of the side of the house, any shot will be a hit if it passes within 6 yards of the central vertical line and within 3 yards of the central horizontal line. Hence we have

$$x = 6 \text{ yds.}, \quad y = 3 \text{ yds.}; \text{ and}$$

$$h_x x = \frac{0.5642x}{\eta_x} = \frac{0.5642 \times 6}{8.3} = 0.407,$$

$$h_y y = \frac{0.5642y}{\eta_y} = \frac{0.5642 \times 3}{4.6} = 0.368.$$

From the probability table we find

$$P_x = 0.435, \quad P_y = 0.397.$$

The chance of a hit for each shot is therefore

$$P = P_x P_y = 0.435 \times 0.397 = 0.173.$$

For 30 shots the number of hits would probably be $30 \times 0.173 = 5.2$ or 5, say.

(b) To find the probability that the door would be hit during the bombardment we assume that the gun is aimed at the geometric center of the side of the house, as in (a). Then the door will be hit if a shot strikes within the rectangle bounded by the lines $x = 5$, $x = 6$, $y = -1$, $y = -3$. The chance of hitting the door at each shot is therefore

$$P = P_x \cdot P_y = \frac{h_x}{\sqrt{\pi}} \int_5^6 e^{-h_x^2 x^2} dx \times \frac{h_y}{\sqrt{\pi}} \int_1^3 e^{-h_y^2 y^2} dy$$

$$= \left[\frac{1}{\sqrt{\pi}} \int_0^6 e^{-(h_x x)^2} d(h_x x) - \frac{1}{\sqrt{\pi}} \int_0^5 e^{-(h_x x)^2} d(h_x x) \right] \left[\frac{1}{\sqrt{\pi}} \int_0^3 e^{-(h_y y)^2} d(h_y y) \right.$$

$$\left. - \frac{1}{\sqrt{\pi}} \int_0^1 e^{-(h_y y)^2} d(h_y y) \right].$$

Hence the two values of $h_x x$ to be used in the probability table are

$$\frac{0.5642}{8.3} \times 6 = 0.407 \quad \text{and} \quad \frac{0.5642}{8.3} \times 5 = 0.340,$$

for which the probabilities are $P_{x6} = 0.435/2$, $P_{x5} = 0.369/2$. Therefore

$$P_x = \frac{0.435}{2} - \frac{0.369}{2} = \frac{0.066}{2}.$$

Likewise, the two values of $h_y y$ are

$$\frac{0.5642}{4.6} \times 3 = 0.368, \qquad \frac{0.5642}{4.6} \times 1 = 0.1226.$$

The corresponding probabilities are found from the table to be

$$P_{y3} = \frac{0.397}{2}, \qquad P_{y1} = \frac{0.138}{2}.$$

Hence $P_y = 0.397/2 - 0.138/2 = 0.159/2$, and we have finally

$$P = P_x \times P_y = \frac{0.066 \times 0.159}{4} = 0.0026.$$

The door will be hit unless every one of the 30 shots misses it. The chance that any shot will miss it is $1 - 0.0026 = 0.9974$. The chance that every one of the 30 shots misses is therefore $(0.9974)^{30} = 0.9249$. The chance of a hit is therefore $1 - 0.9249 = 0.0751$.

The door would probably be hit once out of the every $1/0.0026 = 380$ shots.

Example 3. Find the number of shots necessary to make the odds 10 to 1 in favor of at least one hit on the side of the house mentioned in Example 2.

Solution. The house will certainly be hit at least once unless every shot misses it. The chance that any shot will be a hit was found to be 0.173. The chance that any shot will miss it is therefore $1 - 0.173 = 0.827$. The chance that every one of n shots will miss it is then $(0.827)^n$. The chance of at least one hit is therefore

$$P = 1 - (0.827)^n.$$

Since the odds are to be 10 to 1 in favor of a hit, we have $P = 10/11$. Hence

$$1 - (0.827)^n = \frac{10}{11}, \quad \text{or} \quad (0.827)^n = \frac{1}{11}.$$

$$\therefore \quad n \log (0.827) = - \log 11,$$

or

$$n = \frac{- \log 11}{\log 0.827} = \frac{- 1.0414}{9.9175 - 10} = \frac{- 1.0414}{- 0.0825} = 12.6 = 13, \text{ say.}$$

125. The Principle of Least Squares. Suppose we make a set of n measurements $m_1, m_2, \cdots m_n$ of some object or quantity in an effort to determine as nearly as possible its true magnitude, using the same care, methods, and instruments in making each measurement. If we try to read the measuring instrument to the finest subdivision of its graduated scale and even estimate fractions of a subdivision, we shall find that the results of the several measurements do not agree exactly among themselves, however much care we may use; for each measurement is subject to unavoidable accidental errors. How, then, shall we decide upon the best result obtainable from any given set of measurements or observations?

This question is answered by the *Principle of Least Squares,* which says that the best or most probable value of the measured quantity is that value for which the sum of the squares of the errors is least. This answer is in accord with reason and common sense; for, since the accidental errors are real quantities their squares are positive quantities and the requirement that the sum of these positive quantities shall be as small as possible insures that the errors themselves shall be as small numerically as possible.

Furthermore, the requirement that the sum of the squares of the errors shall be a minimum leads to the result that the arithmetic mean or average of the measurements is the best value obtainable from any set of equally trustworthy direct measurements. This result is also in accord with experience and common sense.

The principle of least squares also follows from the Normal Law of accidental errors, as we shall now show.

If we make a set of measurements all with equal care and use the same methods and instruments for each, the precision constant h of the probability equation will be the same for all the measurements and the frequency of the accidental errors will be given by the same probability curve. If the accidental errors of the n measurements $m_1, m_2, \cdots m_n$ be denoted by $x_1, x_2, \cdots x_n$, respectively, then the respective probabilities of these errors are

$$p_1 = \frac{h}{\sqrt{\pi}} e^{-h^2 x_1^2} dx_1, \quad p_2 = \frac{h}{\sqrt{\pi}} e^{-h^2 x_2^2} dx_2, \cdots p_n = \frac{h}{\sqrt{\pi}} e^{-h^2 x_n^2} dx_n .$$

Since the separate measurements are independent events, the probability that the set of errors $x_1, x_2, \cdots x_n$ will be made is the product of their separate probabilities, or

$$(1) \qquad P = p_1 p_2 \cdots p_n = \left(\frac{h}{\sqrt{\pi}}\right)^n e^{-h^2(x_1^2 + x_2^2 + \cdots + x_n^2)} dx_1 dx_2 \cdots dx_n .$$

Now since small errors occur more frequently than large ones, a set of small errors is a more probable event than a set of large ones in making any set of measurements. Hence the set which has the greatest probability will give us the best or most probable value of the quantity measured; and since the differentials dx_1, dx_2, etc. are perfectly arbitrary quantities (the smallest subdivisions of a graduated scale, for instance) it is evident from equation (1) that this probability P is greatest when the exponent of e is least, that is, when

$$x_1{}^2 + x_2{}^2 + \cdots + x_n{}^2 = \Sigma x^2 \text{ is a minimum.}$$

Thus, by the principles of probability we arrive at the *Principle of Least Squares*, namely:

The best or most probable value obtainable from a set of measurements or observations of equal precision is that value for which the sum of the squares of the errors is a minimum.

Note. Any measurable quantity has a definite, *true* magnitude; and the differences between this unknown magnitude and the several measurements made to determine it are the true errors of those measurements. However, when these errors are required to satisfy the condition that the sum of their squares shall be a minimum, for the purpose of arriving at the most probable magnitude of the quantity, they become residual errors, or simply *residuals* (see Art. 127). But it is shown in Art. 129 that the sum of the squares of the residuals is least when the sum of the squares of the errors is least.

126. Weighted Observations. If the measurements are not of equal precision, the values of h will be different. The probabilities of the errors will then be

$$p_1 = \frac{h_1}{\sqrt{\pi}} e^{-h_1{}^2 x_1{}^2} dx_1, \quad p_2 = \frac{h_2}{\sqrt{\pi}} e^{-h_2{}^2 x_2{}^2} dx_2, \cdots p_n = \frac{h_n}{\sqrt{\pi}} e^{-h_n{}^2 x_n{}^2} dx_n;$$

and the probability of their simultaneous occurrence will be

(1) $\quad P = p_1 p_2 \cdots p_n = \dfrac{h_1 h_2 \cdots h_n}{(\sqrt{\pi})^n} e^{-(h_1{}^2 x_1{}^2 + h_2{}^2 x_2{}^2 + \ldots + h_n{}^2 x_n{}^2)} dx_1 dx_2 \cdots dx_n .$

The best value obtainable from this set of measurements will therefore be that for which

(2) $\qquad \Sigma h^2 x^2 = h_1{}^2 x_1{}^2 + h_2{}^2 x_2{}^2 + \cdots + h_n{}^2 x_n{}^2$ is a minimum.

Since it is not customary in practice to make such an expression as

(2) a minimum, it is necessary to introduce here the idea of *weighted* measurements or observations. By the weight of an observation is meant its relative value or importance when compared with other observations of a set. Thus, if we measure a line three times with the same care and accuracy, we regard the mean of the three measureeents as more reliable than any one of the single measurements. We express this by saying that the weight of the mean is three times that of a single measurement. An observation of weight w is therefore one which is equivalent in importance to w observations of *unit* weight.

To find the relation between weight and precision index let

$$h = \text{precision index corresponding to weight 1,}$$

$$h_1 = \text{precision index corresponding to weight } w_1.$$

Then the probability of an error of magnitude x in the observations of *unit* weight is given by

$$p = \frac{h}{\sqrt{\pi}} e^{-h^2 x^2} dx;$$

and the probability of an error of the *same magnitude* in a set of observations of weight w_1 is

$$p_1 = \frac{h_1}{\sqrt{\pi}} e^{-h_1^2 x^2} dx.$$

The probability of the same error (of magnitude x) in w_1 observations of *unit* weight is

$$P = p \cdot p \cdot p \cdots \text{ to } w_1 \text{ factors} = p^{w_1} = \left(\frac{h}{\sqrt{\pi}}\right)^{w_1} e^{-w_1 h^2 x^2} (dx)^{w_1}.$$

Now if the weighted observation (wt. w_1) is to be worth as much as the w_1 observations of unit weight, an error of magnitude x must have the same probability in it as in the case of the w_1 observations. Hence we must have

$$p_1 = P,$$

or

$$\frac{h_1}{\sqrt{\pi}} e^{-h_1^2 x^2} dx = \left(\frac{h}{\sqrt{\pi}}\right)^{w_1} e^{-w_1 h^2 x^2} (dx)^{w_1}$$

for any x. Taking logarithms to the base e, we have

$$\log_e \frac{h_1}{\sqrt{\pi}} - h_1^2 x^2 = w_1 \log_e \frac{h}{\sqrt{\pi}} - w_1 h^2 x^2 + (w_1 - 1)\log_e dx.$$

Equating coefficients of like powers of x,

$$h_1{}^2 = w_1 h^2, \quad \text{or} \quad w_1 = \frac{h_1{}^2}{h^2}.$$

Likewise, for observations of weights w_2, w_3, etc., we have

$$h_2{}^2 = w_2 h^2, \quad \text{or} \quad w_2 = \frac{h_2{}^2}{h^2};$$

$$h_3{}^2 = w_3 h^2, \quad \text{or} \quad w_3 = \frac{h_3{}^2}{h^2};$$

etc.

The weights are therefore proportional to the squares of the precision indices.

Substituting in (1) the values of $h_1{}^2$, $h_2{}^2$; etc. as given above, we get

$$P = \left(\frac{w_1 w_2 \cdots w_n}{\pi}\right)^{n/2} h^n e^{-h^2(w_1 x_1{}^2 + w_2 x_2{}^2 + \ldots + w_n x_n{}^2)} dx_1 dx_2 \cdots dx_n.$$

In order that P be a maximum we must have

(3) $\Sigma w x^2 = w_1 x_1{}^2 + w_2 x_2{}^2 + \cdots + w_n x_n{}^2$ a minimum.

We can now state the Principle of Least Squares in its most general form:

The best value of an unknown quantity that can be obtained from a set of measurements of unequal precision is that which makes the sum of the weighted squares of the errors a minimum.

127. Residuals. In the preceding articles of the present chapter we have been discussing the *errors* of observations and measurements. The true or exact magnitude of a quantity can not be found by measurement; for the unit of measurement and the quantity to be measured are, in general, incommensurable. Moreover, all measurements are subject to errors of some kind. It is obvious, therefore, that the *error* of a measurement can never be determined, the error being defined as the true value minus the measured value. What we actually do, and all we can do, is to measure the quantity as many times as may be desirable or convenient and then find from these measurements the *most probable* value of the measured quantity. The difference between the most probable value and any particular measurement is called the *residual* for that measurement. For consistency in sign we always write

Error = True Value — Measured Value.

Residual = Most Probable Value — Measured Value.

Let m_0 denote the most probable value of a measured quantity and let $m_1, m_2, \cdots m_n$ denote the values of n separate measurements. Then if $v_1, v_2, \cdots v_n$ denote the residuals of these measurements, we have by definition

$$v_1 = m_0 - m_1,$$
$$v_2 = m_0 - m_2,$$
$$\cdots \cdots$$
$$v_n = m_0 - m_n.$$

128. The Most Probable Value of a Set of Direct Measurements. The definition of residuals leads us up to the problem of finding the most probable value of a set of measurements. Suppose we make n direct measurements on some unknown magnitude, how shall we determine the best value of the magnitude, on the basis of the n measurements? To give a general answer to this question we shall first assume that the measurements are of unequal weight.

Let $m_1, m_2, \cdots m_n$ denote the n measurements and let $w_1, w_2, \cdots w_n$ denote their respective weights. Then if m denote the true value of the unknown magnitude, the *errors* of the several measurements are

$$x_1 = m - m_1, \ x_2 = m - m_2, \cdots x_n = m - m_n.$$

Now the true value m is unknown and can not be found, but we must adopt *some* value for it. The principle of least squares says that the best value is that which makes the sum of the weighted squares of the errors a minimum (Art. 126); that is,

$$(1) \quad f(m) = w_1(m - m_1)^2 + w_2(m - m_2)^2 + \cdots + w_n(m - m_n)^2$$

must be a minimum.

Differentiating (1) with respect to m, putting the derivative equal to zero, and replacing m by m_0, which is to be the adopted value of m, we have

$$w_1(m_0 - m_1) + w_2(m_0 - m_2) + \cdots + w_n(m_0 - m_n) = 0,$$

from which

$$(128. 1) \quad m_0 = \frac{w_1 m_1 + w_2 m_2 + \cdots + w_n m_n}{w_1 + w_2 + \cdots + w_n} = \frac{\sum wm}{\sum w}.$$

This value m_0 is called the *weighted mean* of the several measurements.

If all the measurements are of equal weight, then $w_1 = w_2 = \cdots = w_n$, and (128. 1) reduces to

$$(128. 2) \qquad m_0 = \frac{m_1 + m_2 + \cdots + m_n}{n} \,,$$

which is simply the *average* of all the measurements. This result is in accord with experience and common sense.

Formulas (128. 1) and (128. 2) enable us to prove the following important theorem:

In any set of measurements of equal weight the algebraic sum of the residuals is zero, and in a set of measurements of unequal weight the algebraic sum of the weighted residuals is zero.

To prove this theorem let m_0 denote the most probable value of the n measurements $m_1, m_2, \cdots m_n$; and let $v_1, v_2, \cdots v_n$ denote the residuals. Then

$$v_1 = m_0 - m_1,$$
$$v_2 = m_0 - m_2,$$
$$\cdot \quad \cdot \quad \cdot \quad \cdot \quad \cdot \quad \cdot$$
$$v_n = m_0 - m_n \,.$$

Adding these n equations, we get

$$v_1 + v_2 + \cdots + v_n = nm_0 - (m_1 + m_2 + \cdots + m_n)$$
$$= nm_0 - nm_0 = 0, \text{ by (128. 2)}.$$

To prove the second part of the theorem let $w_1, w_2, \cdots w_n$ denote the weights of the several measurements. The weighted residuals are

$$w_1 v_1 = w_1 m_0 - w_1 m_1 \,,$$
$$w_2 v_2 = w_2 m_0 - w_2 m_2 \,,$$
$$\cdot \quad \cdot \quad \cdot \quad \cdot \quad \cdot \quad \cdot \quad \cdot$$
$$w_n v_n = w_n m_0 - w_n m_n \,.$$

Adding these n equations, as before, we get

$$w_1 v_1 + w_2 v_2 + \cdots w_n v_n = m_0(w_1 + w_2 + \cdots w_n) - (w_1 m_1 + w_2 m_2 + \cdots)$$
$$= 0, \text{ by (128. 1)}.$$

This theorem provides us with a valuable check on the computed residuals in any set of measurements. However, since the residuals in such cases are rounded numbers their algebraic sum will rarely be exactly zero.

129. Law of Error for Residuals. We shall now show that when the errors of a set of measurements follow the Normal Law of error, the residuals likewise follow a similar law. To prove this let m denote the true value of the measured quantity; m_0 the most probable value; $\epsilon_1, \epsilon_2, \cdots \epsilon_n$ the errors of measurement; $v_1, v_2, \cdots v_n$ the residuals; and $w_1, w_2, \cdots w_n$ the weights. Then

$$(v) \qquad\qquad\qquad\qquad (\epsilon)$$

$$v_1 = m_0 - m_1, \qquad\qquad \epsilon_1 = m - m_1,$$
$$v_2 = m_0 - m_2, \qquad\qquad \epsilon_2 = m - m_2,$$
$$\cdots\cdots\cdots \qquad\qquad \cdots\cdots\cdots$$
$$v_n = m_0 - m_n. \qquad\qquad \epsilon_n = m - m_n.$$

For the case of measurements of equal weight we have from column (v)

$$\Sigma v = nm_0 - \Sigma m = 0, \quad \text{or} \quad m_0 = \frac{\Sigma m}{n};$$

and from column (ϵ) we get in a similar manner

$$\Sigma \epsilon = nm - \Sigma m, \quad \text{or} \quad \Sigma m = nm - \Sigma \epsilon.$$

Substituting this value of Σm in the equation $m_0 = \Sigma m/n$, we get

$$(1) \qquad m_0 = \frac{nm - \Sigma \epsilon}{n} = m - \frac{\Sigma \epsilon}{n}.$$

Now substituting this value of m_0 in the equations of column (v), we have

$$(2) \qquad v_1 = m - \frac{1}{n} \Sigma \epsilon - m_1 = m - m_1 - \frac{1}{n} \Sigma \epsilon = \epsilon_1 - \frac{1}{n} \Sigma \epsilon$$

$$= \epsilon_1 - \frac{1}{n} \epsilon_1 - \frac{1}{n} \epsilon_2 - \cdots - \frac{1}{n} \epsilon_n,$$

or

$$v_1 = \left(\frac{n-1}{n}\right) \epsilon_1 - \frac{1}{n} \epsilon_2 - \frac{1}{n} \epsilon_3 - \cdots - \frac{1}{n} \epsilon_n.$$

Similarly,

$$v_2 = -\frac{1}{n} \epsilon_1 + \left(\frac{n-1}{n}\right) \epsilon_2 - \frac{1}{n} \epsilon_3 - \cdots - \frac{1}{n} \epsilon_n,$$

$$\cdots\cdots\cdots\cdots\cdots\cdots\cdots\cdots\cdots$$

$$v_n = -\frac{1}{n} \epsilon_1 - \frac{1}{n} \epsilon_2 - \cdots + \left(\frac{n-1}{n}\right) \epsilon_n.$$

We have thus proved that the residuals are linear functions of the errors. Hence by Art. 122 they follow the Normal Law.

If h is the precision index for the ϵ's and H that for the v's, we have from (122.1)

$$\frac{1}{H^2} = \frac{\left(\dfrac{n-1}{n}\right)^2}{h^2} + \frac{\dfrac{1}{n^2}}{h^2} + \cdots + \frac{\dfrac{1}{n^2}}{h^2} = \frac{1}{n^2 h^2} \left[(n-1)^2 + n - 1 \right],$$

or

$$\frac{1}{H^2} = \frac{n-1}{n} \frac{1}{h^2}.$$

Hence

(3)
$$H = h \sqrt{\frac{n}{n-1}}.$$

Since the residuals follow the Normal Law, the probability equation for them is

(4)
$$y = \frac{H}{\sqrt{\pi}} e^{-H^2 v^2}$$

From (3) it is plain that the precision index for the residuals is a function of both h and n, and that it is always larger than h. This means that the graph of (4) rises higher in the middle and falls off more rapidly on each side than does the graph of (121.1). As the number of measurements increases, the graph of (4) approaches that of (121.1) more and more closely, and would ultimately coincide with it if the number of measurements were increased indefinitely.

When the measurements are of unequal weight, the weighted residuals and weighted errors are as given in the columns (wv) and $(w\epsilon)$ below.

(wv)	$(w\epsilon)$
$w_1 v_1 = w_1 m_0 - w_1 m_1 ,$	$w_1 \epsilon_1 = w_1 m - w_1 m_1 ,$
$w_2 v_2 = w_2 m_0 - w_2 m_2 ,$	$w_2 \epsilon_2 = w_2 m - w_2 m_2 ,$
$\cdots \cdots \cdots$	$\cdots \cdots \cdots$
$w_n v_n = w_1 m_0 - w_n m_n .$	$w_n \epsilon_n = w_n m - w_n w_n .$

On adding the equations (wv) we get

$$\Sigma wv = m_0 \Sigma w - \Sigma wm = 0, \text{ by (128.1).}$$

$$\therefore \quad m_0 = \frac{\Sigma wm}{\Sigma w}.$$

By adding the equations in column $(w\epsilon)$ we obtain

$$\Sigma w\epsilon = m \Sigma w - \Sigma wm, \text{ or } \Sigma wm = m \Sigma w - \Sigma w\epsilon.$$

Substituting this value of Σwm in the expression for m_0 above, we get

(5) $$m_0 = \frac{m\,\Sigma w - \Sigma w\epsilon}{\Sigma w} = m - \frac{\Sigma w\epsilon}{\Sigma w}.$$

Hence

(6) $$v_1 = m_0 - m_1 = m - m_1 - \frac{\Sigma w\epsilon}{\Sigma w} = \epsilon_1 - \frac{\Sigma w\epsilon}{\Sigma w}$$

$$= \epsilon_1 - \frac{w_1\epsilon_1}{\Sigma w} - \frac{w_2\epsilon_2}{\Sigma w} - \frac{w_3\epsilon_3}{\Sigma w} - \cdots - \frac{w_n\epsilon_n}{\Sigma w},$$

or

$$v_1 = \left(1 - \frac{w_1}{\Sigma w}\right)\epsilon_1 - \frac{w_2}{\Sigma w}\epsilon_2 - \frac{w_3}{\Sigma w}\epsilon_3 - \cdots - \frac{w_n}{\Sigma w}\epsilon_n.$$

Similarly,

$$v_2 = -\frac{w_1}{\Sigma w}\epsilon_1 + \left(1 - \frac{w_2}{\Sigma w}\right)\epsilon_2 - \frac{w_3}{\Sigma w}\epsilon_3 - \cdots - \frac{w_n}{\Sigma w}\epsilon_n,$$

etc.

Hence in the case of measurements of unequal weight the residuals are linear functions of the errors and therefore follow the Normal Law. The residual v_1, for example, would follow the law

$$y = \frac{H_1}{\sqrt{\pi}} e^{-H_1^2 v_1^2},$$

where

$$\frac{1}{H_1^2} = \frac{1}{(\Sigma w)^2}\left[\frac{(\Sigma w - w_1)^2}{h_1^2} + \frac{w_2^2}{h_2^2} + \cdots + \frac{w_n^2}{h_n^2}\right].$$

And similarly for the other residuals.

On squaring and adding the n equations $v_1 = \epsilon_1 - (1/n)\Sigma\epsilon$, $v_2 = \epsilon_2 - (1/n)\Sigma\epsilon$, etc., we obtain

(7) $$\Sigma v^2 = \Sigma\epsilon^2 - \frac{1}{n}(\Sigma\epsilon)^2,$$

which gives the relation between the sum of the squares of the residuals and the sum of the squares of the true errors in any set of measurements of equal weight. Since both terms in the right member of (7) are positive quantities, it is evident that the sum of the squares of the residuals is always less than the sum of the squares of the errors, but that the difference is very slight.

Inasmuch as the quantity $\Sigma\epsilon$ is very nearly zero in any set of measurements, the square of this quantity is still smaller and $(1/n)(\Sigma\epsilon)^2$ is practically negligible in comparison with $\Sigma\epsilon^2$. Hence any small shift in the values of the ϵ's would have very little effect on the already negligible quantity $(1/n)(\Sigma\epsilon)^2$. We may therefore consider this quantity constant for small changes in the ϵ's, and then it is plain that Σv^2 is least when $\Sigma\epsilon^2$ is least.

This can also be shown in a different way. From equation (7) we have

$$\Sigma v^2 = \Sigma\epsilon^2 - \frac{(\epsilon_1 + \epsilon_2 + \cdots + \epsilon_n)^2}{n}$$

$$= \Sigma\epsilon^2 - \frac{(\epsilon_1{}^2 + \epsilon_2{}^2 + \cdots + \epsilon_n{}^2 + 2\epsilon_1\epsilon_2 + 2\epsilon_1\epsilon_3 + \cdots + 2\epsilon_{n-1}\epsilon_n)}{n}.$$

Now when the number of measurements is large, the product terms $2\epsilon_1\epsilon_2$, $2\epsilon_1\epsilon_3$, etc. will be about half positive and half negative; and they will average about the same size. Hence they will cancel one another for the most part and then Σv^2 reduces to

$$\Sigma v^2 = \Sigma\epsilon^2 - \frac{(\epsilon_1{}^2 + \epsilon_2{}^2 + \cdots + \epsilon_n{}^2)}{n}$$

$$= \Sigma\epsilon^2 - \frac{\Sigma\epsilon^2}{n} = \left(\frac{n-1}{n}\right)\Sigma\epsilon^2.$$

From the foregoing considerations we are justified in asserting that

The sum of the squares of the residuals is a minimum when the sum of the squares of the true errors is a minimum, and conversely.

In a similar manner, on squaring the n equations $v_1 = \epsilon_1 - \Sigma w\epsilon/\Sigma w$, $v_2 = \epsilon_2 - \Sigma w\epsilon/\Sigma w$, etc., then multiplying the squared equations by the corresponding weights w_1, w_2, etc. and adding the results, we get

$$(8) \qquad \Sigma w v^2 = \Sigma w\epsilon^2 - \frac{1}{\Sigma w}(\Sigma w\epsilon)^2.$$

Here, again, we see that the sum of the weighted squares of the residuals is a minimum when the sum of the weighted squares of the true errors is a minimum, and conversely, since the negligible quantity $(1/\Sigma w)(\Sigma w\epsilon)^2$ may be considered constant for small changes in the ϵ's.

Remarks. Equation (1) shows that the arithmetic mean is equal to the true value of the quantity minus a very small quantity; for since the errors are as likely to be positive as negative the quantity $\Sigma\epsilon$ is not large, and $(1/n)\Sigma\epsilon$ is still smaller. Hence the larger the number of measurements the nearer does m_0 approach the true value of the quantity measured. Equation (5) shows a similar result in the case of weighted measurements.

Equations (2) and (6) show that any residual is equal to the corresponding error minus a very small quantity. Therefore when the number of measurements is large the residuals are practically equal to the true errors. Hence, although we can never determine the true magnitude of a measured quantity we can determine it as closely as we please by taking enough measurements.

130. Agreement between Theory and Experience. At the beginning of this chapter we described an experiment which was designed to show the behavior and distribution of accidental errors. In deriving the Probability Equation we made the assumptions that the probability of an error depended upon its size and that positive and negative errors of the same size were equally likely. These two assumptions were supported by the pencil experiment. The first is based upon experience, but the second is evident on purely *a priori* grounds and also supported by experience. No rigorous deduction of the Normal Law, based upon purely *a priori* considerations, has ever been given. The truth is that, for the kinds of errors considered in this book (errors of measurement and observation), the Normal Law is *proved by experience.* Several substitutes for this law have been proposed, but none fits the facts so well as it does.

To show how well the Normal Law agrees with experience when the number of measurements is large, we give in the table below the results of 470 observations made by Bradley on the right ascensions of the stars Sirius and Altair.

Size of errors	Number computed from theory	Number actually found
$0''.0$ to $0''.1$	95	94
$0''.1$ to $0''.2$	89	88
$0''.2$ to $0''.3$	78	78
$0''.3$ to $0''.4$	64	58
$0''.4$ to $0''.5$	50	51
$0''.5$ to $0''.6$	36	36
$0''.6$ to $0''.7$	24	26
$0''.7$ to $0''.8$	15	14
$0''.8$ to $0''.9$	9	10
$0''.9$ to $1''.0$	5	7
over $1''.0$	5	8

It will be seen that the agreement between theory and experience is remarkably close, with the exception of the number of errors of magnitude from $0''.3$ to $0''.4$.

EXERCISES XIII

1. Compute the value of the integral $\int_0^{1/3} e^{-t^2} dt$ correct to seven decimal places.

2. Compute the value of $\int_0^{2.2} e^{-t^2} dt$ correct to five decimal places.

3. Find the probability of hitting at the first shot a rectangular target 60 feet wide and 24 feet high at a distance of 4000 yards, the mean errors for the gun at this range being

$$\eta_x = 7.4 \text{ yds.}, \quad \eta_y = 5.2 \text{ yds.}$$

4. If 20 shots are fired at a cylindrical standpipe 120 feet high and 40 feet in diameter at a distance of three miles, find the chance that the standpipe will be hit if the probable errors of the gun for this range are

$$r_x = 14.2 \text{ feet}, \quad r_y = 10.6 \text{ feet.}$$

5. If the foretop of a battleship is a cylinder 12 feet in diameter and 8 feet high, find the chance that it will be hit by a shot aimed at a point 80 feet directly below, the mean errors for the gun in this case being

$$\eta_x = 42.6 \text{ feet}, \quad \eta_y = 36.5 \text{ feet.}$$

About how many shots would have to be fired at the ship (aimed at a point 80 feet below the foretop) before the foretop would be hit?

6. Twelve measurements of the length of a line are given below. Find the most probable length of the line.

364.2	364.2	364.3
364.4	363.7	363.8
363.9	364.1	364.3
364.3	364.5	364.0

7. Seven measurements of an object by different methods are given in the following table. If the weights of the different measurements are as given in the table, find the most probable size of the object.

Measurements	Weights
369.2	2
368.3	1
371.1	3
370.2	5
369.1	2
370.6	4
372.2	1

Compute the residuals and weighted residuals. Find the algebraic sum of the weighted residuals and the sum of the weighted squares of the residuals.

CHAPTER XV

THE PRECISION OF MEASUREMENTS

131. Measurements, Direct and Indirect. Direct measurements are those made by methods and instruments whose indications give directly the quantity sought. Such measurements are usually made by reading a scale graduated in terms of the chosen unit. Yard sticks, clocks, voltmeters, chemical balances, etc. are instruments for making direct measurements.

Indirect measurements are those in which the quantity measured is not given directly by observation or readings taken, but must be calculated from them. Thus, in an indirect measurement the quantity sought is a function of one or more directly measured quantities. For example, if we measure two sides and the included angle of a plane triangle we can find the remaining side and the area by means of the formulas

$$a = \sqrt{b^2 + c^2 - 2bc \cos A}, \qquad \text{Area} = \tfrac{1}{2}bc \sin A.$$

Here the directly measured quantities are b, c, A, and the indirectly measured (computed) ones are a and the area.

The relation between observed and computed quantities may be expressed by the general formula

$$y = f(x_1, x_2, x_3, \cdots a, b, c, \cdots),$$

where y and the x's represent observed or computed quantities and a, b, c, etc. represent numerical constants.

132. Precision and Accuracy. The words " precision " and " accuracy," when used in the discussion of measurements, have quite different meanings. Precision has to do with *accidental* errors, and a precise measurement would be one free from accidental errors. An accurate measurement, on the other hand, would be one free from all kinds of errors—mistakes, systematic errors, and accidental errors. Barring mistakes, the systematic error is thus the difference between the precise value and the accurate or true value of the quantity measured. If the systematic error should happen to be large, a precise measurement might be very inaccurate. The accuracy of a measurement can be increased by using more refined instruments and methods, whereas the precision can be increased only by using more care in making the measurement.

411

I. DIRECT MEASUREMENTS.

133. Measures of Precision. The precision of a measurement can be estimated in several ways. The three *measures of precision* in common use are the following: the *mean square error* (M.S.E.), the *probable error* (P.E.), and the *average error*. These three measures are denoted by the letters μ, r, and η, respectively. We shall now derive expressions for them in terms of the precision index h.

(*a*). *The Mean Square Error* (M.S.E.). In discussing the error equation

$$y = \frac{h}{\sqrt{\pi}} e^{-h^2 x^2}$$

in Art. 121, we stated that h is called the index of precision and indicated the reason for this name. Then in Art. 125 we found that the probability of the simultaneous occurrence of a set of errors $x_1, x_2, \cdots x_n$ in a given measurement is

(1) $P = p_1 p_2 \cdots p_n = \left(\frac{h}{\sqrt{\pi}} \right)^n e^{-h^2(x_1^2 + x_2^2 + \ldots + x_n^2)} dx_1 dx_2 \cdots dx_n$.

It was also shown in that article that the best or most probable result obtainable from a set of measurements is that corresponding to the maximum value of P.

Let us now assume that a given set of n measurements has been made and let us try to find the best or most probable value of the precision index h for this set of measurements. It is that value which makes P a maximum and is found by differentiating P with respect to h and putting the derivative equal to zero. We thus get from (1)

$$\frac{dP}{dh} = \left(\frac{h}{\sqrt{\pi}} \right)^n e^{-h^2(x_1^2 + x_2^2 + \ldots)} [- 2h (x_1^2 + x_2^2 + \cdots + x_n^2)]$$
$$+ e^{-h^2(x_1^2 + x_2^2 + \ldots)} n \left(\frac{h}{\sqrt{\pi}} \right)^{n-1} \frac{1}{\sqrt{\pi}} = 0,$$

or

$$e^{-h^2(x_1^2 + x_2^2 + \ldots)} \left(\frac{h}{\sqrt{\pi}} \right)^{n-1} \frac{1}{\sqrt{\pi}} [- 2h^2 (x_1^2 + x_2^2 + \cdots + x_n^2) + n] = 0.$$

$$\therefore \quad - 2h^2 (x_1^2 + x_2^2 + \cdots + x_n^2) + n = 0,$$

or

$$\frac{1}{2h^2} = \frac{x_1^2 + x_2^2 + \cdots + x_n^2}{n},$$

from which

$$\frac{1}{h\sqrt{2}} = \sqrt{\frac{x_1^2 + x_2^2 + \cdots + x_n^2}{n}}$$

The quantity on the right is usually called the *mean square error* (M.S.E.) of a single observation and is denoted by the Greek letter μ. We therefore have

(2) $$\mu = \frac{1}{h\sqrt{2}} = \sqrt{\frac{x_1{}^2 + x_2{}^2 + \cdots + x_n{}^2}{n}}.$$

(*b*). *The Probable Error* (P.E.). The *probable error*, r, of a single measurement of a series is a quantity such that one half the errors of the series are greater than it and the other half less than it. In other words, the probability that the error of a single measurement will fall between r and $-r$ is $\frac{1}{2}$, and the probability that it will fall outside these limits is $\frac{1}{2}$. Hence we must have

$$\int_{-r}^{+r} \frac{h}{\sqrt{\pi}}\, e^{-h^2 x^2} dx = \frac{1}{2}, \quad \text{or} \quad \frac{h}{\sqrt{\pi}} \int_0^r e^{-h^2 x^2} dx = \frac{1}{4},$$

since the probability that an error lies between any given limits is represented by the area under the probability curve between those limits.

To find the value of r from the above equation we put

$$t = hx.$$

Then

$$dt = h\, dx,$$

and we have

$$\int_0^{hr} e^{-t^2} dt = \frac{\sqrt{\pi}}{4}, \quad \text{or} \quad \int_0^\rho e^{-t^2} dt = 0.4431135, \quad \text{where} \quad \rho = hr.$$

Now

$$e^{-t^2} = 1 - t^2 + \frac{t^4}{2} - \frac{t^6}{6} + \frac{t^8}{24} - \frac{t^{10}}{120} \cdots.$$

$$\therefore \int_0^\rho e^{-t^2} dt = \int_0^\rho \left(1 - t^2 + \frac{t^4}{2} - \frac{t^6}{6} + \frac{t^8}{24} - \frac{t^{10}}{120} + \cdots\right) dt = 0.4431135,$$

or

(3) $$\rho - \frac{\rho^3}{3} + \frac{\rho^5}{10} - \frac{\rho^7}{42} + \frac{\rho^9}{216} - \frac{\rho^{11}}{1320} - 0.4431135 = 0.$$

This is the equation which we have already solved in Art. 70 and found $\rho = 0.4769363$. The value of ρ can also be found by interpolation, as we have already done in two ways in Ex. 2, Art. 26 and Ex. 1, Art. 29.

Using now the relation $\rho = hr$, we get

$$r = \frac{\rho}{h} = \frac{0.4769}{h} = 0.4769\left(\frac{1}{h}\right);$$

and from (2) we have

$$\frac{1}{h} = \sqrt{2} \sqrt{\frac{x_1^2 + x_2^2 + \cdots + x_n^2}{n}}.$$

Hence

$$r = 0.4769\sqrt{2} \sqrt{\frac{x_1^2 + x_2^2 + \cdots + x_n^2}{n}}$$

$$= 0.6745 \sqrt{\frac{x_1^2 + x_2^2 + \cdots + x_n^2}{n}},$$

or

(4) $$r = 0.6745 \sqrt{\frac{x_1^2 + x_2^2 + \cdots + x_n^2}{n}}.$$

(c). *The average error* is the arithmetic mean of all the errors of a set, without regard to signs. Thus,

(5) $$\eta = \frac{|x_1| + |x_2| + \cdots + |x_n|}{n}.$$

To find an expression for η in terms of h let us suppose that a set of n measurements has been made, and that each measurement is affected with an error of some size. In the case of any single measurement the probability of an error of magnitude x to $x + \Delta x$ is approximately $y\Delta x = (h/\sqrt{\pi})e^{-h^2x^2}\Delta x$ (Art. 120). Hence the probable *number* of errors of this size in the n measurements is n times this probability, or $(nh/\sqrt{\pi})e^{-h^2x^2}\Delta x$. The *sum* of these errors is therefore the number of errors times the size of a single error, or $(nhx/\sqrt{\pi})e^{-h^2x^2}\Delta x$. The sum of all the errors of all sizes is therefore

$$S = \int_{-\infty}^{\infty} \frac{nhx}{\sqrt{\pi}} e^{-h^2x^2} dx = \frac{2nh}{\sqrt{\pi}} \int_0^{\infty} e^{-h^2x^2} x dx$$

$$= -\frac{n}{h\sqrt{\pi}} \int_0^{\infty} e^{-h^2x^2}(-2h^2x dx) = -\frac{n}{h\sqrt{\pi}} \left[e^{-h^2x^2} \right]_0^{\infty},$$

or

$$S = \frac{n}{h\sqrt{\pi}}.$$

Hence

(6) $$\eta = \frac{S}{n} = \frac{1}{h\sqrt{\pi}}.$$

134. Relations between the Precision Measures. From (2) and (4) of Art. 133 we have

(1) $$r = 0.6745\mu = \tfrac{2}{3}\mu, \text{ roughly,}$$

and

(2)
$$\mu = \frac{r}{0.6745} = 1.4826r.$$

Also, since

$$\frac{1}{h} = \sqrt{2} \sqrt{\frac{x_1{}^2 + x_2{}^2 + \cdots + x_n{}^2}{n}} = \mu\sqrt{2},$$

we have

(3)
$$\eta = \frac{1}{h} \cdot \frac{1}{\sqrt{\pi}} = \mu \sqrt{\frac{2}{\pi}} = 0.79788\mu$$

$$= 0.8\mu, \text{ approximately.}$$

Hence

(4)
$$\mu = \frac{\eta}{0.79788} = 1.2533\eta.$$

Furthermore, from (2) and (4) we get

$$1.4826r = 1.2533\eta.$$

(5)
$$\therefore \quad r = \frac{1.2533}{1.4826}\eta = 0.8453\eta,$$

and

(6)
$$\eta = \frac{1.4826}{1.2533} r = 1.1829r.$$

All these relations are shown concisely in the following table:

	μ	r	η
$\mu =$	1.0000	1.4826	1.2533
$r =$	0.6745	1.0000	0.8453
$\eta =$	0.7979	1.1829	1.0000

135. Geometric Significance of μ, r, and η. From the definition of r it follows that its corresponding ordinate to the probability curve bisects the area under that curve on either side of the y-axis.

The quantity μ is the abscissa of the point of inflection of the probability curve, as we shall now show.

Taking the second derivative of

$$y = \frac{h}{\sqrt{\pi}} e^{-h^2 x^2}$$

and equating it to zero, we have

$$\frac{dy}{dx} = -\frac{2h^3}{\sqrt{\pi}}\,(xe^{-h^2x^2}),$$

$$\frac{d^2y}{dx^2} = -\frac{2h^3}{\sqrt{\pi}}\,e^{-h^2x^2}(1 - 2h^2x^2) = 0.$$

Hence

$$1 - 2h^2x^2 = 0,$$

or

$$x = \pm\frac{1}{h\sqrt{2}} = \pm\mu.$$

The precision measure η is the abscissa of the center of gravity of the area (under the curve) on either side of the y-axis. To prove this we

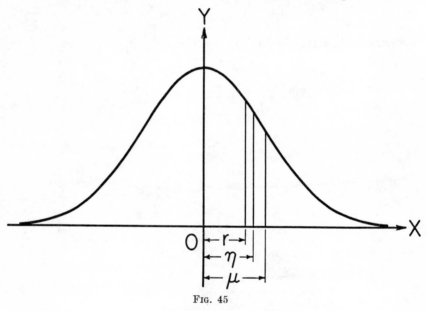

FIG. 45

recall that if x_0 denote the abscissa of the center of gravity of that area we have

$$x_0 = \frac{\displaystyle\int xy\,dx}{\displaystyle\int y\,dx} = \frac{\displaystyle\int_0^\infty x\,\frac{h}{\sqrt{\pi}}e^{-h^2x^2}dx}{\text{area}} = \frac{-\dfrac{1}{2h\sqrt{\pi}}\displaystyle\int_0^\infty e^{-h^2x^2}(-2h^2x)\,dx}{1/2}$$

$$= -\frac{1}{h\sqrt{\pi}}\Big[\,e^{-h^2x^2}\,\Big]_0^\infty = \frac{1}{h\sqrt{\pi}} = \eta\,.$$

The relative sizes of the precision measures and their geometric relations are shown in Fig. 45.

The question naturally arises as to which precision measure is the best for practical use. On this point there is no universal agreement. In continental Europe the M.S.E. is used almost exclusively, but in England and America the P.E. is more often used. The average error is also used in America, but usually under the name *average deviation*.

The M.S.E. is used almost exclusively in Mathematical Statistics, where it is called the *standard deviation* and denoted by σ.

The average error is the easiest of all to compute, and the P.E. is the most laborious, because of the factor 0.6745. Nevertheless, in this book we shall conform to American practice and use the P.E. almost exclusively.

136. Relation between Probable Error and Weight, and the Probable Error of the Arithmetic and Weighted Means. In Art. 126 we derived the relation between the precision index h and the weight w of an observation, namely:

(136. 1)
$$\frac{h_1{}^2}{w_1} = \frac{h_2{}^2}{w_2} = \frac{h_3{}^2}{w_3} = \cdot \cdot \cdot = \frac{h_n{}^2}{w_n} .$$

Then in Art. 133 we found the relation

$$r = \frac{\rho}{h}, \quad \text{where} \quad \rho = 0.4769.$$

Hence

$$h = \frac{\rho}{r} .$$

Let $w_1, w_2, \cdot \cdot \cdot w_n$ be the weights of observations whose probable errors are $r_1, r_2, \cdot \cdot \cdot r_n$, respectively. Then

$$h_1 = \frac{\rho}{r_1}, \quad h_2 = \frac{\rho}{r_2}, \cdot \cdot \cdot h_n = \frac{\rho}{r_n} .$$

Substituting these values for $h_1, h_2, \cdot \cdot \cdot h_n$ in (136. 1), we get

$$\frac{\rho^2}{r_1{}^2 w_1} = \frac{\rho^2}{r_2{}^2 w_2} = \cdot \cdot \cdot = \frac{\rho^2}{r_n{}^2 w_n} ,$$

or

$$\frac{1}{r_1{}^2 w_1} = \frac{1}{r_2{}^2 w_2} = \cdot \cdot \cdot = \frac{1}{r_n{}^2 w_n} .$$

Hence

(136. 2)
$$\frac{w_1}{w_2} = \frac{r_2{}^2}{r_1{}^2}, \quad \text{etc.}$$

The weights are thus inversely proportional to the squares of the probable errors.

This relation (136.2) enables us to find the P.E. of the arithmetic and weighted means of a set of n direct measurements.

To find the P.E. of the arithmetic mean of n direct measurements of *equal* weight, let the weight of each measurement be 1. Then the weight of the mean of all the measurements will be n. Denoting by r the P.E. of any single measurement and by r_0 the P.E. of the mean of all the measurements, we have from (136.2)

$$\frac{1}{n} = \frac{r_0{}^2}{r^2}, \quad \text{or} \quad r_0{}^2 = \frac{r^2}{n}.$$

Hence the P.E. of the mean is

(136.3) $$r_0 = \frac{r}{\sqrt{n}}.$$

If the measurements are not all of equal weight, let $w_1, w_2, \cdots w_n$ denote their weights. Then if r denote the P.E. of a measurement of *unit* weight $(w = 1)$ and r_i the P.E. of a measurement of weight w_i, we have from (136.2)

$$\frac{1}{w_i} = \frac{r_i{}^2}{r^2}, \quad \text{or} \quad r_i{}^2 = \frac{r^2}{w_i}.$$

Hence

(136.4) $$r_i = \frac{r}{\sqrt{w_i}}.$$

Now the weight of the weighted mean is $\Sigma w = w_1 + w_2 + \cdots + w_n$. Hence by (136.4) the P.E. of this mean is

(136.5) $$r_0 = \frac{r}{\sqrt{\Sigma w}} = \frac{r}{\sqrt{w_1 + w_2 + \cdots + w_n}}.$$

Formula (136.3) shows that the P.E. of the arithmetic mean can be decreased by increasing the number of measurements. A glance at the graph of this equation shows, however, (see Fig. 46) that the decrease is very slight after several measurements have been made. Usually it does not pay to make more than ten measurements for the purpose of reducing the P.E. of the arithmetic mean.

137. Computation of the Precision Measures from the Residuals. So far in our discussion of precision we have been considering the *errors* of measurements. Since the true errors can not be found, it is necessary to derive formulas for the precision measures in terms of the residuals.

In Art. 129 it was shown that when the errors of a set of measurements follow the Normal Law of error, the residuals likewise follow a similar law. The probability equation for any residual will therefore be of the form

(1) $$y = \frac{H}{\sqrt{\pi}} e^{-H^2 v^2}$$

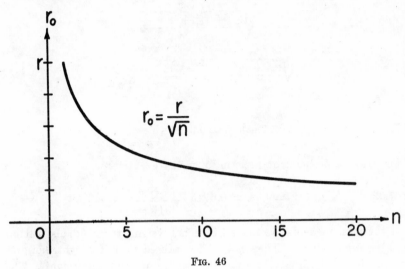

$$r_0 = \frac{r}{\sqrt{n}}$$

FIG. 46

for measurements of equal weight, where $H = h\sqrt{n/(n-1)}$. (See Art. 129.) For a set of n direct measurements of equal weight we therefore have for the n residuals the following probabilities:

$$p_1 = \frac{H}{\sqrt{\pi}} e^{-H^2 v_1^2} dv_1, \quad p_2 = \frac{H}{\sqrt{\pi}} e^{-H^2 v_2^2} dv_2, \cdots p_n = \frac{H}{\sqrt{\pi}} e^{-H^2 v_n^2} dv_n .$$

The chance that this particular set of residuals will be made in any set of measurements is then

(2) $$P = p_1 p_2 \cdots p_n = \left(\frac{H}{\sqrt{\pi}}\right) e^{-H^2(v_1^2 + v_2^2 + \ldots + v_n^2)} dv_1 dv_2 \cdots dv_n .$$

Differentiating (2) with respect to H and putting the derivative equal to zero, exactly as was done in Art. 133, we get

$$\frac{1}{H\sqrt{2}} = \sqrt{\frac{v_1^2 + v_2^2 + \cdots + v_n^2}{n}} .$$

But

$$\frac{1}{H} = \frac{1}{h}\sqrt{\frac{n-1}{n}}, \quad \text{and} \quad \frac{1}{h\sqrt{2}} = \mu.$$

Hence

$$\frac{1}{H\sqrt{2}} = \frac{1}{h\sqrt{2}}\sqrt{\frac{n-1}{n}} = \mu\sqrt{\frac{n-1}{n}}.$$

$$\therefore \quad \mu\sqrt{\frac{n-1}{n}} = \sqrt{\frac{v_1{}^2 + v_2{}^2 + \cdots + v_n{}^2}{n}},$$

or

(3) $$\mu = \sqrt{\frac{v_1{}^2 + v_2{}^2 + \cdots + v_n{}^2}{n-1}} = \sqrt{\frac{\Sigma v^2}{n-1}}.$$

Therefore

(137. 1) $$r = 0.6745\mu = 0.6745\sqrt{\frac{\Sigma v^2}{n-1}}.$$

For the P.E. of the arithmetic mean we have

(137. 2) $$r_0 = \frac{r}{\sqrt{n}} = 0.6745\sqrt{\frac{\Sigma v^2}{n(n-1)}}.$$

If the measurements are not all of equal weight, the residuals will not have the same weight. They can all be reduced to unit weight, however, by multiplying each of them by the square root of its weight. This follows from (136. 4), since $r_i\sqrt{w_i} = r$.

Let $v_1, v_2, \cdots v_n$ be the residuals of n measurements of weights $w_1, w_2, \cdots w_n$. Then the residuals reduced to unit weight are

$$v'_1 = v_1\sqrt{w_1},$$
$$v'_2 = v_2\sqrt{w_2},$$
$$\cdots \cdots \cdots$$
$$v'_n = v_n\sqrt{w_n}.$$

Squaring these equations and adding, we get

(6) $$\Sigma v'^2 = \Sigma w v^2.$$

Now for a set of measurements of equal weight we have from (137. 1)

$$r = 0.6745\sqrt{\frac{\Sigma v'^2}{n-1}}.$$

Replacing $\Sigma v'^2$ by its equal from (6), we get

$$(137.\,3)\quad r = 0.6745\ \sqrt{\frac{\Sigma wv^2}{n-1}} = 0.6745\ \sqrt{\frac{w_1v_1{}^2 + w_2v_2{}^2 + \cdots + w_nv_n{}^2}{n-1}}.$$

This is the P.E. of a single measurement of *unit* weight.

To find the P.E. of a measurement of weight w_i and the P.E. of the weighted mean we have from (136. 4), (136. 5), and (137. 3)

$$(137.\,4)\qquad\qquad r_i = \frac{r}{\sqrt{w_i}} = 0.6745\ \sqrt{\frac{\Sigma wv^2}{(n-1)w_i}}.$$

$$(137.\,5)\qquad\qquad r_0 = \frac{r}{\sqrt{\Sigma w}} = 0.6745\ \sqrt{\frac{\Sigma wv^2}{(n-1)\Sigma w}}.$$

It will be observed that (137. 5) reduces to (137. 2) when all the weights are equal.

We now collect for easy reference the fundamental formulas for computing the P.E. of direct measurements.

(a) *Measurements of equal precision.* P.E. of a single measurement:

$$(137.\,1)\qquad\qquad r = 0.6745\ \sqrt{\frac{v_1{}^2 + v_2{}^2 + \cdots + v_n{}^2}{n-1}}.$$

P.E. of arithmetic mean:

$$(137.\,2)\qquad\qquad r_0 = 0.6745\ \sqrt{\frac{v_1{}^2 + v_2{}^2 + \cdots + v_n{}^2}{n(n-1)}}.$$

(b) *Weighted measurements.* P.E. of a single measurement of *unit* weight:

$$(137.\,3)\qquad\qquad r = 0.6745\ \sqrt{\frac{w_1v_1{}^2 + w_2v_2{}^2 + \cdots + w_nv_n{}^2}{n-1}}.$$

P.E. of measurement of weight w_i:

$$(137.\,4)\qquad\qquad r_i = 0.6745\ \sqrt{\frac{w_1v_2{}^2 + w_2v_2{}^2 + \cdots + w_nv_n{}^2}{(n-1)w_i}}.$$

P.E. of weighted mean:

$$(137.\,5)\quad r_0 = 0.6745\ \sqrt{\frac{w_1v_2{}^2 + w_2v_2{}^2 + \cdots w_nv_n{}^2}{(n-1)(w_1 + w_2 + \cdots + w_n)}}.$$

138. The Combination of Sets of Measurements when the P.E. 's of the Sets are Given. When several separate determinations of the magnitude of a quantity have been made by different observers or by different methods and the probable errors of the separate determinations are given, it is important to know just how to combine these several results so as to obtain from them the best value for the measured quantity and the probable error of this best value. For example, the results of five different determinations of the atomic weight of silver are given below. How can we obtain from them the best value for the atomic weight and how can we find the P.E. of this value?

$$107.9401 \pm 0.0058$$
$$107.9406 \pm 0.0049$$
$$107.9233 \pm 0.0140$$
$$107.9371 \pm 0.0045$$
$$107.9270 \pm 0.0090$$

This is really a problem in indirect measurements, but it can readily be solved by the methods already given. The proper method of procedure in a problem of this type is first to compute by the relation (136. 2) the weights of the several determinations from their given probable errors and then find the weighted mean of the given values of the measured quantity. The P.E. of this weighted mean is to be computed by formula (136. 5). See Example 4.

Note. Some authors compute the P.E. of the weighted mean in this case by finding the residuals of the sets of measurements and then finding the P.E. of the weighted mean by formula (137. 5). Such a method is incorrect, and the P.E. of the weighted mean found by this procedure may be worthless. For an investigation of this matter from several angles, see the following papers:

1. " The Invalidity of a Commonly Used Method for Computing a Certain Probable Error." *Proc. Nat. Acad. Sci.,* Vol. 15, No. 8 (August, 1929), pp. 665-668.

2. " On the Computation of the Probable Error of a Weighted Mean." *Am. Math. Monthly,* Vol. XLII, No. 5 (May, 1935) pp. 286-301.

We shall now show the use of the formulas derived in the preceding sections.

Example 1. The following measurements were made to determine the length of a base line in a geodetic survey. Find the most probable length of the line, the P.E. of a single measurement, and the P.E. of the arithmetic mean.

Solution. The measurements, residuals, etc. are arranged in tabular form as shown below. The first step in the solution is to find the arithmetic mean of the given measurements. Then the residuals are found by subtracting each measurement from the arithmetic mean.

$M_1 = 455.35$	$v_1 = -0.02$	$v_1^2 = 0.0004$
$M_2 = 455.35$	$v_2 = -0.02$	$v_2^2 = 0.0004$
$M_3 = 455.20$	$v_3 = +0.13$	$v_3^2 = 0.0169$
$M_4 = 455.05$	$v_4 = +0.28$	$v_4^2 = 0.0784$
$M_5 = 455.75$	$v_5 = -0.42$	$v_5^2 = 0.1764$
$M_6 = 455.40$	$v_6 = -0.07$	$v_6^2 = 0.0049$
$M_7 = 455.10$	$v_7 = +0.23$	$v_7^2 = 0.0529$
$M_8 = 455.30$	$v_8 = +0.03$	$v_8^2 = 0.0009$
$M_9 = 455.50$	$v_9 = -0.17$	$v_9^2 = 0.0289$
$M_{10} = 455.30$	$v_{10} = +0.03$	$v_{10}^2 = 0.0009$
$\Sigma M = 10 \times 455 + 3.30$	$\Sigma v = 0$	$\Sigma v^2 = 0.3610$

$$M_0 = \frac{10 \times 455 + 3.30}{10} = 455.330.$$

$$r = 0.6745 \sqrt{\frac{0.3610}{9}} = 0.135, \quad \text{by (137.1)}.$$

$$r_0 = \frac{0.135}{\sqrt{10}} = 0.043, \quad \text{by (137.2)}.$$

The length of the line is therefore to be written

$$M = 455.330 \pm 0.043.$$

Note. The number of significant figures to be recorded in the most probable value (arithmetic or general mean) is usually one more than the number given in the individual measurements (Art. 7). If the P.E. of the final result should be relatively large, however, we are not justified in recording this result to more figures than are contained in the separate measurements, and in such cases we record the final result to the same number of figures as given in the data.

The P.E. of the result is recorded to only one or two significant figures— just enough to extend to the last figure of the mean. Slide-rule accuracy is therefore amply sufficient in the computation of probable errors.

In finding the residuals we use only as many figures in the mean as are given in the individual measurements.

Sometimes too much importance it attached to the probable error of a mean and too little to the mean itself. The mean is the important thing in any set of measurements or in any combination of sets; the probable error is of secondary importance. Theoretically, the weights of the separate means shquld be used in computing the general mean, but in the com- bination of only a few sets of measurements—from two to five, for example—such a procedure is of doubtful value. When only a few sets are to be combined, the simple average is usually better than the weighted average and is much easier to compute.

Example 2. The following measurements were made to determine a certain wave length. Find the most probable wave length and its P.E.

Solution. Here we first find the mean and then the residuals as before. The rounded mean is correct to its last figure as given, but since the last digit is slightly less than 5 the mean when rounded to three decimals is 4.505. From this number we subtract the individual measurements to find the residuals.

n	M	v	v^2
1	4.524	— 0.019	0.000361
2	4.500	+ 0.005	0.000025
3	4.515	— 0.010	0.000100
4	4.508	— 0.003	0.000009
5	4.513	— 0.008	0.000064
6	4.511	— 0.006	0.000036
7	4.497	+ 0.008	0.000064
8	4.507	— 0.002	0.000004
9	4.501	+ 0.004	0.000016
10	4.502	+ 0.003	0.000009
11	4.485	+ 0.020	0.000400
12	4.519	— 0.014	0.000196
13	4.517	— 0.012	0.000144
14	4.504	+ 0.001	0.000001
15	4.493	+ 0.012	0.000144
16	4.492	+ 0.013	0.000169
17	4.505	0.000	0.000000

$$M_0 = 4.5055 \qquad \Sigma v = - 0.008 \qquad \Sigma v^2 = 0.001742$$

$$r_0 = 0.6745 \ \sqrt{\frac{0.001742}{17 \times 16}} = 0.0017, \text{ by } (137.2).$$

$$\therefore \ M = 4.5055 \pm 0.0017.$$

Remark. Theoretically the algebraic sum of the residuals should be zero, but since these residuals in any actual problem are necessarily *rounded* numbers their algebraic sum is rarely zero. However, if the algebraic sum of the residuals is not practically zero, there is a numerical mistake either in the mean or in some residual. Hence it is very important to check the computation by noting whether Σv is practically zero.

Example 3. Six measurements of the parallax of a star are given in the following table. Find the most probable value of the parallax and its P.E.

M	w	wM	v	v^2	wv^2
0″.507	8	4.056	−0.104	0.010816	0.086528
0″.438	5	2.190	−0.035	0.001225	0.006125
0″.381	2	0.762	0.022	0.000484	0.000968
0″.371	8	2.968	0.032	0.001024	0.008192
0″.350	13	4.550	0.053	0.002809	0.036517
0″.402	20	8.040	0.001	0.000001	0.000020
	$\Sigma w = 56$	ΣwM $= 22.566$			$\Sigma wv^2 = 0.13835$

$$M_0 = \frac{22.566}{56} = 0''.403.$$

$$r_0 = 0.6745 \sqrt{\frac{0.13835}{5 \times 56}} = 0.015.$$

Hence the final result is

$$\underline{M = 0''.403 \pm 0''.015.}$$

Here the P.E. of the weighted mean is so large (relatively) that we are not justified in recording the result to more figures than are given in the data.

Example 4. Seven separate determinations of the difference of longitude between two places gave the following results. Find the most probable value of the longitude difference and its P.E.

1	19^m $1^s.42 \pm 0^s.044$
2	19 1.37 ± 0.037
3	19 1.38 ± 0.036
4	19 1.45 ± 0.036
5	19 1.60 ± 0.046
6	19 1.55 ± 0.045
7	19 1.57 ± 0.047.

Solution. The first step in the solution of this problem is to find the weights of the different determinations from their given probable errors. From Art. 136 we have

$$\frac{1}{r_1{}^2 w_1} = \frac{1}{r_2{}^2 w_2} = \cdots = \frac{1}{r_7{}^2 w_7} = \frac{1}{c} \text{ , say.}$$

Hence

$$r_1{}^2 w_1 = r_2{}^2 w_2 = \cdots = r_7{}^2 w_7 = c.$$

Let us take the weight of the last determination as unity, that is, let us put

$$w_7 = 1.$$

Then

$$c = r_7{}^2 = (0.047)^2.$$

Hence

$$w_1 = \frac{c}{r_1{}^2} = \left(\frac{0.047}{0.044}\right)^2 = \left(\frac{47}{44}\right)^2 = 1.14,$$

$$w_2 = \frac{c}{r_2{}^2}\left(\frac{0.047}{0.037}\right)^2 = \left(\frac{47}{37}\right)^2 = 1.61.$$

In like manner we find

$$w_3 = 1.70, \quad w_4 = 1.70, \quad w_5 = 1.04, \quad w_6 = 1.09.$$

To save labor in the computation of the weighted mean let us denote by $d_1, d_2, \cdots d_7$ the differences between the various determinations and an assumed approximate value of the weighted mean, say $19^m 1^s.40$. Then the various determinations are $19^m 1^s.40 + d_1$, $19^m 1^s.40 + d_2$, etc.; and their weighted mean is

$$M_0 = \frac{(19^m 1^s.40 + d_1)w_1 + (19^m 1^s.40 + d_2)w_2 + \cdots + (19^m 1^s.40 + d_7)w_7}{w_1 + w_2 + \cdots + w_7}$$

$$= \frac{(w_1 + w_2 + \cdots + w_7)(19^m 1^s.40) + w_1 d_1 + w_2 d_2 + \cdots + w_7 d_7}{w_1 + w_2 + \cdots + w_7}$$

$$= 19^m 1^s.40 + \frac{w_1 d_1 + w_2 d_2 + \cdots + w_7 d_7}{w_1 + w_2 + \cdots + w_7}.$$

This equation shows that it is necessary to multiply only the d's by the weights. We therefore complete the solution by making out the table shown below and then using (136.5).

M	d	w	wd
$19^m\ 1^s.42$	0.02	1.14	0.023
19 1 .37	−0.03	1.61	−0.048
19 1 .38	−0.02	1.70	−0.034
19 1 .45	0.05	1.70	0.085
19 1 .60	0.20	1.04	0.208
19 1 .55	0.15	1.09	0.164
19 1 .57	0.17	1.00	0.170
		$\Sigma w = 9.28$	$\Sigma wd = 0.568$

Hence

$$M_0 = 19^m\ 1^s.40 + \frac{0.568}{9.28} = 19^m\ 1^s.40 + 0.061 = 19^m\ 1^s.461.$$

Then since the weight of M_7 is assumed to be 1, we substitute the value of r_7 in the formula (136.5) and get

$$r_0 = \frac{0.047}{\sqrt{9.28}} = 0^s.015.$$

$$\therefore \quad \underline{M = 19^m\ 1^s.461 \pm 0^s.015.}$$

Note. The reader is reminded that the expression $M = M_0 \pm r$ *does not* mean that the true value of M is somewhere between $M_0 + r$ and $M_0 - r$; nor does it mean that M is probably in error by the amount r. It means that, so far as accidental errors are concerned, the true value of M is just as likely to lie between $M_0 + r$ and $M_0 - r$ as it is to lie outside of these limits.

EXERCISES XIV

1. Ten measurements of equal precision were made to determine the density of a body, the results of the measurements being as follows: 9.662, 9.673, 9.664, 9.659, 9.677, 9.662, 9.663, 9.680, 9.645, 9.654. Find the probable error of a single measurement, the most probable value of the density, and its P.E.

2. Twelve measurements of an angle in a primary triangulation gave the following results. Find the P.E. of a single measurement, the most probable value of the angle, and its P.E.

116 43′ 44″ .45	116 43′ 51″ .75
50 .95	52 .35
49 .20	51 .05
47 .40	49 .05
51 .05	49 .25
50 .60	49 .25

3. Ten measurements of the coefficients of expansion of dry air gave the following results. Find the most probable value of the coefficient and its P.E.

3.643×10^{-3}	3.636×10^{-3}
54	51
44	43
50	43
53	45

4. A certain coefficient of expansion was measured with different apparatus with the following results. Find the best value for the coefficient and its P.E.

Measurement	Weight	Measurement	Weight
0.0045	3	0.0036	2
0.0039	2	0.0026	2
0.0034	5	0.0027	1
0.0030	4	0.0043	3

5. An angle was measured several times with a transit and then several times with a theodolite, with the following results:

Theodolite ....$36° 41' 28'' \pm 11''$
Transit ....$36° 41' 23''.8 \pm 2''.7$

Find the most probable value of the angle and its P.E.

6. Six determinations of the velocity of light by different observers at different times gave the following results, with their probable errors:

$$298000 \pm 1000$$
$$298500 \pm 1000$$
$$299930 \pm 100$$
$$299990 \pm 200$$
$$300100 \pm 1000$$
$$299944 \pm 50$$

Find the most probable value obtainable from these determinations and its P.E.

7. Find the best value of the atomic weight of silver and its P.E. from the following determinations:

$$107.9401 \pm 0.0058$$
$$107.9406 \pm 0.0049$$
$$107.9233 \pm 0.0140$$
$$107.9371 \pm 0.0045$$
$$107.9270 \pm 0.0090$$

II. INDIRECT MEASUREMENTS.

139. The Probable Error of any Function of Independent Quantities Whose P. E.'s are Known.

Let

(1) $$Q = f(q_1, q_2, q_3, \cdots q_n)$$

represent any function of directly measured quantities $q_1, q_2, \cdots q_n$. Then errors $\Delta q_1, \Delta q_2, \cdots \Delta q_n$ in the q's will cause an error ΔQ in the function Q, so that

$$Q + \Delta Q = f(q_1 + \Delta q_1, q_2 + \Delta q_2, \cdots q_n + \Delta q_n).$$

Expanding the right-hand member by Taylor's theorem and proceeding exactly as in Art. 6, we get

$$(2) \qquad \Delta Q = \frac{\partial Q}{\partial q_1} \Delta q_1 + \frac{\partial Q}{\partial q_2} \Delta q_2 + \cdots + \frac{\partial Q}{\partial q_n} \Delta q_n.$$

This expression for ΔQ holds for any kind of errors whatever. If $\Delta q_1, \Delta q_2, \cdots \Delta q_n$ are *accidental* errors, so that they obey the Normal Law of error, then ΔQ is likewise an accidental error which obeys the Normal Law, as proved in Art. 122. In this case equation (2) is exactly like equation (2) of Art. 122, and all the results of that article apply to it. Hence if $H, h_1, h_2, \cdots h_n$ denote the precision indices of $Q_1, q_1, q_2, \cdots q_n$, respectively, we have from (122. 2)

$$(3) \qquad \frac{1}{H^2} = \frac{\left(\dfrac{\partial Q}{\partial q_1}\right)^2}{h_1{}^2} + \frac{\left(\dfrac{\partial Q}{\partial q_2}\right)^2}{h_2{}^2} + \frac{\left(\dfrac{\partial Q}{\partial q_3}\right)^2}{h_3{}^2} + \cdots + \frac{\left(\dfrac{\partial Q}{\partial q_n}\right)^2}{h_n{}^2}.$$

Let us denote the probable errors of $Q, q_1, q_2, \cdots q_n$ by $R_1, r_1, r_2, \cdots r_n$, respectively. Then from the relation $\rho = hr$ found in Art. 133 we have

$$\frac{1}{H^2} = \frac{R^2}{\rho^2}, \frac{1}{h_1{}^2} = \frac{r_1{}^2}{\rho^2}, \frac{1}{h_2{}^2} = \frac{r_2{}^2}{\rho^2}, \cdots \frac{1}{h_n{}^2} = \frac{r_n{}^2}{\rho^2}, \text{ where } \rho = 0.4769.$$

Substituting these values of $1/H^2$, $1/h_1{}^2$, etc. in (3) and reducing, we get

$$(139.\,1) \quad R = \sqrt{\left(\frac{\partial Q}{\partial q_1}\right)^2 r_1{}^2 + \left(\frac{\partial Q}{\partial q_2}\right)^2 r_2{}^2 + \cdots + \left(\frac{\partial Q}{\partial q_n}\right)^2 r_n{}^2}.$$

This formula is of *great importance*, for it includes all possible cases of a function of directly measured quantities. It expresses the law of the *propagation of errors* and is the foundation of the whole subject of indirect measurements.

The terms relative error and percentage error may also be applied to probable errors. The fundamental formula for the relative error in indirect measurements is obtained by dividing (139. 1) throughout by Q. We then have

$$(139.\,2) \qquad \frac{R}{Q} = \sqrt{\left(\frac{\partial Q}{\partial q_1}\right)^2 \frac{r_1{}^2}{Q^2} + \left(\frac{\partial Q}{\partial q_2}\right)^2 \frac{r_2{}^2}{Q^2} + \cdots + \left(\frac{\partial Q}{\partial q_n}\right)^2 \frac{r_n{}^2}{Q^2}}$$

for the probable relative error. The probable percentage error is 100 times this.

Formula (139. 2) assumes a very simple form when Q happens to be a product of several functions or a logarithm of a single function. Suppose, for instance, that

(139. 3) $$Q = K x^m y^n z^p .$$

Then

$$\frac{\partial Q}{\partial x} = \frac{Qm}{x} , \ \frac{\partial Q}{\partial y} = \frac{Qn}{y} , \ \frac{\partial Q}{\partial z} = \frac{Qp}{z} ;$$

and when these are substituted in (139. 2) we get

(139. 4) $$\frac{R}{Q} = \sqrt{ m^2 \left(\frac{r_1}{x}\right)^2 + n^2 \left(\frac{r_2}{y}\right)^2 + p^2 \left(\frac{r_3}{z}\right)^2 }$$

for the probable relative error of Q.

It is worth while to notice here that the P.E. of the weighted mean of several sets of measurements whose P.E.'s are given (Art. 138) can be found by the methods of the present article; for the weighted mean may be written in the form

$$M_0 = \frac{w_1}{\Sigma w} M_1 + \frac{w_2}{\Sigma w} M_2 + \cdots + \frac{w_n}{\Sigma w} M_n ,$$

which is a linear function of the M's. Hence on substituting in (139. 1) the partial derivatives $\partial M_0 / \partial M_1 = w_1 / \Sigma w$, $\partial M_0 / \partial M_2 = w_2 / \Sigma w$, etc., we get

(4) $$R = \sqrt{ \frac{w_1^2}{(\Sigma w)^2} r_1^2 + \frac{w_2^2}{(\Sigma w)^2} r_2^2 + \cdots + \frac{w_n^2}{(\Sigma w)^2} r_n^2 } .$$

But since $r_1^2 = c/w_1$, $r_2^2 = c/w_2$, etc., we have

$$R = \sqrt{ \frac{w_1^2}{(\Sigma w)^2} \frac{c}{w_1} + \frac{w_2^2}{(\Sigma w)^2} \frac{c}{w_2} + \cdots + \frac{w_n^2}{(\Sigma w)^2} \frac{c}{w_n} }$$

$$= \frac{\sqrt{c}}{\Sigma w} \sqrt{ w_1 + w_2 + \cdots + w_n } = \frac{\sqrt{c}}{\Sigma w} \sqrt{\Sigma w} = \frac{\sqrt{c}}{\sqrt{\Sigma w}} .$$

Now if we take $w_i = 1$ $(i = 1, 2, \cdots n)$, we get $\sqrt{c} = r_i$ and therefore

$$R = \frac{r_i}{\sqrt{\Sigma w}} ,$$

which is formula (136. 5).

On putting $w_1 = w_2 = \cdots = w_n$ we get $r_1 = r_2 = \cdots = r_n$, by (136. 2). Then (4) reduces to

$$R = \frac{r}{\sqrt{n}},$$

which is formula (136. 3).

140. The Two Fundamental Problems of Indirect Measurements. The two main problems of indirect measurements are the following:

1. Given the P.E.'s of a number of directly measured quantities, to find the P.E. of any function of these quantities.

2. Given a prescribed P.E. of the function, to find the allowable P.E.'s of the directly measured quantities.

The first of these problems is solved by substituting the data directly in formula (139. 1) or (139. 2), according as the given P.E.'s are absolute or relative.

The second problem is mathematically indeterminate when the number of directly observed quantities is greater than one. For a function of a single quantity, say

$$Q = f(x),$$

we have by (139. 1)

$$R = \sqrt{\left(\frac{\partial Q}{\partial x}\right)^2 r_1{}^2} = \frac{\partial Q}{\partial x} r_1, \quad \text{or} \quad r_1 = \frac{R}{\frac{\partial Q}{\partial x}}.$$

140a). The Method of Equal Effects. If, on the other hand, Q is a function of several directly measured quantities, we obtain a definite solution by using the *method of equal effects,* as explained in Art. 10. This method assumes that all the components (directly measured independent quantities) contribute the same amount to the resultant error in Q. Under these conditions all the terms under the radical in (139. 1) are equal to one another, so that

$$R = \sqrt{n\left(\frac{\partial Q}{\partial q_1}\right)^2 r_1{}^2} = \sqrt{n}\frac{\partial Q}{\partial q_1} r_1 = \sqrt{n}\frac{\partial Q}{\partial q_2} r_2 = \cdots = \sqrt{n}\frac{\partial Q}{\partial q_n} r_n.$$

Hence

(1) $$r_1 = \frac{R}{\sqrt{n}\frac{\partial Q}{\partial q_1}}, \quad r_2 = \frac{R}{\sqrt{n}\frac{\partial Q}{\partial q_2}}, \cdots r_n = \frac{R}{\sqrt{n}\frac{\partial Q}{\partial q_n}}.$$

In some problems the P.E.'s of some of the components are so small in comparison with the others that we may neglect them entirely when applying the method of equal effects, thereby simplifying the problem.

Thus, if we wished to find the local time at any place on the earth's surface, we could compute it from the formula

$$\cos t = \frac{\sin h}{\cos L \cos d} - \tan L \tan d$$

as soon as we knew the altitude (h) and declination (d) of a heavenly body and the latitude (L) of the place. The declination can be found from the *Nautical Almanac* to a hundredth part of a second of arc, but the altitude and latitude have to be measured at the place where the local time is wanted. If these are measured with a sextant or an engineers' transit, they can not be measured much closer than to the nearest *minute* of arc. Hence the declination is known so much more accurately than the altitude and latitude can be measured that we may treat the declination as free from error, so that the error in t will be due entirely to the errors in h and L. If, therefore, we desired the local time to the nearest second, we would treat t as a function of h and L alone, take $n = 2$, and find the allowable P.E.'s of h and L by means of formulas (1).

To find out whether the error in any particular component has a negligible effect in producing an error in the function Q we apply the following criterion:

140b). Criterion for Negligible Effects: If any component q_k has a negligible effect in causing an error in Q, then we must have *

(2)
$$\frac{\partial Q}{\partial q_k} r_k \leqq \frac{1}{3} R,$$

where R is the stipulated P.E. of Q. If several components $q_1, q_2, \cdots q_m$ should each satisfy (2), they may all be neglected provided

(3)
$$\sqrt{\left(\frac{\partial Q}{\partial q_1}\right)^2 r_1{}^2 + \left(\frac{\partial Q}{\partial q_2}\right)^2 r_2{}^2 + \cdots + \left(\frac{\partial Q}{\partial q_m}\right)^2 r_m{}^2} \leqq \frac{1}{3} R.$$

When applying the criteria (2) and (3) to any particular problem, we are supposed to know in advance the size of the P.E.'s of the components we contemplate neglecting, as in the case of the declination d in the astronomical problem mentioned above. If we know nothing concerning the size of the P.E.'s whose effect we contemplate neglecting, then the best we can do is to apply the method of equal effects to the terms under the radical in (3), thereby obtaining

$$\sqrt{m \left(\frac{\partial Q}{\partial q_1}\right)^2 r_1{}^2} = \sqrt{m} \frac{\partial Q}{\partial q_1} r_1 = \sqrt{m} \frac{\partial Q}{\partial q_2} r_2 = \sqrt{m} \frac{\partial Q}{\partial q_m} r_m \leqq \frac{1}{3} R,$$

* See Palmer's *Theory of Measurements*, p. 151.

from which

$$r_1 \leqq \frac{R}{3\sqrt{m}\dfrac{\partial Q}{\partial q_1}}, \quad r_2 \leqq \frac{R}{3\sqrt{m}\dfrac{\partial Q}{\partial q_2}}, \cdots r_m \leqq \frac{R}{3\sqrt{m}\dfrac{\partial Q}{\partial q_m}}.$$

We may therefore neglect the effect of m components $q_1, q_2, \cdots q_m$ if each satisfies the condition

(4) $$r_k \leqq \frac{R}{3\sqrt{m}\dfrac{\partial Q}{\partial q_k}}, \qquad (k = 1, 2, 3, \cdots m).$$

The proofs of criteria (2) and (3) are simple and easy, but they will not be given here.*

We shall now apply the preceding formulas to some examples.

Example 1. From the simple pendulum formula

$$T = \pi \sqrt{\frac{l}{g}}$$

we get

$$g = \frac{\pi^2 l}{T^2} = f(l, T).$$

If $l = 100$ cm. and $T = 1$ sec., find the error in g due to errors of 0.10 cm. in l and 0.0020 sec. in T, respectively.

Solution. Differentiating g with respect to l and T separately, we have

$$\frac{\partial g}{\partial l} = \frac{\pi^2}{T^2}, \frac{\partial g}{\partial T} = -\frac{2\pi^2 l}{T^3}.$$

From this point onward we proceed in one of two ways, depending on the meaning of the errors in l and T.

(a) If the errors in l and T are actual, definite errors of the magnitudes given, then we compute the error in g by the formula

$$\Delta g = \frac{\partial g}{\partial l}\Delta l + \frac{\partial g}{\partial T}\Delta T. \qquad \text{[See (6. 1)]}$$

Hence

$$\Delta g = \frac{\pi^2}{T^2}\Delta l - \frac{2\pi^2 l}{T^3}\Delta T$$
$$= 9.8696\,(0.10 + 200 \times 0.002) = 4.935 \text{ cm./sec.}^2 = \underline{4.9}, \text{ say.}$$

Since we do not know the signs of ΔT and Δl, we disregard the negative

---

* See Palmer's *Theory of Measurements*, p. 151.

sign on the right and take the arithmetic sum of the terms. This gives the maximum numerical value of Δg.

(b) If the given values of l and T are the means of several measurements and their given errors are the P.E.'s of these arithmetic means, then we compute the P.E. of g by formula (139. 1). Hence we have

$$R = \sqrt{\frac{\pi^4}{T^4}(\Delta l)^2 + \frac{4\pi^4}{T^6}l^2(\Delta T)^2} = 9.8696\sqrt{0.01 + 0.16}$$

$$= 9.8696 \times 0.4123 = 4.068 \text{ cm./sec.}^2 = \underline{4.1}, \text{ say.}$$

To find the relative and percentage errors under the two suppositions (a) and (b), we have

(a)   Relative error $= \dfrac{\Delta g}{g} = \dfrac{\Delta l}{l} + 2\dfrac{\Delta T}{T} = \dfrac{0.1}{100} + \dfrac{2(0.002)}{1}$

$$= 0.001 + 0.004 = \underline{0.005}.$$

Percentage error $= 100(\Delta g/g) = 100 \times 0.005 = \underline{0.5}$ per cent.

(b) Since we are here dealing with a product of several quantities, we use formula (139. 4). Hence

$$\frac{R}{g} = \sqrt{\left(\frac{\Delta l}{l}\right)^2 + 4\left(\frac{\Delta T}{T}\right)^2} = \sqrt{(0.001)^2 + 4(0.002)^2}$$

$$= 0.00412 = \underline{0.004}, \text{ say.}$$

Percentage P.E. $= 100(R/g) = 100 \times 0.004 = \underline{0.4}$ percent.

Example 2. Two sides and the included angle of a triangle were measured with the following results:

$$a = 252.52 \pm 0.06 \text{ feet,}$$
$$b = 330.01 \pm 0.06 \text{ feet,}$$
$$C = 42°13'00'' \pm 30''.$$

Find the area of the triangle and its P.E.

Solution. The formula for the area is

$$A = \tfrac{1}{2}ab \sin C.$$

Hence

$$\frac{\partial A}{\partial a} = \frac{b \sin C}{2}, \quad \frac{\partial A}{\partial b} = \frac{a \sin C}{2}, \quad \frac{\partial A}{\partial C} = \frac{ab \cos C}{2}.$$

Since the errors given in this problem are the probable errors of the given measurements, we should use formula (139. 1). The use of that formula in this example, however, would call for a considerable amount of numerical work. To avoid this we calculate the relative error by formula (139. 2) and then get the P.E. from the relative error. Hence we have (139. 2)

$$\frac{R}{A} = \sqrt{\left(\frac{\Delta a}{a}\right)^2 + \left(\frac{\Delta b}{b}\right)^2 + (\Delta C \cot C)^2}.$$

The error in C must be expressed in radians. Hence

$$\Delta C = 30 \times \frac{\pi}{180} \times \frac{1}{3600} = 0.0001454.$$

Also, $\cot C = \cot 42° \, 13' = 1.1022.$

$$\therefore \quad \frac{R}{A} = \sqrt{\left(\frac{0.06}{252.52}\right)^2 + \left(\frac{0.06}{300.01}\right)^2 + (0.0001454 \times 1.1022)^2}$$
$$= 0.00035.$$

The area is

$$A = \frac{252.52 \times 300.01 \times \sin 42°13'}{2} = 25452 \text{ sq. ft.}$$

$$\therefore \quad R = 0.00035 \times A = 0.00035 \times 25452 = 8.9 = 9, \text{ say.}$$

The required result is therefore

$$\underline{A = 25452 \pm 9 \text{ sq. ft.}}$$

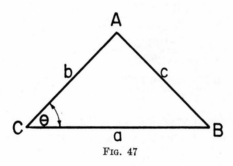

FIG. 47

Example 3. The distance between two inaccessible points A and B is desired to $\pm$ 0.1 foot. The required distance can not be measured directly but must be calculated from the measurements of CA, CB, and $\angle ACB$. If a, b, and θ (see Fig. 47) are approximately equal to 200 ft., 150 ft., and 45°, respectively, find the allowable errors in these directly measured quantities.

Solution. Here

$$c = \sqrt{a^2 + b^2 - 2ab \cos \theta},$$

and

$$R = 0.1.$$

The best way to solve this problem is by the method of equal effects, and we therefore use formulas (1). Differentiating c with respect to a, b, and θ in turn, we have

$$\frac{\partial c}{\partial a} = \frac{a - b \cos \theta}{c}, \quad \frac{\partial c}{\partial b} = \frac{b - a \cos \theta}{c}, \quad \frac{\partial c}{\partial \theta} = \frac{ab \sin \theta}{c}.$$

But $c = \sqrt{40000 + 22500 - 30000 \sqrt{2}} = 141.7$

$$\therefore \frac{\partial c}{\partial a} = \frac{200 - 75\sqrt{2}}{141.7} = \frac{93.93}{141.7} = 0.66,$$

$$\frac{\partial c}{\partial b} = \frac{150 - 100\sqrt{2}}{141.7} = \frac{8.58}{141.7} = 0.060,$$

$$\frac{\partial c}{\partial \theta} = \frac{200 \times 150 \times \dfrac{\sqrt{2}}{2}}{141.7} = \frac{21213}{141.7} = 149.7;$$

and $n = 3$.
Then by (1) we have

$$r_a = \frac{0.1}{\sqrt{3}\dfrac{\partial c}{\partial a}} = \frac{0.1}{\sqrt{3} \times 0.66} = \frac{0.1732}{1.98} = 0.087 = \underline{0.09 \text{ ft.}}$$

$$r_b = \frac{0.1}{\sqrt{3} \times 0.06} = \frac{0.1732}{0.18} = \underline{0.96 \text{ ft.}}$$

$$r_\theta = \frac{0.1}{\sqrt{3} \times 149.7} = \frac{0.1732}{449.1} = 0.000386 \text{ rad.} = \underline{1'20''.}$$

The large allowable error in b is due to the fact that b is nearly perpendicular to c, so that a considerable change in the former has little effect on the latter.

Example 4. The modulus of elasticity of a beam of length l, breadth b, and depth d, supported at the ends and loaded at the center by a weight W, is given by the formula

$$E = \frac{Wl^3}{4ab\ d^3},$$

where a is the deflection produced at the center. If it is desired to

measure E to 1 per cent, and the error in W may be neglected, compute
the allowable errors in a, b, d, and l.

Solution. The formula for E may be written

$$E = \tfrac{1}{4} W l^3 a^{-1} b^{-1} d^{-3}.$$

This is of the form (139.3), where $K = W/4$. Then since $R/E = 1\%$
$= 0.01$, we have from (139.4)

$$0.01 = \sqrt{ 9\left(\frac{\Delta l}{l}\right)^2 + \left(\frac{\Delta a}{a}\right)^2 + \left(\frac{\Delta b}{b}\right)^2 + 9\left(\frac{\Delta d}{d}\right)^2 }.$$

Now using the method of equal effects, we have

$$\sqrt{ 4 \times 9 \left(\frac{\Delta l}{l}\right)^2 } = 0.01, \quad \text{or} \quad 6\left(\frac{\Delta l}{l}\right) = 0.01.$$

$$\therefore \frac{\Delta l}{l} = \frac{0.01}{6}, \quad \text{and} \quad 100\frac{\Delta l}{l} = \frac{1}{6} = \underline{0.167} \text{ per cent.}$$

$$\sqrt{ 4\left(\frac{\Delta a}{a}\right)^2 } = 0.01, \quad \text{or} \quad \frac{\Delta a}{a} = 0.005.$$

$$\therefore \quad 100\frac{\Delta a}{a} = \underline{0.5} \text{ per cent.}$$

Likewise,

$$100\frac{\Delta b}{b} = \underline{0.5} \text{ per cent.}$$

$$100\frac{\Delta d}{d} = \frac{1}{6} = \underline{0.167} \text{ per cent.}$$

Hence if the percentage P.E. of E is to be 1 per cent, the percentage
P.E.'s of a, b, d, l, must not exceed $\tfrac{1}{2}$, $\tfrac{1}{2}$, $\tfrac{1}{6}$, $\tfrac{1}{6}$ of one per cent, respectively.

141. Rejection of Observations and Measurements. Occasionally some
individual measurement may differ so widely from the others of the
same set that we may suspect the discrepancy to be due to a mistake.
In such a case it may be well to reject this measurement entirely. To
decide what to do about it we apply the following rule:

*Find the mean of all the measurements (including the " wild " one)
and find the residual for each. Compute the P.E of a single measurement
by formula (137.1). Reject any measurement whose residual exceeds 5
times the P.E. of a single measurement.*

This rule rests on the following considerations:
Suppose the chance of an error of magnitude x is 1 in 1000. Then

its probability is $p = 1/1000 = 0.001$. The chance that an error of this size will *not* occur is therefore $1 - 0.001 = 0.999$. From the probability table we find the corresponding hx to be 2.326.

Now from Art. 133 we have

$$hr = \rho = 0.4769,$$

from which

$$h = \frac{0.4769}{r}.$$

Hence

$$hx = \frac{0.4769}{r} x = 2.326.$$

$$\therefore \quad x = \frac{2.326}{0.4769} r = 4.9r,$$

to two figures.

The chance of making an error as great as five times the P.E. of a single measurement is therefore less than one in a thousand. An error of such a magnitude is therefore so improbable that we may safely neglect it.

Example. A quantity M was measured with the results given below. Should any of the measurements be rejected?

$$M = 236, \ 251, \ 249, \ 252, \ 248, \ 254, \ 246, \ 257, \ 243, \ 274.$$

Solution. The average of these measurements is

$$M = 251.$$

Hence the residuals are

$$v_1 = +15, \quad v_2 = 0, \quad v_3 = +2, \quad v_4 = -1, \quad v_5 = +3, \quad v_6 = -3,$$
$$v_7 = +5, \quad v_8 = -6, \quad v_9 = +8, \quad v_{10} = -23.$$

The P.E. of a single measurement is

$$r = 0.6745 \sqrt{\frac{225 + 4 + 1 + 9 + 9 + 25 + 36 + 64 + 529}{9}}.$$

$$= 0.6745 \times 10.01 = 6.75.$$

Five times this P.E. is 33.75, and since all the residuals are less than this we retain all the measurements.

EXERCISES XV

1. The side b and the angles B and C of a plane triangle were measured with the following results:

$$b = 106 \pm 0.06 \ \text{ft.}, \quad B = 28°36' \pm 1', \quad C = 120°12' \pm 1'.5.$$

Find the angle A, the side a, and their P.E.'s.

2. Two sides a and b and the included angle C of a town lot were measured to be

$$a = 104.86 \pm 0.02 \text{ ft.}, \quad b = 214.24 \pm 0.03 \text{ ft.},$$
$$C = 47°13' \pm 1'.$$

Find the side c and its P.E.

3. The index of refraction of a prism is given by the formula

$$n = \frac{\sin \frac{1}{2}(a + D)}{\sin \frac{1}{2}a}.$$

If $D = 28°34' \pm 0'.5$ and $a = 62°48' \pm 0'.7$, find n and its P.E.

4. The current in a tangent galvanometer is given by the formula

$$I = K \tan \theta.$$

Find I and its P.E. when $K = 1.963 \pm 0.002$ and $\theta = 35° \pm 0°.1$.

5. The volume of a right circular cylinder is given by the formula

$$V = \frac{\pi}{4}d^2h.$$

Find V and its P.E. when $h = 116.85 \pm 0.28$ mm. and $d = 82.54 \pm 0.28$ mm.

6. The diameter of a rod was measured several times with the following results:

1.034, 1.031, 1.029, 1.032, 1.034, 1.030, 1.034, 1.033, 1.032, 1.031.

Find the P.E. of a single measurement, the P.E. of the mean, the most probable diameter of the rod, its cross-sectional area, and the P.E. of this area.

7. The diameter of a polished steel rod was measured ten times with the following results:

0.5003, 0.5002, 0.4999, 0.4998, 0.4999, 0.5003, 0.5001, 0.5004, 0.5001, 0.4999.

Find the cross-sectional area and its P.E.

8. Explain how you would decide in any given problem whether to use formula (6.1) or formula (139.1). What is the fundamental difference between these two formulas?

CHAPTER XVI

EMPIRICAL FORMULAS

142. Introduction. An empirical formula, or empirical equation, is one whose *form* is inferred from the results of experiment or observation and in which the *constants* are determined from experimental or observational data. Thus, it is known that the speed of a ship varies with the horse power according to the formula

$$P = a + bV^3.$$

The constants to be determined in this formula are a and b, and for the purpose of determining them we should take several sets of readings of the speed and corresponding horse power. These sets of simultaneous values of V and P would, when substituted in the given formula, give several equations in the two unknowns a and b. The next thing to be done would be to find the best values for a and b from the several equations. For the solution of this part of the problem three methods are available: the *graphic method* or *method of selected points,* the *method of averages, and the method of Least Squares.* We shall now consider these methods in the order named and illustrate each by several examples.

143. The Graphic Method, or Method of Selected Points. This method can be used whenever the given formula can be plotted as a straight line either directly or after a suitable transformation. The equation given above, for example, can be reduced to a straight-line form by putting $V^3 = t$, thereby reducing the equation to the form

$$P = a + bt,$$

which is linear in the variables t and P.

To apply the graphic method to this problem we plot on coordinate paper the corresponding values of $t(= V^3)$ and P. The plotted points should lie nearly on a straight line. We then draw a straight line which will be a good compromise for all the plotted points and pass as near as possible to each of them. The slope of this line will be the value of b and its P-intercept will be a. If the line happens to pass through two of the plotted points, or through any other two points whose coordinates are easily determined (points at the corners of squares, for instance), we can substitute their coordinates in the given equation and solve the two resulting equations for a and b, but the points so used should be as far apart as possible. The drawing of the best representative straight line is a matter of good judgment.

This method will give fairly good results when finely divided coordinate paper is used, but in general it is not recommended except for obtaining approximate values of the constants or in cases where the results obtainable by the method are as accurate as the data used.

Example 1. The electrical resistance of a copper wire varies with the temperature according to the equation

$$R = a + bT.$$

For the purpose of determining the constants a and b the measurements of temperature and corresponding resistance given in the following table were made. Find the values of a and b.

T	19.1	25.0	30.1	36.0	40.0	45.1	50.0
R	76.30	77.80	79.75	80.80	82.35	83.90	85.10

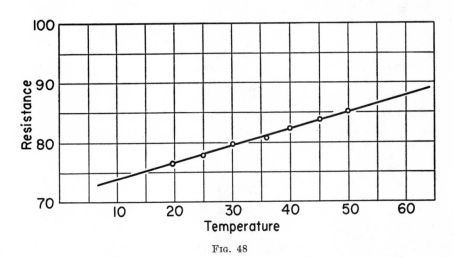

Fig. 48

Solution. Plotting these pairs of values on a large sheet of paper and drawing what seems to be a good compromise line (Fig. 48), we find that this line passes through the points $(21, 77)$ and $(64, 89)$. Substituting in the given equation the coordinates of these points, we have

$$a + 21b = 77$$
$$a + 64b = 89$$
$$\overline{43b = 12} \quad \therefore \quad b = \frac{12}{43} = 0.2790,$$

and

$$a = 77 - 21 \times 0.2790 = 71.14.$$

Hence the required relation between R and T is

$$R = 71.14 + 0.2790T.$$

To see how well this formula fits the data in the table we compute the *residuals* of the several measurements. Writing

$$v = 0.2790T + 71.14 - R,$$

we have

$$v_1 = 0.2790 \times 19.1 + 71.14 - 76.30 = 0.15$$
$$v_2 = 0.2790 \times 25.0 + 71.14 - 77.80 = 0.32$$
$$v_3 = -0.21$$
$$v_4 = \quad 0.39$$
$$v_5 = -0.05$$
$$v_6 = -0.19$$
$$v_7 = -0.01$$
$$\therefore \quad \Sigma v = 0.40, \quad \Sigma v^2 = 0.36.$$

Example 2. The data in the following table fit a formula of the type

(1) $$y = ax^n.$$

Find the values of a and n and thence the required formula.

x	10	20	30	40	50	60	70	80
y	1.06	1.33	1.52	1.68	1.81	1.91	2.01	2.11

Solution. Taking the logarithm of each side of the given equation, we have

(2) $$\log y = \log a + n \log x.$$

Putting

$$y' = \log y, \quad x' = \log x,$$

we get

$$y' = \log a + nx' = a' + nx',$$

where $a' = \log a$.

This is the equation of a straight line in the new variables x' and y'. To plot this line the most conveniently we use logarithmic paper. Plotting the given points on such paper, we find that they lie almost

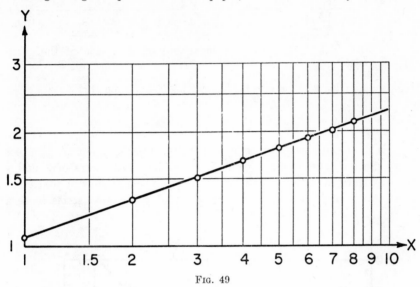

Fig. 49

exactly on a straight line (Fig. 49). Hence we substitute in (2) the coordinates of the first and last of the given points and get

$$\log 1.06 = \log a + n,$$
$$\log 2.11 = \log a + n \log 80;$$

or

$$n + \log a = 0.0253,$$
$$1.9031n + \log a = 0.3243.$$
$$\therefore \quad \overline{0.9031n = 0.2990,}$$

or

$$n = 0.3311.$$

Also,

$$\log a = 0.0253 - n$$
$$= 0.0253 - 0.3311$$
$$= 9.6942 - 10.$$
$$\therefore \quad a = 0.4945.$$

The required formula is therefore

$$\underline{y = 0.4945\, x^{0.3311}.}$$

Example 3.   Find a formula of the form

(3) $$y = ke^{mx}$$

which will fit the data in the table below.

x	1	2	3	4	5	6	7	8
y	15.3	20.5	27.4	36.6	49.1	65.6	87.8	117.6

Solution. Taking the common logarithm of each side of the given equation, we have

$$(4) \qquad \log y = \log k + mx \log e = \log k + (m \log e)x,$$

or

$$y' = \log k + (m \log e)x, \text{ where } y' = \log y.$$

This is the equation of a straight line in the variables x and y'. To plot it we use semilogarithmic paper. Plotting the given values of x and y on semilogarithmic paper, we find that the points lie nearly on a straight line (Fig. 50). Drawing on a large sheet of paper what seems to be a

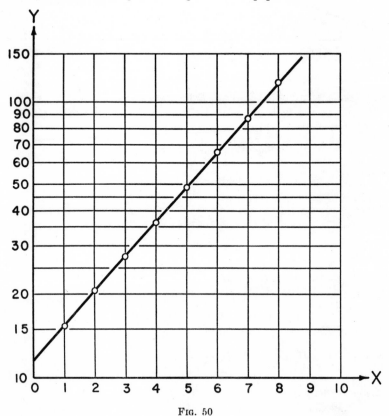

FIG. 50

good representative line, we notice that it passes through the points (0.4, 13) and (8.6, 140). Substituting these values in (4), we have

$$\log 13 = \log k + 0.43429m\,(0.4) = \log k + 0.1737m,$$
$$\log 140 = \log k + 0.43429m\,(8.6) = \log k + 3.7349m.$$

Solving these equations for m and k, we get

$$m = 0.2898,$$
$$k = 11.58.$$

The required equation is therefore

$$y = 11.58e^{0.2898x}.$$

Note. In logarithmic coordinate paper the origin is the point $(1, 1)$. Hence the equations of the axes are $x = 1$, $y = 1$. Putting $x = 1$ in the equation $y = ax^n$, we get $y = a$. Hence *in the straight-line graph of the equation* y $= $ ax^n *on logarithmic paper the constant* a *is the* y*-intercept.*

To find a formula for the exponent n, let (x_1, y_1) and (x_2, y_2) be any two pairs of corresponding values of x and y. Then from (2)

$$\log y_2 = \log a + n \log x_2\,,$$
$$\log y_1 = \log a + n \log x_1\,.$$
$$\therefore \quad \log y_2 - \log y_1 = n\,(\log x_2 - \log x_1),$$

or

(5)
$$n = \frac{\log y_2 - \log y_1}{\log x_2 - \log x_1}\,.$$

The origin of coordinates in semilogarithmic paper is the point $(0, 1)$. The equation of the y-axis is therefore $x = 0$, and that of the x-axis is $y = 1$. Putting $x = 0$ in (3), we get $y = k$. Hence in the straight-line graph of the equation $y = ke^{mx}$ on semilogarithmic paper the constant k is the y-intercept.

To find a formula for the exponent m we substitute in (4) two pairs of corresponding values of x and y, obtaining the two equations

$$\log y_2 = \log k + (m \log e)x_2\,,$$
$$\log y_1 = \log k + (m \log e)x_1\,.$$
$$\therefore \quad \log y_2 - \log y_1 = (x_2 - x_1)m \log e,$$

or

(6)
$$m = \frac{\log y_2 - \log y_1}{(x_2 - x_1)\log e} = 2.3026\,\frac{(\log y_2 - \log y_1)}{x_2 - x_1}\,.$$

If the given points are so plotted that the equations of the axes are not as stated above, the y-intercept will *not* be the value of the constant a or k. For instance, in Example 2 we plotted the point $(10, 1.06)$ *on the y-axis*. This is really equivalent to making the substitution $x = 10x'$, so that the given equation is transformed into the equivalent equation

$$y = a(10x')^n = a \times 10^n x'^n.$$

Putting $x' = 1$, we get $y = a \times 10^n = 0.4945 \times 10^{0.3311} = 1.06$, and this is the actual plotted value of the y-intercept. The student should have no difficulty in deciding whether or not the y-intercept of the plotted straight line gives the true value of the coefficients a and k in any given example.

144. The Method of Averages. The *residuals* of a series of plotted points are the vertical distances of these points from the best representative curve. Some of the residuals will be positive and others negative. The method of averages assumes that the best representative curve is that for which the algebraic sum of the residuals is zero. To find the unknown constants in an empirical formula by this method we first substitute in the given formula the several pairs of observed or measured values of x and y. We thus get as many residuals as there are pairs of observed values. Then we divide the residuals, or residual equations, into as many groups as there are constants in the assumed formula. Each group should contain as nearly as possible the same number of residuals. By placing the sum of the residuals in the first group equal to zero we get a single equation in the unknown constants. Placing the sum of the residuals in the second group equal to zero, we get a second equation in the constants, and so on. Since the sum of the residuals in each group is zero, the sum of all the residuals is necessarily zero. On solving simultaneously the equations obtained from the several groups, we obtain the values of the unknown constants in the original formula. A few examples will make the method clear.

Example 1. The data in the following table will fit a formula of the type

(1) $$y = a + bx + cx^2.$$

Find the formula.

x	87.5	84.0	77.8	63.7	46.7	36.9
y	292	283	270	235	197	181

Solution. Substituting in (1) the several pairs of corresponding values of x and y, we get

$$\text{I} \begin{cases} v_1 = a + 87.5b + 7656c - 292 \\ v_2 = a + 84.0b + 7056c - 283 \end{cases}$$

$$\text{II} \begin{cases} v_3 = a + 77.8b + 6053c - 270 \\ v_4 = a + 63.7b + 4058c - 235 \end{cases} \quad \begin{matrix} \text{Residual} \\ \text{equations.} \end{matrix}$$

$$\text{III} \begin{cases} v_5 = a + 46.7b + 2181c - 197 \\ v_6 = a + 36.9b + 1362c - 181 \end{cases}$$

Dividing these equations into three groups (since there are three constants to be determined), as indicated by the braces at the left, adding the equations of each group, and placing the sums equal to zero, we get the three equations

$$\begin{cases} 2a + 171.5b + 14712c = 575 \\ 2a + 141.5b + 10111c = 505 \\ 2a + 83.6b + 3543c = 378 \end{cases}$$

Solving these three equations simultaneously for a, b, and c, we get

$$a = 107.72, \quad b = 1.7960, \quad c = 0.0035036.$$

Hence the required formula is

$$y = 107.72 + 1.7960x + 0.0035036x^2.$$

This method of averages requires no graph and can be applied to any formula which is *linear* (of the first degree) in the unknown constants or to any formula which is reducible to a form linear in the constants.

Example 2. Solve Example 2, Art. 143, by the method of averages.

Solution. Strictly speaking, the residuals are, by definition,

$$v_1 = ax_1{}^n - y_1, \quad v_2 = ax_2{}^n - y_2, \text{ etc.}$$

But if we divide these equations into groups, add, and attempt to solve the resulting equations for a and n, we get into trouble at once; for the unknown n occurs as an exponent in several terms of a sum.

We can avoid this trouble without much loss in accuracy by proceeding as follows: Instead of equating to zero the sum of the residuals of the y's, we equate to zero the sum of the residuals of the *logarithms* of the y's. For any residual we have from (2) of Art. 143

$$v' = \log a + n \log x - \log y.$$

Hence the several residuals are

$$\text{I} \begin{cases} v'_1 = \log a + 1.0000n - 0.0253 \\ v'_2 = \log a + 1.3010n - 0.1239 \\ v'_3 = \log a + 1.4771n - 0.1818 \\ v'_4 = \log a + 1.6021n - 0.2253 \end{cases}$$

$$\text{II} \begin{cases} v'_5 = \log a + 1.6990n - 0.2577 \\ v'_6 = \log a + 1.7782n - 0.2810 \\ v'_7 = \log a + 1.8451n - 0.3032 \\ v'_8 = \log a + 1.9031n - 0.3243. \end{cases}$$

In actual practice we do not write down these equations in this form, but in the form given below:

$$\log a + 1.0000n = 0.0253 \qquad \log a + 1.6990n = 0.2577$$
$$\log a + 1.3010n = 0.1239 \qquad \log a + 1.7782n = 0.2810$$
$$\log a + 1.4771n = 0.1818 \qquad \log a + 1.8451n = 0.3032$$
$$\underline{\log a + 1.6021n = 0.2253} \qquad \underline{\log a + 1.9031n = 0.3243}$$

(2) $\quad 4\log a + 5.3802n = 0.5563.$ (3) $\quad 4\log a + 7.2254n = 1.1662.$

Solving (2) and (3) simultaneously, we get

$$n = 0.3305, \quad \log a = -0.3055 = 9.6945 - 10 \quad \therefore \ a = 0.4949.$$

The required formula is therefore

$$\underline{y = 0.4949x^{0.3305}}.$$

Note. The method of averages is the shortest and easiest method for finding the constants in an empirical formula, but it must not be used blindly. The residual equations can be grouped in several ways,* and

---

* The number of possible groupings is given by the following formulas:

a) Two groups. The number of different ways in which $p + q$ different things can be divided into *two* groups of p things and q things, respectively, is

$$\frac{(p + q)!}{p!q!}.$$

b) Three groups. The number of different ways in which $p + q + r$ different things can be divided into *three* groups of p things, q things, and r things, respectively, is

$$\frac{(p + q + r)!}{p!q!r!}.$$

c) Four or more groups. The number of ways in which we can divide $p+q+r+s$ different things into *four* groups of p things, q things, r things, and s things, respectively, is

$$\frac{(p + q + r + s)!}{p!q!r!s!}.$$

And so on for any other case. For the proof of these formulas see Wentworth's *College Alegbra*, pp. 263-264; or Whitworth's *Choice and Chance*, pp. 63-64.

each different grouping will give different values for the unknown constants, even though the algebraic sum of the residuals be zero in every case. The resulting formulas will thus be different, and some of them will fit the data much better than the others.

There is no way to determine in advance just what grouping will give the best result. As a general rule the best formula is obtained by grouping the residual equations in consecutive order, as was done in Examples 1 and 2. The following example will serve to clear up the matter of grouping.

Example 3. Find by the method of averages a formula of the type

$$y = a + bx^3$$

which will fit the following data:

x	5	7	9	11	12
y	290	560	1044	1810	2300

Solution. The residual equations are

$$v_1 = a + \ 125b - \ \ 290$$
$$v_2 = a + \ 343b - \ \ 560$$
$$v_3 = a + \ 729b - 1044$$
$$v_4 = a + 1331b - 1810$$
$$v_5 = a + 1728b - 2300.$$

The number of possible groupings of these equations is $5!/(3!2!) = 10$. The ten different groupings and the resulting formulas corresponding to them are given below.

1.
$$\begin{cases} v_1 \\ \ \\ v_2 \end{cases} \quad y = 130.87 + 1.2570x^3.$$

$$\begin{cases} v_3 \\ v_4 \\ v_5 \end{cases} \quad \Sigma v = 0.000010, \quad \Sigma v^2 = 64.065.$$

2.
$$\begin{cases} v_1 \\ v_2 \\ v_3 \end{cases} \quad y = 128.86 + 1.2593x^3.$$

$$\begin{cases} v_4 \\ \ \\ v_5 \end{cases} \quad \Sigma v = 0.000071, \quad \Sigma v^2 = 72.500.$$

3.
$$\begin{cases} v_1 \\ \\ v_3 \end{cases} \quad y = 129.68 + 1.2584x^3.$$

$$\begin{cases} v_2 \\ v_4 \\ v_5 \end{cases} \quad \Sigma v = 0.00028, \quad \Sigma v^2 = 66.668.$$

4.
$$\begin{cases} v_1 \\ \\ v_4 \end{cases} \quad y = 158.91 + 1.2240x^3.$$

$$\begin{cases} v_2 \\ v_3 \\ v_5 \end{cases} \quad \Sigma v = -0.000017. \quad \Sigma v^2 = 2038.694.$$

5.
$$\begin{cases} v_1 \\ \\ v_5 \end{cases} \quad y = 135.95 + 1.2510x^3.$$

$$\begin{cases} v_2 \\ v_3 \\ v_4 \end{cases} \quad \Sigma v = -0.000004, \quad \Sigma v^2 = 132.197.$$

6.
$$\begin{cases} v_2 \\ \\ v_4 \end{cases} \quad y = 253.69 + 1.1127x^3.$$

$$\begin{cases} v_1 \\ v_3 \\ v_5 \end{cases} \quad \Sigma v = -0.000001, \quad \Sigma v^2 = 37626.548.$$

7.
$$\begin{cases} v_1 \\ v_2 \\ v_4 \end{cases} \quad y = 137.76 + 1.2489x^3.$$

$$\begin{cases} v_3 \\ \\ v_5 \end{cases} \quad \Sigma v = -0.000002, \quad \Sigma v^2 = 187.328.$$

8.
$$\begin{cases} v_1 \\ v_2 \\ v_5 \end{cases} \quad y = 123.95 + 1.2651x^3.$$

$$\begin{cases} v_3 \\ \\ v_4 \end{cases} \quad \Sigma v = 0.0000001, \quad \Sigma v^2 = 177.705.$$

9.

$$\begin{cases} v_2 \\ \\ v_3 \end{cases} \quad y = 123.84 + 1.2652x^3.$$

$$\begin{cases} v_1 \\ v_4 \\ v_5 \end{cases} \quad \sum v = -0.000002, \quad \sum v^2 = 181.389.$$

10.

$$\begin{cases} v_2 \\ \\ v_5 \end{cases} \quad y = 142.23 + 1.2436x^3.$$

$$\begin{cases} v_1 \\ v_3 \\ v_4 \end{cases} \quad \sum v = -0.000001. \quad \sum v^2 = 393.303.$$

The best formulas are those for which $\sum v^2$ is least and are evidently 1, 2, 3. The poorest are 4 and 6.

The best formula obtainable is found by the method of Least Squares to be

$$y = 130.71 + 1.2572x^3,$$

for which $\sum v = -0.0000016$ and $\sum v^2 = 64.004$.

A carefully constructed graph, obtained by putting $x^3 = u$ and plotting the straight line $y = a + bu$ on a large sheet of finely squared paper, gave

$$y = 125 + 1.33x^3,$$

for which $\sum v = 281.48$, $\sum v^2 = 25460.154$. This formula obtained from a good graph is far inferior to nine of the ten formulas obtained by the method of averages.

When the number of residual equations is large enough to allow three or more to each group, the method of averages can be depended upon to give good results. If we have only a few sets of data (readings or measurements) and can not easily obtain more, we should always use the method of Least Squares. This method gives only one formula and that is always the best possible one.

Every empirical formula, however obtained, should always be tested by computing the residuals and seeing whether they are within allowable limits.

145. The Method of Least Squares. This method says that the best representative curve is that for which the sum of the squares of the residuals is a minimum. Since the squares of the residuals are positive quantities, the requirement that their sum shall be as small as possible insures that the numerical values of the residuals will be small; and this means that in the case of a series of plotted points the best representative curve will pass as closely as possible to all the points. Before applying this method to empirical formulas we shall first derive a fundamental rule which reduces the method to a simple procedure.

For simplicity let us consider the formula

$$(1) \qquad\qquad y = a + bx + cx^2$$

and find the values of a, b, and c which will make the graph of (1) pass as near as possible to each of the n points (x_1, y_1), (x_2, y_2), $\cdots$ (x_n, y_n); or, stated otherwise, let us find an equation of the form (1) which will be satisfied as nearly as possible by *each* of the n pairs of observed values (x_1, y_1), (x_2, y_2), $\cdots$ (x_n, y_n). The equation will not, in general, be satisfied exactly by any of the n pairs. Substituting in (1) each of the n pairs of values in turn, we get the following *residual equations*:

$$(2) \qquad \begin{aligned} v_1 &= a + bx_1 + cx_1{}^2 - y_1, \\ v_2 &= a + bx_2 + cx_2{}^2 - y_2, \\ &\;\cdot\quad\cdot\quad\cdot\quad\cdot\quad\cdot\quad\cdot\quad\cdot\quad\cdot \\ v_n &= a + bx_n + cx_n{}^2 - y_n. \end{aligned}$$

The principle of least squares says that the best values of the unknown constants a, b, and c are those which make the sum of the squares of the residuals a minimum, or

$$\Sigma v^2 = v_1{}^2 + v_2{}^2 + \cdots + v_n{}^2$$

must be a minimum. Hence

$$\Sigma(a + bx + cx^2 - y)^2 = (a + bx_1 + cx_1{}^2 - y_1)^2 + (a + bx_2 + cx_2{}^2 - y_2)^2$$
$$+ \cdots + (a + bx_n + cx_n{}^2 - y_n)^2 = f(a, b, c)$$

is to be a minimum.

The condition that $f(a, b, c)$ be a maximum or a minimum is that its partial derivatives with respect to a, b, and c shall each be zero. We therefore have

$$\frac{\partial f}{\partial a} = 2(a + bx_1 + cx_1{}^2 - y_1) + 2(a + bx_2 + cx_2{}^2 - y_2) + \cdots = 0,$$

$$\frac{\partial f}{\partial b} = 2(a + bx_1 + cx_1{}^2 - y_1)x_1 + 2(a + bx_2 + cx_2{}^2 - y_2)x_2 + \cdots = 0,$$

$$\frac{\partial f}{\partial c} = 2(a + bx_1 + cx_1{}^2 - y_1)x_1{}^2 + 2(a + bx_2 + cx_2{}^2 - y_2)x_2{}^2 + \cdots = 0.$$

Dividing through by 2, we get the following three *normal equations*:

$$(3) \quad \begin{cases} (a + bx_1 + cx_1{}^2 - y_1) + (a + bx_2 + cx_2{}^2 - y_2) \\ \quad + \cdots + (a + bx_n + cx_n{}^2 - y_n) = 0, \\ x_1(a + bx_1 + cx_1{}^2 - y_1) + x_2(a + bx_2 + cx_2{}^2 - y_2) \\ \quad \cdot \ + \cdots + x_n(a + bx_n + cx_n{}^2 - y_n) = 0, \\ x_1{}^2(a + bx_1 + cx_1{}^2 - y_1) + x_2{}^2(a + bx_2 + cx_2{}^2 - y_2) \\ \quad + \cdots + x_n{}^2(a + bx_n + cx_n{}^2 - y_n) = 0. \end{cases}$$

It will be observed that these normal equations can be written down immediately by applying the following

Rule: To find the *first* normal equation multiply the right-hand member of each residual equation by the coefficient of the *first unknown* in that member, add the products thus obtained, and equate their sum to zero; to get the *second* normal equation multiply the right-hand member of each residual equation by the coefficient of the *second unknown* in that member, add the products so obtained, and place their sum equal to zero; and so on for the remaining normal equations.

The normal equations are solved by the ordinary methods of algebra for solving simultaneous equations of the first degree in two or more unknowns. When there are several equations and the coefficients contain several digits, solve by the methods of Arts. 158 or 164.

The number of normal equations is always the same as the number of unknown constants to be determined, whereas the number of residual equations is equal to the number of observations. The number of observations must always be *greater* than the number of undetermined constants if the method of least squares is to be of any benefit in the solution.

The rule above is applicable to any formula which is *linear in the constants* or to any formula which can be reduced to a form linear in the constants.

Example 1. Find the equation of the straight line which comes nearest to passing through the following points:

x	0.5	1.0	1.5	2.0	2.5	3.0
y	0.31	0.82	1.29	1.85	2.51	3.02

Solution. Let the equation of the line be

$$y = a + bx.$$

Substituting in this equation the several pairs of values of x and y, we get the following *residual equations*:

$$v_1 = a + 0.5b - 0.31$$
$$v_2 = a + \quad b - 0.82$$
$$v_3 = a + 1.5b - 1.29$$
$$v_4 = a + \quad 2b - 1.85$$
$$v_5 = a + 2.5b - 2.51$$
$$v_6 = a + \quad 3b - 3.02$$

Residual equations.

Adding the right-hand members and equating their sum to zero, we get

$$6a + 10.5b - 9.80 = 0.$$

Multiplying the right-hand member of the first residual equation by 0.5, the second by 1, the third by 1.5, etc., adding the products, and equating their sum to zero, we get

$$10.5a + 22.75b - 21.945 = 0.$$

Hence the normal equations are

$$6a + 10.5b = \quad 9.80$$
$$10.5a + 22.75b = 21.945$$

Normal equations.

Solving these by determinants, we have

$$a = \frac{\begin{vmatrix} 9.80 & 10.5 \\ 21.945 & 22.75 \end{vmatrix}}{\begin{vmatrix} 6 & 10.5 \\ 10.5 & 22.75 \end{vmatrix}} = \frac{222.950 - 230.422}{136.50 - 110.25} = -\frac{7.472}{26.25} = -0.285.$$

$$b = \frac{\begin{vmatrix} 6 & 9.80 \\ 10.5 & 21.945 \end{vmatrix}}{26.25} = \frac{131.670 - 102.900}{26.25} = \frac{28.770}{26.25} = 1.096$$

$$= 1.10, \text{ say.}$$

The required equation is therefore

$$y = -0.285 + 1.10x.$$

Computing the residuals by substituting the given points in this formula, we have

$$v_1 = -0.045, \quad v_2 = -0.005, \quad v_3 = 0.075,$$
$$v_4 = 0.065, \quad v_5 = -0.045, \quad v_6 = -0.005.$$
$$\therefore \ \Sigma v = 0.04, \quad \Sigma v^2 = 0.014.$$

Example 2. Find a formula of the form

$$y = a + bx + cx^2$$

which will fit the following data:

x	0	0.1	0.2	0.3	0.4	0.5	0.6	0.7	0.8	0.9
y	3.1950	3.2299	3.2532	3.2611	3.2516	3.2282	3.1807	3.1266	3.0594	2.9759

Solution. Substituting in the assumed formula the corresponding values of x and y as given in the table, we get

$$
\begin{aligned}
v_1 &= a + 0b + 0c - 3.1950 \\
v_2 &= a + 0.1b + 0.01c - 3.2299 \\
v_3 &= a + 0.2b + 0.04c - 3.2532 \\
v_4 &= a + 0.3b + 0.09c - 3.2611 \\
v_5 &= a + 0.4b + 0.16c - 3.2516 \\
v_6 &= a + 0.5b + 0\ 25c - 3.2282 \\
v_7 &= a + 0.6b + 0.36c - 3.1807 \\
v_8 &= a + 0.7b + 0.49c - 3.1266 \\
v_9 &= a + 0.8b + 0.64c - 3.0594 \\
v_{10} &= a + 0.9b + 0.81c - 2.9759
\end{aligned}
\quad\right\} \text{ Residual equations.}
$$

Applying the rule of page 453 to these equations, we get

$$
\left.
\begin{aligned}
10a + 4.5b + 2.85c &= 31.7616 \\
4.5a + 2.85b + 2.025c &= 14.0896 \\
2.85a + 2.025b + 1.5333c &= 8.82881
\end{aligned}
\right\} \text{ Normal equations.}
$$

Solving these for a, b, c, we find

$$
\begin{aligned}
a &= 3.1951, \\
b &= 0.44254, \\
c &= -0.76531.
\end{aligned}
$$

Hence the required equation is

$$\underline{y = 3.1951 + 0.44254x - 0.76531x^2.}$$

If we compute the residuals by substituting in this formula the values of x and y given in the table, we find

$$\Sigma v = 0.0001, \qquad \Sigma v^2 = 0.0000549.$$

The following example is given to illustrate how the solution of a problem in a routine, perfunctory manner can lead to a worthless result. The first computation is the perfunctory one in which the work is done in a routine, careless manner. The second computation improves on the first by preventing errors of computation in the evaluation of the determinants. The third computation prevents errors of computation from the very beginning.

Example 3. The indicated horse power, I, required to drive a ship of displacement D tons at a ten-knot speed is given by the following data. Find a formula of the form $I = aD^n$ which will fit the data.

D	1720	2300	3200	4100
I	655	789	1000	1164

Solution. We have

$$I = aD^n.$$
$$\therefore \quad \log I = \log a + n \log D.$$

The residuals are really

$$v_1 = aD_1{}^n - I_1, \quad v_2 = aD_2{}^n - I_2, \text{ etc.,}$$

but we save a great deal of labor and commit very little error by writing

$$(4) \qquad \begin{cases} v'_1 = \log a + n \log D_1 - \log I_1, \\ v'_2 = \log a + n \log D_2 - \log I_2, \\ \qquad \text{etc.,} \end{cases}$$

and making the sum of the squares of the v''s a minimum.

(a). Perfunctory Computation. Substituting in these equations the corresponding values of D and I, we get

$$\left. \begin{array}{l} v'_1 = \log a + 3.236n - 2.816 \\ v'_2 = \log a + 3.362n - 2.897 \\ v'_3 = \log a + 3.505n - 3.000 \\ v'_4 = \log a + 3.613n - 3.066 \end{array} \right\} \text{ Residual equations.}$$

Since these equations are *linear* in the constants n and *log a*, we can apply the rule stated on page 453. Adding the right-hand members and equating their sum to zero, we find the first normal equation to be

$$4 \log a + 13.716n = 11.779.$$

Multiplying the right-hand member of the first residual equation by 3.236, the second by 3.362, etc., adding the products, and equating their sum to zero, we get

$$13.716 \log a + 47.11n = 40.445$$

for the second normal equation. Rounding off these numbers to four figures, we have

$$47.11n + 13.72 \log a = 40.44 \brace 13.72n + 4 \log a = 11.78}$$ Normal equations.

Solving these equations by determinants, we have

$$n = \frac{\begin{vmatrix} 40.44 & 13.72 \\ 11.78 & 4 \end{vmatrix}}{\begin{vmatrix} 47.11 & 13.72 \\ 13.72 & 4 \end{vmatrix}} = \frac{161.76 - 161.62}{188.44 - 188.24} = \frac{0.14}{0.20} = 0.700,$$

$$\log a = \frac{\begin{vmatrix} 47.11 & 40.44 \\ 13.72 & 11.78 \end{vmatrix}}{0.20} = \frac{554.96 - 554.84}{0.20} = \frac{0.12}{0.20} = 0.600.$$

$$\therefore \quad a = 3.981.$$

The resulting formula is therefore

$$I = 3.98 D^{0.700}.$$

Computing the residuals by substituting the data in this formula, we get

$$v_1 = -77, \quad v_2 = -108, \quad v_3 = -131, \quad v_4 = -182.$$

Hence

$$\Sigma v^2 = 67,878.$$

The formula which we have found is evidently so poor as to be worthless; for the residuals are large, all of the same sign, and the sum of their squares is exceedingly large.

The results would have been far worse if we had rounded off to four figures the products obtained in evaluating the determinants, for in that case we would have had

$$n = \frac{161.8 - 161.6}{188.4 - 188.2} = \frac{0.2}{0.2} = 1$$

$$\log a = \frac{555.0 - 554.8}{0.2} = \frac{0.2}{0.2} = 1.$$

$$\therefore \quad a = 10.$$

Hence the formula would have been

$$I = 10D,$$

which is totally worthless in this case.

The poor result obtained above is due primarily to the fact that in the process of solving the normal equations three of the most important significant figures *disappeared by subtraction* (see Art. 7); for n and $\log a$ were determined from the simple fractions $0.14/0.20$ and $0.12/0.20$, respectively, in each of which the second figure in both numerator and denominator is doubtful. This loss of significant figures did not seriously affect n, but in the case of a the effect was disastrous. The reason for the greater effect on a is this: An error ϵ in $\log N$ will cause an error $2.3026\,N\epsilon$ in the antilog (Art. 7).

(*b*). *Improved Computation.* Treating the elements of the determinants as exact numbers and retaining all the figures in the products, we have

$$n = \frac{\begin{vmatrix} 40.44 & 13.72 \\ 11.78 & 4 \end{vmatrix}}{\begin{vmatrix} 47.11 & 13.72 \\ 13.72 & 4 \end{vmatrix}} = \frac{161.76 - 161.6216}{188.44 - 188.2384} = \frac{0.1384}{0.2016} = 0.6865.$$

$$\log a = \frac{\begin{vmatrix} 47.11 & 40.44 \\ 13.72 & 11.78 \end{vmatrix}}{0.2016} = \frac{554.9558 - 554.8368}{0.2016} = \frac{0.1190}{0.2016} = 0.5903,$$

whence

$$a = 3.893.$$

The resulting formula is therefore

$$I = 3.893 D^{0.6865}.$$

The residuals in this case are

$$v_1 = 7.16, \quad v_2 = -1.88, \quad v_3 = 7.87, \quad v_4 = -12.1; \quad \text{and}$$

$$\Sigma v^2 = 263.1.$$

(*c*). *Accurate Solution.*

One way to get the required constants correct to four significant figures in this example is to solve the problem anew and carry all computations to *eight significant figures*, so that we shall have five left after the first three disappear by subtraction. We therefore make a new computation, using 7-place logs. The results are as follows:

$$n = \frac{161.773154 - 161.554945}{188.43257 \ \ - 188.10644} = \frac{0.21821}{0.32613} = 0.6691$$

$$\log a = \frac{554.89958 - 554.68739}{0.32613} = \frac{0.21219}{0.32613} = 0.65063$$

and

$$\therefore \ \ a = 4.4733 = 4.473, \text{ say.}$$

Hence the final formula is

$$\underline{I = 4.473 \ D^{0.6691}.}$$

The residuals are found to be

$$v_1 = -1.1, \quad v_2 = 5.2, \quad v_3 = -9.4, \quad v_4 = 5.3 \ ;$$

and therefore

$$\Sigma v = 0.0, \quad \Sigma v^2 = 144.7.$$

Note. This example serves to bring out an important point which must be kept in mind when determining the constants in empirical formulas. The point is this: The data used in determining the constants should be treated as *exact* numbers, and the computer must be careful about rounding off and dropping seemingly superfluous digits at any stage of the computation. The final values of the constants should be given to as many significant figures as are given in the original data.

When it happens that some of the most important significant figures disappear by subtraction, as in the example above, the computation must be carried through with enough significant figures at all stages to give a reliable result. As a general rule it may be stated that if the constants are desired to m significant figures and if a preliminary calculation shows that the first p figures will disappear by subtraction, the calculation must be performed with $m + p + 1$ significant figures throughout from beginning to end.

In the solution of systems of linear equations the occasional loss of the leading significant figures by subtraction cannot be prevented, but the harmful effect of such loss can be lessened by preventing subsequent errors of computation.

146. Weighted Residuals. It sometimes happens that the residuals are not all of the same weight. This is the case when we use the residuals of a *function* of y instead of those of y itself. In Ex. 2, Art. 143, and Ex. 3, Art. 145, for example, we found it necessary to use the residuals of $\log y$ instead of those of y. In these cases the residuals were no longer of equal weight, as we shall now show.

Using the notation of Art. 139, let

$$Q = f(y).$$

Then

$$\frac{\partial Q}{\partial y} = f'(y).$$

Substituting this in (139.1), we get

$$R = f'(y)r,$$

where r denotes the P. E. of y and R the P. E. of $f(y)$. Hence

$$\frac{R}{r} = f'(y).$$

Since the same relations hold between residuals as between probable errors, we may write

$$\frac{R}{r} = \frac{V}{v},$$

where v and V denote the residuals of y and $f(y)$, respectively. Hence

$$\frac{V}{v} = f'(y).$$

Denoting by w_y and w_f the weights of y and $f(y)$, respectively, we have from (136.2)

$$\frac{w_f}{w_y} = \frac{r^2}{R^2} = \frac{v^2}{V^2} = \frac{1}{[f'(y)]^2}.$$

(146. 1) $$\therefore \quad w_f = \frac{w_y}{[f'(y)]^2}.$$

Now if $f(y) = \log_{10} y = M \log_e y$, where $M = 0.43429$, we have

$$f'(y) = \frac{M}{y}.$$

Hence from (146.1)

$$w_f = \frac{y^2 w_y}{M^2};$$

and if all the y's are of equal weight, then $w_y = 1$ and we have

(146. 2) $$w_f = \frac{y^2}{M^2}.$$

We shall next derive the fundamental rule for writing down the normal equations when the residuals have different weights.

By Art. 126 the best result obtainable from measurements of unequal weight is that for which the sum of the weighted squares of the residuals is a minimum. Hence we must have

$$\Sigma wv^2 = w_1v_1{}^2 + w_2v_2{}^2 + \cdots + w_nv_n{}^2 \text{ a minimum.}$$

In the case of the equation $y = a + bx + cx^2$ (Art. 145) we therefore have

$$w_1(a + bx_1 + cx_1{}^2 - y_1)^2 + w_2(a + bx_2 + cx_2{}^2 - y_2)^2 + \cdots \text{ a minimum.}$$

Calling this expression $f(a, b, c)$, taking the partial derivatives with repect to a, b, c in turn, and equating each to zero, we have

$$\frac{\partial f}{\partial a} = 2w_1(a + bx_1 + cx_1{}^2 - y_1) + 2w_2(a + bx_2 + cx_2{}^2 - y_2) + \cdots = 0,$$

$$\frac{\partial f}{\partial b} = 2w_1x_1(a + bx_1 + cx_1{}^2 - y_1) + 2w_2x_2(a + bx_2 + cx_2{}^2 - y_2) + \cdots = 0,$$

$$\frac{\partial f}{\partial c} = 2w_1x_1{}^2(a + bx_1 + cx_1{}^2 - y_1) + 2w_2x_2{}^2(a + bx_2 + cx_2{}^2 - y_2) + \cdots = 0,$$

Hence on dividing through by 2 we get

$$\left.\begin{array}{l} w_1(a + bx_1 + cx_1{}^2 - y_1) + w_2(a + bx_2 + cx_2{}^2 - y_2) \\ \quad + \cdots + w_n(a + bx_n + cx_n{}^2 - y_n) = 0 \\ w_1x_1(a + bx_1 + cx_1{}^2 - y_1) + w_2x_2(a + bx_2 + cx_2{}^2 - y_2) \\ \quad + \cdots + w_nx_n(a + bx_n + cx_n{}^2 - y_n) = 0 \\ w_1x_1{}^2(a + bx_1 + cx_1{}^2 - y_1) + w_2x_2{}^2(a + bx_2 + cx_2{}^2 - y_2) \\ \quad + \cdots + w_nx_n{}^2(a + bx_n + cx_n{}^2 - y_n) = 0 \end{array}\right\} \begin{array}{l} \text{Weighted} \\ \text{normal} \\ \text{equations.} \end{array}$$

In the case of *weighted* residuals we can therefore write down the normal equations according to the following

Rule: To get the *first* normal equation multiply the right-hand side of each residual equation by its weight and by the coefficient of the *first unknown* in that equation, add the products thus obtained, and equate their sum to zero; to find the *second* normal equation multiply the right-hand member of each residual equation by its weight and by the coefficient of the *second · unknown* in that member, add the products, and equate their sum to zero; and so on for the others.

We shall now work Ex. 3 of the preceding article by the method of weights. By (146. 2) the weights of the residuals are $I_1{}^2/M^2$, $I_2{}^2/M^2$, $I_3{}^2/M^2$, and $I_4{}^2/M^2$; but since the factor $1/M^2$ will divide out in the normal equations we do not write it down at all. The solution given below should be self-expanatory.

$$I = aD^n.$$

$$\therefore \quad \log I = \log a + n \log D.$$

D	1720	2300	3200	4100
I	655	789	1000	1164
I^2	429025	622521	1000000	1354896

Weights

$$
\begin{aligned}
v_1 &= \log a + 3.2355284n - 2.8162413 & 429025 \\
v_2 &= \log a + 3.3617278n - 2.8970770 & 622521 \\
v_3 &= \log a + 3.5051500n - 3.0000000 & 1000000 \\
v_4 &= \log a + 3.6127839n - 3.0659530 & 1354896
\end{aligned}
\left.\begin{aligned} \\ \\ \\ \\ \end{aligned}\right\}
\begin{aligned} \text{Residual} \\ \text{equations.} \end{aligned}
$$

Now applying the rule for writing down the weighted normal equations, we find them to be

$$
\begin{aligned}
11880965.2n + 3406442 \log a &= 10165776.6 \\
41497013.1n + 11880965.2 \log a &= 35495260.6
\end{aligned}
\left.\begin{aligned} \\ \\ \end{aligned}\right\}
\begin{aligned} \text{Weighted normal} \\ \text{equations.} \end{aligned}
$$

Solving these by determinants, we find

$$n = 0.6671, \quad a = 4.546.$$

The required formula is therefore

$$\underline{I = 4.546D^{0.6671}.}$$

The residuals are found to be

$$v_1 = -0.3, \quad v_2 = 5.8, \quad v_3 = -9.4, \quad v_4 = 4.8.$$
$$\therefore \quad \Sigma v = 0.9, \quad \Sigma v^2 = 145.1.$$

Here the values of Σv and Σv^2 are slightly larger than in the unweighted previous solution, but the lack of improvement is not the fault of the weighting method. It is due to the singular nature of the example treated. After applying this weighting method to several simple examples of different types and comparing the results with those obtained by ignoring differences in weight, the author is of the opinion that ordinarily it is not worth while to bother about the weights of the residuals; but problems sometimes arise in which the weights must be considered.*

---

* For a striking example of the effect of weighting in some problems see an important paper by C. E. Van Orstrand: "On the Empirical Representation of Certain

Remark. Since the weights in the preceding example are approximately as the numbers 43, 62, 100, and 135, the student may wonder why it is not sufficient to multiply the residuals by these smaller numbers instead of by the actual weights 429025, 622521, etc. The answer is that if we did this the corresponding products would be true to only two or three significant figures and these would disappear in this problem by subtraction in solving the normal equations, so that the results found would be very uncertain. We can state as a general rule that the number of significant figures used in the weights must not be less than the number of significant figures which are to be retained throughout the computation, unless the exact values of the weights happen to contain fewer figures than the number retained throughout the computation.

147. Non-Linear Formulas.—The General Case.

Not all empirical formulas can be handled by the methods thus far considered. For example, the relation between the pressure p and temperature t of saturated steam can be expressed by a formula of the type

$$p = a(10)^{bt/(c+t)},$$

where a, b, c, are unknown constants. These constants do not enter the formula linearly, and no transformation of the formula will give a linear relation among them. Consequently they can not be determined by the methods previously given. We are now going to develop a method which will apply to any type of formula, however complicated it may be.

Let us consider a formula involving two variables, x and y, and three undetermined constants, a, b, c. Such a formula may be written in the symbolic form

$$(1) \qquad y = f(x, a, b, c).$$

Let a_0, b_0, c_0 be approximate values of a, b, c, obtained from a graph or by any other means, and let α, β, γ denote corrections which are to be applied to a_0, b_0, c_0, respectively, so that

$$(2) \qquad \begin{cases} a = a_0 + \alpha, \\ b = b_0 + \beta, \\ c = c_0 + \gamma. \end{cases}$$

Then

$$(3) \qquad y' = f(x, a_0, b_0, c_0)$$

will be a function whose graph approximates the graph (1) more or less closely. The values of this approximating function corresponding to $x_1, x_2, \cdots x_n$ will be

(4)
$$\begin{cases} y'_1 = f(x_1, a_0, b_0, c_0), \\ y'_2 = f(x_2, a_0, b_0, c_0), \\ \cdots \cdots \cdots \cdots \\ y'_n = f(x_n, a_0, b_0, c_0). \end{cases}$$

If we take (1) to be the best or most probable function and its graph to be the best representative curve, then the residuals will be

(5)
$$\begin{cases} v_1 = f(x_1, a, b, c) - y_1 \\ v_2 = f(x_2, a, b, c) - y_2 \\ \cdots \cdots \cdots \cdots \\ v_n = f(x_n, a, b, c) - y_n, \end{cases}$$

where $y_1, y_2, \cdots y_n$ are the *observed* y's corresponding to $x_1, x_2, \cdots x_n$, respectively. Substituting in (5) the values of a, b, c as given by (2). we have for the first residual

$$v_1 = f(x_1, a_0 + \alpha, b_0 + \beta, c_0 + \gamma) - y_1,$$

or

(6) $$v_1 + y_1 = f(x_1, a_0 + \alpha, b_0 + \beta, c_0 + \gamma).$$

Considering the right-hand member of (6) as a function of a, b, c and expanding it by Taylor's theorem for a function of several variables, we have

(7) $$v_1 + y_1 = f(x_1, a_0, b_0, c_0)$$

$$+ \alpha \left(\frac{\partial f_1}{\partial a} \right)_0 + \beta \left(\frac{\partial f_1}{\partial b} \right)_0 + \gamma \left(\frac{\partial f_1}{\partial c} \right)_0$$

+ terms involving higher powers and products of α, β, γ,

where $(\partial f_1 / \partial a)_0$ means

$$\left(\frac{\partial f}{\partial a} \right)_{\substack{x = x_1 \\ a = a_0 \\ b = b_0 \\ b = c_0}}, \text{ etc.}$$

Then since $y'_1 = f(x_1, a_0, b_0, c_0)$, (7) becomes

$$v_1 + y_1 = y'_1 + \alpha \left(\frac{\partial f_1}{\partial a} \right)_0 + \beta \left(\frac{\partial f_1}{\partial b} \right)_0 + \gamma \left(\frac{\partial f_1}{\partial c} \right)_0 + \cdots,$$

or

$$v_1 = \alpha \left(\frac{\partial f_1}{\partial a}\right)_0 + \beta \left(\frac{\partial f_1}{\partial b}\right)_0 + \gamma \left(\frac{\partial f_1}{\partial c}\right)_0 + y'_1 - y_1 .$$

Let

$$r_1 = y'_1 - y_1, \quad r_2 = y'_2 - y_2, \quad \cdots r_n = y'_n - y_n .$$

Then the residuals become

$$(147.1) \quad \left. \begin{aligned} v_1 &= \alpha \left(\frac{\partial f_1}{\partial a}\right)_0 + \beta \left(\frac{\partial f_1}{\partial b}\right)_0 + \gamma \left(\frac{\partial f_1}{\partial c}\right)_0 + r_1 \\ v_2 &= \alpha \left(\frac{\partial f_2}{\partial a}\right)_0 + \beta \left(\frac{\partial f_2}{\partial b}\right)_0 + \gamma \left(\frac{\partial f_2}{\partial c}\right)_0 + r_2 \\ &\cdots \cdots \cdots \cdots \cdots \cdots \cdots \cdots \cdots \cdots \\ v_n &= \alpha \left(\frac{\partial f_n}{\partial a}\right)_0 + \beta \left(\frac{\partial f_n}{\partial b}\right)_0 + \gamma \left(\frac{\partial f_n}{\partial c}\right)_0 + r_n \end{aligned} \right\} \begin{array}{l} \text{Residual} \\ \text{equations.} \end{array}$$

These equations are *linear* (of the first degree) *in the corrections* α, β, γ, and we may therefore deal with the problem from this point onward either by the method of averages or by the method of least squares. If we use the latter method, we write down the normal equations by the rule stated on page 453.

The quantities $r_1, r_2, \cdots r_n$ are the residuals for the approximation curve $y' = f(x, a_0, b_0, c_0)$, since they are the differences between the observed ordinates and the ordinates to this curve.

We shall now apply this general method to two examples.

Example 1. Find a formula of the form

$$y = mx + b$$

which will fit the following data:

x	27	33	40	55	68
y	109.9	112.0	114.7	120.1	125.0

Solution. When these values are plotted on ordinary coordinate paper, the points are found to lie nearly on a straight line (Fig. 51). The line which seems (to the eye) to fit them best has a slope of 0.37 and a y-intercept of 99.7. Hence we take

$$m_0 = 0.37, \quad b_0 = 99.7.$$

The approximation curve is therefore the line

$$y' = 0.37x + 99.7.$$

Substituting in this equation the observed values of x, we get

$$y'_1 = 0.37 \times 27 + 99.7 = 109.7,$$
$$y'_2 = 0.37 \times 33 + 99.7 = 111.9,$$
$$y'_3 = 114.7, \quad y'_4 = 120.0, \quad y'_5 = 124.9.$$

Hence

$$r_1 = 109.7 - 109.9 = -0.2,$$
$$r_2 = 111.9 - 112.0 = -0.1,$$
$$r_3 = 0.0, \quad r_4 = -0.1, \quad r_5 = -0.1.$$

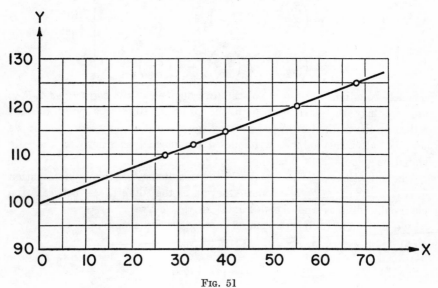

FIG. 51

Also, since

$$f(x, m, b) = mx + b.$$

we have

$$\frac{\partial f}{\partial m} = x, \quad \frac{\partial f}{\partial b} = 1.$$

$$\therefore \frac{\partial f_1}{\partial m} = x_1 = 27,$$

$$\frac{\partial f_2}{\partial m} = x_2 = 33,$$

$$\frac{\partial f_3}{\partial m} = 40, \quad \frac{\partial f_4}{\partial m} = 55, \quad \frac{\partial f_5}{\partial m} = 68;$$

and

$$\frac{\partial f_1}{\partial b} = 1 = \frac{\partial f_2}{\partial b} = \frac{\partial f_3}{\partial b} = \frac{\partial f_4}{\partial b} = \frac{\partial f_5}{\partial b}.$$

Substituting in (147.1) these values of the r's and partial derivatives, we get

$$\left.\begin{aligned}
v_1 &= 27\alpha + \beta - 0.2 \\
v_2 &= 33\alpha + \beta - 0.1 \\
v_3 &= 40\alpha + \beta + 0.0 \\
v_4 &= 55\alpha + \beta - 0.1 \\
v_5 &= 68\alpha + \beta - 0.1
\end{aligned}\right\} \quad \begin{aligned}\text{Residual} \\ \text{equations.}\end{aligned}$$

We shall complete the problem by finding the best values of α and β by the method of least squares. Forming the normal equations according to the rule on page 453, we get

$$\left.\begin{aligned}
11068\alpha + 223\beta &= 21.0 \\
223\alpha + 5\beta &= 0.5
\end{aligned}\right\} \quad \begin{aligned}\text{Normal} \\ \text{equations.}\end{aligned}$$

Solving these for α and β, we find

$$\alpha = -0.0012, \quad \beta = 0.152.$$

Hence

$$m = 0.37 - 0.0012 = 0.3688,$$

$$b = 99.7 + 0.15 = 99.85.$$

The required formula is therefore

$$\underline{\quad y = 0.3688x + 99.85.\quad}$$

Example 2. Find more accurate values for the constants a, b, c, in the formula

$$p = a(10)^{bt/(c+t)},$$

given the approximate values

$$a_0 = 4.53, \quad b_0 = 7.45, \quad c_0 = 234.7.$$

Solution. For the partial derivatives $(\partial p/\partial a)_0$, $(\partial p/\partial b)_0$, $(\partial p/\partial c)_0$ we have

$$\left(\frac{\partial p}{\partial a}\right)_0 = (10)^{b_0 t/(c_0+t)}, \quad \left(\frac{\partial p}{\partial b}\right)_0 = a_0(10)^{b_0 t/(c_0+t)} \cdot \frac{t}{c_0 + t} \cdot \log_e 10,$$

$$\left(\frac{\partial p}{\partial c}\right)_0 = -a_0(10)^{b_0 t/(c_0+t)} \cdot \frac{b_0 t}{(c_0 + t)^2} \log_e 10.$$

Also

$$p'_1 = a_0(10)^{b_0 t_1/(c_0+t_1)}, \quad p'_2 = a_0(10)^{b_0 t_2/(c_0+t_2)}, \text{ etc.};$$

and

$$r_1 = p'_1 - p_1, \quad r_2 = p'_2 - p_2, \text{ etc.}$$

In the following table are given the observed values of t and p, the corresponding values of the partial derivatives, and the corresponding r's.

No.	$t°\ C$	p	$\left(\dfrac{\partial p}{\partial a}\right)_0$	$\left(\dfrac{\partial p}{\partial b}\right)_0$	$\left(\dfrac{\partial p}{\partial c}\right)_0$	r	Group
1	−5.31	2.95	0.672	−0.161	+0.005	+0.095	
2	−3.64	3.45	0.763	−0.124	+0.005	+0.007	
3	0.00	4.52	1.000	0.000	0.000	+0.005	
4	8.01	7.93	1.761	0.605	−0.018	+0.049	I
5	11.98	9.88	2.300	1.165	−0.035	+0.541	
6	16.82	13.52	3.149	2.196	−0.064	+0.746	
7	23.85	22.24	4.867	4.681	−0.136	−0.194	
8	35.95	43.96	9.763	13.523	−0.373	+0.265	
9	44.90	71.20	15.717	26.326	−0.726	−0.002	
10	52.12	101.40	22.583	42.806	−1.112	+0.903	
11	58.68	139.72	30.910	64.490	−1.636	+0.893	II
12	74.47	281.55	62.300	156.520	−3.723	+0.649	
13	78.83	330.58	73.152	190.924	−4.543	+1.248	
14	82.25	387.56	85.765	232.136	−5.455	+1.365	
15	86.21	453.31	100.319	281.098	−6.528	+3.807	
16	91.34	552.20	122.213	357.103	−8.160	+0.592	
17	93.66	602.53	133.354	396.752	−9.003	+2.314	
18	99.39	743.49	164.564	510.637	−11.381	+1.916	III
19	100.87	784.07	173.547	544.065	−12.079	+6.439	
20	104.64	895.83	198.293	637.758	−13.999	−3.435	

Denoting the corrections to a, b, c by α, β, γ, respectively, and substituting in (147.1) the values of the r's and partial derivatives given in the table, we get 20 residual equations for determining α, β, γ. In this problem we are going to use the method of averages; so it is not necessary to write down the residual equations. We simply divide the coefficients into three groups, as indicated in the table, and add the coefficients in each group. We thus get the following three equations:

$$\left\{ \begin{array}{l} 14.512\alpha + \quad 8.362\beta - \quad 0.243\gamma = -\quad 1.249, \\ 300.190\alpha + \quad 726.725\beta - 17.568\gamma = -\quad 5.321, \\ 892.290\alpha + 2727.413\beta - 61.150\gamma = -11.633. \end{array} \right.$$

Solving these equations for α, β, γ, we get

$$\alpha = -0.131, \quad \beta = -0.0603, \quad \gamma = -4.437,$$

so that the corrected values of the constants are

$$a = \quad 4.53 - 0.131 \quad = 4.399,$$
$$b = \quad 7.45 - 0.0603 = 7.390,$$
$$c = 234.70 - 4.44 \quad = 230.26.$$

The final equation is therefore

$$p = 4.399(10)^{7.390t/(230.26+t)}.$$

148. Determination of the Constants when Both Variables are Subject to Error. In Arts. 144-147 it was tacitly assumed that the given values of the independent variable were absolutely correct and free from all error; the values of the function alone were supposed to be subject to error. This assumption is legitimate in most cases, for it is usually possible and practicable to obtain the values of one variable more accurately than the other.

If both variables are subject to errors of the same order of magnitude, the problem of finding the best values of the empirical constants is more complicated except in those cases in which the data can be plotted as a straight-line graph, either directly or after a suitable change of one or both variables. In the present article we shall treat only the simple case in which both variables are of equal weight. This is sufficient for most problems; for, as was seen in Art. 146, it is not often necessary to take account of differences in weight.

Let us consider n pairs of values $(x_1, y_1), (x_2, y_2), \cdots (x_n, y_n)$, and let these be plotted as points on a straight-line graph. The line which best fits these points will evidently be that for which the sum of the squares of the *perpendicular distances* from the points to it is a minimum. The equation of any straight line may be written in the form

$$(1) \qquad\qquad ax + by + 1 = 0,$$

this symmetrical form being used because both x and y are equally subject to error. The perpendicular distance from any point (x', y') to the line (1) is given by the formula

$$(2) \qquad\qquad d = \frac{ax' + by' + 1}{\sqrt{a^2 + b^2}}.$$

The sum of the squares of the perpendicular distances from the points $(x_1, y_1), (x_2, y_2)$, etc. to the line (1) is therefore

$$(3) \quad F(a, b) = \Sigma d^2 = \frac{1}{a^2 + b^2}[(ax_1 + by_1 + 1)^2$$
$$+ (ax_2 + by_2 + 1)^2 + \cdots + (ax_n + by_n + 1)^2].$$

Since this is to be a minimum, its partial derivatives with respect to a and b must each be zero.

Taking the partial derivative of (3) with respect to a, we have

$$\frac{\partial F}{\partial a} = -\frac{2a}{(a^2 + b^2)^2} [(ax_1 + by_1 + 1)^2 + (ax_2 + by_2 + 1)^2$$
$$+ \cdots + (ax_n + by_n + 1)^2]$$
$$+ \frac{2}{a^2 + b^2} [x_1(ax_1 + by_1 + 1) + x_2(ax_2 + by_2 + 1)$$
$$+ \cdots + x_n(ax_n + by_n + 1)].$$

Expanding the terms within the brackets, reducing to a common denominator, and collecting terms, we get

(4) $\qquad \dfrac{\partial F}{\partial a} = \dfrac{2}{(a^2 + b^2)^2} [b(b^2 - a^2)\Sigma xy + (b^2 - a^2)\Sigma x$
$$+ ab^2(\Sigma x^2 - \Sigma y^2) - 2ab\,\Sigma y - an].$$

Likewise, by symmetry,

(5) $\qquad \dfrac{\partial F}{\partial b} = \dfrac{2}{(a^2 + b^2)^2} [a(a^2 - b^2)\Sigma xy + (a^2 - b^2)\Sigma y$
$$+ a^2 b(\Sigma y^2 - \Sigma x^2) - 2ab\,\Sigma x - bn].$$

Multiplying (4) by a, (5) by b, adding the results, and simplifying, we get

(6) $\qquad a\dfrac{\partial F}{\partial a} + b\dfrac{\partial F}{\partial b} = -\dfrac{2}{a^2 + b^2} [a\,\Sigma x + b\,\Sigma y + n].$

But since $\partial F/\partial a = 0$ and $\partial F/\partial b = 0$ for a minimum, (6) reduces to

$$a\,\Sigma x + b\,\Sigma y + n = 0,$$

or

(148. 1) $\qquad a\left(\dfrac{\Sigma x}{n}\right) + b\left(\dfrac{\Sigma y}{n}\right) + 1 = 0,$

which shows that equation (1) is satisfied by the values

$$x = \left(\frac{\Sigma x}{n}\right) = \bar{x}, \quad y = \left(\frac{\Sigma y}{n}\right) = \bar{y}.$$

In other words, *the best representative line always passes through the centroid of the given points.*

Since $\partial F/\partial a$ and $\partial F/\partial b$ must be zero for a minimum, we have from (4) and (5), respectively,

(148. 2) $\quad b(b^2 - a^2)\Sigma xy + (b^2 - a^2)\Sigma x - 2ab\,\Sigma y$
$$+ ab^2(\Sigma x^2 - \Sigma y^2) - an = 0,$$

(148. 3) $\quad a(a^2 - b^2)\Sigma xy + (a^2 - b^2)\Sigma y - 2ab\,\Sigma x$
$$- a^2 b(\Sigma x^2 - \Sigma y^2) - bn = 0.$$

Problems of the type treated in this article are to be solved by means of formulas (148. 1) and (148. 2) or (148. 1) and (148. 3), always using (148. 1) first. We shall apply this method to Example 1 of Art 145.

Example.

x	y	xy	x^2	y^2
0.5	0.31	0.155	0.25	0.0961
1.0	0.82	0.820	1.00	0.6724
1.5	1.29	1.935	2.25	1.6641
2.0	1.85	3.700	4.00	3.4225
2.5	2.51	6.275	6.25	6.3001
3.0	3.02	9.060	9.00	9.1204
Sums 10.5	9.80	21.945	22.75	21.2756

To facilitate the computation, the several known quantities are arranged in tabular form as shown above.

Since

$$\frac{\Sigma x}{n} = \frac{10.5}{6} = 1.75, \quad \frac{\Sigma y}{n} = \frac{9.80}{6} = \frac{4.90}{3},$$

we have by (148. 1)

$$1.75a + \frac{4.90}{3}\,b + .1 = 0,$$

or

$$b = -\frac{5.25a + 3}{4.9}.$$

Substituting this value of b in (148. 3) and reducing, we get

$$5.7187a^3 + 23.4548a^2 + 6.165a = 0.$$

Solving for a, we find

$$a = 0, \quad -3.8191, \quad -0.28227.$$

The corresponding values of b are found from the equation
$b = -(5.25a + 3)/4.9$ to be

$$b = -0.61224, \quad 3.4796, \quad -0.30981.$$

Since the slope of the line (1) is $-a/b$, it is obvious that the values $a = -3.8191$, $b = 3.4796$ are the only ones which will fit the data of this example. The required line is therefore

$$-3.8191x + 3.4796y + 1 = 0,$$

or

$$3.819x - 3.480y = 1,$$

or

$$\underline{y = -0.2874 + 1.097x.}$$

This last equation agrees closely with that found by the ordinary method in Art. 145.

If we compute the sum of the squares of the perpendicular distances from the several points to this line, we find

$$\Sigma d^2 = 0.00618.$$

For the line found in Ex. 1, Art. 145, we find

$$\Sigma d^2 = 0.00619 ;$$

the two results are thus practically identical.

Remark. The reader will observe that the determination of the best representative line by the method of the present article involves but little, if any, more labor than the ordinary method of Art. 145.

149. Finding the Best Type of Formula. There exists no general method for finding the best type of formula to fit any given set of data. Probably the best one can do is to proceed as follows:

1. Plot the data on rectangular coordinate paper, taking care to choose the proper scales along the two axes so as to make the graph show up to the best advantage.

2. If the graph is a straight line, or nearly so, assume a formula of the type

$$y = a + bx.$$

3. If the graph is not a straight line but is a fairly smooth curve without sharp turns or bends, it is likely that the data can be fitted by some one of the following formulas:

Remarks and Suggestions.

(a) $\quad y = a + bx + cx^2 + dx^3.$ Linear in the constants.

(b) $\quad y = a + \dfrac{b}{x}$ Linear in constants. Put $1/x = t$ to plot.

Remarks and Suggestions.

(c) $y = \dfrac{1}{a + bx}$, or $\dfrac{1}{y} = a + bx.$ Put $1/y = u$ and plot the straight
line $u = a + bx.$

(d) $y^2 = a + bx + cx^2 + dx^3.$ Linear in constants.

(e) $y = ab^x,$ or $\log y = \log a + x \log b.$

(f) $y = ae^{bx},$ or $\log y = \log a + bx \log e.$

(g) $\log y = a + bx + cx^2.$ Linear in constants.

(h) $y = \dfrac{x}{a + bx + cx^2}$,

or

$\dfrac{x}{y} = a + bx + cx^2.$ Linear in constants.

(i) $y = ax^n,$ or $\log y = \log a + n \log x.$

(j) $y = ax^n + b.$ Use general method of Art. 147.

(k) $y = ae^{bx} + c.$ "   "   "   "   "   "

(l) $y = \dfrac{x}{a + bx} + c.$ "   "   "   "   "   "

(m) $y = ae^{bx} + ce^{dx}.$ "   "   "   "   "   "

(n) $y = ax^m + bx^n.$ "   "   "   "   "   "

4. As aids in determining which of the formulas (a)-(n) to use in any given problem, the following suggestions are offered:

(a) If the observed data give a straight-line graph when plotted on *logarithmic* paper, use the formula

$$y = ax^n.$$

(b) If the data give a straight line when plotted on *semi*logarithmic paper, the proper formula is

$$y = ae^{bx}, \quad \text{or} \quad y = ab^x.$$

(c) If the points $(1/x, y)$ or $(x, 1/y)$ lie on a straight line when plotted on ordinary coordinate paper, the proper formula is $y = a + b/x$ in the first case and $y = 1/(a + bx)$ or $1/y = a + bx$ in the second case.

5. The polynomial formula

$$y = a + bx + cx^2 + dx^3 + \cdots + qx^n$$

can be used to fit any set of data by taking a sufficient number of terms. The requisite number of terms is given by the following

Theorem: If the values of x *are in arithmetic progression (equidistant) and the* nth *differences of the* y*'s are constant, the last term in the required polynomial is* x^n.

This theorem is simply a corollary of the theorem proved in Art. 19.

For example, the third differences in the following data are nearly constant; so the required polynomial is

$$y = a + bx + cx^2 + dx^3.$$

x	y	$\Delta_1 y$	$\Delta_2 y$	$\Delta_3 y$
0	0			
0.1	0.212	0.212		
0.2	0.463	0.251	0.039	
0.3	0.772	0.309	0.058	0.019
0.4	1.153	0.381	0.072	0.014
0.5	1.625	0.472	0.091	0.019
0.6	2.207	0.582	0.110	0.019
0.7	2.917	0.710	0.128	0.018
0.8	3.776	0.859	0.149	0.021
0.9	4.798	1.022	0.163	0.014
1.0	6.001	1.203	0.181	0.018

This theorem applies *only* when the x's are taken at *equal intervals* apart. It rarely pays to take more than three or four terms in a polynomial formula, on account of the labor involved in determining the constants.

EXERCISES XVI

1. Find by the method of averages a formula of the form $y = ax^n$ which will fit the following data:

x	273	283	288	293	313	333	353	373
y	29.4	33.3	35.2	37.2	45.8	55.2	65.6	77.3

2. Plot on logarithmic paper the data of the above example and find a and n graphically or from selected points.

3. Find by the method of least squares a formula of the form $y = a + bx^2$ which will fit the following data:

x	19	25	31	38	44
y	1900	3230	4900	7330	9780

4. The data in the following table can be fitted by a formula of the type $y = ax^n$. Find the formula by the method of averages.

x	53.92	26.36	14.00	6.992	4.280	2.748	1.853
y	6.86	14.70	28.83	60.40	101.9	163.3	250.3

5. The data given below can be fitted by an exponential formula of the type $y = ae^{bx}$. Plot the data on semilogarithmic paper and find values for a and b.

x	2	5	8	11	14	17	27	31	35	44
y	94.8	89.7	81.3	74.9	68.7	64.0	49.3	44.0	39.1	31.6

6. Solve the preceding example by the method of averages.

7. Find by the method of least squares a formula of the type $y = a + bx^2$ which will fit the following data:

x	7.87	11.50	16.40	22.60	32.80
y	0.2	0.4	0.8	1.6	3.2

8. The data in the table below can be fitted by a formula of the type $x/y = a + bx$. Find the formula by the method of averages.

x	3.8	7.0	9.5	11.3	17.5	31.5	45.0	64.0	95.0
y	10.0	12.5	13.5	14.0	15.0	16.0	16.5	17.0	17.5

9. Work the preceding example by plotting the points $(x, x/y)$ on ordinary coordinate paper and finding the values of a and b.

Hint: Put $x/y = u$. Then the equation becomes $u = a + bx$, the graph of which is a straight line.

10. In Exercise 3 put $x^2 = t$ and plot the equation $y = a + bt$. Find from the graph the approximate values of a and b and then find corrections to these values by the general method of Art. 147.

11. Find by the method of averages a polynomial formula which will fit the data in the following table:

x	8.5	9.5	10.5	11.5	12.5	13.5	14.5	15.5	16.5	17.5
y	1260	1660	2150	2850	3670	· 4730	6050	7750	10000	13050

12. The data in the table below are to be fitted by a formula having $y = 20$ as an asymptote. Find the formula by any method.

x	0	1	2	3	4	5	6	7	8	9	10
y	84.9	79.9	75.0	70.7	67.2	64.3	61.9	59.9	57.6	55.6	53.4

13. The table below gives the atmospheric refraction for a star at various altitudes above the horizon. Assume that $R'' = a/(b + \tan h)$, omit the first and last values in the table, and find a and b by the method of least squares.

h	0°	2°	4°	6°	8°	10°	20°	40°	60°	90°
R	34'50"	18'06"	11'37"	8'23"	6'29"	5'16"	2'37"	1'09"	0'33"	0

CHAPTER XVII

HARMONIC ANALYSIS OF EMPIRICAL FUNCTIONS

150. Introduction. Any periodic function can be represented by a trignonometric series of the form

(1) $y = a_0 + a_1 \cos x + a_2 \cos 2x + \cdots + a_n \cos nx$
$$+ b_1 \sin x + b_2 \sin 2x + \cdots + b_n \sin nx.$$

This function is periodic and has the period 2π. A periodic function having a period different from 2π can be reduced to the form (1) by a suitable change of the independent variable (Art. 153).

When we wish to find an empirical formula to represent a phenomenon that is known to be periodic—such, for example, as the tides, alternating currents and voltages, mean monthly temperatures, etc.—, we should always assume a formula of the type (1). If the values of the function are known for certain equidistant values of the independent variable—from readings of an instrument, measurements of a graph, or otherwise—, it is an easy matter to find the unknown constants $a_0, a_1, \cdots a_n, b_1, b_2, \cdots b_n$. In the present chapter we shall give explicit formulas for computing these coefficients when the number of equally-spaced ordinates is either 12 or 24. We shall also give schemes for reducing the numerical work to a minimum.

151. Case of 12 Ordinates. We assume that the period of the unknown function is 2π and that the value of the function is known for 12 equidistant values of the independent variable. The appropriate formula is then

(151. 1) $y = a_0 + a_1 \cos x + a_2 \cos 2x + a_3 \cos 3x + a_4 \cos 4x$
$$+ a_5 \cos 5x + a_6 \cos 6x + b_1 \sin x + b_2 \sin 2x$$
$$+ b_3 \sin 3x + b_4 \sin 4x + b_5 \sin 5x.$$

Let the corresponding values of x and y be as given in the table below.

x	0°	30°	60°	90°	120°	150°	180°	210°	240°	270°	300°	330°
y	y_0	y_1	y_2	y_3	y_4	y_5	y_6	y_7	y_8	y_9	y_{10}	y_{11}

Then on substituting in (151. 1) each of these corresponding sets of values we obtain the following *conditional equations*:

$$y_0 = a_0 + a_1 + a_2 + a_3 + a_4 + a_5 + a_6 + 0 \cdot b_1 + 0 \cdot b_2 + 0 \cdot b_3 + 0 \cdot b_4 + 0 \cdot b_5,$$

$$y_1 = a_0 + \frac{\sqrt{3}}{2}a_1 + \frac{1}{2}a_2 + 0 \cdot a_3 - \frac{1}{2}a_4 - \frac{\sqrt{3}}{2}a_5 - a_6 + \frac{1}{2}b_1 + \frac{\sqrt{3}}{2}b_2$$
$$+ b_3 + \frac{\sqrt{3}}{2}b_4 + \frac{1}{2}b_5,$$

$$y_2 = a_0 + \frac{1}{2}a_1 - \frac{1}{2}a_2 - a_3 - \frac{1}{2}a_4 + \frac{1}{2}a_5 + a_6 + \frac{\sqrt{3}}{2}b_1 + \frac{\sqrt{3}}{2}b_2$$
$$+ 0 \cdot b_3 - \frac{\sqrt{3}}{2}b_4 - \frac{\sqrt{3}}{2}b_5,$$

$$y_3 = a_0 + 0 \cdot a_1 - a_2 + 0 \cdot a_3 + a_4 + 0 \cdot a_5 - a_6 + b_1 + 0 \cdot b_2$$
$$- b_3 + 0 \cdot b_4 + b_5,$$

$$y_4 = a_0 - \frac{1}{2}a_1 - \frac{1}{2}a_2 + a_3 - \frac{1}{2}a_4 - \frac{1}{2}a_5 + a_6 + \frac{\sqrt{3}}{2}b_1$$
$$- \frac{\sqrt{3}}{2}b_2 + 0 \cdot b_3 + \frac{\sqrt{3}}{2}b_4 - \frac{\sqrt{3}}{2}b_5,$$

$$y_5 = a_0 - \frac{\sqrt{3}}{2}a_1 + \frac{1}{2}a_2 + 0 \cdot a_3 - \frac{1}{2}a_4 + \frac{\sqrt{3}}{2}a_5 - a_6 + \frac{1}{2}b_1$$
$$- \frac{\sqrt{3}}{2}b_2 + b_3 - \frac{\sqrt{3}}{2}b_4 + \frac{1}{2}b_5,$$

$$y_6 = a_0 - a_1 + a_2 - a_3 + a_4 - a_5 + a_6 + 0 \cdot b_1 + 0 \cdot b_2$$
$$+ 0 \cdot b_3 + 0 \cdot b_4 + 0 \cdot b_5,$$

$$y_7 = a_0 - \frac{\sqrt{3}}{2}a_1 + \frac{1}{2}a_2 + 0 \cdot a_3 - \frac{1}{2}a_4 + \frac{\sqrt{3}}{2}a_5 - a_6 - \frac{1}{2}b_1$$
$$+ \frac{\sqrt{3}}{2}b_2 - b_3 + \frac{\sqrt{3}}{2}b_4 - \frac{1}{2}b_5,$$

$$y_8 = a_0 - \frac{1}{2}a_1 - \frac{1}{2}a_2 + a_3 - \frac{1}{2}a_4 - \frac{1}{2}a_5 + a_6 - \frac{\sqrt{3}}{2}b_1$$
$$+ \frac{\sqrt{3}}{2}b_2 + 0 \cdot b_3 - \frac{\sqrt{3}}{2}b_4 + \frac{\sqrt{3}}{2}b_5,$$

$$y_9 = a_0 + 0 \cdot a_1 - a_2 + 0 \cdot a_3 + a_4 + 0 \cdot a_5 - a_6 - b_1 + 0 \cdot b_2$$
$$+ b_3 + 0 \cdot b_4 - b_5,$$

$$y_{10} = a_0 + \frac{1}{2}a_1 - \frac{1}{2}a_2 - a_3 - \frac{1}{2}a_4 + \frac{1}{2}a_5 + a_6 - \frac{\sqrt{3}}{2}b_1 - \frac{\sqrt{3}}{2}b_2$$
$$+ 0 \cdot b_3 + \frac{\sqrt{3}}{2}b_4 + \frac{\sqrt{3}}{2}b_5,$$

$$y_{11} = a_0 + \frac{\sqrt{3}}{2}a_1 + \frac{1}{2}a_2 + 0 \cdot a_3 - \frac{1}{2}a_4 - \frac{\sqrt{3}}{2}a_5 - a_6 - \frac{1}{2}b_1 - \frac{\sqrt{3}}{2}b_2$$

$$- b_3 - \frac{\sqrt{3}}{2}b_4 - \frac{1}{2}b_5 .$$

To solve these equations for the a's and b's we apply the rule of Art. 145 for writing down normal equations. Thus, to find a_0 we multiply each equation by the coefficient of a_0 in that equation and add the results. We then get

$$12a_0 = y_0 + y_1 + y_2 + y_3 + y_4 + y_5 + y_6 + y_7 + y_8 + y_9 + y_{10} + y_{11} ,$$

which gives a_0 explicitly in terms of the known quantities $y_0, y_1, \cdots y_{11}$.

To find a_1 we multiply each equation by the coefficient of a_1 in that equation and add the results. This gives *

$$6a_1 = y_0 + \frac{\sqrt{3}}{2}y_1 + \frac{1}{2}y_2 - \frac{1}{2}y_4 - \frac{\sqrt{3}}{2}y_5 - y_6 - \frac{\sqrt{3}}{2}y_7 - \frac{1}{2}y_8$$

$$+ \frac{1}{2}y_{10} + \frac{\sqrt{3}}{2}y_{11} .$$

Continuing in this manner, we get the following equations for finding the remaining a's and b's:

---

* The reason for the disappearance of all the a's and b's except one in the normal equations is as follows:

Since the multipliers used in obtaining the normal equations are sines and cosines, the coefficients of the a's and b's in the resulting normal equations are all of some one of the forms

$$\sum_r \sin p x_r, \quad \sum_r \cos q x_r, \quad \sum_r \sin p x_r \sin q x_r, \quad \sum_r \sin p x_r \cos q x_r, \quad \sum_r \cos p x_r \cos q x_r,$$

$$\sum_r \sin^2 p x_r, \qquad \sum_r \cos^2 q x_r,$$

where r takes the values $0, 1, 2, \cdots (m-1)$, and m is the number of equidistant ordinates. But

$$\sum_r \sin p x_r = 0, \quad \sum_r \cos q x_r = 0, \quad \sum_r \sin p x_r \cos q x_r = 0,$$

$$\left. \begin{array}{l} \sum_r \sin p x_r \sin q x_r = 0 \\[4pt] \sum_r \cos p x_r \cos q x_r = 0 \end{array} \right\} \text{ if } p \neq q,$$

$$\sum_r \sin^2 p x_r = \frac{m}{2}, \quad \sum_r \cos^2 q x_r = \frac{m}{2} .$$

Since only one of the a's or b's in each normal equation has a coefficient of the form $\sum_r \sin^2 p x_r$ or $\sum_r \cos^2 q x_r$, it is evident that all but one must disappear.

For a simple and elegant proof of the relations given above, the reader is referred to Runge and König's *Numerisches Rechnen*, page 212.

$$6a_2 = y_0 + \frac{1}{2}y_1 - \frac{1}{2}y_2 - y_3 - \frac{1}{2}y_4 + \frac{1}{2}y_5 + y_6 + \frac{1}{2}y_7 - \frac{1}{2}y_8 - y_9$$
$$- \frac{1}{2}y_{10} + \frac{1}{2}y_{11} ,$$

$$6a_3 = y_0 - y_2 + y_4 - y_6 + y_8 - y_{10} ,$$

$$6a_4 = y_0 - \frac{1}{2}y_1 - \frac{1}{2}y_2 + y_3 - \frac{1}{2}y_4 - \frac{1}{2}y_5 + y_6 - \frac{1}{2}y_7 - \frac{1}{2}y_8$$
$$+ y_9 - \frac{1}{2}y_{10} - \frac{1}{2}y_{11} ,$$

$$6a_5 = y_0 - \frac{\sqrt{3}}{2}y_1 + \frac{1}{2}y_2 - \frac{1}{2}y_4 + \frac{\sqrt{3}}{2}y_5 - y_6 + \frac{\sqrt{3}}{2}y_7 - \frac{1}{2}y_8$$
$$+ \frac{1}{2}y_{10} - \frac{\sqrt{3}}{2}y_{11} ,$$

$$12a_6 = y_0 - y_1 + y_2 - y_3 + y_4 - y_5 + y_6 - y_7 + y_8 - y_9 + y_{10} - y_{11} ,$$

$$6b_1 = \frac{1}{2}y_1 + \frac{\sqrt{3}}{2}y_2 + y_3 + \frac{\sqrt{3}}{2}y_4 + \frac{1}{2}y_5 - \frac{1}{2}y_7 - \frac{\sqrt{3}}{2}y_8$$
$$- y_9 - \frac{\sqrt{3}}{2}y_{10} - \frac{1}{2}y_{11} ,$$

$$6b_2 = \frac{\sqrt{3}}{2}(y_1 + y_2 - y_4 - y_5 + y_7 + y_8 - y_{10} - y_{11}),$$

$$6b_3 = y_1 - y_3 + y_5 - y_7 + y_9 - y_{11} ,$$

$$6b_4 = \frac{\sqrt{3}}{2}(y_1 - y_2 + y_4 - y_5 + y_7 - y_8 + y_{10} - y_{11}),$$

$$6b_5 = \frac{1}{2}y_1 - \frac{\sqrt{3}}{2}y_2 + y_3 - \frac{\sqrt{3}}{2}y_4 + \frac{1}{2}y_5 - \frac{1}{2}y_7 + \frac{\sqrt{3}}{2}y_8 - y_9$$
$$+ \frac{\sqrt{3}}{2}y_{10} - \frac{1}{2}y_{11} .$$

We could find the values of the a's and b's directly from these equations, but it would he a tedious process on account of the large number of terms in the right-hand members. We therefore reduce the number of terms on the right by grouping terms and substituting new variables for the different groups. The first grouping gives

$$12a_0 = (y_0 + y_6) + (y_1 + y_{11}) + (y_2 + y_{10}) + (y_3 + y_9) + (y_4 + y_8)$$
$$+ (y_5 + y_7),$$

$$6a_1 = (y_0 - y_6) + \frac{\sqrt{3}}{2}(y_1 + y_{11}) + \frac{1}{2}(y_2 + y_{10}) - \frac{1}{2}(y_4 + y_8)$$
$$- \frac{\sqrt{3}}{2}(y_5 + y_7),$$

$$6a_2 = (y_0 + y_6) + \frac{1}{2}(y_1 + y_{11}) - \frac{1}{2}(y_2 + y_{10}) - (y_3 + y_9)$$
$$- \frac{1}{2}(y_4 + y_8) + \frac{1}{2}(y_5 + y_7),$$

$$6a_3 = (y_0 - y_6) - (y_2 + y_{10}) + (y_4 + y_8),$$

$$6a_4 = (y_0 + y_6) - \frac{1}{2}(y_1 + y_{11}) - \frac{1}{2}(y_2 + y_{10}) + (y_3 + y_9)$$
$$- \frac{1}{2}(y_4 + y_8) - \frac{1}{2}(y_5 + y_7),$$

$$6a_5 = (y_0 - y_6) - \frac{\sqrt{3}}{2}(y_1 + y_{11}) + \frac{1}{2}(y_2 + y_{10}) - \frac{1}{2}(y_4 + y_8)$$
$$+ \frac{\sqrt{3}}{2}(y_5 + y_7),$$

$$12a_6 = (y_0 + y_6) - (y_1 + y_{11}) + (y_2 + y_{10}) - (y_3 + y_9) + (y_4 + y_8)$$
$$- (y_5 + y_7),$$

$$6b_1 = \frac{1}{2}(y_1 - y_{11}) + \frac{\sqrt{3}}{2}(y_2 - y_{10}) + (y_3 - y_9) + \frac{\sqrt{3}}{2}(y_4 - y_8)$$
$$+ \frac{1}{2}(y_5 - y_7),$$

$$6b_2 = \frac{\sqrt{3}}{2}[(y_1 - y_{11}) + (y_2 - y_{10}) - (y_4 - y_8) - (y_5 - y_7)],$$

$$6b_3 = (y_1 - y_{11}) - (y_3 - y_9) + (y_5 - y_7),$$

$$6b_4 = \frac{\sqrt{3}}{2}[(y_1 - y_{11}) - (y_2 - y_{10}) + (y_4 - y_8) - (y_5 - y_7)],$$

$$6b_5 = \frac{1}{2}(y_1 - y_{11}) - \frac{\sqrt{3}}{2}(y_2 - y_{10}) + (y_3 - y_9) - \frac{\sqrt{3}}{2}(y_4 - y_8)$$
$$+ \frac{1}{2}(y_5 - y_7).$$

Let us now put

$$
\begin{array}{ll}
y_0 + y_6 = u_0 & y_0 - y_6 = v_0 \\
y_1 + y_{11} = u_1 & y_1 - y_{11} = v_1 \\
y_2 + y_{10} = u_2 & y_2 - y_{10} = v_2 \\
y_3 + y_9 = u_3 & y_3 - y_9 = v_3 \\
y_4 + y_8 = u_4 & y_4 - y_8 = v_4 \\
y_5 + y_7 = u_5 & y_5 - y_7 = v_5 .
\end{array}
$$

Then the normal equations become

$$12a_0 = u_0 + u_1 + u_2 + u_3 + u_4 + u_5 = (u_0 + u_3) + (u_1 + u_5) + (u_2 + u_4),$$

$$6a_1 = v_0 + \frac{\sqrt{3}}{2}u_1 + \frac{1}{2}u_2 - \frac{1}{2}u_4 - \frac{\sqrt{3}}{2}u_5 = v_0 + \frac{\sqrt{3}}{2}(u_1 - u_5)$$
$$+ \frac{1}{2}(u_2 - u_4),$$

$$6a_2 = u_0 + \frac{1}{2}u_1 - \frac{1}{2}u_2 - u_3 - \frac{1}{2}u_4 + \frac{1}{2}u_5 = (u_0 - u_3)$$
$$+ \frac{1}{2}(u_1 + u_5) - \frac{1}{2}(u_2 + u_4),$$

$$6a_3 = v_0 - u_2 + u_4 = v_0 - (u_2 - u_4),$$

$$6a_4 = u_0 - \frac{1}{2}u_1 - \frac{1}{2}u_2 + u_3 - \frac{1}{2}u_4 - \frac{1}{2}u_5 = (u_0 + u_3) - \frac{1}{2}(u_1 + u_5)$$
$$- \frac{1}{2}(u_2 + u_4),$$

$$6a_5 = v_0 - \frac{\sqrt{3}}{2}u_1 + \frac{1}{2}u_2 - \frac{1}{2}u_4 + \frac{\sqrt{3}}{2}u_5 = v_0 - \frac{\sqrt{3}}{2}(u_1 - u_5)$$
$$+ \frac{1}{2}(u_2 - u_4),$$

$$12a_6 = u_0 - u_1 + u_2 - u_3 + u_4 - u_5 = (u_0 - u_3) - (u_1 + u_5) + (u_2 + u_4),$$

$$6b_1 = \frac{1}{2}v_1 + \frac{\sqrt{3}}{2}v_2 + v_3 + \frac{\sqrt{3}}{2}v_4 + \frac{1}{2}v_5 = \frac{1}{2}(v_1 + v_5)$$
$$+ \frac{\sqrt{3}}{2}(v_2 + v_4) + v_3,$$

$$6b_2 = \frac{\sqrt{3}}{2}(v_1 + v_2 - v_4 - v_5) = \frac{\sqrt{3}}{2}[(v_1 - v_5) + (v_2 - v_4)],$$

$$6b_3 = v_1 - v_3 + v_x = (v_1 + v_5) - v_3,$$

$$6b_4 = \frac{\sqrt{3}}{2}(v_1 - v_2 + v_4 - v_5) = \frac{\sqrt{3}}{2}[(v_1 - v_5) - (v_2 - v_4)],$$

$$6b_5 = \frac{1}{2}v_1 - \frac{\sqrt{3}}{2}v_2 + v_3 - \frac{\sqrt{3}}{2}v_4 + \frac{1}{2}v_5 = \frac{1}{2}(v_1 + v_5)$$

$$- \frac{\sqrt{3}}{2}(v_2 + v_4) + v_3.$$

If we make the further substitutions

$$u_0 + u_3 = r_0 \qquad u_0 - u_3 = s_0 \qquad v_1 + v_5 = p_1 \qquad v_1 - v_5 = q_1$$

$$u_1 + u_5 = r_1 \qquad u_1 - u_5 = s_1 \qquad v_2 + v_4 = p_2 \qquad v_2 - v_4 = q_2,$$

$$u_2 + u_4 = r_2 \qquad u_2 - u_4 = s_2$$

the normal equations take the simpler forms

$$12a_0 = r_0 + r_1 + r_2 = r_0 + (r_1 + r_2),$$

$$6a_1 = v_0 + \frac{\sqrt{3}}{2}s_1 + \frac{1}{2}s_2,$$

$$6a_2 = s_0 + \frac{1}{2}r_1 - \frac{1}{2}r_2 = s_0 + \frac{1}{2}(r_1 - r_2),$$

$$6a_3 = v_0 - s_2,$$

$$6a_4 = r_0 - \frac{1}{2}r_1 - \frac{1}{2}r_2 = r_0 - \frac{1}{2}(r_1 + r_2),$$

$$6a_5 = v_0 - \frac{\sqrt{3}}{2}s_1 + \frac{1}{2}s_2,$$

$$12a_6 = s_0 - r_1 + r_2 = s_0 - (r_1 - r_2),$$

$$6b_1 = \frac{1}{2}p_1 + \frac{\sqrt{3}}{2}p_2 + v_3 = v_3 + \frac{1}{2}p_1 + \frac{\sqrt{3}}{2}p_2,$$

$$6b_2 = \frac{\sqrt{3}}{2}(q_1 + q_2),$$

$$6b_3 = p_1 - v_3,$$

$$6b_4 = \frac{\sqrt{3}}{2}(q_1 - q_2),$$

$$6b_5 = \frac{1}{2}p_1 - \frac{\sqrt{3}}{2}p_2 + v_3 = v_3 + \frac{1}{2}p_1 - \frac{\sqrt{3}}{2}p_2.$$

Finally, we write

$$r_1 + r_2 = l \qquad q_1 + q_2 = g$$
$$r_1 - r_2 = m \qquad q_1 - q_2 = h.$$

Then the equations for finding the coefficients in the trigonometric series are

$$(151.2) \quad \begin{cases} a_0 = \dfrac{1}{12}(r_0 + l), \\[2mm] a_1 = \dfrac{1}{6}\left(v_0 + \dfrac{\sqrt{3}}{2}s_1 + \dfrac{1}{2}s_2\right), \\[2mm] a_2 = \dfrac{1}{6}\left(s_0 + \dfrac{1}{2}m\right), \\[2mm] a_3 = \dfrac{1}{6}(v_0 - s_2), \\[2mm] a_4 = \dfrac{1}{6}\left(r_0 - \dfrac{1}{2}l\right), \\[2mm] a_5 = \dfrac{1}{6}\left(v_0 - \dfrac{\sqrt{3}}{2}s_1 + \dfrac{1}{2}s_2\right), \\[2mm] a_6 = \dfrac{1}{12}(s_0 - m), \\[2mm] b_1 = \dfrac{1}{6}\left(v_3 + \dfrac{1}{2}p_1 + \dfrac{\sqrt{3}}{2}p_2\right), \\[2mm] b_2 = \dfrac{\sqrt{3}}{12}g, \\[2mm] b_3 = \dfrac{1}{6}(p_1 - v_3), \\[2mm] b_4 = \dfrac{\sqrt{3}}{12}h, \\[2mm] b_5 = \dfrac{1}{6}\left(v_3 + \dfrac{1}{2}p_1 - \dfrac{\sqrt{3}}{2}p_2\right). \end{cases}$$

The several substitutions made above can be accomplished very simply by the addition and subtraction scheme given below,* starting with the given y's.

* Such schemes for computing the a's and b's were first devised by Runge about the year 1903. See *Zeitschrift für Math. und Physik.*, XLVIII (1903), p. 443, and LII (1905), p. 117.

	y_0	y_1	y_2	y_3	y_4	y_5
	y_6	y_{11}	y_{10}	y_9	y_8	y_7
Sum	u_0	u_1	u_2	u_3	u_4	u_5
Diff.	$\boldsymbol{v_0}$	v_1	v_2	$\boldsymbol{v_3}$	v_4	v_5

	u_0	u_1	u_2		v_1	v_2
	u_3	u_5	u_4		v_5	v_4
Sum	$\boldsymbol{r_0}$	r_1	r_2		p_1	p_2
Diff.	s_0	s_1	s_2		q_1	q_2

	r_1	q_1
	r_2	q_2
Sum	l	h
Diff.	m	g

The quantities v_0, v_3, and r_0 are printed in heavy type because they are somewhat isolated from the other quantities which appear in the final formulas for the coefficients.

Check formulas. Since the chances of making an error in the additions and subtractions are considerable, it is important to have a reliable check on the computed a's and b's. As a check on the a's we have from the first conditional equation

$$y_0 = a_0 + a_1 + a_2 + a_3 + a_4 + a_5 + a_6.$$

To find a check for the b's we subtract the twelfth conditional equation from the second, giving

$$y_1 - y_{11} = b_1 + \sqrt{3}b_2 + 2b_3 + \sqrt{3}b_4 + b_5;$$

or, since

$$v_1 = y_1 - y_{11},$$
$$v_1 = b_1 + b_5 + 2b_3 + \sqrt{3}(b_2 + b_4).$$

The check formulas are therefore

$$(151.3) \qquad \begin{cases} \Sigma a = y_0, \\ (b_1 + b_5) + 2b_3 + \sqrt{3}(b_2 + b_4) = v_1. \end{cases}$$

We shall now work an example to show the application of the above scheme.

Example 1. Find an empirical formula to fit the following data:

x	0°	30°	60°	90°	120°	150°	180°	210°	240°	270°	300°	330°
y	9.3	15.0	17.4	23.0	37.0	31.0	15.3	4.0	−8.0	−13.2	−14.2	−6.0

Solution. The first part of the computation is carried out according to the scheme given above and should be self-explanatory.

	0	1	2	3	4	5
y's	9.3	15.0	17.4	23.0	37.0	31.0
	15.3	— 6.0	— 14.2	— 13.2	— 8.0	4.0
Sum (u)	24.6	9.0	3.2	9.8	29.0	35.0
Diff. (v)	— 6.0	21.0	31.6	36.2	45.0	27.0

	0	1	2			1	2
u's	24.6	9.0	3.2		v's	21.0	31.6
	9.8	35.0	29.0			27.0	45.0
Sum (r)	34.4	44.0	32.2	Sum (p)		48.0	76.6
Diff. (s)	14.8	— 26.0	25.8	Diff. (q)		— 6.0	— 13.4

$$r\text{'s} \quad 44.0 \qquad q\text{'s} \quad - 6.0$$
$$32.2 \qquad\qquad\quad - 13.4$$
$$l = 76.2 \qquad g = -19.4$$
$$m = 11.8 \qquad h = 7.4$$

Now substituting these quantities in equations (151.2), we get

$$a_0 = \frac{1}{12}(34.4 + 76.2) = 9.22,$$

$$a_1 = \frac{1}{6}\left(- 6.0 - 26\frac{\sqrt{3}}{2} - 12.9\right) = - 6.90,$$

$$a_2 = \frac{1}{6}(14.8 + 5.9) = 3.45,$$

$$a_3 = \frac{1}{6}(- 6.0 + 25.8) = 3.30,$$

$$a_4 = \frac{1}{6}(34.4 - 38.1) = - 0.62,$$

$$a_5 = \frac{1}{6}\left(- 6.0 + 26\frac{\sqrt{3}}{2} - 12.9\right) = 0.60,$$

$$a_6 = \frac{1}{12}(14.8 - 11.8) = 0.25,$$

$$b_1 = \frac{1}{6}(36.2 + 24.0 + 66.3) = 21.09,$$

$$b_2 = \frac{\sqrt{3}}{12}(-19.4) = -2.80,$$

$$b_3 = \frac{1}{6}(48.0 - 36.2) = 1.97,$$

$$b_4 = \frac{\sqrt{3}}{12}(7.4) = 1.07,$$

$$b_5 = \frac{1}{6}(36.2 + 24.0 - 66.3) = -1.02.$$

Applying the check formulas (151. 3), we have

$$\Sigma a = 9.30 = y_0,$$
$$(b_1 + b_5) + 2b_3 + \sqrt{3}(b_2 + b_4) = 21.01 = v_1.$$

The coefficients are therefore correct and the final formula is

$$y = 9.22 - 6.90 \cos x + 3.45 \cos 2x + 3.30 \cos 3x - 0.62 \cos 4x$$
$$+ 0.60 \cos 5x + 0.25 \cos 6x + 21.09 \sin x - 2.80 \sin 2x$$
$$+ 1.97 \sin 3x + 1.07 \sin 4x - 1.02 \sin 5x.$$

Note. Since the terms of a trigonometric series are *additive*, it is necessary that the coefficients all be computed to the same number of *decimal places* (Art. 7).

152. Case of 24 Ordinates. For 24 equally-spaced ordinates the values of x are taken at equal intervals of $15°$ apart from $0°$ to $345°$ inclusive. The appropriate formula for this case is

$$(152. 1) \quad y = a_0 + a_1 \cos x + a_2 \cos 2x + a_3 \cos 3x + a_4 \cos 4x + a_5 \cos 5x$$
$$+ a_6 \cos 6x + a_7 \cos 7x + a_8 \cos 8x + a_9 \cos 9x + a_{10} \cos 10x$$
$$+ a_{11} \cos 11x + a_{12} \cos 12x + b_1 \sin x + b_2 \sin 2x + b_3 \sin 3x$$
$$+ b_4 \sin 4x + b_5 \sin 5x + b_6 \sin 6x + b_7 \sin 7x + b_8 \sin 8x$$
$$+ b_9 \sin 9x + b_{10} \sin 10x + b_{11} \sin 11x.$$

x	0°	15°	30°	45°	60°	75°	90°	105°	120°	135°	150°	165°	180°
y	y_0	y_1	y_2	y_3	y_4	y_5	y_6	y_7	y_8	y_9	y_{10}	y_{11}	y_{12}

x	195°	210°	225°	240°	255°	270°	285°	300°	315°	330°	345°
y	y_{13}	y_{14}	y_{15}	y_{16}	y_{17}	y_{18}	y_{19}	y_{20}	y_{21}	y_{22}	y_{23}

Let the corresponding values of x and y be as given in the table above. Then on substituting in (152. 1) these corresponding values of x and y we get 24 conditional equations. Applying to these the rule for obtaining normal equations, we get 24 equations in which the a's and b's are given explicitly in terms of the y's. Then we group the terms in the right-hand members, substitute new variables for the different groups, group again, etc., just as in the case of 12 ordinates. The final formulas for computing the a's and b's are found to be as follows:

$$a_0 = \frac{1}{24}(l_0 + e),$$

$$a_1 = \frac{1}{12}\left(v_0 + C s_1 + \frac{\sqrt{3}}{2} s_2 + \frac{1}{\sqrt{2}} s_3 + \frac{1}{2} s_4 + S s_5 \right),$$

$$a_2 = \frac{1}{12}\left(s_0 + \frac{\sqrt{3}}{2} m_1 + \frac{1}{2} m_2 \right),$$

$$a_3 = \frac{1}{12}\left(v_0 + \frac{1}{\sqrt{2}}(s_1 - s_3 - s_5) - s_4 \right),$$

$$a_4 = \frac{1}{12}\left(m_0 + \frac{1}{2} f \right),$$

$$a_5 = \frac{1}{12}\left(v_0 + S s_1 - \frac{\sqrt{3}}{2} s_2 - \frac{1}{\sqrt{2}} s_3 + \frac{1}{2} s_4 + C s_5 \right),$$

$$a_6 = \frac{1}{12}(s_0 - m_2),$$

$$a_7 = \frac{1}{12}\left(v_0 - S s_1 - \frac{\sqrt{3}}{2} s_2 + \frac{1}{\sqrt{2}} s_3 + \frac{1}{2} s_4 - C s_5 \right),$$

$$a_8 = \frac{1}{12}\left(l_0 - \frac{1}{2} e \right),$$

$$a_9 = \frac{1}{12}\left(v_0 - \frac{1}{\sqrt{2}}(s_1 - s_3 - s_5) - s_4 \right),$$

$$a_{10} = \frac{1}{12}\left(s_0 - \frac{\sqrt{3}}{2} m_1 + \frac{1}{2} m_2 \right),$$

$$a_{11} = \frac{1}{12}\left(v_0 - C s_1 + \frac{\sqrt{3}}{2} s_2 - \frac{1}{\sqrt{2}} s_3 + \frac{1}{2} s_4 - S s_5 \right),$$

$$a_{12} = \frac{1}{24}(m_0 - f),$$

(152. 2)

$$b_1 = \frac{1}{12}\left(S p_1 + \frac{1}{2} p_2 + \frac{1}{\sqrt{2}} p_3 + \frac{\sqrt{3}}{2} p_4 + C p_5 + v_6 \right),$$

$$b_2 = \frac{1}{12}\left(\frac{1}{2}g_1 + \frac{\sqrt{3}}{2}g_2 + q_3\right),$$

$$b_3 = \frac{1}{12}\left(p_2 - v_6 + \frac{1}{\sqrt{2}}(p_1 + p_3 - p_5)\right),$$

$$b_4 = \frac{\sqrt{3}}{24}c,$$

$$b_5 = \frac{1}{12}\left(Cp_1 + \frac{1}{2}p_2 - \frac{1}{\sqrt{2}}p_3 - \frac{\sqrt{3}}{2}p_4 + Sp_5 + v_6\right),$$

$$b_6 = \frac{1}{12}(g_1 - q_3),$$

$$b_7 = \frac{1}{12}\left(Cp_1 - \frac{1}{2}p_2 - \frac{1}{\sqrt{2}}p_3 + \frac{\sqrt{3}}{2}p_4 + Sp_5 - v_6\right),$$

$$b_8 = \frac{\sqrt{3}}{24}d,$$

$$b_9 = \frac{1}{12}\left(v_6 - p_2 + \frac{1}{\sqrt{2}}(p_1 + p_3 - p_5)\right),$$

$$b_{10} = \frac{1}{12}\left(\frac{1}{2}g_1 - \frac{\sqrt{3}}{2}g_2 + q_3\right),$$

$$b_{11} = \frac{1}{12}\left(Sp_1 - \frac{1}{2}p_2 + \frac{1}{\sqrt{2}}p_3 - \frac{\sqrt{3}}{2}p_4 + Cp_5 - v_6\right),$$

where $C = \cos 15° = 0.9659258$, $S = \sin 15° = 0.2588190$, and the other quantities are obtained from the given y's according to the following scheme:

y_0	y_1	y_2	y_3	y_4	y_5	y_6	y_7	y_8	y_9	y_{10}	y_{11}
y_{12}	y_{23}	y_{22}	y_{21}	y_{20}	y_{19}	y_{18}	y_{17}	y_{16}	y_{15}	y_{14}	y_{13}
Sum u_0	u_1	u_2	u_3	u_4	u_5	u_6	u_7	u_8	u_9	u_{10}	u_{11}
Diff. v_0	v_1	v_2	v_3	v_4	v_5	v_6	v_7	v_8	v_9	v_{10}	v_{11}

u_0	u_1	u_2	u_3	u_4	u_5		v_1	v_2	v_3	v_4	v_5
u_6	u_{11}	u_{10}	u_9	u_8	u_7		v_{11}	v_{10}	v_9	v_8	v_7
Sum r_0	r_1	r_2	r_3	r_4	r_5	Sum p_1	p_2	p_3	p_4	p_5
Diff. s_0	s_1	s_2	s_3	s_4	s_5	Diff. q_1	q_2	q_3	q_4	q_5

r_0	r_1	r_2		q_1	q_2	l_1	h_1
r_3	r_5	r_4		q_5	q_4	l_2	h_2
Sum l_0	l_1	l_2	Sum g_1	g_2	Sum e	Sum c
Diff. m_0	m_1	m_2	Diff. h_1	h_2	Diff. f	Diff. d

Here the quantities v_0, v_6, and q_3 are printed in heavy type because they are somewhat isolated from the other quantities which appear in the final formulas for the coefficients.

A check formula for the a's is given by the first conditional equation, and is

$$\Sigma a = y_0.$$

To find a check formula for the b's we subtract the 23d conditional equation from the second and obtain

$$y_1 - y_{23} = v_1 = 2S(b_1 + b_{11}) + (b_2 + b_{10}) + \sqrt{2}(b_3 + b_9)$$
$$+ \sqrt{3}(b_4 + b_8) + 2C(b_5 + b_7) + 2b_6.$$

The check formulas are therefore

$$(152. 3) \quad \begin{cases} \Sigma a = y_0, \\ 2S(b_1 + b_{11}) + (b_2 + b_{10}) + \sqrt{2}(b_3 + b_9) + \sqrt{3}(b_4 + b_8) \\ \qquad + 2C(b_5 + b_7) + 2b_6 = v_1. \end{cases}$$

Example 2. Find an empirical formula to fit the data in the following table:

x	0°	15°	30°	45°	60°	75°	90°	105°	120°	135°	150°	165°	180°
y	149	137	128	126	128	135	159	178	189	191	189	187	178

x	195°	210°	225°	240°	255°	270°	285°	300°	315°	330°	345°
y	170	177	183	181	179	179	185	182	176	166	160

Solution. The preliminary quantities are found by the scheme below:

	0	1	2	3	4	5	6	7	8	9	10	11
y's	149	137	128	126	128	135	159	178	189	191	189	187
	178	160	166	176	182	185	179	179	181	183	177	170
Sum (u)	327	297	294	302	310	320	338	357	370	374	366	357
Diff. (v)	—29	—23	—38	—50	—54	—50	—20	—1	8	8	12	17

	0	1	2	3	4	5
u's	327	297	294	302	310	320
	338	357	366	374	370	357
Sum (r)	665	654	660	676	680	677
Diff. (s)	— 11	— 60	— 72	— 72	— 60	— 37

		1	2	3	4	5
v's		− 23	− 38	− 50	− 54	− 50
		17	12	8	8	− 1
Sum (p)		− 6	− 26	− 42	− 46	− 51
Diff. (q)		− 40	− 50	− 58	− 62	− 49

	0	1	2			1	2
r's	665	654	660		q's	− 40	− 50
	676	677	680			− 49	− 62
Sum (l)	1341	1331	1340		Sum (g)	− 89	− 112
Diff. (m)	− 11	− 23	− 20		Diff. (h)	9	12

$$l\text{'s} \quad 1331 \qquad h\text{'s} \quad 9$$
$$1340 \qquad\qquad 12$$
$$\overline{\hspace{2cm}} \qquad \overline{\hspace{2cm}}$$
$$e = 2671 \qquad c = 21$$
$$f = -9 \qquad d = -3.$$

Now substituting these quantities in (152. 2), we find

$a_0 = 167.167,$ $a_1 = -19.983,$ $a_2 = -3.410,$ $a_3 = 5.471,$

$a_4 = -1.292,$ $a_5 = 0.250,$ $a_6 = 0.750$ $a_7 = 0.309,$

$a_8 = 0.458,$ $a_9 = -0.304,$ $a_{10} = -0.090,$ $a_{11} = -0.243,$

$a_{12} = -0.083.$

$b_1 = -12.779,$ $b_2 = -16.625,$ $b_3 = -0.323,$ $b_4 = 1.516,$

$b_5 = 1.462,$ $b_6 = -2.583,$ $b_7 = 0.322,$ $b_8 = -0.216,$

$b_9 = 0.677,$ $b_{10} = -0.459,$ $b_{11} = -0.640.$

The check formulas (152. 3) give

$$\Sigma a = 149.000 = y_0,$$

$$2S(b_1 + b_{11}) + (b_2 + b_{10}) + \sqrt{2}(b_3 + b_9) + \sqrt{3}(b_4 + b_8) + 2C(b_5 + b_7)$$
$$+ 2b_6 = -22.997 = v_1,$$

practically.

Hence the required formula is

$$y = 167.167 - 19.983 \cos x - 3.410 \cos 2x + 5.471 \cos 3x$$
$$- 1.292 \cos 4x + 0.250 \cos 5x + 0.750 \cos 6x + 0.309 \cos 7x$$
$$+ 0.458 \cos 8x - 0.304 \cos 9x - 0.090 \cos 10x - 0.243 \cos 11x$$
$$- 0.083 \cos 12x - 12.779 \sin x - 16.625 \sin 2x - 0.323 \sin 3x$$
$$+ 1.516 \sin 4x + 1.462 \sin 5x - 2.583 \sin 6x + 0.323 \sin 7x$$
$$- 0.216 \sin 8x + 0.677 \sin 9x - 0.459 \sin 10x - 0.640 \sin 11x.$$

153. Miscellaneous Matters.

(a). *Computation of the Coefficients for Any Number of Equidistant Ordinates.* In this chapter we have considered only the cases where the number of given ordinates is 12 or 24, because these are the most important cases from a practical standpoint. It is possible, however, to derive formulas for the a's and b's in the case of any number of equidistant ordinates, such as 6, 8, 10, 16, 20, etc. The method of procedure in all these cases is exactly the same as that in the case of 12 ordinates. Computing schemes for the cases just mentioned are given in Running's *Empirical Formulas*, pp. 76-85.

Pollak's *Rechentafeln zur Harmonischen Analyse* enable one to find the a's and b's directly from the normal equations for any number of equidistant ordinates from 3 to 40 inclusive. The tables are accompanied by full directions for their use.

(b) *Periods other than 2π.* When a function is periodic and has a period different from 2π, we change the independent variable by a linear substitution. Thus, if x is the independent variable and the given function is $y = f(x)$, we write

$$(1) \qquad x = k + m\theta.$$

If the limits for x are g and h and we wish the limits of θ to be 0 and 2π, we have only to substitute in (1) these corresponding values of x and θ and then solve the resulting equations for k and m. Hence in this case we have from (1)

$$g = k + 0, \quad \text{or} \quad k = g;$$

and

$$h = k + 2\pi m = g + 2\pi m.$$

Hence $m = (h - g)/2\pi$, and the desired formula of transformation is

$$(153.1) \qquad x = g + \frac{(h - g)}{2\pi}\, \theta, \quad \text{or} \quad \theta = \frac{2\pi(x - g)}{h - g}.$$

In all these cases the proper formula to assume for y is

$$(153.2) \qquad y = a_0 + a_1 \cos \theta + a_2 \cos 2\theta + \cdots + a_n \cos n\theta$$
$$+ b_1 \sin \theta + b_2 \sin 2\theta + \cdots + b_{n-1} \sin (n - 1)\theta.$$

For example, if the period of a phenomenon is known to be 18.3 days and we wish to use 12 equidistant ordinates, the values of x corresponding to these ordinates would be $x_0 = 0$, $x_1 = 18.3/12 = 1.525$, $x_2 = 3.050$, etc.

The corresponding values of θ would be $0°$, $30°$, $60°$, etc. The values of the a's and b's in (153.2) would be found by substituting in (153.2) these values of θ and the corresponding y's, or simply applying the 12-ordinate scheme to the given y's. The resulting formula in terms of x would then be, by (153.1) and (153.2),

$$(2) \qquad y = a_0 + a_1 \cos\left(\frac{2\pi x}{18 \cdot 3}\right) + a_2 \cos 2\left(\frac{2\pi x}{18 \cdot 3}\right) + \cdots$$
$$+ b_1 \sin\left(\frac{2\pi x}{18 \cdot 3}\right) + b_2 \sin 2\left(\frac{2\pi x}{18 \cdot 3}\right) + \cdots.$$

(c). *Caution in the Use of Empirical Formulas.* Empirical formulas are really interpolation formulas of particular forms, and are therefore subject to all the limitations of interpolation formulas. They can be relied upon for all values of the independent variable within the range of values used in determining the coefficients, but should not be trusted outside of these limits, except possibly for very short distances outside the range of values used. Stated otherwise, empirical formulas may be used for interpolation but not for extrapolation.

If, however, the given function is known to have a certain form for *all* values of the independent variable, we may use the formula for computing *rough* values of the function outside the range of values used in determining the coefficients.

EXERCISES XVII

1. Find a periodic function that will fit the following data:

x	0°	30°	60°	90°	120°	150°	180°	210°	240°	270°	300°	330°
y	38.4	11.8	4.3	13.8	3.9	-18.1	-22.9	-27.2	-23.8	8.2	31.7	34.2

2. Do the same for the following:

x	0°	15°	30°	45°	60°	75°	90°	105°	120°	135°	150°	165°	180°
y	45	110	142	128	138	88	-2	-12	-25	-39	-21	-38	-69

195°	210°	225°	240°	255°	270°	285°	300°	315°	330°	345°
-78	-90	-112	-92	-70	-45	25	68	59	40	54

3. The equation of time for twelve equidistant intervals in a certain year is given in the following table. Taking the period of this phenomenon to be 365.2 days, find an empirical formula that will give its value at any instant in that year.

$3^m10^s.9$, $13^n.30^s.4$, $12^m20^s.6$, $3^m53^s.6$, $-3^m2^s.7$, $-2^m22^s.6$, $3^m42^s.0$,

$9^m10^s.0$, $0^m9^s.3$, $-10^m13^s.8$, $-16^m18^s.2$, $-10^m59^s.6$.

4. The period of a certain phenomenon is 14.4 days. Twenty-four values for equal time intervals are given below. Find an empirical formula to represent this phenomenon.

2.4, 5.6, 6.7, 7.4, 8.8, 9.9, 10.4, 12.0, 13.8, 14.9, 16.4, 16.8, 17.5, 18.4, 19.2, 20.8, 21.4, 20.5, 18.5, 16.0, 15.1, 14.8, 12.2, 6.4.

CHAPTER XVIII

NUMERICAL SOLUTION OF SIMULTANEOUS LINEAR EQUATIONS

Various methods have been devised for the numerical solution of simultaneous linear equations. Some of the methods are of general applicability, while others are somewhat restricted in their application. Perhaps no single method is best in all cases. In the present chapter some of the best general methods are explained and illustrated by numerical examples.

I. SOLUTION BY DETERMINANTS

154. Evaluation of Numerical Determinants. In the following pages it is assumed that the reader is familiar with the elementary properties of determinants to the extent given in the usual college algebras.

a) Expansion in terms of minors. The *minor* of any element of a determinant is the determinant which remains after deletion of the row and column containing the element. Any determinant may be expanded in terms of the minors of the elements of any row or column. The elements of the first row or first column are usually the most convenient for expansions in terms of minors. Thus, the determinant

$$D = \begin{vmatrix} a_1 & a_2 & a_3 & a_4 \\ b_1 & b_2 & b_3 & b_4 \\ c_1 & c_2 & c_3 & c_4 \\ d_1 & d_2 & d_3 & d_4 \end{vmatrix}$$

may be expanded with respect to the elements of the first row as

$$D = a_1 \begin{vmatrix} b_2 & b_3 & b_4 \\ c_2 & c_3 & c_4 \\ d_2 & d_3 & d_4 \end{vmatrix} - a_2 \begin{vmatrix} b_1 & b_3 & b_4 \\ c_1 & c_3 & c_4 \\ d_1 & d_3 & d_4 \end{vmatrix} + a_3 \begin{vmatrix} b_1 & b_2 & b_4 \\ c_1 & c_2 & c_4 \\ d_1 & d_2 & d_4 \end{vmatrix} - a_4 \begin{vmatrix} b_1 & b_2 & b_3 \\ c_1 & c_2 & c_3 \\ d_1 & d_2 & d_3 \end{vmatrix},$$

or with respect to the elements of the first column as

$$D = a_1 \begin{vmatrix} b_2 & b_3 & b_4 \\ c_2 & c_3 & c_4 \\ d_2 & d_3 & d_4 \end{vmatrix} - b_1 \begin{vmatrix} a_2 & a_3 & a_4 \\ c_2 & c_3 & c_4 \\ d_2 & d_3 & d_4 \end{vmatrix} + c_1 \begin{vmatrix} a_2 & a_3 & a_4 \\ b_2 & b_3 & b_4 \\ d_2 & d_3 & d_4 \end{vmatrix} - d_1 \begin{vmatrix} a_2 & a_3 & a_4 \\ b_2 & b_3 & b_4 \\ c_2 & c_3 & c_4 \end{vmatrix}.$$

The resulting third-order determinants can be expanded by the rule for expanding determinants of the second and third orders.

495

Note that in the above expansions by minors *the signs alternate,* whether the expansion is with respect to the elements of the row or with respect to the elements of the column.

Example. To evaluate the determinant

$$D = \begin{vmatrix} 3 & -1 & 2 & 5 \\ -2 & 3 & 4 & 1 \\ 1 & -3 & 2 & 6 \\ 2 & 4 & 3 & 1 \end{vmatrix},$$

we expand it in terms of the elements of the first row and have

$$D = 3 \begin{vmatrix} 3 & 4 & 1 \\ -3 & 2 & 6 \\ 4 & 3 & 1 \end{vmatrix} + 1 \begin{vmatrix} -2 & 4 & 1 \\ 1 & 2 & 6 \\ 2 & 3 & 1 \end{vmatrix} + 2 \begin{vmatrix} -2 & 3 & 1 \\ 1 & -3 & 6 \\ 2 & 4 & 1 \end{vmatrix} - 5 \begin{vmatrix} -2 & 3 & 4 \\ 1 & -3 & 2 \\ 2 & 4 & 3 \end{vmatrix}$$

$$= 129 + 75 + 194 - 385 = 13.$$

Although the method of expansion by minors is simple and is very important theoretically, it is too long for practical use in determinants higher than the fourth order.

b) The pivotal method. In this method of evaluating a determinant the order of the determinant is systematically reduced step by step, the leading element (called the *pivot*) playing a more important role than any other element. To derive the formula for the pivotal expansion, let us consider the nth-order determinant

$$(1) \qquad D = \begin{vmatrix} a_1 & a_2 & a_3 & a_4 \cdots \\ b_1 & b_2 & b_3 & b_4 \cdots \\ c_1 & c_2 & c_3 & c_4 \cdots \\ d_1 & d_2 & d_3 & d_4 \cdots \\ \cdots \cdots \cdots \cdots \\ \cdots \cdots \cdots \cdots \end{vmatrix}.$$

Multiply the elements of the 2d, 3d, $\cdots$ nth columns by a_1 and compensate by dividing the determinant by a_1^{n-1}. Then

$$(2) \qquad D = 1/a_1^{n-1} \begin{vmatrix} a_1 & a_1 a_2 & a_1 a_3 & a_1 a_4 \cdots \\ b_1 & a_1 b_2 & a_1 b_3 & a_1 b_4 \cdots \\ c_1 & a_1 c_2 & a_1 c_3 & a_1 c_4 \cdots \\ d_1 & a_1 d_2 & a_1 d_3 & a_1 d_4 \cdots \\ \cdots \cdots \cdots \cdots \cdots \end{vmatrix}.$$

Now multiply the elements of the first column of (1) by $a_2, a_3, \cdots, a_n$ in succession and subtract the results from the 2d, 3d, $\cdots nth$ columns of (2). We thus get

$$D = 1/a_1^{n-1} \begin{vmatrix} a_1 & 0 & 0 & 0 & \cdots \\ b_1 & a_1b_2 - a_2b_1 & a_1b_3 - a_3b_1 & a_1b_4 - a_4b_1 & \cdots \\ c_1 & a_1c_2 - a_2c_1 & a_1c_3 - a_3c_1 & a_1c_4 - a_4c_1 & \cdots \\ d_1 & a_1d_2 - a_2d_1 & a_1d_3 - a_3d_1 & a_1d_4 - a_4d_1 & \cdots \\ \cdots & \cdots & \cdots & \cdots & \\ \cdots & \cdots & \cdots & \cdots & \end{vmatrix},$$

which becomes

$$D = 1/a_1^{n-2} \begin{vmatrix} a_1b_2 - a_2b_1 & a_1b_3 - a_3b_1 & a_1b_4 - a_4b_1 & \cdots \\ a_1c_2 - a_2c_1 & a_1c_3 - a_3c_1 & a_1c_4 - a_4c_1 & \cdots \\ a_1d_2 - a_2d_1 & a_1d_3 - a_3d_1 & a_1d_4 - a_4d_1 & \cdots \\ \cdots & \cdots & \cdots & \\ \cdots & \cdots & \cdots & \end{vmatrix}$$

when expanded by minors with respect to the elements of the first row. We have thus derived the important reduction formula:

$$(3) \quad \begin{vmatrix} a_1 & a_2 & a_3 & a_4 & \cdots \\ b_1 & b_2 & b_3 & b_4 & \cdots \\ c_1 & c_2 & c_3 & c_4 & \cdots \\ d_1 & d_2 & d_3 & d_4 & \cdots \\ \cdots & & & & \end{vmatrix} = 1/a_1^{n-2} \begin{vmatrix} a_1b_2 - a_2b_1 & a_1b_3 - a_3b_1 & a_1b_4 - a_4b_1 & \cdots \\ a_1c_2 - a_2c_1 & a_1c_3 - a_3c_1 & a_1c_4 - a_4c_1 & \cdots \\ a_1d_2 - a_2d_1 & a_1d_3 - a_3d_1 & a_1d_4 - a_4d_1 & \cdots \\ \cdots & \cdots & \cdots & \end{vmatrix}.$$

Since each application of (3) lowers the order of a determinant by one, a continued application of it will reduce any determinant to the third order or even to the second order.

Formula (3) shows that the first column of the new determinant of lower order is obtained by multiplying by a_1 each element in the first column of the minor of a_1 and then subtracting the product of the element at the top by the element at the extreme left. The elements in the second column of the new determinant are obtained in the same manner. This procedure should be memorized and applied as a working rule: a_1 *times any element, minus the element at the top times the element at the extreme left.*

Example. Applying this rule to the numerical determinant evaluated above by minors, we have

$$D = \begin{vmatrix} 3 & -1 & 2 & 5 \\ -2 & 3 & 4 & 1 \\ 1 & -3 & 2 & 6 \\ 2 & 4 & 3 & 1 \end{vmatrix} = \frac{1}{9} \begin{vmatrix} 7 & 16 & 13 \\ -8 & 4 & 13 \\ 14 & 5 & -7 \end{vmatrix}$$

$$= \frac{1}{9}(-196 + 2912 - 520 - 728 - 455 - 896) = \frac{117}{9} = 13.$$

c). *The triangular method.* Another important method of evaluating a numerical determinant is to reduce it to triangular form and then take the product of the elements in the leading diagonal of the triangular determinant. A triangular determinant is one in which all the elements on one side of the leading diagonal are zero. Any determinant

$$(4) \qquad D = \begin{vmatrix} a_{11} & a_{12} & a_{13} \cdot \cdot \cdot a_{1n} \\ a_{21} & a_{22} & a_{23} \cdot \cdot \cdot a_{2n} \\ a_{31} & a_{32} & a_{33} \cdot \cdot \cdot a_{3n} \\ \cdot & \cdot & \cdot \cdot \cdot \cdot \cdot \cdot \\ a_{n1} & a_{n2} & a_{n3} \cdot \cdot \cdot a_{nn} \end{vmatrix}$$

can be reduced to triangular form by the following procedure:

Multiply the first row successively by $\dfrac{a_{21}}{a_{11}}$, $\dfrac{a_{31}}{a_{11}}$, $\cdot \cdot \cdot \dfrac{a_{n1}}{a_{11}}$ and subtract the results from the 2d, 3d, $\cdot \cdot \cdot$ nth rows. We thus obtain

$$(5) \qquad D = \begin{vmatrix} a_{11} & a_{12} & a_{13} \cdot \cdot \cdot a_{1n} \\ 0 & b_{22} & b_{23} \cdot \cdot \cdot b_{2n} \\ 0 & b_{32} & b_{33} \cdot \cdot \cdot b_{3n} \\ 0 & b_{42} & b_{43} \cdot \cdot \cdot b_{4n} \\ \cdot & \cdot & \cdot \cdot \cdot \cdot \cdot \cdot \\ 0 & b_{n2} & b_{n3} \cdot \cdot \cdot b_{nn} \end{vmatrix},$$

where

$$b_{22} = a_{22} - \frac{a_{21}}{a_{11}} a_{12}, \quad b_{23} = a_{23} - \frac{a_{21}}{a_{11}} a_{13}, \text{ etc.}$$

$$b_{32} = a_{32} - \frac{a_{31}}{a_{11}} a_{12}, \quad b_{33} = a_{33} - \frac{a_{31}}{a_{11}} a_{13}, \text{ etc.}$$

Now leaving the first row of (5) as it stands, we multiply the second row successively by $\dfrac{b_{32}}{b_{22}}$, $\dfrac{b_{42}}{b_{22}}$, $\cdot \cdot \cdot \dfrac{b_{n2}}{b_{22}}$ and subtract the results from the 3d, 4th, $\cdot \cdot \cdot$ nth rows of (5) and thereby obtain

$$(6) \qquad D = \begin{vmatrix} a_{11} & a_{12} & a_{13} \cdots a_{1n} \\ 0 & b_{22} & b_{23} \cdots b_{2n} \\ 0 & 0 & c_{33} \cdots c_{3n} \\ 0 & 0 & c_{43} \cdots c_{4n} \\ \cdot & \cdot & \cdot \cdot \cdot \cdot \cdot \\ 0 & 0 & c_{n3} \cdots c_{nn} \end{vmatrix},$$

where

$$c_{33} = b_{33} - \frac{b_{32}}{b_{22}} \, b_{23}, \text{ etc.}$$

$$c_{43} = b_{43} - \frac{b_{32}}{b_{22}} \, b_{23}, \text{ etc.}$$

By continuing this process we reduce (4) to the triangular form

$$(7) \qquad D = \begin{vmatrix} a_{11} & a_{12} & a_{13} \cdots \cdots a_{1n} \\ 0 & b_{22} & b_{23} \cdots \cdots b_{2n} \\ 0 & 0 & c_{33} \cdots \cdots c_{3n} \\ 0 & 0 & 0 & d_{44} \cdots d_{4n} \\ \cdot & \cdot & \cdot \cdot \cdot \cdot \cdot \cdot \\ 0 & 0 & 0 & 0 \cdots l_{nn} \end{vmatrix}.$$

The value of the original determinant (4) is the product of the diagonal elements of (7), or

$$(8) \qquad D = a_{11}b_{22}c_{33}d_{44} \cdots l_{nn}.$$

To prove this fact we expand (7) successively in minors with respect to the elements of the first column of each successive determinant. Thus:

$$D = a_{11} \begin{vmatrix} b_{22} & b_{23} \cdots b_{2n} \\ 0 & c_{33} \cdots c_{3n} \\ \cdot & \cdot \cdot \cdot \cdot \cdot \cdot \\ 0 & 0 \\ 0 & 0 \\ \cdot & \cdot \cdot \cdot \cdot \cdot \cdot \\ 0 & 0 & l_{nn} \end{vmatrix} = a_{11}b_{22} \begin{vmatrix} c_{33} & c_{34} \cdots c_{3n} \\ 0 & d_{44} \cdots d_{4n} \\ 0 & 0 \\ \cdot & \cdot \cdot \cdot \cdot \cdot \cdot \\ 0 & 0 & l_{nn} \end{vmatrix}$$

$$= a_{11}b_{22}c_{33} \begin{vmatrix} d_{44} & d_{45} \cdots d_{4n} \\ 0 & e_{55} \cdots e_{5n} \\ 0 & 0 \\ \cdot & \cdot \cdot \cdot \cdot \cdot \cdot \\ 0 & 0 & l_{nn} \end{vmatrix},$$

and continue the expansions until we arrive at (8).

If the elements of the determinant are inexact or rounded numbers, the denominators a_{11}, b_{22}, etc. of the fractional multipliers should be as large as possible in order to reduce errors as much as possible. Interchanges of rows or columns will usually enable the computer to bring the largest elements to the positions of a_{11}, b_{22}, etc.

Example. We now apply the triangular method to the determinant previously evaluated by other methods.

$$D = \begin{vmatrix} 3 & -1 & 2 & 5 \\ -2 & 3 & 4 & 1 \\ 1 & -3 & 2 & 6 \\ 2 & 4 & 3 & 1 \end{vmatrix}.$$

On multiplying the first row successively by $\frac{2}{3}$, $\frac{1}{3}$, $\frac{2}{3}$, then adding the first result to the second row and subtracting the next two results from the third and fourth rows, respectively, we get

$$D = \begin{vmatrix} 3 & -1 & 2 & 5 \\ 0 & \dfrac{7}{3} & \dfrac{16}{3} & \dfrac{13}{3} \\ 0 & -\dfrac{8}{3} & \dfrac{4}{3} & \dfrac{13}{3} \\ 0 & \dfrac{14}{3} & \dfrac{5}{3} & -\dfrac{7}{3} \end{vmatrix}.$$

Now multiplying the second row by $\dfrac{8}{7}$ and 2 in succession, adding the first result to the third row and subtracting the second result from the fourth row, we get

$$D = \begin{vmatrix} 3 & -1 & 2 & 5 \\ 0 & \dfrac{7}{3} & \dfrac{16}{3} & \dfrac{13}{3} \\ 0 & 0 & \dfrac{52}{7} & \dfrac{65}{7} \\ 0 & 0 & -9 & -11 \end{vmatrix}.$$

Finally, on multiplying the third row by $\dfrac{63}{52}$ and adding the result to the fourth row, we obtain

$$D = \begin{vmatrix} 3 & -1 & 2 & 5 \\ 0 & \dfrac{7}{3} & \dfrac{16}{3} & \dfrac{13}{3} \\ 0 & 0 & \dfrac{52}{7} & \dfrac{65}{7} \\ 0 & 0 & 0 & \dfrac{1}{4} \end{vmatrix} .$$

Hence

$$D = 3 \times \frac{7}{3} \times \frac{52}{7} \times \frac{1}{4} = 13.$$

Concerning the merits of the three methods given above for evaluating a numerical determinant, the method of expansion in terms of minors is the least desirable of the three. As to the other two methods, the pivotal method is preferable when the elements of a determinant are simple numbers of one or two digits such that they can be multiplied and subtracted mentally. When the elements are numbers of several digits, the triangular method is the best method of evaluation.

155. Cramer's Rule. A simple method of solving simultaneous linear equations by determinants was discovered by Gabriel Cramer * in 1750. To derive Cramer's rule, as it is called, we consider a system of **three** equations

(1)
$$\begin{cases} a_1 x + a_2 y + a_3 z = k_1 \\ b_1 x + b_2 y + b_3 z = k_2 \\ c_1 x + c_2 y + c_3 z = k_3. \end{cases}$$

We first write down arbitrarily the determinant

(2)
$$\begin{vmatrix} (a_1 x + a_2 y + a_3 z) & a_2 & a_3 \\ (b_1 x + b_2 y + b_3 z) & b_2 & b_3 \\ (c_1 x + c_2 y + c_3 z) & c_2 & c_3 \end{vmatrix} .$$

From (1) the elements in the first column of (2) are equal to k_1, k_2, k_3, respectively. Hence we may write

(3)
$$\begin{vmatrix} (a_1 x + a_2 y + a_3 z) & a_2 & a_3 \\ (b_1 x + b_2 y + b_3 z) & b_2 & b_3 \\ (c_1 x + c_2 y + c_3 z) & c_2 & c_3 \end{vmatrix} = \begin{vmatrix} k_1 & a_2 & a_3 \\ k_2 & b_2 & b_3 \\ k_3 & c_2 & c_3 \end{vmatrix} .$$

* Swiss mathematician (1704–1752).

The addition law of determinants states that the left member of (3) may be expressed as the sum of three determinants, as follows:

$$\begin{vmatrix} a_1x & a_2 & a_3 \\ b_1x & b_2 & b_3 \\ c_1x & c_2 & c_3 \end{vmatrix} + \begin{vmatrix} a_2y & a_2 & a_3 \\ b_2y & b_2 & b_3 \\ c_2y & c_2 & c_3 \end{vmatrix} + \begin{vmatrix} a_3z & a_2 & a_3 \\ b_3z & b_2 & b_3 \\ c_3z & c_2 & c_3 \end{vmatrix}.$$

Factoring out x, y, and z from the first columns of these determinants and replacing the left member of (3) by the above sum, we have

$$\begin{vmatrix} a_1 & a_2 & a_3 \\ b_1 & b_2 & b_3 \\ c_1 & c_2 & c_3 \end{vmatrix} x + \begin{vmatrix} a_2 & a_2 & a_3 \\ b_2 & b_2 & b_3 \\ c_3 & c_2 & c_3 \end{vmatrix} y + \begin{vmatrix} a_3 & a_2 & a_3 \\ b_3 & b_2 & b_3 \\ c_3 & c_2 & c_3 \end{vmatrix} z = \begin{vmatrix} k_1 & a_2 & a_3 \\ k_2 & b_2 & b_3 \\ k_3 & c_2 & c_3 \end{vmatrix}.$$

Since two columns of the second and third determinants on the left are identical, those determinants are each equal to zero and we are left with

$$\begin{vmatrix} a_1 & a_2 & a_3 \\ b_1 & b_2 & b_3 \\ c_1 & c_2 & c_3 \end{vmatrix} x = \begin{vmatrix} k_1 & a_2 & a_3 \\ k_2 & b_2 & b_3 \\ k_3 & c_2 & c_3 \end{vmatrix},$$

from which

$$x = \frac{\begin{vmatrix} k_1 & a_2 & a_3 \\ k_2 & b_2 & b_3 \\ k_3 & c_2 & c_3 \end{vmatrix}}{\begin{vmatrix} a_1 & a_2 & a_3 \\ b_1 & b_2 & b_3 \\ c_1 & c_2 & c_3 \end{vmatrix}}.$$

To find the value of y we write down the determinant

$$\begin{vmatrix} a_1 & (a_1x + a_2y + a_3z) & a_3 \\ b_1 & (b_1x + b_2y + b_3z) & b_3 \\ c_1 & (c_1x + c_2y + c_3z) & c_3 \end{vmatrix},$$

replace the elements in the second column by k_1, k_2, k_3 from (1), and then proceed as in finding x. The result is

$$y = \frac{\begin{vmatrix} a_1 & k_1 & a_3 \\ b_1 & k_2 & b_3 \\ c_1 & k_3 & c_3 \end{vmatrix}}{\begin{vmatrix} a_1 & a_2 & a_3 \\ b_1 & b_2 & b_3 \\ c_1 & c_2 & c_3 \end{vmatrix}}.$$

To find z we start with the determinant

$$\begin{vmatrix} a_1 & a_2 & (a_1x + a_2y + a_3z) \\ b_1 & b_2 & (b_1x + b_2y + b_3z) \\ c_1 & c_2 & (c_1x + c_2y + c_3z) \end{vmatrix},$$

and proceed as in the case of x. This gives

$$z = \frac{\begin{vmatrix} a_1 & a_2 & k_1 \\ b_1 & b_2 & k_2 \\ c_1 & c_2 & k_3 \end{vmatrix}}{\begin{vmatrix} a_1 & a_2 & a_3 \\ b_1 & b_2 & b_3 \\ c_1 & c_2 & c_3 \end{vmatrix}}.$$

Note that the nuemrators of the fractions giving x, y, and z are the same as the denominator except that the coefficients of the desired unknown are replaced by the known quantities (the k's). Hence Cramer's rule may be stated as follows:

Write down the determinant of the coefficients of the unknowns. Any unknown is equal to the fraction whose denominator is the determinant of the coefficients and whose numerator is the same determinant with the coefficients of the desired unknown replaced by the known (constant) terms.

Cramer's rule holds for systems of any number of equations in the same number of unknowns and can be derived as was done above in the case of three equations.

Example. Find y from the equations

(A)
$$\begin{cases} 3x + 2y - z + t = 1 \\ x - y - 2z + 4t = 3 \\ 2x + 3y + z - 2t = -2 \\ 5x - 2y + 3z + 2t = 0. \end{cases}$$

Solution. The denominator of the fractions for all the unknowns is

$$D = \begin{vmatrix} 3 & 2 & -1 & 1 \\ 1 & -1 & -2 & 4 \\ 2 & 3 & 1 & -2 \\ 5 & -2 & 3 & 2 \end{vmatrix} = \frac{1}{9} \begin{vmatrix} -5 & -5 & 11 \\ 5 & 5 & -8 \\ -16 & 14 & 1 \end{vmatrix}$$

$$= \frac{1}{9}(-25 - 640 + 770 + 880 + 25 - 560) = 50.$$

Hence

$$y = \frac{\begin{vmatrix} 3 & 1 & -1 & 1 \\ 1 & 3 & -2 & 4 \\ 2 & -2 & 1 & -2 \\ 5 & 0 & 3 & 2 \end{vmatrix}}{50} = \frac{\dfrac{1}{9}\begin{vmatrix} 8 & -5 & 11 \\ -8 & 5 & -8 \\ -5 & 14 & 1 \end{vmatrix}}{50} = -\frac{29}{50}.$$

The other unknowns are found to be $x = \dfrac{19}{50}$, $z = -\dfrac{51}{50}$, $t = 0$. It will be found on substitution that these values satisfy equations (A).

Although Cramer's rule is simple and easy to apply, its use requires a great deal of labor when the number of equations exceeds four or five, because of the labor in evaluating the determinants involved.

II. SOLUTION BY SUCCESSIVE ELIMINATION OF THE UNKNOWNS

Several methods have been devised for solving systems of linear equations by successive or step-by-step elimination of the unknowns. Three of the most important of these methods will be explained in the following pages.

156. The Method of Division by the Leading Coefficients. The simplest of the step-by-step elimination methods is that in which each equation is first divided throughout by its leading coefficient, the equations being thereby transformed into a second set in which all leading coefficients are unity. To complete the first step, one of the transformed equations, which will be called the *pivotal equation*, is subtracted from each of the others (if all leading coefficients are positive), thus eliminating one unknown from the set. If the original set contained n unknowns, the first step reduced it to a set in $n-1$ unknowns.

If the same procedure is applied to the new system in $n-1$ unknowns, we get a third set of equations in $n-2$ unknowns; and by continuing the process we finally arrive at a single equation in one unknown. When the unknown has been found from this last equation, it is substituted into the preceding pivotal equation. The method of back substitution is continued until all the unknowns have been found, the back substitutions always being made into the immediately preceding pivotal equations. The following example should make the method clear.

Example. Solve the equations

$$475x - 316y - 407z + 253t = 521$$

$$296x - 482y - 395z + 242t = 720$$

$$364x - 421y - 643z + 342t = 634$$

$$282x - 286y - 315z + 448t = 266.$$

Solution. On dividing each equation throughout by its leading coefficient, we get

(a_1) $x - 0.66527y - 0.85684z + 0.53264t = 1.09685$

(a_2) $x - 1.6284y - 1.3345z + 0.81758t = 2.4324$

(a_3) $x - 1.1566y - 1.7665z + 0.93958t = 1.7418$

(a_4) $x - 1.0142y - 1.1170z + 1.5887t = 0.94326.$

Now taking the first of these equations as pivotal equation and subtracting it from each of the others, we get the new set

$$-0.9631y - 0.4777z + 0.28494t = 1.3356$$

$$-0.4913y - 0.9097z + 0.40694t = 0.6450$$

$$-0.3489y - 0.2602z + 1.0561t = -0.15359.$$

This completes the first step. Succeeding steps are carried out in exactly the same manner.

In practice, the solution is exhibited in compact form as shown below, the unknowns being written at the top of the table and only the coefficients shown in the work. Since errors are liable to be made in the computation, checks are provided in each line of the table. The column headed "Sum" gives the algebraic sum of the coefficients and constant term in each equation. The check numbers were obtained by performing on the previous sums the same operations (divisions and subtractions) as were performed on the corresponding previous equations. For example, the check number 2.5869 in row (b_1) was obtained by dividing -2.4915 by -0.9631; and the check number 0.7492 in row $(b_2) - (b_1)$ came from subtracting 2.5869 from 3.3361. The truth of the checks is evident from the axioms that if equals are divided by equals the quotients are equal, and if equals are subtracted from equals the remainders are equal. Hence the sums should agree with the check numbers in the same row.

		x	y	z	t	c	Sum	Check
		475	—316	—407	253	—521	—516	
		296	—482	—395	242	—720	—1059	
		364	—421	—643	342	—634	—992	
		282	—286	—315	448	—266	—137	
(a_1)		1	—0.66527	—0.85684	0.53264	—1.09685	—1.08632	—1.0863
(a_2)		1	—1.6284	—1.3345	0.81758	—2.4324	—3.5777	—3.5778
(a_3)		1	—1.1566	—1.7665	0.93958	—1.7418	—2.7253	—2.7252
(a_4)		1	—1.0142	—1.1170	1.5887	—0.94326	—0.4858	—0.4858
$(a_2)-(a_1)$			—0.9631	—0.4777	0.28494	—1.3356	—2.4915	—2.4914
$(a_3)-(a_1)$			—0.4913	—0.9097	0.40694	—0.6450	—1.6391	—1.6390
$(a_4)-(a_1)$			—0.3489	—0.2602	1.0561	0.15359	0.6006	0.6005
(b_1)			1	0.49601	—0.29586	1.3868	2.5869	2.5869
(b_2)			1	1.8516	—0.82828	1.31284	3.3361	3.3362
(b_3)			1	0.74578	—3.0269	—0.44021	—1.7213	—1.7214
$(b_2)-(b_1)$				1.3556	—0.53242	—0.0740	0.7492	0.7492
$(b_3)-(b_1)$				0.24977	—2.7310	—1.8270	—4.3082	—4.3082
(c_1)				1	—0.39276	—0.05459	0.55265	0.55267
(c_2)				1	—10.934	—7.3148	—17.249	—17.249
$(c_2)-(c_1)$					—10.541	—7.2602	—17.801	—17.802

Having reduced the given system to the single equation

$$-10.541t - 7.2602 = 0,$$

we find

$$t = -0.68877.$$

Now substituting this value of t into (c_1), we have

$$z - 0.39276(-0.68877) - 0.05459 = 0,$$

whence

$$z = -0.21593.$$

On substituting into (b_1) these values of t and z, we find

$$y = -1.4835.$$

Then these known values are substituted into (a_1) to find

$$x = 0.29177.$$

As a final check we substitute the above values of x, y, z, and t into the original equations and find that the left members become 520.99, 720.01, 634.02, and 266.02, respectively. The discrepancies are thus only —0.01, 0.01, 0.02, and 0.02, respectively.

157. The Method of Gauss. In the Gauss method of solving simultaneous linear equations, as explained in detail and with great clarity by Encke,* the unknowns are eliminated successively by solving some equation for one unknown in terms of all the others; then substituting this value for the same unknown in all the remaining equations, thereby eliminating the unknown from the set. The process is repeated on the new set of equations, thus eliminating another unknown; and so on until the system is reduced to a single equation in one unknown.

The equations which express one unknown explicitly in terms of all the others are called *pivotal equations*. After one unknown has been found, the remaining unknowns are found by back substitution into the pivotal equations.

In the solution of numerical equations by Gauss's method, one should always select as pivotal equation the equation which has the largest coefficient of the unknown it is desired to eliminate. For example, if the unknowns are to be eleminated in the order x, y, z, t (or x_1, x_2, x_3,), the first pivotal equation is obtained by solving for x that equation which has the largest x-coefficient. Then the second pivotal equation is obtained by solving for y that equation (in the new set) which has the largest y-coefficient, etc. A slightly better result may be obtained by disregarding the order of elimination and solving, at each step in the elimination process, the equation in which the largest coefficient in the entire set occurs, this equation being solved for the unknown to which the largest coefficient is attached. The reason for preferring the largest coefficients will appear later. The following example illustrates the Gauss method.

Example. Solve the following set of equations by Gauss's method, assuming that the coefficients and known terms are exact numbers:

(1) $2.63x + 5.21y - 1.694z + 0.938t - 4.23 = 0$

(2) $3.16x - 2.95y + 0.813z - 4.21t + 0.716 = 0$

(3) $5.36x + 1.88y - 2.15z - 4.95t - 1.28 = 0$

(4) $1.34x + 2.98y - 0.432z - 1.768t - 0.419 = 0.$

Solution. The variables will be eliminated in the order x, y, z, t. Since the largest coefficient of x occurs in (3), we take that as the pivotal equation. Solving it for x, we get

(5) $x = -\dfrac{1.88}{5.36}y + \dfrac{2.15}{5.36}z + \dfrac{4.95}{5.36}t + \dfrac{1.28}{5.36}$

$= -0.350746y + 0.401119z + 0.923506t + 0.238806.$

* *Berliner Astronomisches Jahrbuch*: 1835, pp. 267–272; 1836, pp. 256–259.

Substituting this value of x into (1), (2), and (4), and reducing, we get

(6) $4.287538y - 0.63906z + 3.36682t - 3.601940 = 0$

(7) $-4.05836y + 2.08054z - 1.29172t + 1.470627 = 0$

(8) $2.510000y + 0.105500z - 0.530500t - 0.099000 = 0.$

Since (6) has the largest y-coefficient, we solve it for y and get

(9) $y = 0.149051z - 0.785258t + 0.840096.$

Substituting this value of y into (7) and (8), we get

(10) $1.47564z + 1.89514t - 1.93879 = 0$

(11) $0.479618z - 2.501500t + 2.00964 = 0.$

Here we take (10) as the pivotal equation and get

(12) $z = -1.28428t + 1.31386.$

Substituting this value of z into (11), we get the final equation

(13) $-3.117463t + 2.63979 = 0,$

from which $t = 0.846775.$

The values of z, y, and x are found by back substitution into (12), (9), and (5), respectively. Substituting the value of t into (12), we find

$$z = 0.22636.$$

Then substituting the values of t and z into (9), we find

$$y = 0.208898.$$

Finally, on substituting the values of t, z, and y into (5), we get

$$x = 1.038335.$$

The solution of the given system of equations is thus

$$x = 1.038335$$
$$y = 0.208898$$
$$z = 0.22636$$
$$t = 0.846775.$$

When these values are substituted into the original equations (1), (2), (3), (4), the left members of those equations have the values 0.00000, 0.00000, 0.00001, 0.00000, respectively.

It will be observed that the Gauss method reduced the original system of equations to the triangular system of pivotal equations:

$$5.36x \quad + 1.88y \quad - 2.15z \quad - 4.95t \quad - 1.28 = 0$$

$$4.287538y - 0.63906z + 3.36682t - 3.601940 = 0$$

$$1.47564z + 1.89514t - 1.93897 = 0$$

$$- 3.117463t + 2.63979 = 0.$$

Since the value of the determinant of the coefficients in the given system is equal to the product of the leading coefficients in the triangular system (Art. 154), we have

$$\Delta = (5.36)(4.287538)(1.47564)(-3.117463) = -105.720.$$

158. Another Version of the Gauss Method. If we apply the method of the previous article to the equations

$$(1) \qquad \begin{cases} a_1x + a_2y + a_3z = k_1 & \text{(a)} \\ b_1x + b_2y + b_3z = k_2 & \text{(b)} \\ c_1x + c_2y + c_3z = k_3 & \text{(c)} \end{cases}$$

and assume that a_1 is larger than either b_1 or c_1, we take (a) as the pivotal equation and solve it for x, obtaining

$$x = \frac{k_1}{a_1} - \frac{a_2}{a_1}y - \frac{a_3}{a_1}z.$$

On substituting this into (b) and (c), we get

$$(2) \qquad \begin{cases} (b_2 - \dfrac{b_1}{a_1}a_2)y + (b_3 - \dfrac{b_1}{a_1}a_3)z = k_2 - \dfrac{b_1}{a_1}k_1 & \text{(d)} \\[2mm] (c_2 - \dfrac{c_1}{a_1}a_2)y + (c_3 - \dfrac{c_1}{a_1}a_3)z = k_3 - \dfrac{c_1}{a_1}k_1. & \text{(e)} \end{cases}$$

Equations (2) are exactly what would have been obtained if we had multiplied (1) (a) successively by $\dfrac{b_1}{a_1}$ and $\dfrac{c_1}{a_1}$ and then subtracted the resulting equations from (1) (b) and (1) (c), respectively. Equations (2) will also be obtained if we first divide (1) (a) throughout by a_1, then multiply the resulting equation successively by b_1 and c_1, and then subtract these resulting equations from (1) (b) and (1) (c), respectively. The Gauss method is therefore equivalent to either of the following procedures:

1. Choose the pivotal equation just as in Art. 157. Multiply this pivotal equation successively by such positive numbers as will make its leading coefficient in each case numerically equal to the leading coefficients of the other equations of the set. Then subtract the multiplied pivotal equations from the other equations having the same leading coefficients, thereby eliminating one unknown completely. Follow the same procedure with the new equations in $n-1$ unknowns. Or:

2. Divide the pivotal equation throughout by its leading coefficient. Then multiply the resulting equation successively by the leading coefficients of the other equations and subtract the multiplied pivotal equations from the other equations having the same leading coefficients. Follow the same procedure with the new set in $n-1$ unknowns.

In case the leading coefficients in some of the other equations are negative (or have signs opposite that of the leading coefficient of the pivotal equation), the multiplied pivotal equations are added to the other equations instead of subtracted from them.

Example. Solve the equations

$$(A) \quad \begin{cases} 2.63x + 5.21y - 1.694z + 0.938t - 4.23 = 0 & \text{(a)} \\ 3.16x - 2.95y + 0.813z - 4.21t + 0.716 = 0 & \text{(b)} \\ 5.36x + 1.88y - 2.15z - 4.95t - 1.28 = 0 & \text{(c)} \\ 1.34x + 2.98y - 0.432z - 1.768t - 0.419 = 0 & \text{(d)} \end{cases}$$

by the first method stated above.

Solution. We take (c) as the pivotal equation and multiply it succesively by $\dfrac{2.63}{5.36}$, $\dfrac{3.16}{5.36}$, and $\dfrac{1.34}{5.36}$, thereby obtaining the equations

$$(B) \quad \begin{cases} 2.63x + 0.92246y - 1.05494z - 2.42882t - 0.62806 = 0 \\ 3.16x + 1.10836y - 1.26754z - 2.91828t - 0.754627 = 0 \\ 1.34x + 0.47000y - 0.53750z - 1.23750t - 0.32000 = 0. \end{cases}$$

Now subtracting the first of these equations from (a), the second from (b), and the third from (d), we get

$$(C) \quad \begin{cases} 4.28754y - 0.63906z + 3.36682t - 3.60194 = 0 \\ -4.05836y + 2.08054z - 1.29172t + 1.47063 = 0 \\ 2.51000y + 0.10550z - 0.53050t - 0.09900 = 0. \end{cases}$$

These equations are the same as (6), (7), (8) of Art. 157.

The computation is usually presented in tabular form as given below:

x	y	z	t	k	Sum	Check
2.63	5.21	—1.694	0.938	—4.23	2.854	
3.16	—2.95	0.813	—4.21	0.716	—2.471	
5.36	1.88	—2.15	—4.95	—1.28	—1.14	
1.34	2.98	—0.432	—1.768	—0.419	—1.701	
	4.28754	—0.63906	3.36682	—3.60194	3.41336	3.41337
	—4.05836	2.08054	—1.29172	1.47063	—1.79891	—1.79891
	2.51000	0.10550	—0.53050	—0.09900	1.98600	1.98600
		1.47564	1.89514	—1.93879	1.43199	1.43200
		0.47962	—2.50150	2.00964	—0.01224	—0.01224
			—3.11747	2.63979	—0.47768	—0.47767

From the last equation we find

$$t = \frac{2.63979}{3.11747} = 0.846773.$$

Back substitution into the other pivotal equations gives

$$z = 0.22637$$
$$y = 0.208901$$
$$x = 1.03834.$$

When these values are substituted into the given equations, the left members of those equations become 0.00001, 0.00000, 0.00000, and 0.00001, respectively. The slight discrepancies between the results found above and those found in Art. 157 are due to the fact that some of the numbers in the above table were rounded off to the same number of decimal places as some other numbers to which they had to be added to obtain the "sums."

The numbers in the check column were obtained from the "sums" found in the preceding sets of equations, by applying to those sums the same operations as were applied to the pivotal equations. For example, the check numbers 1.43200 and —0.01224 were obtained as follows:

$$-1.79891 + \frac{4.05836}{4.28754} \times 3.41336 = 1.43200$$

$$1.98600 - \frac{2.51000}{4.28754} \times 3.41336 = -0.01224.$$

In case a check number fails to agree with the sum immediately to the left of it, a mistake has been made in the computation and should be found and corrected at once.

If we wished to solve the given set of equations by the second method outlined above, we would first divide equation (c) throughout by 5.36, thereby obtaining the pivotal equation,

$$x + 0.350746y - 0.401119z - 0.923506t - 0.238806 = 0.$$

Then we would multiply this equation successively by 2.63, 3.16, and 1.34. The resulting equations would then be subtracted from (a), (b), and (d), respectively, thus obtaining equations which should agree with equations (C). The solution would be continued by dividing the first of the new equations throughout by 4.28754 to get a new pivotal equation, etc. After finding t, we would find the other unknowns by back substitution into the pivotal equations. As a final step, we would substitute the computed values of x, y, z, and t into equations (A) as a check.

We may now state the reason for choosing as pivotal equations those equations having the largest coefficients of the unknowns we desire to eliminate. A glance at equations (2) shows that fractional terms are present in the coefficients and in the constant terms. It is desirable that such fractional terms be as small as possible, and this necessitates that the denominator a_1 be as large as possible. Moreover, if the numerators of such fractions contain rounding errors, the effects of such errors are diminished when the denominator a_1 is large.

III. SOLUTION BY INVERSION OF MATRICES

159. Definitions. A *matrix* is a rectangular array of quantities or numbers, such as

$$a_1 a_2 a_3 a_4$$
$$b_1 b_2 b_3 b_4$$
$$c_1 c_2 c_3 c_4.$$

To distinguish such an array from a determinant, which it resembles in appearance, it is always enclosed by square brackets, large parentheses, or double bars, as:

$$\begin{bmatrix} a_1 a_2 a_3 a_4 \\ b_1 b_2 b_3 b_4 \\ c_1 c_2 c_3 c_4 \end{bmatrix}, \quad \begin{pmatrix} a_1 a_2 a_3 a_4 \\ b_1 b_2 b_3 b_4 \\ c_1 c_2 c_3 c_4 \end{pmatrix}, \quad \text{or} \quad \begin{Vmatrix} a_1 a_2 a_3 a_4 \\ b_1 b_2 b_3 b_4 \\ c_1 c_2 c_3 c_4 \end{Vmatrix}.$$

We shall use the square-bracket notation and write a general matrix in the form

$$\begin{bmatrix} a_{11}a_{12}a_{13} \cdot \cdot \cdot a_{1n} \\ a_{21}a_{22}a_{23} \cdot \cdot \cdot a_{2n} \\ a_{31}a_{32}a_{33} \cdot \cdot \cdot a_{3n} \\ \cdot \cdot \cdot \cdot \cdot \cdot \cdot \cdot \cdot \\ a_{m1}a_{m2}a_{m3} \cdot \cdot \cdot a_{mn} \end{bmatrix}.$$

The quantities a_{11}, a_{12}, etc., are called the *elements* of the matrix, as in the case of determinants. It is to be noted that the first digit in the double subscript of an element denotes the row and the second digit denotes the column in which the element stands. A matrix of m rows and n columns is an $m \times n$ matrix.

If $m = n$, the matrix is a square matrix of order n.

A matrix may consist of only a single column, as $\begin{bmatrix} a_1 \\ a_2 \\ a_3 \\ a_4 \end{bmatrix}$,

in which case it is called a *column* matrix. It is merely a special case of a general matrix.

If all the elements in the leading diagonal of a square matrix are unity and all the other elements are zeros, the matrix is called a *unit* matrix. Thus,

$$\begin{bmatrix} 1 & 0 & 0 & 0 \\ 0 & 1 & 0 & 0 \\ 0 & 0 & 1 & 0 \\ 0 & 0 & 0 & 1 \end{bmatrix}$$

is a unit matrix of the fourth order. A unit matrix of any order will be denoted by the symbol I. Unit matrices play an important role in the application of matrices.

If all the elements of a matrix are zero, the matrix itself is zero.

Although the elements of a matrix are numbers, the matrix itself is not a number. It plays the role of an *operator*, as we shall see later.

160. Addition and Subtraction of Matrices. Two matrices of the same order can be added or substracted by adding or subtracting their corresponding elements. Thus, the sum of the two matrices

$$A = \begin{bmatrix} a_{11}a_{12}a_{13} \\ a_{21}a_{22}a_{23} \\ a_{31}a_{32}a_{33} \end{bmatrix} \text{ and } B = \begin{bmatrix} b_{11}b_{12}b_{13} \\ b_{21}b_{22}b_{23} \\ b_{31}b_{32}b_{33} \end{bmatrix}$$

is the matrix

$$C = \begin{bmatrix} a_{11} + b_{11} & a_{12} + b_{12} & a_{13} + b_{13} \\ a_{21} + b_{21} & a_{22} + b_{22} & a_{23} + b_{23} \\ a_{31} + b_{31} & a_{32} + b_{32} & a_{33} + b_{33} \end{bmatrix}.$$

We therefore write

$$A + B = C.$$

The difference of two matrices is found in the same manner, and we therefore write

$$A - B = C',$$

where the elements of C' are those of C with the signs of the b's changed.

Examples:

$$\begin{bmatrix} 2 & 3 & -4 \\ 5 & -1 & 0 \end{bmatrix} + \begin{bmatrix} 1 & -2 & 4 \\ 3 & 5 & 2 \end{bmatrix} = \begin{bmatrix} 3 & 1 & 0 \\ 8 & 4 & 2 \end{bmatrix}$$

$$\begin{bmatrix} 3 & -2 & 5 \\ 6 & 0 & 3 \\ 1 & 5 & 4 \end{bmatrix} - \begin{bmatrix} 2 & 3 & -1 \\ 4 & 1 & 0 \\ 5 & 2 & -1 \end{bmatrix} = \begin{bmatrix} 1 & -5 & 6 \\ 2 & -1 & 3 \\ -4 & 3 & 5 \end{bmatrix}.$$

161. Multiplication of Matrices. a) *Multiplication of a matrix by a simple number or scalar.* To multiply a matrix by a number or scalar quantity, we multiply every element of the matrix by that number. For example,

$$m \begin{bmatrix} a_1 a_2 a_3 \\ b_1 b_2 b_3 \end{bmatrix} = \begin{bmatrix} ma_1 & ma_2 & ma_3 \\ mb_1 & mb_2 & mb_3 \end{bmatrix}.$$

To see the reason for this rule of multiplication, let us consider the sum of three matrices of the second order,

$$A + B + C = \begin{bmatrix} a_{11} a_{12} \\ a_{21} a_{22} \end{bmatrix} + \begin{bmatrix} b_{11} b_{12} \\ b_{21} b_{22} \end{bmatrix} + \begin{bmatrix} c_{11} c_{12} \\ c_{21} c_{22} \end{bmatrix}.$$

Let us suppose now that the three matrices become identical, so that $B = C = A$ and $b_{rs} = c_{rs} = a_{rs}$. Then we have

$$3A = \begin{bmatrix} 3a_{11} 3a_{12} \\ 3a_{21} 3a_{22} \end{bmatrix},$$

and so in general.

Note that this multiplication differs from the multiplication of a determinant by a scalar, for in the latter case the elements of only *one* row or column are multiplied by the scalar.

b) *Multiplication of a matrix by another matrix.* In the system of equations

(1)
$$\begin{cases} a_1x_1 + a_2x_2 + a_3x_3 = k_1 \\ b_1x_1 + b_2x_2 + b_3x_3 = k_2 \\ c_1x_1 + c_2x_2 + c_3x_3 = k_3 \end{cases}$$

the array

$$a_1a_2a_3$$
$$b_1b_2b_3$$
$$c_1c_2c_3$$

is called the *matrix of the coefficients.* This matrix may be regarded as an *operator* which operates on the x's to produce the k's on the right side of the equations. The operation is seen to be a type of multiplication. If the x's be arranged in a vertical column, as

$$x_1$$
$$x_2$$
$$x_3,$$

the left member of the first equation of (1) is seen to be the sum of the products of the elements of the top row of the coefficient matrix by the corresponding x's in the vertical column. The left members of the other equations can be obtained in the same manner. We are therefore justified in writing (1) in the form

(2)
$$\begin{bmatrix} a_1a_2a_3 \\ b_1b_2b_3 \\ c_1c_2c_3 \end{bmatrix} \begin{bmatrix} x_1 \\ x_2 \\ x_3 \end{bmatrix} = \begin{bmatrix} k_1 \\ k_2 \\ k_3 \end{bmatrix}.$$

With (2) as a starting point we utilize a linear transformation to derive the rule for the multiplication of matrices in general.

Consider the two systems of equations

(3)
$$\begin{cases} y_1 = a_{11}x_1 + a_{12}x_2 + a_{13}x_3 \\ y_2 = a_{21}x_1 + a_{22}x_2 + a_{23}x_3, \end{cases} \text{ or } \begin{bmatrix} a_{11}a_{12}a_{13} \\ a_{21}a_{22}a_{23} \end{bmatrix} \begin{bmatrix} x_1 \\ x_2 \\ x_3 \end{bmatrix} = \begin{bmatrix} y_1 \\ y_2 \end{bmatrix};$$

and

(4)
$$\begin{cases} z_1 = b_{11}y_1 + b_{12}y_2 \\ z_2 = b_{21}y_1 + b_{22}y_2 \\ z_3 = b_{31}y_1 + b_{32}y_2, \end{cases} \text{ or } \begin{bmatrix} b_{11}b_{12} \\ b_{21}b_{22} \\ b_{31}b_{32} \end{bmatrix} \begin{bmatrix} y_1 \\ y_2 \end{bmatrix} = \begin{bmatrix} z_1 \\ z_2 \\ z_3 \end{bmatrix}.$$

Eliminating y_1 and y_2 by substituting in (4) their values as given in (3), we get

$$z_1 = (b_{11}a_{11} + b_{12}a_{21})x_1 + (b_{11}a_{12} + b_{12}a_{22})x_2 + (b_{11}a_{13} + b_{12}a_{23})x_3$$

$$z_2 = (b_{21}a_{11} + b_{22}a_{21})x_1 + (b_{21}a_{12} + b_{22}a_{22})x_2 + (b_{21}a_{13} + b_{22}a_{23})x_3$$

$$z_3 = (b_{31}a_{11} + b_{32}a_{21})x_1 + (b_{31}a_{12} + b_{32}a_{22})x_2 + (b_{31}a_{13} + b_{32}a_{23})x_3;$$

or, in matrix form,

$$(6) \quad \begin{bmatrix} b_{11}a_{11} + b_{12}a_{21} & b_{11}a_{12} + b_{12}a_{22} & b_{11}a_{13} + b_{12}a_{23} \\ b_{21}a_{11} + b_{22}a_{21} & b_{21}a_{12} + b_{22}a_{22} & b_{21}a_{13} + b_{22}a_{23} \\ b_{31}a_{11} + b_{32}a_{21} & b_{31}a_{12} + b_{32}a_{22} & b_{31}a_{13} + b_{32}a_{23} \end{bmatrix} \begin{bmatrix} x_1 \\ x_2 \\ x_3 \end{bmatrix} = \begin{bmatrix} z_1 \\ z_2 \\ z_3 \end{bmatrix}.$$

Now replacing the column matrix $\begin{bmatrix} y_1 \\ y_2 \end{bmatrix}$ of (4) by its value as given in (3), we get

$$(7) \quad \begin{bmatrix} b_{11}b_{12} \\ b_{21}b_{22} \\ b_{31}b_{32} \end{bmatrix} \begin{bmatrix} a_{11}a_{12}a_{13} \\ a_{21}a_{22}a_{23} \end{bmatrix} \begin{bmatrix} x_1 \\ x_2 \\ x_3 \end{bmatrix} = \begin{bmatrix} z_1 \\ z_2 \\ z_3 \end{bmatrix}.$$

Comparison of the left members of (6) and (7) gives the relation

$$(8) \quad \begin{bmatrix} b_{11}b_{12} \\ b_{21}b_{22} \\ b_{31}b_{32} \end{bmatrix} \begin{bmatrix} a_{11}a_{12}a_{13} \\ a_{21}a_{22}a_{23} \end{bmatrix}$$

$$= \begin{bmatrix} b_{11}a_{11} + b_{12}a_{21} & b_{11}a_{12} + b_{12}a_{22} & b_{11}a_{13} + b_{12}a_{23} \\ b_{21}a_{11} + b_{22}a_{21} & b_{21}a_{12} + b_{22}a_{22} & b_{21}a_{13} + b_{22}a_{23} \\ b_{31}a_{11} + b_{32}a_{21} & b_{31}a_{12} + b_{32}a_{22} & b_{31}a_{13} + b_{32}a_{23} \end{bmatrix}.$$

Formula (8) expresses the rule for the multiplication of matrices. If the first of the two matrices in the left member of (8) be denoted by B and the second by A, a glance at (8) shows that the elements in the product matrix in the right member can be obtained by following the procedure outlined below. It is best to compute the product by columns; that is, compute one column at a time, beginning with the first.

First column of product:

To find the *first element* in the first column of the product, multiply the elements in the *first row* of B into the corresponding elements in the *first column* of A and sum the products thus obtained. To find the *second element* in the first column of the product, multiply the elements in the *second row* of B into the corresponding elements in the first column of A and sum the products thus obtained. The *third element* in the first column of the product is found by multiplying the elements in the *third row* of B into the corresponding elements in the first column of A, and so on for the remaining elements in the first column of the product.

Second column of product:

To find the *first element* in the second column of the product matrix, multiply the elements in the *first row* of B into the corresponding elements in the *second column* of A and sum the products thus obtained. To find the *second element* in the .second column of the product, multiply the elements in the *second row* of B into the corresponding elements in the *second column* of A and sum the products thus obtained. The remaining elements in the second column of the product are found in a similar manner.

Third column of product:

Proceed as for first and second columns, except that the elements in the rows of B must be multiplied into the corresponding elements in the *third column* of A.

Example.

$$\begin{bmatrix} 3 & 1 & 2 \\ -1 & 2 & 3 \\ 2 & -5 & 7 \end{bmatrix} \times \begin{bmatrix} -2 & 4 & 1 \\ 3 & -1 & 2 \\ 4 & 1 & 3 \end{bmatrix}$$

$$= \begin{bmatrix} 3(-2) + 1(3) + 2(4) & 3(4) + 1(-1) + 2(1) & 3(1) + 1(2) + 2(3) \\ (-1)(-2) + 2(3) + 3(4) & (-1)4 + 2(-1) + 3(1) & (-1)1 + 2(2) + 3(3) \\ 2(-2) + (-5)3 + 7(4) & 2(4) + (-5)(-1) + 7(1) & 2(1) + (-5) + 7(3) \end{bmatrix}$$

$$= \begin{bmatrix} 5 & 13 & 11 \\ 20 & -3 & 12 \\ 9 & 20 & 13 \end{bmatrix}.$$

Note that in matrix multiplication:

(a) Rows are always multiplied into columns.

(b) The number of rows in the product is the same as the number of rows in B, and the number of columns in the product is the same as the number of columns in A.

(c) The number of rows in one factor must be the same as the number of columns in the other factor.

If A and B denote any two matrices and C denotes the product AB, then

$$AB = C.$$

But $BA \neq C$, in general.

That is, matrix multiplication is *not commutative* in general. For example,

$$\begin{bmatrix} 2 & 3 \\ 5 & -1 \end{bmatrix}\begin{bmatrix} 1 & 4 \\ -3 & -2 \end{bmatrix} = \begin{bmatrix} -7 & 2 \\ 8 & 22 \end{bmatrix};$$

but

$$\begin{bmatrix} 1 & 4 \\ -3 & -2 \end{bmatrix}\begin{bmatrix} 2 & 3 \\ 5 & -1 \end{bmatrix} = \begin{bmatrix} 22 & -1 \\ -16 & -7 \end{bmatrix},$$

an entirely different result.

An important exception occurs in the case of the product any matrix by a unit matrix. For example,

$$\begin{bmatrix} a_1 a_2 a_3 \\ b_1 b_2 b_3 \\ c_1 c_2 c_3 \end{bmatrix}\begin{bmatrix} 1 & 0 & 0 \\ 0 & 1 & 0 \\ 0 & 0 & 1 \end{bmatrix}$$

$$= \begin{bmatrix} a_1 + 0 + 0 & 0 + a_2 + 0 & 0 + 0 + a_3 \\ b_1 + 0 + 0 & 0 + b_2 + 0 & 0 + 0 + b_3 \\ c_1 + 0 + 0 & 0 + c_2 + 0 & 0 + 0 + c_3 \end{bmatrix} = \begin{bmatrix} a_1 a_2 a_3 \\ b_1 b_2 b_3 \\ c_1 c_2 c_3 \end{bmatrix}$$

and

$$\begin{bmatrix} 1 & 0 & 0 \\ 0 & 1 & 0 \\ 0 & 0 & 1 \end{bmatrix}\begin{bmatrix} a_1 a_2 a_3 \\ b_1 b_2 b_3 \\ c_1 c_2 c_3 \end{bmatrix}$$

$$= \begin{bmatrix} a_1 + 0 + 0 & a_2 + 0 + 0 & a_3 + 0 + 0 \\ 0 + b_1 + 0 & 0 + b_2 + 0 & 0 + b_3 + 0 \\ 0 + 0 + c_1 & 0 + 0 + c_2 & 0 + 0 + c_3 \end{bmatrix} = \begin{bmatrix} a_1 a_2 a_3 \\ b_1 b_2 b_3 \\ c_1 c_2 c_3 \end{bmatrix},$$

which is the same result in both cases.

It is to be noted that *the multiplication of a matrix by a unit matrix does not change its value.* More generally,

$$AI = AI^2 = \cdots = AI^n = A.$$

In the product $AB = C$, B is said to be *pre*multiplied by A; whereas in the product $BA = D$, B is said to be *post*multiplied by A. Because matrix multiplication is not commutative in general, premultiplication and postmultiplication do not give the same result in general.

The multiplication of one matrix by another is a most important process and should be thoroughly learned and kept in mind by everybody who works with matrices. It is used constantly in checking the inversion of matrices.

162. Inversion of Matrices. The operation of dividing one matrix directly by another does not exist in matrix theory, but the equivalent of division can be accomplished in most cases by a process called the inversion of matrices. The inverse of a square matrix A is another square matrix A^{-1} of the same order, such that

$$(1) \qquad\qquad AA^{-1} = I,$$

where I denotes a unit matrix of the same order. Moreover, it can be shown that

$$A^{-1}A = I,$$

so that

$$AA^{-1} = A^{-1}A.$$

Hence a matrix is commutative with its inverse. The process of finding A^{-1} when A is given is called the inversion of A. Before showing how to find A^{-1}, we digress for a moment to consider the condition necessary for its existence.

If A denotes any square matrix such as

$$A = \begin{bmatrix} a_1 a_2 a_3 \\ b_1 b_2 b_3 \\ c_1 c_2 c_3 \end{bmatrix},$$

the determinant

$$|A| = \begin{vmatrix} a_1 a_2 a_3 \\ b_1 b_2 b_3 \\ c_1 c_2 c_3 \end{vmatrix}$$

is called the determinant of the matrix. If the determinant of a matrix is not zero, the matrix is said to be non-singular and can always be inverted. That is, if $|A| \neq 0$, A^{-1} can always be found. The reason for this is as follows:

It is shown in most books dealing with matrix theory that

$$(2) \qquad A^{-1} = \begin{bmatrix} \dfrac{A_1}{|A|} & \dfrac{A_2}{|A|} & \dfrac{A_3}{|A|} \\[2mm] \dfrac{B_1}{|A|} & \dfrac{B_2}{|A|} & \dfrac{B_3}{|A|} \\[2mm] \dfrac{C_1}{|A|} & \dfrac{C_2}{|A|} & \dfrac{C_3}{|A|} \end{bmatrix} = \dfrac{1}{|A|} \begin{bmatrix} A_1 & A_2 & A_3 \\ B_1 & B_2 & B_3 \\ C_1 & C_2 & C_3 \end{bmatrix},$$

where A_1, B_2, etc., are the cofactors of the elements a_1, b_2, etc., in the determinant $|A|$. Evidently A^{-1} could not exist if $|A| = 0$.

Several methods have been devised for finding the inverse of a matrix. It can be found, for example, by means of formula (2). Although (2) is of value theoretically, it is of little value in the inversion of numerical matrices, because of the large number of determinants (the cofactors) that must be evaluated. The method of inversion explained below is simple, direct, and reasonably short.* By a procedure similar to the Gauss method explained in Art. 158, the given matrix is transformed into its inverse by means of a unit matrix of the same order. The transformation is made in consecutive steps, the number of steps being equal to the order of the matrix. A single column of the unit matrix is used in each step. The aim in each step is to reduce to zero all the elements in the first column except one, and that element is reduced to unity by dividing its row throughout by such a number as will make it unity. The matrix at the beginning of each step is augmented by the appropriate column of the unit matrix, and all elements in each row of the augmented matrix are subjected to the same operations. The underlying theory of this method of inverting matrices will not be given. The fact that the method always gives the correct result is a sufficient indication of its soundness. The simplest case of the method and a more general case will be explained by means of examples. The first element in the pivot line of every matrix will be in bold type.

a) *The simplest case.*

Example 1. Find the inverse of the matrix

$$A = \begin{bmatrix} 2 & -2 & 4 \\ 2 & 3 & 2 \\ -1 & 1 & -1 \end{bmatrix}.$$

Solution. The given matrix is first augmented by inserting the first column of a unit matrix of the third order, as follows:

$$\begin{bmatrix} \mathbf{2} & -2 & 4 & \vdots & 1 \\ 2 & 3 & 2 & \vdots & 0 \\ -1 & 1 & -1 & \vdots & 0 \end{bmatrix}.$$

---

* This method is used at the National Bureau of Standards and perhaps elsewhere.

The first row is then divided throughout by 2, giving

$$\begin{bmatrix} 1 & -1 & 2 & | & 1/2 \\ 2 & 3 & 2 & | & 0 \\ -1 & 1 & -1 & | & 0 \end{bmatrix}.$$

We now multiply the first row by 2 and subtract the result from the second row, and we also add the first row to the third row, thereby obtaining

$$\begin{bmatrix} 1 & -1 & 2 & | & 1/2 \\ 0 & 5 & -2 & | & -1 \\ 0 & 0 & 1 & | & 1/2 \end{bmatrix}.$$

This ends the first step of the transformation.

To start on the second step, we discard the first column of the old matrix and augment the last three columns by the second column of the unit matrix. Thus,

$$\begin{bmatrix} -1 & 2 & 1/2 & | & 0 \\ 5 & -2 & -1 & | & 1 \\ 0 & 1 & 1/2 & | & 0 \end{bmatrix}.$$

We now divide the second row throughout by 5 and add the result to the first row, thus obtaining

$$\begin{bmatrix} 0 & 8/5 & 3/10 & | & 1/5 \\ 1 & -2/5 & -1/5 & | & 1/5 \\ 0 & 1 & 1/2 & | & 0 \end{bmatrix}.$$

This ends the second step. Note that nothing was done to the third row, because its element in the first column was already 0.

We begin the third and last step of the transformation by discarding the first column of the matrix just found and then augmenting the remaining columns by the third column of the unit matrix. Then we have

$$\begin{bmatrix} 8/5 & 3/10 & 1/5 & | & 0 \\ -2/5 & -1/5 & 1/5 & | & 0 \\ 1 & 1/2 & 0 & | & 1 \end{bmatrix}.$$

Now multiply the third row by 8/5 and subtract the result from the first row, and also multiply the third row by 2/5 and add the result to the second row. This gives

$$\begin{bmatrix} 0 & -1/2 & 1/5 & | & -8/5 \\ 0 & 0 & 1/5 & | & 2/5 \\ 1 & 1/2 & 0 & | & 1 \end{bmatrix}.$$

This ends the third step of the transformation. On dropping the first column of the matrix just obtained, we have

$$\begin{bmatrix} -1/2 & 1/5 & -8/5 \\ 0 & 1/5 & 2/5 \\ 1/2 & 0 & 1 \end{bmatrix}.$$

as the inverse of the given matrix.

Since mistakes are easily made in the transformations, we check the result by seeing whether the inverse premultiplied by the given matrix gives the unit matrix. We therefore have

$$\begin{bmatrix} 2 & -2 & 4 \\ 2 & 3 & 2 \\ -1 & 1 & -1 \end{bmatrix} \times \begin{bmatrix} -1/2 & 1/5 & -8/5 \\ 0 & 1/5 & 2/5 \\ 1/2 & 0 & 1 \end{bmatrix}$$

$$= \begin{bmatrix} -1+0+2 & 2/5-2/5+0 & -16/5-4/5+4 \\ -1+0+1 & 2/5+3/5+0 & -16/5+6/5+2 \\ 1/2+0-1/2 & -1/5+1/5+0 & 8/5+2/5-1 \end{bmatrix} = \begin{bmatrix} 1 & 0 & 0 \\ 0 & 1 & 0 \\ 0 & 0 & 1 \end{bmatrix}.$$

The inverse found is therefore correct.

Example 2. Find the inverse of the matrix

$$\begin{bmatrix} 2 & -2 & 0 & -1 \\ 0 & 2 & 1 & 2 \\ 1 & -2 & 3 & -2 \\ 0 & 1 & 2 & 2 \end{bmatrix}.$$

Solution. The steps in the solution are shown below.

$$\begin{bmatrix} 2 & -2 & 0 & -1 & \vdots & 1 \\ 0 & 2 & 1 & 2 & \vdots & 0 \\ 1 & -2 & 3 & -2 & \vdots & 0 \\ 0 & 1 & 2 & 2 & \vdots & 0 \end{bmatrix} = \begin{bmatrix} 1 & -1 & 0 & -1/2 & \vdots & 1/2 \\ 0 & 2 & 1 & 2 & \vdots & 0 \\ 1 & -2 & 3 & -2 & \vdots & 0 \\ 0 & 1 & 2 & 2 & \vdots & 0 \end{bmatrix}.$$

Subtract row 1 from row 3. Then we have

$$\begin{bmatrix} 1 & -1 & 0 & -1/2 & \vdots & 1/2 \\ 0 & 2 & 1 & 2 & \vdots & 0 \\ 0 & -1 & 3 & -3/2 & \vdots & -1/2 \\ 0 & 1 & 2 & 2 & \vdots & 0 \end{bmatrix} \quad \text{End of step 1}$$

$$\begin{bmatrix} -1 & 0 & -1/2 & 1/2 & \vdots & 0 \\ 2 & 1 & 2 & 0 & \vdots & 1 \\ -1 & 3 & -3/2 & -1/2 & \vdots & 0 \\ 1 & 2 & 2 & 0 & \vdots & 0 \end{bmatrix} = \begin{bmatrix} -1 & 0 & -1/2 & 1/2 & \vdots & 0 \\ 1 & 1/2 & 1 & 0 & \vdots & 1/2 \\ -1 & 3 & -3/2 & -1/2 & \vdots & 0 \\ 1 & 2 & 2 & 0 & \vdots & 0 \end{bmatrix}.$$

Add row 2 to rows 1 and 3 and subtract it from row 4, obtaining

$$
\begin{bmatrix}
0 & 1/2 & 1/2 & 1/2 & \vdots & 1/2 \\
1 & 1/2 & 1 & 0 & \vdots & 1/2 \\
0 & 7/2 & -1/2 & -1/2 & \vdots & 1/2 \\
0 & 3/2 & 1 & 0 & \vdots & -1/2
\end{bmatrix} \quad \text{End of step 2}
$$

$$
\begin{bmatrix}
1/2 & 1/2 & 1/2 & 1/2 & \vdots & 0 \\
1/2 & 1 & 0 & 1/2 & \vdots & 0 \\
7/2 & -1/2 & -1/2 & 1/2 & \vdots & 1 \\
3/2 & 1 & 0 & -1/2 & \vdots & 0
\end{bmatrix}
=
\begin{bmatrix}
1/2 & 1/2 & 1/2 & 1/2 & \vdots & 0 \\
1/2 & 1 & 0 & 1/2 & \vdots & 0 \\
\tfrac{1}{2} & -1/14 & -1/14 & 1/14 & \vdots & 1/7 \\
3/2 & 1 & 0 & -1/2 & \vdots & 0
\end{bmatrix}.
$$

Subtract row 3 from rows 1 and 2, and subtract three times row 3 from row 4. The result is

$$
\begin{bmatrix}
0 & 4/7 & 4/7 & 3/7 & \vdots & -1/7 \\
0 & 15/14 & 1/14 & 3/7 & \vdots & -1/7 \\
\tfrac{1}{2} & -1/14 & -1/14 & 1/14 & \vdots & 1/7 \\
0 & 17/14 & 3/14 & -5/7 & \vdots & -3/7
\end{bmatrix}
$$

$$
=
\begin{bmatrix}
0 & 4/7 & 4/7 & 3/7 & \vdots & -1/7 \\
0 & 15/14 & 1/14 & 3/7 & \vdots & -1/7 \\
1 & -1/7 & -1/7 & 1/7 & \vdots & 2/7 \\
0 & 17/14 & 3/14 & -5/7 & \vdots & -3/7
\end{bmatrix} \quad \text{End of step 3}
$$

$$
\begin{bmatrix}
4/7 & 4/7 & 3/7 & -1/7 & \vdots & 0 \\
15/14 & 1/14 & 3/7 & -1/7 & \vdots & 0 \\
-1/7 & -1/7 & 1/7 & 2/7 & \vdots & 0 \\
17/14 & 3/14 & -5/7 & -3/7 & \vdots & 1
\end{bmatrix}
$$

$$
=
\begin{bmatrix}
4/7 & 4/7 & 3/7 & -1/7 & \vdots & 0 \\
15/14 & 1/14 & 3/7 & -1/7 & \vdots & 0 \\
-1/7 & -1/7 & 1/7 & 2/7 & \vdots & 0 \\
1 & 3/17 & -10/17 & -6/17 & \vdots & 14/17
\end{bmatrix}.
$$

Multiply row 4 by 4/7 and subtract result from row 1, multiply row 4 by 15/14 and subtract the result from row 2, and multiply row 4 by 1/7 and add the result to row 3. The result is

$$
\begin{bmatrix}
0 & 8/17 & 13/17 & 1/17 & \vdots & -8/17 \\
0 & -2/17 & 18/17 & 4/17 & \vdots & -15/17 \\
0 & -2/17 & 1/17 & 4/17 & \vdots & 2/17 \\
1 & 3/17 & -10/17 & -6/17 & \vdots & 14/17
\end{bmatrix} \quad \text{End of step 4.}
$$

Hence

$$
\begin{bmatrix}
8/17 & 13/17 & 1/17 & -8/17 \\
-2/17 & 18/17 & 4/17 & -15/17 \\
-2/17 & 1/17 & 4/17 & 2/17 \\
3/17 & -10/17 & -6/17 & 14/17
\end{bmatrix}
= 1/17
\begin{bmatrix}
8 & 13 & 1 & -8 \\
-2 & 18 & 4 & -15 \\
-2 & 1 & 4 & 2 \\
3 & -10 & -6 & 14
\end{bmatrix}.
$$

is the desired inverse matrix. Premultiplication of this by the given matrix will give a unit matrix of the fourth order, as the reader may verify.

Example 3.   Invert the matrix

$$
\begin{bmatrix}
1.254 & 0.831 & 1.109 \\
0.532 & 1.105 & 0.702 \\
0.957 & 1.342 & 0.642
\end{bmatrix}.
$$

Solution.   We have

$$
\begin{bmatrix}
1.254 & 0.831 & 1.109 & \vdots & 1 \\
0.532 & 1.105 & 0.702 & \vdots & 0 \\
0.957 & 1.342 & 0.642 & \vdots & 0
\end{bmatrix}
=
\begin{bmatrix}
1 & 0.6627 & 0.8844 & \vdots & 0.7974 \\
0.532 & 1.105 & 0.702 & \vdots & 0 \\
0.957 & 1.342 & 0.642 & \vdots & 0
\end{bmatrix},
$$

where we have divided row 1 by 1.254. Now multiply row 1 of the matrix on the right by 0.532 and subtract the result from row 2, and also multiply row 1 by 0.957 and subtract the result from row 3. We thus get

$$
\begin{bmatrix}
1 & 0.6627 & 0.8844 & \vdots & 0.7974 \\
0 & 0.7524 & 0.2315 & \vdots & -0.4242 \\
0 & 0.7078 & -0.2044 & \vdots & -0.7631
\end{bmatrix} \quad \text{End of step 1}
$$

$$
\begin{bmatrix}
0.6627 & 0.8844 & 0.7974 & \vdots & 0 \\
0.7524 & 0.2315 & -0.4242 & \vdots & 1 \\
0.7078 & -0.2044 & -0.7631 & \vdots & 0
\end{bmatrix}
$$

$$
=
\begin{bmatrix}
0.6627 & 0.8844 & 0.7974 & \vdots & 0 \\
1 & 0.3077 & -0.5638 & \vdots & 1.3291 \\
0.7078 & -0.2044 & -0.7631 & \vdots & 0
\end{bmatrix}.
$$

Now multiply row 2 by 0.6627 and subtract result from row 1. Also multiply row 2 by 0.7078 and subtract result from row 3. Then we have

$$\begin{bmatrix} 0 & 0.6805 & 1.1710 & | & -0.8808 \\ 1 & 0.3077 & -0.5638 & | & 1.3291 \\ 0 & -0.4217 & -0.3640 & | & -0.9407 \end{bmatrix} \text{End of step 2}$$

$$\begin{bmatrix} 0.6805 & 1.1710 & -0.8808 & | & 0 \\ 0.3077 & -0.5638 & 1.3291 & | & 0 \\ -\mathbf{0.4217} & -0.3640 & -0.9407 & | & 1 \end{bmatrix}$$

$$= \begin{bmatrix} 0.6805 & 1.1710 & -0.8808 & | & 0 \\ 0.3077 & -0.5638 & 1.3291 & | & 0 \\ 1 & 0.8632 & 2.2308 & | & -2.3714 \end{bmatrix}.$$

On multiplying row 3 by 0.6805 and 0.3077 and subtracting the respective results from rows 1 and 2, we get

$$\begin{bmatrix} 0 & 0.5836 & -2.3988 & | & 1.614 \\ 0 & -0.8294 & 0.6427 & | & 0.7297 \\ 1 & 0.8632 & 2.2308 & | & -2.3714 \end{bmatrix} \text{End of step 3.}$$

The required inverse is therefore

$$\begin{bmatrix} 0.5836 & -2.3988 & 1.614 \\ -0.8294 & 0.6427 & 0.7297 \\ 0.8632 & 2.2308 & -2.3714 \end{bmatrix}.$$

When this is premultiplied by the given matrix, the result is

$$\begin{bmatrix} 0.9997 & 0.0000 & 0.0006 \\ -0.0001 & 1.0001 & 0.0002 \\ -0.0005 & -0.0009 & 1.0014 \end{bmatrix},$$

which is practically a unit matrix.

b) Inversion in the more general case. In the preceding examples the pivot lines have been taken in consecutive order, always bginning with the first line of the given matrix. This procedure cannot be followed if the first element in the pivotal line is zero. Furthermore, if the first element in the pivotal line is not zero, it is sometimes desirable to take pivotal lines in any order. However, when the pivotal lines are not taken in consecutive order, the matrix obtained at the end of the last step will not be the desired inverse, but will be that inverse with its rows and columns permuted. The matrix obtained in the last step must therefore be unscrambled to obtain the desired inverse. The unscrambling process will be explained by means of an example.

Example 4. Find the inverse of the matrix

$$\begin{bmatrix} 1 & -2 & 3 & 4 \\ 3 & -1 & 2 & 5 \\ 2 & 4 & -5 & 1 \\ 4 & 2 & -1 & 3 \end{bmatrix}.$$

Solution. Here we take as pivotal row the one having the largest element in the first column: the fourth row. Augmenting the given matrix by the fourth column of a unit matrix of the fourth order, we have

$$\begin{bmatrix} 1 & -2 & 3 & 4 & \vdots & 0 \\ 3 & -1 & 2 & 5 & \vdots & 0 \\ 2 & 4 & -5 & 1 & \vdots & 0 \\ \mathbf{4} & 2 & -1 & 3 & \vdots & 1 \end{bmatrix} = \begin{bmatrix} 1 & -2 & 3 & 4 & \vdots & 0 \\ 3 & -1 & 2 & 5 & \vdots & 0 \\ 2 & 4 & -5 & 1 & \vdots & 0 \\ 1 & 1/2 & -1/4 & 3/4 & \vdots & 1/4 \end{bmatrix}.$$

Subtracting row 4 from row 1, three times row 4 from row 2, and twice row 4 from row 3, we get

$$\begin{bmatrix} 0 & -5/2 & 13/4 & 13/4 & \vdots & -1/4 \\ 0 & -5/2 & 11/4 & 11/4 & \vdots & -3/4 \\ 0 & 3 & -9/2 & -1/2 & \vdots & -1/2 \\ 1 & 1/2 & -1/4 & 3/4 & \vdots & 1/4 \end{bmatrix} \quad \text{End of step 1}$$

$$\begin{bmatrix} -5/2 & 13/4 & 13/4 & -1/4 & \vdots & 0 \\ -5/2 & 11/4 & 11/4 & -3/4 & \vdots & 0 \\ \mathbf{3} & -9/2 & -1/2 & -1/2 & \vdots & 1 \\ 1/2 & -1/4 & 3/4 & 1/4 & \vdots & 0 \end{bmatrix}$$

$$= \begin{bmatrix} -5/2 & 13/4 & 13/4 & -1/4 & \vdots & 0 \\ -5/2 & 11/4 & 11/4 & -3/4 & \vdots & 0 \\ 1 & -3/2 & -1/6 & -1/6 & \vdots & 1/3 \\ 1/2 & -1/4 & 3/4 & 1/4 & \vdots & 0 \end{bmatrix}.$$

Now adding 5/2 times row 3 to rows 1 and 2, and subtracting 1/2 of row 3 from row 4, we get

$$\begin{bmatrix} 0 & -1/2 & 17/6 & -2/3 & \vdots & 5/6 \\ 0 & -1 & 7/3 & -7/6 & \vdots & 5/6 \\ 1 & -3/2 & -1/6 & -1/6 & \vdots & 1/3 \\ 0 & 1/2 & 5/6 & 1/3 & \vdots & -1/6 \end{bmatrix} \quad \text{End of step 2}$$

$$\begin{bmatrix} -1/2 & 17/6 & -2/3 & 5/6 & \vdots & 0 \\ -1 & 7/3 & -7/6 & 5/6 & \vdots & 1 \\ -3/2 & -1/6 & -1/6 & 1/3 & \vdots & 0 \\ -1/2 & 5/6 & 1/3 & -1/6 & \vdots & 0 \end{bmatrix}$$

$$= \begin{bmatrix} -1/2 & 17/6 & -2/3 & 5/6 & \vdots & 0 \\ 1 & -7/3 & 7/6 & -5/6 & \vdots & -1 \\ -3/2 & -1/6 & -1/6 & 1/3 & \vdots & 0 \\ 1/2 & 5/6 & 1/3 & -1/6 & \vdots & 0 \end{bmatrix}.$$

Adding 1/2 row 2 to row 1, 3/2 row 2 to row 3, and subtracting 1/2 row 2 from row 4, we get

$$\begin{bmatrix} 0 & 5/3 & -1/12 & 5/12 & \vdots & -1/2 \\ 1 & -7/3 & 7/6 & -5/6 & \vdots & -1 \\ 0 & -11/3 & 19/12 & -11/12 & \vdots & -3/2 \\ 0 & 2 & -1/4 & 1/4 & \vdots & 1/2 \end{bmatrix} \text{ End of step 3}$$

$$\begin{bmatrix} \mathbf{5/3} & -1/12 & 5/12 & -1/2 & \vdots & 1 \\ -7/3 & 7/6 & -5/6 & -1 & \vdots & 0 \\ -11/3 & 19/12 & -11/12 & -3/2 & \vdots & 0 \\ 2 & -1/4 & 1/4 & 1/2 & \vdots & 0 \end{bmatrix}$$

$$= \begin{bmatrix} 1 & -1/20 & 1/4 & -3/10 & \vdots & 3/5 \\ -7/3 & 7/6 & -5/6 & -1 & \vdots & 0 \\ -11/3 & 19/12 & -11/12 & -3/2 & \vdots & 0 \\ 2 & -1/4 & 1/4 & 1/2 & \vdots & 0 \end{bmatrix}.$$

Now add 7/3 of row 1 to row 2 and 11/3 of row 1 to row 3. Also subtract twice row 1 from row 4. Then we have

$$\begin{bmatrix} 1 & -1/20 & 1/4 & -3/10 & \vdots & 3/5 \\ 0 & 21/20 & -1/4 & -17/10 & \vdots & 7/5 \\ 0 & 7/5 & 0 & -13/5 & \vdots & 11/5 \\ 0 & -3/20 & -1/4 & 11/10 & \vdots & -6/5 \end{bmatrix} \text{ End of step 4.}$$

Hence the permuted inverse is

(A)
$$\begin{bmatrix} -1/20 & 1/4 & -3/10 & 3/5 \\ 21/20 & -1/4 & -17/10 & 7/5 \\ 7/5 & 0 & -13/5 & 11/5 \\ -3/20 & -1/4 & 11/10 & -6/5 \end{bmatrix}.$$

To unscramble this matrix, we first permute its rows and then permute the columns of the resultant matrix. In order to make the permutations in a systematic and infallible manner, we construct a table showing the pivotal row used in each step of the transformation. The table for the present example is:

$$\text{Steps:} \quad 1 \quad 2 \quad 3 \quad 4 \quad \text{(for rows)}$$

$$\text{Pivot rows:} \quad 4 \quad 3 \quad 2 \quad 1 \quad \text{(for columns).}$$

The use of this table is as follows: To find the *rows* in the first permuted matrix, we fix our attention on the numbers in the *top row* of the table and note the number directly under any particular number. For example, the number directly under 2 in the top row is 3, and this means that row 2 of the new matrix will be row 3 of the previous matrix (the scrambled inverse found in the last step of the transformation).

To find the *columns* in the final inverse matrix, we fix our attention on the numbers in the *bottom row* of the table and note the number directly over any particular number. For example, the number directly over 1 in the bottom row is 4, and this means that column 1 in the final matrix is column 4 of the previous matrix (the one having the unscrambled rows). We now proceed to unscramble (A), first unscrambling the rows.

To find row 1 of the next matrix after (A), we look for 1 in the top row of the table and find that the number immediately under it is 4. Hence row 1 of the new matrix is row 4 of (A). Likewise, under 2 of the top row we find 3 and therefore row 2 of the new matrix is row 3 of (A). The remaining rows of the new matrix are found in the same manner and we therefore get the matrix

(B)
$$\begin{bmatrix} -3/20 & -1/4 & 11/10 & -6/5 \\ 7/5 & 0 & -13/5 & 11/5 \\ 21/20 & -1/4 & -17/10 & 7/5 \\ -1/20 & 1/4 & -3/10 & 3/5 \end{bmatrix}.$$

We now unscramble the columns by applying the table to (B). To find column 1 of the final inverse matrix, we look for 1 in the bottom row of the table and find 4 immediately above it. Column 1 of the inverse is therefore column 4 of (B). To find column 2 of the inverse, we look for 2 in the bottom row of the table and find 3 immediately above it. Column 2 of the inverse is therefore column 3 of (B). The remaining columns are found in the same manner and we thus get

(C)
$$\begin{bmatrix} -6/5 & 11/10 & -1/4 & -3/20 \\ 11/5 & -13/5 & 0 & 7/5 \\ 7/5 & -17/10 & -1/4 & 21/20 \\ 3/5 & -3/10 & 1/4 & -1/20 \end{bmatrix},$$

as the desired inverse matrix. The reader will find that if (C) be multiplied by the original matrix the result will be a unit matrix of the fourth order. That shows that (C) is the correct inverse.

The fact that the numbers of the pivotal rows were the inverse of the numbers of the steps in the above example was more or less accidental. The third row was used as pivotal row in the second step because its first element, 3, was the largest .of the first elements in the remaining *unused* rows. In the third step there was little choice between the first and second rows. So we used the second row as pivot.

In further explanation of the unscrambling process, we consider the simple matrix

$$\begin{bmatrix} 1 & -2 & 3 \\ 3 & -1 & 4 \\ 2 & 1 & -2 \end{bmatrix}.$$

Carrying out the inversion transformations, we have

$$\begin{bmatrix} 1 & -2 & 3 & \vdots & 0 \\ \mathbf{3} & -1 & 4 & \vdots & 1 \\ 2 & 1 & -2 & \vdots & 0 \end{bmatrix} = \begin{bmatrix} 1 & -2 & 3 & \vdots & 0 \\ \mathbf{1} & -1/3 & 4/3 & \vdots & 1/3 \\ 2 & 1 & -2 & \vdots & 0 \end{bmatrix}$$

$$= \begin{bmatrix} 0 & -5/3 & 5/3 & \vdots & -1/3 \\ 1 & -1/3 & 4/3 & \vdots & 1/3 \\ 0 & 5/3 & -14/3 & \vdots & -2/3 \end{bmatrix} \text{End of step 1}$$

$$\begin{bmatrix} -5/3 & 5/3 & -1/3 & \vdots & 0 \\ -1/3 & 4/3 & 1/3 & \vdots & 0 \\ \mathbf{5/3} & -14/3 & -2/3 & \vdots & 1 \end{bmatrix} = \begin{bmatrix} 0 & -3 & -1 & \vdots & 1 \\ 0 & 2/5 & -1/5 & \vdots & 1/5 \\ \mathbf{5/3} & -14/3 & -2/3 & \vdots & 1 \end{bmatrix}$$

$$= \begin{bmatrix} 0 & -3 & -1 & \vdots & 1 \\ 0 & 2/5 & 1/5 & \vdots & 1/5 \\ 1 & -14/5 & -2/5 & \vdots & 3/5 \end{bmatrix} \text{End of step 2}$$

$$\begin{bmatrix} -3 & -1 & 1 & \vdots & 1 \\ 2/5 & 1/5 & 1/5 & \vdots & 0 \\ -14/5 & -2/5 & 3/5 & \vdots & 0 \end{bmatrix} = \begin{bmatrix} 1 & 1/3 & -1/3 & \vdots & -1/3 \\ 2/5 & 1/5 & 1/5 & \vdots & 0 \\ -14/5 & -2/5 & 3/5 & \vdots & 0 \end{bmatrix}$$

$$= \begin{bmatrix} 1 & 1/3 & -1/3 & \vdots & -1/3 \\ 0 & 1/15 & 1/3 & \vdots & 2/15 \\ 0 & 8/15 & -1/3 & \vdots & -14/15 \end{bmatrix} \text{End of step 3}$$

(A) $\begin{bmatrix} 1/3 & -1/3 & -1/3 \\ 1/15 & 1/3 & 2/15 \\ 8/15 & -1/3 & -14/15 \end{bmatrix}$ Permuted inverse.

The table showing the pivotal rows for the three steps is:

Steps: 1   2   3   (for rows)

Pivot rows: 2   3   1   (for columns).

The table shows that row 1 of the next matrix is row 2 of (A), that row 2 is row 3 of (A), and that row 3 is row 1 of (A). Hence we have

(B) $\begin{bmatrix} 1/15 & 1/3 & 2/15 \\ 8/15 & -1/3 & -14/15 \\ 1/3 & -1/3 & -1/3 \end{bmatrix}.$

Now looking at the bottom row of the table, we see that column 1 of the inverse is column 3 of (B), that column 2 is column 1 of (B), and that column 3 is column 2 of (B). Hence we write

(C) $\begin{bmatrix} 2/15 & 1/15 & 1/3 \\ -14/15 & 8/15 & -1/3 \\ -1/3 & 1/3 & 1/3 \end{bmatrix}$ Inverse of given matrix.

If we multiply (C) by the given matrix, we get

$$\begin{bmatrix} 1 & 0 & 0 \\ 0 & 1 & 0 \\ 0 & 0 & 1 \end{bmatrix},$$

which shows that (C) is the desired inverse.

The reader will note that in any step of the transformation *the number of the augmenting column from the unit matrix must agree with the number of the row used as pivot.* For example, if the third row of a matrix is the pivotal row, the matrix must be augmented by the third column of the unit matrix.

The reader should also bear in mind that any row can be used as pivot only once in the transformation. In other words, a different row must be used as pivot for each step.

163. Solution of Equations by Matrix Methods. In matrix notation any system of simultaneous linear equations can be represented by the simple equation

(1) $$Ax = k,$$

where A denotes the matrix of the coefficients, x denotes a column matrix of the unknown x's, and k denotes a column matrix of the known terms. On premultiplying (1) by A^{-1}, we get

(2) $$x = A^{-1}k.$$

Equation (2) gives the solution of the given system. From this it is seen that in the solution of a system of linear equations by the matrix method, the chief problem is the inversion of the matrix of the coefficients. After the inverse matrix has been found, all the unknowns can be found in one short step. A few examples will show how this is done.

Example 1. Solve the system of equations

$$\begin{cases} 2x_1 - 2x_2 + 4x_3 = -12 \\ 2x_1 + 3x_2 + 2x_3 = 8 \\ -x_1 + x_2 - x_3 = 7/2. \end{cases}$$

Solution. In matrix form this system is written

$$\begin{bmatrix} 2 & -2 & 4 \\ 2 & 3 & 2 \\ -1 & 1 & -1 \end{bmatrix} \begin{bmatrix} x_1 \\ x_2 \\ x_3 \end{bmatrix} = \begin{bmatrix} -12 \\ 8 \\ 7/2 \end{bmatrix}.$$

The matrix of the coefficients is the same as Example 1, Art. 162, wherein the inverse matrix was found to be

$$\begin{bmatrix} -1/2 & 1/5 & -8/5 \\ 0 & 1/5 & 2/5 \\ 1/2 & 0 & 1 \end{bmatrix}. \text{ Hence by (2) we have}$$

$$\begin{bmatrix} x_1 \\ x_2 \\ x_3 \end{bmatrix} = \begin{bmatrix} -1/2 & 1/5 & -8/5 \\ 0 & 1/5 & 2/5 \\ 1/2 & 0 & 1 \end{bmatrix} \times \begin{bmatrix} -12 \\ 8 \\ 7/2 \end{bmatrix}.$$

On performing the indicated multiplication in the right member, we get

$$\begin{bmatrix} x_1 \\ x_2 \\ x_3 \end{bmatrix} = \begin{bmatrix} 6 + 8/5 - 28/5 \\ 0 + 8/5 + 7/5 \\ -6 + 0 + 7/2 \end{bmatrix} = \begin{bmatrix} 2 \\ 3 \\ -5/2 \end{bmatrix}.$$

Hence

$$x_1 = 2, \qquad x_2 = 3, \qquad x_3 = -5/2.$$

Example 2. Solve the system

$$\begin{cases} x - 2y + 3z + 4t = 9/2 \\ 3x - y + 2z + 5t = 19/2 \\ 2x + 4y - 5z + t = 15 \\ 4x + 2y - z + 3t = 12. \end{cases}$$

Solution. Here we have

$$\begin{bmatrix} 1 & -2 & 3 & 4 \\ 3 & -1 & 2 & 5 \\ 2 & 4 & -5 & 1 \\ 4 & 2 & -1 & 3 \end{bmatrix} \begin{bmatrix} x \\ y \\ z \\ t \end{bmatrix} = \begin{bmatrix} 9/2 \\ 19/2 \\ 15 \\ 12 \end{bmatrix}.$$

The matrix of the coefficients is seen to be the same as the matrix of Example 4, Art. 162, whose inverse was found to be (C). Then by (2) we have

$$\begin{bmatrix} x \\ y \\ z \\ t \end{bmatrix} = \begin{bmatrix} -6/5 & 11/10 & -1/4 & -3/20 \\ 11/5 & -13/5 & 0 & 7/5 \\ 7/5 & -17/10 & -1/4 & 21/20 \\ 3/5 & -3/10 & 1/4 & -1/20 \end{bmatrix} \times \begin{bmatrix} 9/2 \\ 19/2 \\ 15 \\ 12 \end{bmatrix} = \begin{bmatrix} -1/2 \\ 2 \\ -1 \\ 3 \end{bmatrix}.$$

Hence

$$x = -1/2, \qquad y = 2, \qquad z = -1, \qquad t = 3.$$

It will be seen from the above examples that the solution of a system of non-homogeneous linear equations by the matrix method consists of two distinct operations: (1) inverting the matrix of the coefficients and (2) premultiplying the column matrix of the known quantities by the inverted matrix.

IV. SOLUTION BY ITERATION

164. Systems Solvable by Iteration. All the preceding methods of solving systems of linear equations involve many subtractions of terms of the same order of magnitude. When such terms are nearly equal, their difference is nearly zero. The inaccuracies due to this inherent weakness of the methods cannot be entirely avoided. The best the computer can do is to treat all given quantities as exact numbers, use as many significant figures as practicable throughout the computation, and do as little rounding as possible until the final results are reached. The results will then be no more accurate than the given quantities, and may be much less accurate.

The method of iteration explained in Art. 74 is free from the inherent inaccuracy of the preceding methods. Moreover, it is a self-correcting method; any errors made at any step in the computation are corrected in the subsequent iterations.

Unfortunately, however, the method of iteration is not applicable to all systems of equations. In order for iteration to succeed, each equation of the system must contain one large coefficient (much larger than the others in that equation), and the large coefficient must be attached to a different unknown in each equation. This requirement is met when the large coefficients are along the leading diagonal of the matrix of the coefficients, as is sometimes the case. In solving a system of equations by iteration, each equation is first solved for the unknown having the large coefficient, thereby expressing it explicitly in terms of the other unknowns. Further steps in the process are best explained by examples.

Example 1. Solve the following equations by iteration:

$$(1) \quad \begin{cases} 27x + 6y - z = 85 \\ 6x + 15y + 2z = 72 \\ x + y + 54z = 110. \end{cases}$$

Solution. Since these equations meet the requirement for iteration, we solve each equation for the unknown having the large coefficient and thus get the system

$$(2) \quad \begin{cases} x = \dfrac{1}{27}(85 - 6y + z) & \text{(a)} \\[2mm] y = \dfrac{1}{15}(72 - 6x - 2z) & \text{(b)} \\[2mm] z = \dfrac{1}{54}(110 - x - y) & \text{(c).} \end{cases}$$

We start the iteration by putting $y = 0$, $z = 0$ in (2) (a), thus getting

$$x^{(1)} = \frac{85}{27} = 3.15.$$

Now substituting $x = 3.15$, $z = 0$ in (2) (b), we get

$$y^{(1)} = \frac{1}{15}(72 - 18.90) = 3.54.$$

Then putting $x = 3.15$, $y = 3.54$ in (2) (c), we get

$$z^{(1)} = \frac{1}{54}(110 - 3.15 - 3.54) = 1.91.$$

For the second iteration we have

$$x^{(2)} = \frac{1}{27} \, (85 - 21.24 + 1.91) = 2.43$$

$$y^{(2)} = \frac{1}{15} \, (72 - 14.58 - 3.82) = 3.57$$

$$z^{(2)} = \frac{1}{54} \, (110 - 2.43 - 3.57) = 1.926.$$

By continuing in this manner and denoting the successive iterations by I_1, I_2, etc., we get tthe following table:

	x	y	z
I_1	3.15	3.54	1.91
I_2	2.43	3.57	1.926
I_3	2.423	3.574	1.926
I_4	2.425	3.573	1.926
I_5	2.425	3.573	1.926

The solution of the system (1) is therefore

$$x = 2.425, \qquad y = 3.573, \qquad z = 1.926.$$

Example 2. Solve the following system by iteration:

$$(3) \quad \left\{ \begin{array}{l} 3.122x + 0.5756y - 0.1565z - 0.0067t = 1.571 \\ 0.5756x + 2.938y + 0.1103z - 0.0015t = -0.9275 \\ -0.1565x + 0.1103y + 4.127z + 0.2051t = -0.0652 \\ -0.0067x - 0.0015y + 0.2051z + 4.133t = -0.0178. \end{array} \right.$$

These equations meet the requirement for iteration. Solving each for the unknown having the largest coefficient, we have

$$(4) \quad \left\{ \begin{array}{ll} x = \dfrac{1}{3.122} \, (1.571 - 0.5756y + 0.1565z + 0.0067t) & \text{(a)} \\[2mm] y = \dfrac{1}{2.938} \, (-0.9275 - 0.5756x - 0.1103z + 0.0015t) & \text{(b)} \\[2mm] z = \dfrac{1}{4.127} \, (-0.0652 + 0.1565x - 0.1103y - 0.2051t) & \text{(c)} \\[2mm] t = \dfrac{1}{4.133} \, (-0.0178 + 0.0067x + 0.0015y - 0.2051z) & \text{(d)} \end{array} \right.$$

Putting $y = 0$, $z = 0$, $t = 0$ in (a), we get

$$x^{(1)} = \frac{1.571}{3.122} = 0.503.$$

Then putting $x = 0.503$, $z = 0$, $t = 0$ in (b), we get

$$y^{(1)} = \frac{1}{2.938} \, (-0.9275 - 0.5756 \times 0.503) = -0.414.$$

To find $z^{(1)}$ we put $x = 0.503$, $y = -0.414$, $t = 0$ in (c) and get

$$z^{(1)} = \frac{1}{4.127} \, (-0.0652 + 0.1565 \times 0.503 + 0.1103 \times 0.414) = 0.0143.$$

Then for $t^{(1)}$ we have

$$t^{(1)} = \frac{1}{4.133} \, (-0.0178 + 0.0067 \times 0.503 - 0.0015 \times 0.414$$
$$- 0.2051 \times 0.0143) = -0.00435.$$

To start the second iteration, we substitute in (4) (a) the above values of $y^{(1)}$, $z^{(1)}$, $t^{(1)}$ and get

$$x^{(2)} = 0.580.$$

Then

$$y^{(2)} = \frac{1}{2.938} \, [-0.9275 - (0.5756)(0.580) - (0.1103)(0.0143)$$
$$- (0.0015)(0.00435)] = -0.430.$$

The reader will note that *as soon as a new value is found, it is used at once in the immediately following equations.* By continuing the iteration as outlined above, we get the following table:

	x	y	z	t
I_1	0.503	-0.414	0.0143	-0.00435
I_2	0.580	-0.430	0.0179	-0.00441
I_3	0.5834	-0.4307	0.01805	-0.004413
I_4	0.5835	-0.4307	0.01806	-0.004413
I_5	0.5835	-0.4307	0.01806	-0.004413

The solution of the system (3) is thus

$$x = 0.5835, \qquad y = -0.4307, \qquad z = 0.01806, \qquad t = -0.004413.$$

After one or two iterations in an example to which the method of iteration is applicable, the changes in the computed values of the unknowns should be gradual. Erratic changes will usually mean that an error of some kind has been made in obtaining the erratic value, and therefore the value should be checked before proceeding further.

165. Conditions for the Convergence of the Iteration Process. In Art. 75 we derived the conditions for the convergence of the iteration process for a system of two equations of any nature. Those results can be extended to systems in any number of unknowns. For example, in the case of the system in four unknowns

$$x = F_1(x, y, z, t)$$
$$y = F_2(x, y, z, t)$$
$$z = F_3(x, y, z, t)$$
$$t = F_4(x, y, z, t),$$

the conditions for convergence are

$$\left|\frac{\partial F_1}{\partial x}\right| + \left|\frac{\partial F_2}{\partial x}\right| + \left|\frac{\partial F_3}{\partial x}\right| + \left|\frac{\partial F_4}{\partial x}\right| < 1$$

and three similar inequalities involving partial derivatives with respect to y, z, and t, respectively. On adding the four inequalities and grouping the terms of the resultant inequality in the vertical direction, we readily see that the latter inequality is satisfied by the four conditions

$$\left|\frac{\partial F_1}{\partial x}\right| + \left|\frac{\partial F_1}{\partial y}\right| + \left|\frac{\partial F_1}{\partial z}\right| + \left|\frac{\partial F_1}{\partial t}\right| < 1$$

$$\left|\frac{\partial F_2}{\partial x}\right| + \left|\frac{\partial F_2}{\partial y}\right| + \left|\frac{\partial F_2}{\partial z}\right| + \left|\frac{\partial F_2}{\partial t}\right| < 1$$

$$\left|\frac{\partial F_3}{\partial x}\right| + \left|\frac{\partial F_3}{\partial y}\right| + \left|\frac{\partial F_3}{\partial z}\right| + \left|\frac{\partial F_3}{\partial t}\right| < 1$$

$$\left|\frac{\partial F_4}{\partial x}\right| + \left|\frac{\partial F_4}{\partial y}\right| + \left|\frac{\partial F_4}{\partial z}\right| + \left|\frac{\partial F_4}{\partial t}\right| < 1.$$

Now applying these results to a system of linear equations in which the coefficients are a_1, b_1, c_1, d_1; a_2, b_2, c_2, d_2; etc., we find

$$|b_1| + |c_1| + |d_1| < |a_1|$$
$$|a_2| + |c_2| + |d_2| < |b_2|, \text{ etc.}$$

Hence for a system of linear equations the necessary conditions for the convergence of the iteration process are given by the following simple rule:

In each equation of the system the absolute value of the largest coefficient must be greater than the sum of the absolute values of all the remaining coefficients in that equation.

This rule can be applied at a glance and is seen to hold for the two examples worked above.

166. Concluding Remarks, and References for Further Study. In the preceding pages several standard methods of solving systems of linear equations have been explained in sufficient detail to permit the reader to see the advantages and disadvantages of each. No one method can be called the best for any and all systems of equations that may arise. The method of iteration is probably the best method in all cases where it is applicable, provided the convergence is reasonably rapid. It is the best for these reasons: (1) it has no inherent inaccuracy; (2) it is self-correcting; and (3) it is applicable to systems of any number of unknowns. The best of the remaining methods are the second version of Gauss's method (Art. 158) and the method by inversion of matrices (Art. 163).

Additional methods of solving systems of linear equations will be found in P. S. Dwyer's *Linear Computations* (New York, 1951) and in " Practical Solution of Linear Equations and Inversion of Matrices," by L. Fox. This paper constitutes the first chapter in *Contributions to the Solution of Systems of Linear Equations and the Determination of Eigenvalues,* being National Bureau of Standards Applied Mathematics Series 39 (Washington, 1954).

Further information on matrices and their application to the solution of systems of linear equations will be found in *Elementary Matrices,* by Frazer, Duncan, and Collar (Cambridge University Press, 1938).

Methods of investigating the inherent errors in the solutions of systems of linear equations and in the values of numerical determinants have been given in Chapter I of this book.

The errors associated with the inversion of matrices are discussed by P. S. Dwyer in Chapter 17 of his *Linear Computations* and in a paper entitled " Errors of Matrix Computations," published in National Bureau of Standards Applied Mathematics Series 29 (Washington, 1953). A more exhaustive study of the errors associated with matrix inversion will be found in two lengthy papers by John Von Neumann and H. H. Goldstine entitled " Numerical Inverting of Matrices of High Order " and published in the *Bulletin of the American Mathematical Society,* Vol. 53, No. 11 (November, 1947) and in *Proceedings of the American Mathematical*

Society, Vol. 2 (1951). These papers are concerned primarily with matrices of the tenth order and higher.

EXERCISES XVIII

1. Evaluate

$$\begin{vmatrix} 2 & -3 & 1 & 5 \\ 1 & -2 & 4 & 3 \\ -1 & 3 & 2 & 4 \\ 3 & -1 & 2 & 1 \end{vmatrix}$$

by the pivotal method.

2. Evaluate the above determinant by the triangular method.

3. Solve for z by Cramer's Rule:

$$x - 7y + 2z - t = 10$$
$$3x + 4y - z + t = 4$$
$$2x - y + 4z - 2t = 7$$
$$5x + 2y - 3z + 2t = 9.$$

4. Solve the following system by the Gauss method of Art. 158:

$$2.38x_1 + 1.95x_2 - 3.27x_3 + 1.58x_4 = 2.16$$
$$3.21x_1 - 0.86x_2 + 2.42x_3 - 3.20x_4 = 3.28$$
$$1.44x_1 + 2.95x_2 - 2.14x_3 + 1.86x_4 = 1.42$$
$$4.17x_1 + 3.62x_2 - 1.68x_3 - 2.26x_4 = 5.21.$$

5. Evaluate the determinant of the coefficients in the above exercise. *Hint:* Use the product of the leading coefficients of the pivotal equations.

6. Solve Exercise 3 completely by inverting the matrix of the coefficients.

7. Solve Exercise 4 completely by inverting the matrix of the coefficients.

8. Solve the following system by the iteration process:

$$0.89x + 4.32y - 0.47z + 0.95t = 3.36$$
$$1.13x - 0.89y + 0.61z + 5.63t = 4.27$$
$$6.32x - 0.73y - 0.65z + 1.06t = 2.95$$
$$0.74x + 1.01y + 5.28z - 0.88t = 1.97.$$

APPENDIX
VALUES OF THE PROBABILITY INTEGRAL

$$P = \frac{2}{\sqrt{\pi}} \int_0^t e^{-t^2} dt, \quad \text{where } t = hx.$$

hx	0	1	2	3	4	5	6	7	8	9
0.00	0.00000	00113	00226	00339	00451	00564	00677	00790	00903	01016
0.01	0.01128	01241	01354	01467	01580	01692	01805	01918	02031	02144
0.02	0.02256	02369	02482	02595	02708	02820	02933	03046	03159	03271
0.03	0.03384	03497	03610	03722	03835	03948	04060	04173	04286	04398
0.04	0.04511	04624	04736	04849	04962	05074	05187	05299	05412	05525
0.05	0.05637	05750	05862	05975	06087	06200	06312	06425	06537	06650
0.06	0.06762	06875	06987	07099	07212	07324	07437	07549	07661	07773
0.07	0.07886	07998	08110	08223	08335	08447	08559	08671	08784	08896
0.08	0.09008	09120	09232	09344	09456	09568	09680	09792	09904	10016
0.09	0.10128	10240	10352	10464	10576	10687	10799	10911	11023	11135
0.10	0.11246	11358	11470	11581	11693	11805	11916	12028	12139	12251
0.11	0.12362	12474	12585	12697	12808	12919	13031	13142	13253	13365
0.12	0.13476	13587	13698	13809	13921	14032	14143	14254	14365	14476
0.13	0.14587	14698	14809	14919	15030	15141	15252	15363	15473	15584
0.14	0.15695	15805	15916	16027	16137	16248	16358	16468	16579	16689
0.15	0.16800	16910	17020	17130	17241	17351	17461	17571	17681	17791
0.16	0.17901	18011	18121	18231	18341	18451	18560	18670	18780	18890
0.17	0.18999	19109	19218	19328	19437	19547	19656	19766	19875	19984
0.18	0.20094	20203	20312	20421	20530	20639	20748	20857	20966	21075
0.19	0.21184	21293	21402	21510	21619	21728	21836	21945	22053	22162
0.20	0.22270	22379	22487	22595	22704	22812	22920	23028	23136	23244
0.21	0.23352	23460	23568	23676	23784	23891	23999	24107	24214	24322
0.22	0.24430	24537	24645	24752	24859	24967	25074	25181	25288	25395
0.23	0.25502	25609	25716	25823	25930	26037	26144	26250	26357	26463
0.24	0.26570	26677	26783	26889	26996	27102	27208	27314	27421	27527
0.25	0.27633	27739	27845	27950	28056	28162	28268	28373	28479	28584
0.26	0.28690	28795	28901	29006	29111	29217	29322	29427	29532	29637
0.27	0.29742	29847	29952	30056	30161	30266	30370	30475	30579	30684
0.28	0.30788	30892	30997	31101	31205	31309	31413	31517	31621	31725
0.29	0.31828	31922	32036	32139	32243	32346	32450	32553	32656	32760
0.30	0.32863	32966	33069	33172	33275	33378	33480	33583	33686	33788
0.31	0.33891	33993	34096	34198	34300	34403	34505	34607	34709	34811
0.32	0.34913	35014	35116	35218	35319	35421	35523	35624	35725	35827
0.33	0.35928	36029	36130	36231	36332	36433	36534	36635	36735	36836
0.34	0.36936	37037	37137	37238	37338	37438	37538	37638	37738	37838
0.35	0.37938	38038	38138	38237	38337	38436	38536	38635	38735	38834
0.36	0.38933	39032	39131	39230	39329	39428	39526	39625	39724	39822
0.37	0.39921	40019	40117	40215	40314	40412	40510	40608	40705	40803
0.38	0.40901	40999	41096	41194	41291	41388	41486	41583	41680	41777
0.39	0.41874	41971	42068	42164	42261	42358	42454	42550	42647	42743
0.40	0.42839	42935	43031	43127	43223	43319	43415	43510	43606	43701
0.41	0.43797	43892	43988	44083	44178	44273	44368	44463	44557	44652
0.42	0.44747	44841	44936	45030	45124	45219	45313	45407	45501	45595
0.43	0.45689	45782	45876	45970	46063	46157	46250	46343	46436	46529
0.44	0.46623	46715	46808	46901	46994	47086	47179	47271	47364	47456
0.45	0.47548	47640	47732	47824	47916	48008	48100	48191	48283	48374
0.46	0.48466	48557	48648	48739	48830	48921	49012	49103	49193	49284
0.47	0.49375	49465	49555	49646	49736	49826	49916	50006	50096	50185
0.48	0.50275	50365	50454	50543	50633	50722	50811	50900	50989	51078
0.49	0.51167	51256	51344	51433	51521	51609	51698	51786	51874	51962

VALUES OF THE PROBABILITY INTEGRAL

$$P = \frac{2}{\sqrt{\pi}} \int_0^t e^{-t^2}dt, \quad \text{where } t = hx.$$

hx	0	1	2	3	4	5	6	7	8	9
0.50	0.52050	52138	52226	52313	52401	52488	52576	52663	52750	52837
0.51	0.52924	53011	53098	53185	53272	53358	53445	53531	53617	53704
0.52	0.53790	53876	53962	54048	54134	54219	54305	54390	54476	54561
0.53	0.54646	54732	54817	54902	54987	55071	55156	55241	55325	55410
0.54	0.55494	55578	55662	55746	55830	55914	55998	56082	56165	56249
0.55	0.56332	56416	56499	56582	56665	56748	56831	56914	56996	57079
0.56	0.57162	57244	57326	57409	57491	57573	57655	57737	57818	57900
0.57	0.57982	58063	58144	58226	58307	58388	58469	58550	58631	58712
0.58	0.58792	58873	58953	59034	59114	59194	59274	59354	59434	59514
0.59	0.59594	59673	59753	59832	59912	59991	60070	60149	60228	60307
0.60	0.60386	60464	60543	60621	60700	60778	60856	60934	61012	61090
0.61	0.61168	61246	61323	61401	61478	61556	61633	61710	61787	61864
0.62	0.61941	62018	62095	62171	62248	62324	62400	62477	62553	62629
0.63	0.62705	62780	62856	62932	63007	63083	63158	63233	63309	63384
0.64	0.63459	63533	63608	63683	63757	63832	63906	63981	64055	64129
0.65	0.64203	64277	64351	64424	64498	64572	64645	64718	64791	64865
0.66	0.64938	65011	65083	65156	65229	65301	65374	65446	65519	65591
0.67	0.65663	65735	65807	65878	65950	66022	66093	66165	66236	66307
0.68	0.66378	66449	66520	66591	66662	66732	66803	66873	66944	67014
0.69	0.67084	67154	67224	67294	67364	67433	67503	67572	67642	67711
0.70	0.67780	67849	67918	67987	68056	68125	68193	68262	68330	68398
0.71	0.68467	68535	68603	68671	68738	68806	68874	68941	69009	69076
0.72	0.69143	69210	69278	69344	69411	69478	69545	69611	69678	69744
0.73	0.69810	69877	69943	70009	70075	70140	70206	70272	70337	70403
0.74	0.70468	70533	70598	70663	70728	70793	70858	70922	70987	71051
0.75	0.71116	71180	71244	71308	71372	71436	71500	71563	71627	71690
0.76	0.71754	71817	71880	71943	72006	72069	72132	72195	72257	72320
0.77	0.72382	72444	72507	72569	72631	72693	72755	72816	72878	72940
0.78	0.73001	73062	73124	73185	73246	73307	73368	73429	73489	73550
0.79	0.73610	73671	73731	73791	73851	73911	73971	74031	74091	74151
0.80	0.74210	74270	74329	74388	74447	74506	74565	74624	74683	74742
0.81	0.74800	74859	74917	74976	75034	75092	75150	75208	75266	75323
0.82	0.75381	75439	75496	75553	75611	75668	75725	75782	75839	75896
0.83	0.75952	76009	76066	76122	76178	76234	76291	76347	76403	76459
0.84	0.76514	76570	76626	76681	76736	76792	76847	76902	76957	77012
0.85	0.77067	77122	77176	77231	77285	77340	77394	77448	77502	77556
0.86	0.77610	77664	77718	77771	77825	77878	77932	77985	78038	78091
0.87	0.78144	78197	78250	78302	78355	78408	78460	78512	78565	78617
0.88	0.78669	78721	78773	78824	78876	78928	78979	79031	79082	79133
0.89	0.79184	79235	79286	79337	79388	79439	79489	79540	79590	79641
0.90	0.79691	79741	79791	79841	79891	79941	79990	80040	80090	80139
0.91	0.80188	80238	80287	80336	80385	80434	80482	80531	80580	80628
0.92	0.80677	80725	80773	80822	80870	80918	80966	81013	81061	81109
0.93	0.81156	81204	81251	81299	81346	81393	81440	81487	81534	81580
0.94	0.81627	81674	81720	81767	81813	81859	81905	81951	81997	82043
0.95	0.82089	82135	82180	82226	82271	82317	82362	82407	82452	82497
0.96	0.82542	82587	82632	82677	82721	82766	82810	82855	82899	82943
0.97	0.82987	83031	83075	83119	83162	83206	83250	83293	83337	83380
0.98	0.83423	83466	83509	83552	83595	83638	83681	83723	83766	83808
0.99	0.83851	83893	83935	83977	84020	84061	84103	84145	84187	84229

VALUES OF THE PROBABILITY INTEGRAL

$$P = \frac{2}{\sqrt{\pi}} \int_{0}^{t} e^{-t^2}dt, \quad \text{where } t = hx.$$

hx	0	1	2	3	4	5	6	7	8	9
1.00	0.84270	84312	84353	84394	84435	84477	84518	84559	84600	84640
1.01	0.84681	84722	84762	84803	84843	84883	84924	84964	85004	85044
1.02	0.85084	85124	85163	85203	85243	85282	85322	85361	85400	85439
1.03	0.85478	85517	85556	85595	85634	85673	85711	85750	85788	85827
1.04	0.85865	85903	85941	85979	86017	86055	86093	86131	86169	86206
1.05	0.86244	86281	86318	86356	86393	86430	86467	86504	86541	86578
1.06	0.86614	86651	86688	86724	86760	86797	86833	86869	86905	86941
1.07	0.86977	87013	87049	87085	87120	87156	87191	87227	87262	87297
1.08	0.87333	87368	87403	87438	87473	87507	87542	87577	87611	87646
1.09	0.87680	87715	87749	87783	87817	87851	87885	87919	87953	87987
1.10	0.88021	88054	88088	88121	88155	88188	88221	88254	88287	88320
1.11	0.88353	88386	88419	88452	88484	88517	88549	88582	88614	88647
1.12	0.88679	88711	88743	88775	88807	88839	88871	88902	88934	88966
1.13	0.88997	89029	89060	89091	89122	89154	89185	89216	89247	89277
1.14	0.89308	89339	89370	89400	89431	89461	89492	89522	89552	89582
1.15	0.89612	89642	89672	89702	89732	89762	89792	89821	89851	89880
1.16	0.89910	89939	89968	89997	90027	90056	90085	90114	90142	90171
1.17	0.90200	90229	90257	90286	90314	90343	90371	90399	90428	90456
1.18	0.90484	90512	90540	90568	90595	90623	90651	90678	90706	90733
1.19	0.90761	90788	90815	90843	90870	90897	90924	90951	90978	91005
1.20	0.91031	91058	91085	91111	91138	91164	91191	91217	91243	91269
1.21	0.91296	91322	91348	91374	91399	91425	91451	91477	91502	91528
1.22	0.91553	91579	91604	91630	91655	91680	91705	91730	91755	91780
1.23	0.91805	91830	91855	91879	91904	91929	91953	91978	92002	92026
1.24	0.92051	92075	92099	92123	92147	92171	92195	92219	92243	92266
1.25	0.92290	92314	92337	92361	92384	92408	92431	92454	92477	92500
1.26	0.92524	92547	92570	92593	92615	92638	92661	92684	92706	92729
1.27	0.92751	92774	92796	92819	92841	92863	92885	92907	92929	92951
1.28	0.92973	92995	93017	93039	93061	93082	93104	93126	93147	93168
1.29	0.93190	93211	93232	93254	93275	93296	93317	93338	93359	93380
1.30	0.93401	93422	93442	93463	93484	93504	93525	93545	93566	93586
1.31	0.93606	93627	93647	93667	93687	93707	93727	93747	93767	93787
1.32	0.93807	93826	93846	93866	93885	93905	93924	93944	93963	93982
1.33	0.94002	94021	94040	94059	94078	94097	94116	94135	94154	94173
1.34	0.94191	94210	94229	94247	94266	94284	94303	94321	94340	94358
1.35	0.94376	94394	94413	94431	94449	94467	94485	94503	94521	94538
1.36	0.94556	94574	94592	94609	94627	94644	94662	94679	94697	94714
1.37	0.94731	94748	94766	94783	94800	94817	94834	94851	94868	94885
1.38	0.94902	94918	94935	94952	94968	94985	95002	95018	95035	95051
1.39	0.95067	95084	95100	95116	95132	95148	95165	95181	95197	95213
1.40	0.95229	95244	95260	95276	95292	95307	95323	95339	95354	95370
1.41	0.95385	95401	95416	95431	95447	95462	95477	95492	95507	95523
1.42	0.95538	95553	95568	95582	95597	95612	95627	95642	95656	95671
1.43	0.95686	95700	95715	95729	95744	95758	95773	95787	95801	95815
1.44	0.95830	95844	95858	95872	95886	95900	95914	95928	95942	95956
1.45	0.95970	95983	95997	96011	96024	96038	96051	96065	96078	96092
1.46	0.96105	96119	96132	96145	96159	96172	96185	96198	96211	96224
1.47	0.96237	96250	96263	96276	96289	96302	96315	96327	96340	96353
1.48	0.96365	96378	96391	96403	96416	96428	96440	96453	96465	96478
1.49	0.96490	96502	96514	96526	96539	96551	96563	96575	96587	96599

VALUES OF THE PROBABILITY INTEGRAL

$$P = \frac{2}{\sqrt{\pi}} \int_0^t e^{-t^2} dt, \text{ where } t = hx.$$

hx	0	2	4	6	8	hx	0	2	4	6	8
1.50	0.96611	96634	96658	96681	96705	2.00	0.99532	99536	99540	99544	99548
1.51	0.96728	96751	96774	96796	96819	2.01	0.99552	99556	99560	99564	99568
1.52	0.96841	96864	96886	96908	96930	2.02	0.99572	99576	99580	99583	99587
1.53	0.96952	96973	96995	97016	97037	2.03	0.99591	99594	99598	99601	99605
1.54	0.97059	97080	97100	97121	97142	2.04	0.99609	99612	99616	99619	99622
1.55	0.97162	97183	97203	97223	97243	2.05	0.99626	99629	99633	99636	99639
1.56	0.97263	97283	97302	97322	97341	2.06	0.99642	99646	99649	99652	99655
1.57	0.97360	97379	97398	97417	97436	2.07	0.99658	99661	99664	99667	99670
1.58	0.97455	97473	97492	97510	97528	2.08	0.99673	99676	99679	99682	99685
1.59	0.97546	97564	97582	97600	97617	2.09	0.99688	99691	99694	99697	99699
1.60	0.97635	97652	97670	97687	97704	2.10	0.99702	99705	99707	99710	99713
1.61	0.97721	97738	97754	97771	97787	2.11	0.99715	99718	99721	99723	99726
1.62	0.97804	97820	97836	97852	97868	2.12	0.99728	99731	99733	99736	99738
1.63	0.97884	97900	97916	97931	97947	2.13	0.99741	99743	99745	99748	99750
1.64	0.97962	97977	97993	98008	98023	2.14	0.99753	99755	99757	99759	99762
1.65	0.98038	98052	98067	98082	98096	2.15	0.99764	99766	99768	99770	99773
1.66	0.98110	98125	98139	98153	98167	2.16	0.99775	99777	99779	99781	99783
1.67	0.98181	98195	98209	98222	98236	2.17	0.99785	99787	99789	99791	99793
1.68	0.98249	98263	98276	98289	98302	2.18	0.99795	99797	99799	99801	99803
1.69	0.98315	98328	98341	98354	98366	2.19	0.99805	99806	99808	99810	99812
1.70	0.98379	98392	98404	98416	98429	2.20	0.99814	99815	99817	99819	99821
1.71	0.98441	98453	98465	98477	98489	2.21	0.99822	99824	99826	99827	99829
1.72	0.98500	98512	98524	98535	98546	2.22	0.99831	99832	99834	99836	99837
1.73	0.98558	98569	98580	98591	98602	2.23	0.99839	99840	99842	99843	99845
1.74	0.98613	98624	98635	98646	98657	2.24	0.99846	99848	99849	99851	99852
1.75	0.98667	98678	98688	98699	98709	2.25	0.99854	99855	99857	99858	99859
1.76	0.98719	98729	98739	98749	98759	2.26	0.99861	99862	99863	99865	99866
1.77	0.98769	98779	98789	98798	98808	2.27	0.99867	99869	99870	99871	99873
1.78	0.98817	98827	98836	98846	98855	2.28	0.99874	99875	99876	99877	99879
1.79	0.98864	98873	98882	98891	98900	2.29	0.99880	99881	99882	99883	99885
1.80	0.98909	98918	98927	98935	98944	2.30	0.99886	99887	99888	99889	99890
1.81	0.98952	98961	98969	98978	98986	2.31	0.99891	99892	99893	99894	99896
1.82	0.98994	99003	99011	99019	99027	2.32	0.99897	99898	99899	99900	99901
1.83	0.99035	99043	99050	99058	99066	2.33	0.99902	99903	99904	99905	99906
1.84	0.99074	99081	99089	99096	99104	2.34	0.99906	99907	99908	99909	99910
1.85	0.99111	99118	99126	99133	99140	2.35	0.99911	99912	99913	99914	99915
1.86	0.99147	99154	99161	99168	99175	2.36	0.99915	99916	99917	99918	99919
1.87	0.99182	99189	99196	99202	99209	2.37	0.99920	99920	99921	99922	99923
1.88	0.99216	99222	99229	99235	99242	2.38	0.99924	99924	99925	99926	99927
1.89	0.99248	99254	99261	99267	99273	2.39	0.99928	99928	99929	99930	99930
1.90	0.99279	99285	99291	99297	99303	2.40	0.99931	99932	99933	99933	99934
1.91	0.99309	99315	99321	99326	99332	2.41	0.99935	99935	99936	99937	99937
1.92	0.99338	99343	99349	99355	99360	2.42	0.99938	99939	99939	99940	99940
1.93	0.99366	99371	99376	99382	99387	2.43	0.99941	99942	99942	99943	99943
1.94	0.99392	99397	99403	99408	99413	2.44	0.99944	99945	99945	99946	99946
1.95	0.99418	99423	99428	99433	99438	2.45	0.99947	99947	99948	99949	99949
1.96	0.99443	99447	99452	99457	99462	2.46	0.99950	99950	99951	99951	99952
1.97	0.99466	99471	99476	99480	99485	2.47	0.99952	99953	99953	99954	99954
1.98	0.99489	99494	99498	99502	99507	2.48	0.99955	99955	99956	99956	99957
1.99	0.99511	99515	99520	99524	99528	2.49	0.99957	99958	99958	99958	99959
2.00	0.99532	99536	99540	99544	99548	2.50	0.99959	99960	99960	99961	99961

VALUES OF THE PROBABILITY INTEGRAL

$$P = \frac{2}{\sqrt{\pi}} \int_0^t e^{-t^2} dt, \quad \text{where } t = hx.$$

hx	0	1	2	3	4	5	6	7	8	9
2.5	0.99959	99961	99963	99965	99967	99969	99971	99972	99974	99975
2.6	0.99976	99978	99979	99980	99981	99982	99983	99984	99985	99986
2.7	0.99987	99987	99988	99989	99989	99990	99991	99991	99992	99992
2.8	0.99992	99993	99993	99994	99994	99994	99995	99995	99995	99996
2.9	0.99996	99996	99996	99997	99997	99997	99997	99997	99997	99998
3.0	0.99998	99998	99998	99998	99998	99998	99998	99998	99999	99999

INDEX

(The numbers refer to pages)

A

Absolute error, 4
Acceleration of gravity, formula for, 47
Accidental errors, 378
Accuracy in determination of arguments, 28
 in evaluation of formulas, 24
 of addition, 10
 of averages, 11, 12
 of division, 15, 16
 of interpolation formulas, 97
 of linear interpolation, 107
 of logs and antilogs, 19
 of measurements, 411
 of multiplication, 14
 of powers and roots, 18
 of products and quotients, 14, 15, 16, 17
 of series approximations, 32
 of subtraction, 12, 13, 14
 of solution of difference equations, 323, 324
  of differential equations, 303
  of systems of linear equations, 38
Adams, J. C., 247, 251
Addition, errors of, 10
Adopted values of constants, 25
Algebraic equations, special procedure for, 198
Alternating series, error in, 34
Analysis, harmonic, of empirical functions, 477
Antilogarithms, accuracy of, 19, 20
Approximate numbers, 2
Arguments, accuracy in determination of, 28
Astronomy, practical, fundamental equations of, 48, 49
Asymptotic series, 157, 393
Average deviation, 417
 error, 414
Averages, accuracy of, 11
 method of, 446

B

Backward interpolation, Newton's formula for, 64

Ballistic equations, 276, 277, 278
Ballistics, fundamental equation of, 276
Bairstow, L., 233
Barker, J. E., 279
Barker method, 279, 286
 how to use, 282
Bashforth, F., 247
Bessel's formula of interpolation, 77, 78
 for interpolating to halves, 77
 symmetrical form of, 78
Best type of empirical formula, finding, 472
Biermann, O., 59, 117
Binomial series, remainder in, 35
Block relaxation, 336
Borel, E., 97
Boundary-value problems, 368
Bradley, J., 409
Brodetsky, S., 233

C

Cajori, F., 192
Carvallo, 233, 234
Caution in use of empirical formulas, 493
 in use of quadrature formulas, 159
Central-difference formulas,
 of interpolation, 70
 quadrature, 138, 141
  geometric significance of, 141
  remainder terms in, 181
Charlier, C. V. L., 156, 158
Chauvenet, W., 393
Check formula for coefficients in root-squared equations, 221
Check formulas, for 12 ordinates, 485
 for 24 ordinates, 490
Combination of sets of measurements, 421, 422
Complex roots, detection of, 222
 computation of, by Graeffe's method, 222
Conditional equations, 477, 478
Conditions for convergence of iteration process for algebraic and transcendental equations, 201, 209, 536
 of Picard's method, 274

544

ANSWERS TO EXERCISES

I, Page 46

1. 63.85, 93490 or 9349 × 10, 0.006394,
   83620 or 8362 × 10, 3630 × 10², 0.09004,
   53910 or 5391 × 10.

2. Beam measurement.   **3.** 571.   **4.** 5529 or 5528.

5. 6804.0 or 6804.1.   **6.** 0.0206850.

7. Between 860 and 865.   **8.** 9 ft./sec.

9. 37.1 ± 1.4 ft./sec.

10. 6,250,000 ft. lbs.;   6,211,180 ft. lbs.;
    6,216,972 ft. lbs.

11. $\dfrac{dl}{l} = 0.00025$, $\dfrac{dT}{T} = 0.000125$.

12. $100 \dfrac{dr}{r} = 0.177$; $100 \dfrac{dh}{h} = 0.98$.

13. $\Delta\theta = 0.00106$ radian $= 3'\,39''$.

14. 0.1%.   **15.** $dL = 1'\,\dfrac{1}{13}''$.

16. $dh = 0'.5$, $dt = 0.144$ radian $= 0^h.553 = 33^m\,2^s$.

17. $dL_1 = 18''.9$, $dL_2 = 45''.4$, $d\lambda_1 = 30''.6$, $d\lambda_2 = 30''.6$.

18. For $A = 10°$, $dL = 1'\,21''$;
    for $A = 80°$, $dL = 12'\,54''$.

19. (a) $dh = 29''.5$, $dt = 14^s.8$;
    (b) $dh = 7''.8$, $dt = 0^s.7$.

20. For $A = 10°$, $dt = 145^s.2 = 2^m\,25^s.2$;
    for $A = 80°$, $dt = 9^s.9$.

21. For $A = 10°$, $dL = 3''.0$, $dh = 3''.0$;
    for $A = 80°$, $dL = 1'\,37''.8$, $dh = 17''.0$.

22. For $A = 10°$, $dL = 1'.1$;
    for $A = 80°$, $dL = 9'.0$.

23. Δk is most potent as t increases.

24. 0.77210.   **25.** 1.5051.

26. $x = 1.9273537,\quad \Delta x = \pm\, 0.052$;
$y = -\, 2.0198504,\quad \Delta y = \mp\, 0.049$;
$z = 0.7584232,\quad \Delta z = \mp\, 0.0602.$
Hence we take $x = 1.9,\quad y = -\,2.0,\quad z = 0.8.$

27. $x = 0.359496660,\quad \Delta x = \pm\, 0.00872$;
$y = 0.444855496,\quad \Delta y = \mp\, 0.00066$;
$z = 0.712148773,\quad \Delta z = \mp\, 0.00242$;
$u = -\, 1.122082546,\quad \Delta u = \pm\, 0.00097.$
Hence we take
$x = 0.36,\quad y = 0.445,\quad z = 0.71,\quad u = -\, 1.122.$

II, Page 68

1. 65540 should be corrected to 65536.
2. Fourth line should be $19°51'\,59''.8$.
3. $8.0363956 - 10.$ **4.** $261°\,54'\,14''.7.$
5. $8.0891991 - 10.$ **6.** $274°\,43'\,22''.$

III, Page 83

1. $8.2175401 - 10.$ **2.** $0.691960629.$
3. $0.6448325.$ **4.** $1'\,52''.4.$ **5.** $12°\,55'\,12''.94.$
6. $0.436185128.$

IV, Page 95

1. $y = 15.79;\quad x = 97.66.$ **2.** $0.73811340.$

V, Page 108

1. Ex. 3, $R_n = 0.030$; Ex. 4, $R_n = 0''.023.$
2. Ex. 2, $R_n = 0.015$; Ex. 3, $R_n = 0.16$;
Ex. 4, $R_n = 0.00117$; Ex. 6, $R_n = 0.055.$

VI, Page 127

1. $5^h\,48^m\,25^s.$

VII, Page 171

1. 5.6972.   2. 0.4623.   3. $6^h 5^m 21^s.9$ A. M., June 22.
4. By Simpson's Rule, 1.505103;
   by Weddle's Rule, 1.505103.
5. 0.9289011.   6. 293.4.   7. 1.010784.
8. 0.90452.   9. 0.113822.   10. — 0.09485.
11. 0.9480, by Simpson's Rule.   12. 0.13340.
13. (a) 0.3585;   (b) 0.3201;   (c) 0.3104;   (d) 0.2444.

IX, Page 211

3. 3.7893.   4. 6.1647.   5. 2.883238.   6. 0.12243.
7. 1.723.   8. 0.93825.   9. 0.15368.
10. 2.138, — 1.069 $\pm$ 2.257i.   11. 1.0649.
12. 1.44575.   13. $x = 0.22684$, $y = 0.36962$.
14. $x = 0.567325$, $y = 1.857378$.
15. $\pm$ 0.20292, $\pm$ 0.37077, $\pm$ 0.47455.

X, Page 234

3. 5.2555,   0.9676 $\pm$ 0.3272i,
   — 0.7870 $\pm$ 0.5764i,   0.3833.

XIII, Page 410

3. 0.331.   5. 0.00115;   870.

XIV, Page 427

1. $r = 0.0071$; $M_0 = 9.6639 \pm 0.0022$.
4. $M_0 = 0.00356 \pm 0.00016$.   6. $M_0 = 299937 \pm 44$.
7. $M_0 = 107.9374 \pm 0.0027$.

XVI, Page 474

1. $y = 0.000000864 x^{3.0936}$.   5. $y = 101 e^{-0.0265x}$.
6. $y = 100.61 e^{-0.026596x}$.   8. $x/y = 0.173 + 0.0560x$.
12. $\dfrac{1}{y - 20} = 0.0152778 + 0.0014414x$.
13. $R = \dfrac{58.275}{0.010133 + \tan h}$.

XVIII, Page 538

1. 239. 2. 239. 3. $z = 3$. 4. $x_1 = 0.8072$, $x_2 = 0.2372$, $x_3 = -0.1046$,
$x_4 = -0.3581$. 5. 79.98. 6. $x = 2$, $y = -1$, $z = 3$, $t = 5$. 8. $x = 0.444$,
$y = 0.563$, $z = 0.324$, $t = 0.723$.